# MECHANICS OF UNDERWATER NOISE

*OTHER PERGAMON TITLES OF INTEREST*

| | |
|---|---|
| Bugliarello, et al. — | *The Impact of Noise Pollution — A Socio-Technological Introduction* |
| Eckart — | *Hydrodynamics of Oceans and Atmospheres* |

*Deep-Sea Research and Oceanographic Abstracts*

*Progress in Oceanography*

*Water Research*

# MECHANICS OF UNDERWATER NOISE

DONALD ROSS

Assistant to the President
Tetra Tech, Inc.
Pasadena, California

PERGAMON PRESS
New York / Oxford / Toronto / Sydney / Frankfurt / Paris

*Pergamon Press Offices:*

U.S.A. Pergamon Press Inc., Maxwell House, Fairview Park, Elmsford, New York 10523, U.S.A.

U.K. Pergamon Press Ltd., Headington Hill Hall, Oxford OX3, OBW, England

CANADA Pergamon of Canada, Ltd., 207 Queen's Quay West, Toronto 1, Canada

AUSTRALIA Pergamon Press (Aust) Pty. Ltd., 19a Boundary Street, Rushcutters Bay,sN.S.W. 2011, Australia

FRANCE Pergamon Press SARL, 24 rue des Ecoles, 75240 Paris, Cedex 05, France

WEST GERMANY Pergamon Press GmbH, 6242 Kronberg/Taunus, Frankfurt-am-Main, West Germany

---



**Library of Congress Cataloging in Publication Data**

Ross, Donald, 1922 -
Mechanics of underwater noise.

Includes bibliographical references and indexes.
1. Underwater acoustics. s!. Title.
QC242.2.R67 1976 534'.23 76-18731
ISBN 0-08-021182-8
ISBN 0-08-021181-X pbk.

---



*Sponsored in part by the U.S. Navy, Office of Naval Research, Washington, D.C.*

Printed in the United States of America

**Dedication**

To my present and former colleagues, especially the many officers and men of the U.S. Navy with whom I've been fortunate to have spent time at sea.

# CONTENTS


Preface . . . . . . . . . . . . . . . . . . . . . . . . . . . . . . xiii

Acknowledgments . . . . . . . . . . . . . . . . . . . . . . . . . xiv

I. INTRODUCTION . . . . . . . . . . . . . . . . . . . . . . . . . 1

1.1 Noise: Unwanted Sound . . . . . . . . . . . . . . . . . . . . 1

Underwater noise; noise is unavoidable; acoustic conversion efficiency; noise control; types of underwater noise.

1.2 Decibels and Levels . . . . . . . . . . . . . . . . . . . . . . 4

Decibels; transmission loss; levels; reference pressures; source level; power level; spectrum level; decibel arithmetic.

1.3 Significance of Spectra . . . . . . . . . . . . . . . . . . . . 9

1.4 Passive Sonar Equation . . . . . . . . . . . . . . . . . . . . 9

1.5 Some Mathematics . . . . . . . . . . . . . . . . . . . . . . . 11

Scalars, vectors and tensors; tensor notation; vector operations; vector operators; scalar potentials; spherical symmetry; line, surface and volume integrals; complex quantities; Fourier series; Fourier integrals and transforms.

References . . . . . . . . . . . . . . . . . . . . . . . . . . . 18

2. SOUND WAVES IN LIQUIDS . . . . . . . . . . . . . . . . . 19

2.1 Description of Waves . . . . . . . . . . . . . . . . . . . . . 19

Plane waves; retarded time; harmonic representation of waves; Helmholtz equation; wave vectors.

2.2 Wave Equation for Sound in Fluids . . . . . . . . . . . . . . 23

Assumptions; equation of state; equation of continuity; equation of motion; acoustic wave equation; velocity potential; harmonic solutions.

2.3 Plane Sound Waves . . . . . . . . . . . . . . . . . . . . . . 31

Acoustic potential; particle velocity; specific acoustic impedance; acoustic intensity.

2.4 Spherical Waves . . . . . . . . . . . . . . . . . . . . . . . . 33

Acoustic potential; particle velocity; specific acoustic impedance; acoustic intensity; ideal transmission loss; acoustic power; damped sound waves; spherical waves from plane waves.

2.5 Transmission at Media Interfaces . . . . . . . . . . . . . . . 38

Snell's law; reflection from a plane boundary; transmission through a plane boundary; transmission from air to water; transmission from water into air; reflection of underwater sound by ocean surfaces.

2.6 Finite-Amplitude Effects . . . . . . . . . . . . . . . . . . . 43

References . . . . . . . . . . . . . . . . . . . . . . . . . . . 44

3. ACOUSTIC RADIATION FUNDAMENTALS . . . . . . . . . . . . . 45
3.1 General Characterization of Noise Sources . . . . . . . . . . . . 45
Monopoles, dipoles and quadrupoles; radiation impedance; radiation efficiency.
3.2 General Equation for Sound Generation . . . . . . . . . . . . . . 47
Derivation; interpretation.
3.3 General Spherical Sources . . . . . . . . . . . . . . . . . . 50
3.4 Hydrodynamic Sources . . . . . . . . . . . . . . . . . . . . 51
Radiation efficiencies; fluctuating-volume acoustic sources; fluctuating-force sources; turbulence noise; noise from wake turbulence; flow noise.
3.5 Sources in Motion . . . . . . . . . . . . . . . . . . . . . 55
Doppler shift; effect of steady motion on level; periodic motions.
References . . . . . . . . . . . . . . . . . . . . . . . . 56

4. RADIATION BY FLUCTUATING-VOLUME (MONOPOLE) SOURCES . . . . . . . . . . . . . . . . . . . . . . 57
4.1 Uniformly Pulsating Spherical Source . . . . . . . . . . . . . 57
Intensity and power; radiation impedance; radiation efficiency; entrained mass.
4.2 Monopole Radiation . . . . . . . . . . . . . . . . . . . . . 61
4.3 Sounds from Gas Bubbles in Liquids . . . . . . . . . . . . . . 62
Linear bubble pulsations; frequency of bubble oscillation; damping mechanisms; sound radiation.
4.4 Sounds from Splashes . . . . . . . . . . . . . . . . . . . . 68
Franz's measurements; wind-generated ambient sea noise; rain noise.
4.5 Radiation by Two Equal Monopoles . . . . . . . . . . . . . . 72
General equation for pressure field; far-field pressure pattern; directivity function; electrical steering; two equal in-phase sources; out-of-phase sources; dipoles.
4.6 Near-Surface Sources . . . . . . . . . . . . . . . . . . . . 78
Surface image; interference patterns; effects on noise measurements.
4.7 Linear Arrays . . . . . . . . . . . . . . . . . . . . . . . 81
Arrays of equally-spaced monopoles; continuous line radiators; directivity factor; directivity index; arrays of directional sources; arrays as spatial filters.
4.8 Radiation from Rigid Pistons . . . . . . . . . . . . . . . . . 89
Elementary piston radiator; circular piston in a baffle; near field of a piston radiator; radiation impedance and efficiency; directivity factor and index; pistons of other shapes; planar arrays; pistons in non-rigid baffles; unbaffled and partially baffled pistons; pistons on non-planar baffles; effect of flow on piston radiation.
4.9 Radiation from Hull Openings . . . . . . . . . . . . . . . . . 95
Radiation from pipe ends; radiation from tank resonances; radiation from exhaust pipes.
4.10 Radiation from Arbitrary Bodies . . . . . . . . . . . . . . . 97
Integral equation methods; spheroidal wave functions; slender body theory; radiation from cylinders; finite-element methods.
4.11 Radiation from Hulls . . . . . . . . . . . . . . . . . . . . 100
Definition of frequency regimes; low frequencies; medium frequencies; high frequencies.
References . . . . . . . . . . . . . . . . . . . . . . . . 102

5. STRUCTURAL VIBRATIONS . . . . . . . . . . . . . . . . . . . . 106
5.1 Structure-Borne Sound . . . . . . . . . . . . . . . . . . . . . . 106
5.2 Wave Motions in Solids . . . . . . . . . . . . . . . . . . . . . 106
Longitudinal waves in bars; shear waves; compressional waves in bulk solids; Poisson's ratio; longitudinal waves in plates; surface waves; flexural (bending) waves.
5.3 Beam Bending Equations . . . . . . . . . . . . . . . . . . . . 110
Forces and moments; transverse acceleration; rotational acceleration; considerations of shear; differential equation for bending; equation for uniform beams; Euler-Bernoulli (E-B) equation.
5.4 Speed of Flexural Waves . . . . . . . . . . . . . . . . . . . . 116
Harmonic solutions of the Timoshenko equation; low-frequency approximation; high-frequency limit; intermediate-frequency approximation; solid rectangular bars.
5.5 Flexural Resonances . . . . . . . . . . . . . . . . . . . . . . . 123
Uniform thin beams; correction for shear and rotatory inertia; wave approach.
5.6 Non-Uniform Beams . . . . . . . . . . . . . . . . . . . . . . . 130
Finite-element methods; wave method; tapered cantilever beams.
5.7 Forced Vibrations of Non-Resonant Structures . . . . . . . . . . 135
Mechanical impedances; semi-infinite beams; infinite beams; role of damping.
5.8 Forced Vibrations of Resonant Structures . . . . . . . . . . . . 140
Role of resonances; modal responses; broadband excitation.
5.9 Attenuation of Structural Vibrations . . . . . . . . . . . . . . . 143
Isolation mounts; applied damping; impedance mismatches; vibration absorbers and suppressors.
5.10 Fluid Loading . . . . . . . . . . . . . . . . . . . . . . . . . . 150
Entrained mass; hydrodynamic damping; sound radiation.
5.11 Flexural Resonances of Ship Hulls . . . . . . . . . . . . . . . 152
References . . . . . . . . . . . . . . . . . . . . . . . . . . . . 153
6. RADIATION BY PLATE FLEXURAL VIBRATIONS . . . . . . . . 158
6.1 Plate Flexural Vibrations . . . . . . . . . . . . . . . . . . . . 158
Bending rigidity of plates; thick plate bending equations; flexural wave speed; plate vibrations; input impedance.
6.2 Fluid Loading . . . . . . . . . . . . . . . . . . . . . . . . . . 162
Boundary conditions; coincidence; entrained mass; radiation.
6.3 Point-Excited Infinite Plates . . . . . . . . . . . . . . . . . . 169
Radiation below coincidence; directional radiation at high frequencies.
6.4 Radiation from Finite Plates . . . . . . . . . . . . . . . . . . 173
Radiation resistance; modal approach; effect of damping; orthotropic plates; beam on a plate; periodic structures; cylindrical shells; radiation from hull sections.
6.5 Transmission through Structures . . . . . . . . . . . . . . . . 180
Response of structures to sound waves; low-frequency transmission through walls; use of impedance concepts; role of flexural vibrations; sound isolation by walls.
6.6 Boundary-Layer Flow Noise . . . . . . . . . . . . . . . . . . . 184
Turbulent boundary layers; boundary-layer friction; boundary-layer turbulence; intermittency effects; wall pressure fluctuations; self-noise of flush-mounted hydrophones; arrays of flush-mounted hydrophones; radiated flow noise; domed sonar self-noise.
References . . . . . . . . . . . . . . . . . . . . . . . . . . . . 196

7. CAVITATION . . . . . . . . . . . . . . . . . . . . . . . . . . 202
7.1 Introduction . . . . . . . . . . . . . . . . . . . . . . . . . . 202
7.2 Tensile Strength of Liquids . . . . . . . . . . . . . . . . . . 203
Static tensile strength; cavitation nuclei; dynamic tensile strengths.
7.3 Single Bubble Growth and Collapse . . . . . . . . . . . . . . . 205
Classical theory; pressure inside a bubble; effects of compressibility; effects of permanent gases; asymmetrical bubble collapse; summary and conclusions.
7.4 Single Bubble Cavitation Noise . . . . . . . . . . . . . . . . 215
Expression for radiated energy; growth phase; collapse phase; acoustic pressures; spectrum; experimental results.
7.5 Broadband Cavitation Noise . . . . . . . . . . . . . . . . . . 220
7.6 Other Effects of Cavitation . . . . . . . . . . . . . . . . . . 222
Sonoluminescence; chemical reactions; erosion damage.
7.7 Hydrodynamically-Produced Cavitation . . . . . . . . . . . . . 223
Cavitation parameter; body cavitation; scale effects; effects of surface roughness; vortex cavitation; wakes and jets.
7.8 Hydrofoil Cavitation . . . . . . . . . . . . . . . . . . . . . 231
Symmetric struts; lifting hydrofoils; effects of cavitation on section performance scale effects; wing-tip vortex cavitation; supercavitating hydrofoils.
7.9 Hydraulic Cavitation . . . . . . . . . . . . . . . . . . . . . 240
Pipe constructions; valves; pipe bends; hydraulic machinery.
7.10 Underwater Explosions . . . . . . . . . . . . . . . . . . . . 242
References . . . . . . . . . . . . . . . . . . . . . . . . . . 246

8. PROPELLER CAVITATION NOISE . . . . . . . . . . . . . . . . . 253
8.1 Types of Propeller Cavitation . . . . . . . . . . . . . . . . . 253
8.2 Blade-Surface Cavitation Noise . . . . . . . . . . . . . . . . 253
Rotating blade experiments; scaling relationships; dependence of noise on depth; effect of gas content.
8.3 Propellers in Uniform Inflows . . . . . . . . . . . . . . . . . 260
Blade-element analysis; momentum theory analysis; cavitation in uniform inflows.
8.4 Wake-Operating Propellers . . . . . . . . . . . . . . . . . . . 265
Wake diagrams; effect of radially varying inflow; effects of circumferential variations; effect on cavitation; low-frequency cavitation tonals.
8.5 Submarine Propeller Cavitation . . . . . . . . . . . . . . . . 270
8.6 Surface Ship Radiated Noise . . . . . . . . . . . . . . . . . . 272
Importance of propeller cavitation; World War II noise data; dependence on speed; estimation formulas; acoustic efficiencies of surface ships; modulation effects; tonal spectra; merchant ship trends.
8.7 Ship-Generated Ambient Noise . . . . . . . . . . . . . . . . . 280
Recognition of ships as sources of ambient noise; reverberant room theory of ambient noise; geographical variations; importance of coastal shipping; directional characteristics; temporal fluctuations; long-term trends.
References . . . . . . . . . . . . . . . . . . . . . . . . . . 285

9. RADIATION BY FLUCTUATING-FORCE (DIPOLE) SOURCES . . . 288

9.1 Dipole Sound Sources . . . 288
Acoustic field of a concentrated force; oscillating rigid sphere; spheres pulsating out of phase; dipole fields from monopole fields.

9.2 Propeller Blade Tonals . . . 293
General oscillating hydrodynamic force; noise from oscillating thrust; factors affecting oscillating thrust; propeller-induced hull forces; blade-vortex interaction noise; shaft-rate components; rotor-stator interactions; blade-turbulence interactions.

9.3 Vortex Shedding Sounds . . . 299
Aeolian tones; vortex wakes of bluff bodies; oscillating forces associated with vortex wakes; three-dimensional character of vortex wakes; effects of vibration; effects of sound fields; vortex sounds from cylinders; sounds from rotating rods; vortex wakes of airfoils; vortex sounds from rotating blades.

9.4 Noise from Fans and Blowers . . . 313
Noise mechanisms; spectra; noise levels; positive displacement blowers.

9.5 Propeller Singing . . . 316

9.6 Flow-Excited Cavity Resonances . . . 318

References . . . 319

10. MECHANICAL NOISE SOURCES . . . 326

10.1 Mechanical Unbalances . . . 326
Rotational unbalances; reciprocating unbalances.

10.2 Electromagnetic Force Fluctuations . . . 328
Magnetostriction; magnetic force variations.

10.3 Impact Sounds . . . 329
Impact vibratory relations; gear noise.

10.4 Piston-Slap Noise in Reciprocating Machinery . . . 332
Piston slap; significance of piston slap; piston impact velocity; cylinder wall vibrations; experimental verification; empirical noise formulas; underwater noise implications.

10.5 Bearing Noise . . . 345

References . . . 346

Appendix A NOMENCLATURE . . . 349
General; nomenclature by chapter; nomenclature used in references

Appendix B DECIBEL ARITHMETIC . . . 360

AUTHOR INDEX . . . 363

SUBJECT INDEX . . . 370

# Preface

Like so many of my fellow workers in underwater acoustics, I entered the field with a background in physics and engineering but without any formal education in this specific subject. Following the theory that a good way to learn about any subject is to teach it, I have participated as much as possible in formal courses and professional meetings. Over the past sixteen years I have organized and taught graduate-level courses on underwater acoustics at M.I.T., Catholic University, American University and the University of California at San Diego in addition to industry-sponsored commercial courses.

While there now are a number of books covering various aspects of underwater sound, none covers the area of underwater noise in depth. Aware of this, and knowing that this aspect of underwater sound has been my particular interest, Marvin Lasky, then Head of the Acoustics Branch of the Office of Naval Research (O.N.R.), proposed that I write a book on this subject to be used as a self-education text and as a reference for workers in the field.

This is the book. It represents the culmination of thirty years of research and teaching and has been written over a period of three years with contractual support from O.N.R.

My approach has been to stress physical explanations of the basic mechanisms by which noise is generated, transmitted by structures and radiated into the sea. Despite the complexity of many of these phenomena, most can be explained in straightforward ways which emphasize dominant mechanisms and which have considerable practical application.

Chapter organization is by basic source mechanisms. Descriptions of practical manifestations follow discussions of the pertinent fundamental phenomena. Thus, the topic of wind-generated ocean ambient noise is treated in Chapter 4 following a discussion of splash noise, which in turn has been related to noise produced by oscillating gas bubbles. Similarly, ship-generated ambient noise is found in Chapter 8 on propeller cavitation noise which is its main source. The engineering topics of vibration isolation and structural damping are covered in Chapter 5 on structural vibrations. Flow noise, which often involves the excitation of plates by turbulence and their subsequent radiation, is treated in Chapter 6 on radiation by plate flexural vibrations. I have attempted to cover the field completely, and have at the same time placed particular emphasis on topics with which I am personally most familiar.

Much of the work done in underwater acoustics is classified and such areas have, of course, been omitted. Most of the topics discussed in the book have been the subject of articles in the open literature to which I have referred extensively.

In addition to acoustics, I have drawn from the disciplines of fluid mechanics, aerodynamics, thermodynamics, electrical, mechanical and marine engineering, and naval architecture. This breadth of material has led to occasional difficulty in selecting symbols to represent the more than

450 different quantities included in equations. Care has been taken to avoid confusion, but some problems may still exist for readers who are more familiar with these other fields than with acoustics. In this case, use of the lists of symbols and abbreviations in Appendix A will be of assistance.

To the extent that this book is more readable than my usual writings, full credit goes to the editing done by Nancy I. Ross.

*San Diego, California* *Donald Ross*
*July 1976*

**Acknowledgments**

The 140 line drawings were produced from rough originals by James N. Stansil of Sensors, Data, Decisions, Inc. The remainder of the production work was accomplished at Tetra Tech, Inc. Esther H. Riggs typed and retyped the entire draft manuscript many times and with great patience. Production of the camera-ready copy was the work of Bobbie J. Bosley, using an IBM MTST/MTSC. This brief mention cannot express the full extent of my appreciation for her diligence, meticulous attention to detail and artistic talent.

I also wish to express my gratitude to Dr. Lloyd F. Bell, head of Tetra Tech's San Diego Office, and to Dr. Harry A. Schenck of the Naval Undersea Center, who made possible completion of this volume on a timely basis.

# CHAPTER 1

# INTRODUCTION

## 1.1 Noise: Unwanted Sound

Usually when a person uses the word *noise* he is referring to sounds such as those of jet aircraft flying overhead, the rumble of trucks from a nearby highway, or the racket being made by his neighbor's children. These sounds are annoying because they intrude on him and interfere with activities such as conversation and sleep; they may even interfere with his ability to think. *Noise is unwanted sound that interferes with the normal functioning of a system.* The seriousness of the noise and the degree to which noise-control measures are required depend not so much on the level of the noise as on the amount of interference it causes with other functions.

### Underwater Noise

*Underwater noise* is sound in water that limits the military effectiveness of naval systems. Submarines are particularly prone to experiencing such limitations, since sounds which they radiate can reveal their presence to an enemy. In addition, they depend upon acoustic signals for communications and use sonar to detect the presence of any enemy, which functions are also limited by noise.

Submarines are not the only naval systems for which noise plays a vital role in limiting ability to perform assigned functions. Sounds radiated by surface ships reveal their presence to enemy submarines; and, like the submarine, sonar self-noise limits their ability to detect targets. In some cases, sounds radiated by one surface ship may even interfere with sonar performance on another. Another example of limitation by self-noise is that of passive acoustic homing torpedoes which use sounds radiated by ships and submarines to locate these targets. Finally, the effectiveness of otherwise quiet systems, such as buoys, may be determined by the ambient noise background of the sea.

That underwater noise plays a dominant role in naval warfare is today recognized in most Navy circles. Appreciable efforts are devoted both to reducing noise and to developing methods to exploit it. Of necessity, much of this work is classified. However, the phenomena involved are related to topics in physics and mechanics and can be discussed in a general way without divulging classified aspects of specific military systems.

### Noise Is Unavoidable

According to the Second Law of Thermodynamics, no useful mechanical process can take place without generating some heat. If heat were not produced, it would be possible to create a perpetual motion machine. It is not as well recognized, but it is probably equally true that no useful mechanical process can occur without generating some vibration and therefore at least a little noise. Thus, noise is also an unavoidable by-product of machines. Associated with each steady, work-producing force there are always small unsteadinesses, or vibrations, and these vibrations are transmitted to the surfaces of the machine, from which they radiate as sound. Likewise, when a body moves through a fluid, turbulent motions are created. Not only do these turbulent motions eventually decay into heat, but also they radiate a small amount of sound. Only in a vacuum would it be possible to do useful work without producing sound. The acoustician may well be tempted to modify the well-known Second Law of Thermodynamics to include sound along with heat as necessary by-products of mechanical processes.

The amount of sound power radiated into air by various mechanisms varies from as low as a microwatt for a very small fan to many kilowatts for airplanes and over a megawatt for a large rocket. Power levels in water tend to be much lower. A modern submarine proceeding at slow speed produces on the order of 10 mW acoustic power, while surface ships generally radiate from five to 100 Watts. When one realizes that mechanical powers of the order of many thousands of horsepower are involved in operating ships and submarines, it is apparent that only a very small fraction of this mechanical power is actually converted into underwater sound.

Although power levels radiated into water by ships, submarines and torpedoes are relatively low, this does not mean that radiated underwater noise is of no consequence. Sources that radiate as much as one Watt of acoustic power can be detected at relatively long ranges by modern passive sonars. The same power in air might carry only several blocks. The reason for this difference is that in water relatively high acoustic pressures are associated with low power levels; since detection systems respond to acoustic pressures rather than to power density (intensity), it is pressure levels rather than power levels that determine the detectability of underwater sounds.

### Acoustic Conversion Efficiency

A useful concept in analyzing noise mechanisms is that of acoustic conversion efficiency, defined as the ratio of the sound power radiated to the mechanical power of the source:

$$\eta_{ac} \equiv \frac{Acoustic\ Power}{Mechanical\ Power} = \frac{W_{ac}}{W_{mech}} . \qquad (1.1)$$

This ratio finds its greatest use in sorting out noise sources, since different sound-producing mechanisms have different relationships for their acoustic conversion efficiencies.

Acoustic conversion efficiencies are much lower in water than they are in air. Conversion efficiencies as low as $10^{-8}$ are common for sources in water, while values as high as $10^{-4}$ to $10^{-2}$ are often found for sounds radiated into air. This difference between the two media is caused by their relative compressibilities: water is much less compressible than air. Since it is the compressibility of a medium that makes sound possible, the same mechanical power generates more sound power in air than it does in water.

The parameter that measures the relative importance of compressibility is the Mach number, $M$, defined as the ratio of a pertinent mechanical speed to the speed of sound waves:

$$M \equiv \frac{U}{c} . \qquad (1.2)$$

If a medium were totally incompressible, its speed of sound would be infinite, and the Mach number would always be zero. Thus, although water is for many purposes practically incompressible, it does have slight compressibility; and Mach numbers, though low, are finite. In

Chapter 3, which covers basic sound radiation mechanisms, it will be shown that acoustic conversion efficiencies can usually be expressed as functions of Mach number of the form

$$\eta_{ac} \sim M^n \tag{1.3}$$

where the exponent $n$ is equal to or greater than unity. The low acoustic conversion efficiencies found in underwater sound are related to relatively low values of the Mach number in water.

In dealing with many noise sources, it is useful to divide the noise-production process into three parts: generation of a vibratory motion, transmission of this vibration to a radiating surface, and radiation of sound into the medium. The acoustic conversion efficiency can thus be expressed as the product of three conversion efficiencies, one for each of the three processes:

$$\eta_{ac} = \eta_{vibr} \cdot \eta_{trans} \cdot \eta_{rad} \; . \tag{1.4}$$

It is the last term, the radiation efficiency, which is controlled by the Mach number and which differs most between air and water. The other terms are usually independent of the fluid medium. Obviously, the over-all acoustic conversion efficiency is always less than the radiation efficiency.

### Noise Control

It is not practical, economical or even desirable to attempt to eliminate all noise from mechanical systems. Noise control is the technology that evaluates the need for noise reduction and then attempts to achieve acceptable noise levels in a manner consistent with economic and operational considerations. An understanding of basic noise mechanisms is essential to successful noise control.

Equation 1.4 serves as a useful guide to the principles used in noise control. Noise reduction can be accomplished in three different ways:

1. by reducing the fraction of the source mechanical power converted into vibratory power, or by selecting machinery with lower rated mechanical powers;
2. by isolating the source from radiating surfaces, i.e., by reducing the efficiency of vibration transmission; or
3. by reducing the radiation efficiency of the radiating surfaces.

Of the three, the second, isolation of the source from the radiating surface, is generally the most easily accomplished. Reduction of noise at a source often requires redesign of a mechanical system, and reducing the radiation efficiency may require extensive application of anti-radiation coatings. Although noise reduction *per se* is not the purpose of the present volume, many topics pertinent to noise control are considered; the reader may expect to gain some understanding of methods of noise reduction.

### Types of Underwater Noise

There are a number of different manifestations of underwater noise. While consistent definitions for all of the principal types encountered in naval systems have not been universally adopted, the following definitions are consistent with those adopted by the American Standards Association:

*Radiated Noise* – noise radiated into the water that can be used by a passive listening sonar to detect the presence of a vehicle at a considerable distance.

*Ambient Noise* – all noises associated with the medium in which a sonar operates that would exist in the medium if the sonar platform or vehicle itself were not present.

*Platform Noise* – that noise measured by a single, omnidirectional, platform-mounted hydrophone in the presence of an operational platform. Conceptually, platform noise should be simply noise attributable to the presence of the platform, but actual measurements of platform noise invariably include the contribution of ambient ocean noise.

*Sonar Self-Noise* – noise associated with a platform and its sonar hydrophones and preamplifiers, as measured through the sonar hydrophone array.

*Sonar Background Noise* – all noise at the output of a sonar array that limits the detection of signals by a signal processor. Sonar background noise includes the contribution of the medium as well as platform noise and any noises contributed by hydrophones, cables or preamplifiers. (Actually, most sonar self-noise measurements are really background noise measurements, since such measurements are generally made under circumstances that do not permit separate measurement of ambient noise and there is no practical method to estimate the contribution of the medium.)

## 1.2 Decibels and Levels

Acoustic measurements are almost invariably expressed in decibels, which are units involving logarithms of various ratios. The need for a logarithmic measurement unit arose in acoustics for two reasons: first, the range of sound intensities found in practice varies from about $10^{-9}$ W/m$^2$ for a barely intelligible whisper to over a kW/m$^2$ near a jet aircraft; second, human response to acoustic stimuli is approximately logarithmic. For these reasons, it seemed logical to adopt logarithmic units for acoustic measurements. Use of logarithmic measures is not unique to acoustics; such quantities are quite common in thermodynamics. Problems have arisen in acoustics due to inconsistent choices of reference quantities.

### Decibels

Decibels were originally defined in the early 1920's by workers in the electrical communications industry who were interested in the power transmission capability of networks. They noted that as long as a network was linear the output power maintained a constant ratio to the input power. Since these ratios were often quite large, they expressed them by a logarithmic quantity:

$$\text{transmission ratio} = \log_{10} \frac{W_2}{W_1} . \tag{1.5}$$

The unit was named *Bel* after Alexander Graham Bell, inventor of the telephone. To avoid dealing in fractions of Bels, a unit one-tenth as big was chosen, namely, the *decibel*:

$$\text{trans. ratio in dB} = 10 \log \frac{W_2}{W_1} . \tag{1.6}$$

When high impedance networks became common, interest switched to voltage ratios rather than power ratios. Since, for constant resistance, power is proportional to the square of the voltage, twenty times the logarithm to the base ten was chosen for voltage ratios,

$$\text{trans. ratio in dB} = 20 \log \frac{e_2}{e_1} . \tag{1.7}$$

thus maintaining constancy of numerical values of transmission ratios when expressed in decibels.

**Transmission Loss**

In acoustics, intensity is a power-like quantity and pressure corresponds to voltage. When the use of decibels was extended from electric networks to acoustics, it was logical to define acoustic transmission ratios by

$$\text{trans. ratio in dB} = 10 \log \frac{I_2}{I_1} = 20 \log \frac{p_2}{p_1} . \tag{1.8}$$

Actually, in underwater sound it is more common to express transmission ratios as transmission losses, since pressures and intensities usually decrease with increasing distance from a source. Assuming position one to be closer to the source, the *transmission loss in dB* is defined by

$$TL = 20 \log \frac{p_1}{p_2} , \tag{1.9}$$

where the pressures are usually root-mean-square (rms) values. While invariably positive, transmission loss is usually plotted in a negative sense since received signals decrease as transmission loss increases.

**Levels**

Use of decibels in acoustics causes no concern when the application involves comparison of intensity or pressure close to a source with that at a distant measurement point, as in transmission loss. Some confusion has arisen, however, from the practice of expressing quantities measured at a single location in terms of their decibel values, called *levels*. The intensity and pressure at a point are expressed as levels by taking logarithms of their ratios to reference values,

$$IL \equiv 10 \log \frac{I}{I_o} , \tag{1.10}$$

$$SPL \equiv 20 \log \frac{p}{p_o} , \tag{1.11}$$

where $I_o$ and $p_o$ are reference values. This procedure is in itself straightforward. However, problems have arisen in the selection of reference quantities, especially for underwater acoustics.

**Reference Pressures**

It would seem logical to write a pressure level simply as $20 \log_{10} p$, where $p$ would be measured in Newton/m$^2$ if one were using the MKS system, or in dyne/cm$^2$ if one were using cgs units. The problem is that most measured acoustic pressures are smaller than 1 N/m$^2$ or 1 dyne/cm$^2$, and the corresponding levels would be negative. The early producers of sound level meters wanted their decibel readings to be positive. They, therefore, sought to measure intensity and pressure not relative to unity in cgs units but relative to a value small enough to assure positive levels. In the early 1930's, a number of references were proposed, varying from $2 \times 10^{-4}$ to $1.4 \times 10^{-2}$ dyne/cm$^2$.

In 1932, a subcommittee of the newly formed American Standards Association Sectional Committee Z24 for Acoustics tackled the problem of finding a standard reference for noise measurement. Its deliberations were strongly influenced by a desire to consider intensity as a fundamental quantity. It chose $10^{-16}$ W/cm$^2$, which equals $10^{-12}$ W/m$^2$, as the primary reference. However, intensity is seldom measured directly; it is usually inferred from a pressure measurement. For unidirectional plane and spherical waves, acoustic intensity and pressure are related by

$$I = \frac{\overline{p^2}}{\rho_o c_o}, \tag{1.12}$$

where $\rho_o$ is the density and $c_o$ the speed of sound of the medium. For standard air, pressure levels will equal intensity levels if the reference pressure is taken to be 0.000204 dyne/cm$^2$. Since the difference is small, this has been rounded off to 0.0002 dyne/cm$^2$, which is now the reference for all pressure measurements in airborne acoustics.

While the selection of 0.0002 dyne/cm$^2$ had validity for airborne sound, it had no physical significance for other media. While many workers in underwater acoustics adopted this reference, others chose 1 dyne/cm$^2$. This use of two references by different groups has lasted until very recently. Only in the past several years has the underwater sound community agreed on a single pressure reference. It is interesting to trace the history of reference pressures in underwater acoustics and to see how a new third unit came to supplant two established ones.

When underwater noises of ships and other vehicles were first measured, workers used existing noise measuring gear already calibrated relative to 0.0002 dyne/cm$^2$. Graphs were simply marked "sound pressure level in decibels." However, groups involved in transducer calibration during World War II desired a larger unit. Noting that the then standard pressure had no physical significance relative to intensity in water, they chose 1 dyne/cm$^2$, often called one microbar, as their reference pressure. Use of this reference spread, and by the end of WWII about half of the community was using each standard.

An attempt at standardization after WWII failed, and the situation continued for about 20 years. It might have continued indefinitely, but naval personnel were making increased use of acoustic data, and presentation of such data using two different references caused much unnecessary confusion. In 1961, Writing Group S1-W44 was appointed by the American Standards Association at the request of the U.S. Navy Bureau of Ships to recommend a reference sound pressure for underwater acoustics. A survey of the community revealed a near 50-50 split, and neither side was willing to concede. After several years of debate, support gradually developed for the idea of adopting a new fundamental unit to be used in the MKS system and small enough that all measured levels would be positive. The reference pressure ultimately recommended was $10^{-6}$ N/m$^2$, called a *micropascal* and abbreviated $\mu$Pa. In 1970, by order of the Chief of Naval Operations, this unit was adopted by the U.S. Navy, and it is rapidly becoming the standard for all underwater measurements. All numerical values presented in the present volume are referenced to this unit.

Since the new standard reference pressure is so new, many currently used texts and reports use the old references. Values relative to 1 dyne/cm$^2$ can be converted to micropascals by simply adding 100 dB, while values referenced to 0.0002 dyne/cm$^2$ require the addition of 26 dB.

**Source Level**

Acoustic noise measurements are sometimes presented as measured, but more often they are presented in terms of constructs that are derived from actual measurements through certain assumptions. One of these constructs is *source level.* It would be convenient if the total acoustic power radiated by a source were itself measurable, but power is not a directly measurable quantity. What is usually measured is acoustic pressure at some distance from the source. Since pressure varies with distance, pressure alone is not a unique measure of source strength. Some attempts have been made to standardize measurement distances: 3 and 10 feet from machines in air, and 20 and 100 yards or meters from ships and submarines. However, it is not always possible to make measurements at standard distances. Source level is a construct which enables measurements made at a variety of distances to be used as comparable indicators of source strength.

*Source level* is defined as the pressure level that would be measured at a reference distance of one foot, one yard or one meter from an ideal point source radiating the same amount of sound as the actual source being measured. Since most practical sources have directional radiation patterns, source level is properly a function of direction. Source levels are never measured directly. Rather, they are inferred from measurements at greater distances. The complete specification of source level includes the reference distance, thus:

*dB re 0.0002 dyne/cm² at 1 foot* (in air), and

*dB re 1 μPa at 1 meter or 1 yard* (in water).

The concept of source level as a measure of the strength of a noise source has become entrenched in underwater acoustics largely because of its role in sonar performance prediction.

**Power Level**

While not usually directly measurable, acoustic power is often calculated directly in theoretical equations. It can be expressed as a logarithmic quantity, called *power level,* by

$$PWL \equiv 10 \log \frac{W_{ac}}{W_o} , \tag{1.13}$$

where the reference power, $W_o$, is usually 1 pW ($10^{-12}$ W) in airborne acoustics and 1 W in underwater sound. Power levels and source levels are related in a simple manner only when sources radiate uniformly in all directions. In air the relationship is

$$PWL \doteq L_S , \tag{1.14}$$

where $L_S$ is the source level in dB re 0.0002 dyne/cm² at 1 ft and *PWL* is power level in dB re $10^{-12}$ W. In water, the relationship is

$$PWL \doteq L_S - 171 , \tag{1.15}$$

where $L_S$ is in dB re 1 μPa at 1 yd or 1 m, and power level is relative to 1 W.

**Spectrum Level**

When dealing with single-frequency tonal components, source levels refer to the total pressure of the signal. The situation is not so simple when dealing with broadband sources, since the measured level is then a function of filter width. Since different measurement activities use different filter widths, their results are not directly comparable. In order to be able to compare and average values obtained using different filters, the concept of *equivalent spectrum level* is used. This is defined as the level that would have been measured using an ideal 1-Hz filter. Measured spectra are readily converted to spectrum level if the distribution of energy is relatively uniform throughout the measurement band. In this case

$$L_s = L_S - 10 \log \Delta f \,, \tag{1.16}$$

where $\Delta f$ is the filter bandwidth and a lower case subscript refers to spectrum level, while upper case continues to represent total or band level. Even when a spectrum is not flat, Eq. 1.16 is used as the definition of equivalent spectrum level. Thus, calculated equivalent spectrum levels are measures of average levels within a filter band.

It is common practice to plot each spectrum level at the *effective center frequency* of the filter, defined as the geometric mean of the upper and lower cut-off frequencies:

$$f_c = \sqrt{f_u f_\ell} \,. \tag{1.17}$$

Calculated spectrum level is a good measure of the actual spectrum level at the filter center frequency provided the spectrum is continuous and does not change much within the filter band. It can be shown by integrating over a filter band that this procedure is valid provided actual levels do not vary by more than about 9 dB within the band. If the variation is greater than this, errors in excess of a decibel will be introduced.

One-third-octave filters are widely used today. While it is common practice to convert one-third-octave data to spectrum level, some measurement groups prefer presenting their results as actually measured, rather than making the conversion. The reason is that many actual spectra contain tonal components, and spectrum levels can then be quite misleading. Spectrum levels are distinguished from band levels by adding an *s* to *dB*. Thus, *dBs* means "dB in a 1-Hz band," not the plural of dB.

**Decibel Arithmetic**

When using decibels, equations that otherwise would have involved multiplication or division of numbers become simple additions and subtractions. Difficulties occur, however, when performing operations that would be additions or subtractions of linear functions. Thus, the addition or subtraction of sounds from several sources requires transformation of the decibel values to linear values by use of antilogs and transformation back to logarithmic values after performance of the addition or subtraction. Results of source addition and subtraction also depend on whether the several signals are at the same single frequency, or are either broadband or at different frequencies. In the first case, the signals are coherent; otherwise they are incoherent. Formulas for coherent and incoherent decibel arithmetic are given in Appendix B.

## 1.3 Significance of Spectra

In recent years, emphasis in noise measurements has increasingly been placed on narrowband spectra. There are several reasons for this trend. Most important is the fact that its detailed spectral distribution is a most important clue as to the nature of a noise source. Before noise reduction measures can be applied, it is essential that dominant sources be identified. Narrowband spectral analysis is a potent tool in diagnostic noise studies.

The reason that spectral analysis enables classification of noise sources is that, through the Fourier transform, there is a direct relationship between the shape of a signal in the time domain and its spectrum. The simplest signal to contemplate is a pure sine wave, of frequency $f_o$. In frequency space, the spectrum of a pure sine wave is a spike of near-zero width at frequency $f_o$. Nearly pure sine waves are generated by mechanical unbalance forces of rotating machinery running at constant speed. In practice, slight variations in speed usually modulate the frequency, thereby producing tones with finite width in spectral space. The spectral width of a tone is a direct measure of source stability. It can be expressed in terms of the $Q$ of the tone, defined as the ratio of its frequency to its bandwidth,

$$Q \equiv \frac{f_o}{\Delta f} , \tag{1.18}$$

where $\Delta f$ is the half-power bandwidth.

Some sources produce noise through repeated impacts, with each impact generating a sharp pulse in the time domain. The resultant spectrum consists of a large number of tonal components separated in frequency by the fundamental pulse repetition frequency, the number of strong tonal components being a function of the decay time of the individual pulses. Since time between impacts is never exactly constant, individual tones have finite spectral widths which are dependent on source stability. Other noise sources, notably cavitation, produce noise through impulses which are random both in time of occurrence and in amplitude and duration. They produce continuous spectra having some energy at all frequencies, and generally having a broad spectral peak at a frequency which is related to the most prevalent decay time.

The important point is that characteristics of a spectrum are directly related to the nature of the phenomena producing them, and that through detailed spectral analysis one can deduce a great deal about noise sources. In the present volume, as each type of source is discussed, the nature of its spectrum will be developed and any special characteristics noted.

## 1.4 Passive Sonar Equation

The *sonar equation* is an expression in decibels of signal-to-noise relationships for a passive sonar. Figure 1.1 is a simplified schematic of a passive sonar system, showing its essential elements. The *signal level* in the water at the hydrophones of a receiving sonar can be expressed by

$$SL = L_S - TL , \tag{1.19}$$

provided the reference distance for transmission loss is taken to be the same as that used in defining the source level. Thus, in underwater sound, *transmission loss* at distance $r$ is defined by

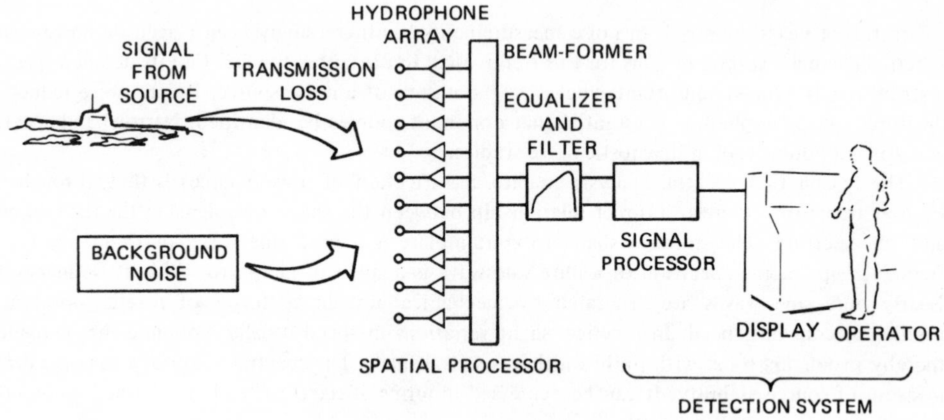


Fig. 1.1. Passive Sonar System

$$TL \equiv 20 \log \frac{p(1)}{p(r)}, \tag{1.20}$$

where $p(1)$ is the rms pressure that would be measured one yard or one meter from an ideal point source. Representing the *background noise level* in the water by $L_N$, the *signal-to-noise ratio* at a hydrophone is

$$\left(\frac{S}{N}\right)_{water} \equiv SL - L_N = L_S - TL - L_N . \tag{1.21}$$

The array of a sonar is a spatial processor that discriminates against background noise. It improves the signal-to-noise ratio by an amount equal to the *array gain, AG*. The output of an array is the input to the signal processor, so that

$$\left(\frac{S}{N}\right)_{in} \equiv \left(\frac{S}{N}\right)_{water} + AG = L_S - TL - \left(L_N - AG\right) . \tag{1.22}$$

The level of signal-to-noise into the signal processor for which the probability of detection is 50% is called the *detection threshold, DT*, or *recognition differential,* $N_{RD}$, of the processor. Detection is more likely whenever the signal-to-noise ratio into the processor exceeds the detection threshold, and is less likely when it is lower. The difference is called *signal excess*:

$$SE \equiv \left(\frac{S}{N}\right)_{in} - N_{RD} = L_S - TL - \left(L_N - AG\right) - N_{RD} . \tag{1.23}$$

This equation for signal excess is one form of the passive sonar equation.

The passive sonar equation is relatively simple, but its application is complex. One problem is that most sonars are broadband sonars, and quantities such as array gain and transmission loss are not constant across a frequency band. Another problem arises from effects of temporal and spatial fluctuations of various quantities. Still another difficulty is that the effective transmission loss for a directional receiver may differ from the omnidirectional value that is usually measured. Normally, the sonar equation applies to a relatively short sample time, yet often what is wanted is a prediction of detection performance over long periods. Despite these difficulties in its application, the sonar equation is nevertheless the basic framework used in treating topics in underwater acoustics.

## 1.5 Some Mathematics

While emphasis in the present volume is on physical principles and on understanding fundamental mechanisms whereby noise is generated, a number of mathematical derivations are included and equations are used extensively to describe functional relationships. The following paragraphs discuss a number of mathematical concepts and also serve to indicate the nomenclature used.

### Scalars, Vectors and Tensors

Physical quantities are classified as scalars, vectors or tensors, according to their dependence on direction.

*Scalars* are physical quantities that are fully described by numbers and are independent of direction. Examples are temperature, density, speed and energy.

*Vectors* are physical quantities that involve direction as well as magnitude. Examples are velocity, force and momentum. Vectors are indicated by arrows over symbols. In cartesian coordinates

$$\vec{A} = \hat{\imath} A_x + \hat{\jmath} A_y + \hat{k} A_z \,, \tag{1.24}$$

where $\hat{\imath}$, $\hat{\jmath}$ and $\hat{k}$ are unit vectors in the $x$, $y$ and $z$ directions. The magnitude of a vector is related to its components by

$$A = |\vec{A}| = \sqrt{A_x^2 + A_y^2 + A_z^2} \,. \tag{1.25}$$

A *tensor* of the second rank is a physical quantity whose full description requires specification of two directions. Examples are mechanical strain and stress, for which both the direction of a surface and that of a force must be specified. Such quantities can be written in cartesian coordinates in terms of nine independent components, each of which is given a double subscript to account for the two directions.

In the most general sense, all physical quantities are described by tensors of various ranks. A vector is a tensor of first rank, while a scalar is a tensor of zero rank. Second rank tensors are sometimes called *dyadics*.

### Tensor Notation

In the present volume, a mixture of vector and tensor notation is used in such a way as to attempt to convey the physics being described by the equations. In tensor notation, directions are represented by subscript indices and quantities are summed for all values of the index whenever the same index appears twice in a single term of an equation. The rank of the tensor is indicated by the number of indices required to specify it. Thus, the components of a vector are represented by a symbol having a single subscript, as $A_i$. Tensor notation is most readily interpreted when using cartesian coordinates, for which the subscript indices represent the $x$, $y$ and $z$ directions in sequence.

A useful symbol in tensor notation is the *Kronecker Delta* symbol. This is a delta with two subscript indices. When the two indices are the same, its value is unity; otherwise it is zero. Using this symbol,

$$\delta_{ij} \frac{\partial A_i}{\partial x_j} = \frac{\partial A_i}{\partial x_i} = \frac{\partial A_x}{\partial x} + \frac{\partial A_y}{\partial y} + \frac{\partial A_z}{\partial z} . \tag{1.26}$$

When several tensor quantities of various rank are combined, the rank of the resulting combination is equal to the number of indices that do not appear twice. Thus Eq. 1.26 is a scalar equation, since each index appears twice.

### Vector Operations

Vectors may be added, subtracted, multiplied and differentiated, but the rules differ somewhat from the corresponding operations for scalars.

*Vector addition and subtraction* are performed by carrying out the specified operation on each of the components:

$$\vec{A} \pm \vec{B} = \hat{\imath}(A_x \pm B_x) + \hat{\jmath}(A_y \pm B_y) + \hat{k}(A_z \pm B_z) . \tag{1.27}$$

*Scalar multiplication* of two vectors produces a scalar having its value equal to the product of their magnitudes times the cosine of the angle between them:

$$\vec{A} \cdot \vec{B} = A_i B_i = A_x B_x + A_y B_y + A_z B_z = AB \cos (A,B) . \tag{1.28}$$

The scalar product is sometimes called the *dot product*.

*Vector multiplication* of two vectors yields a vector perpendicular to their plane in the direction of a right-handed screw, having its magnitude equal to the product of their magnitudes times the sine of the angle between them:

$$\vec{A} \times \vec{B} = \begin{vmatrix} \hat{\imath} & \hat{\jmath} & \hat{k} \\ A_x & A_y & A_z \\ B_x & B_y & B_z \end{vmatrix} = \hat{\imath}(A_y B_z - A_z B_y) + \dots . \tag{1.29}$$

$$|\vec{A} \times \vec{B}| = AB \sin (A,B) . \tag{1.30}$$

Since direction depends upon order,

$$\vec{B} \times \vec{A} = -\left[\vec{A} \times \vec{B}\right] . \tag{1.31}$$

The vector product is often referred to as the *cross product*.

The *derivative* of a vector is a vector having as its components the derivatives of the individual components:

$$\frac{d\vec{A}}{ds} = \hat{\imath}\frac{dA_x}{ds} + \hat{\jmath}\frac{dA_y}{ds} + \hat{k}\frac{dA_z}{ds} . \tag{1.32}$$

Derivatives of scalar and vector products are obtained by applying the product rule for differentiation:

$$\frac{d(\vec{A} \cdot \vec{B})}{ds} = \vec{A} \cdot \frac{d\vec{B}}{ds} + \vec{B} \cdot \frac{d\vec{A}}{ds}, \tag{1.33}$$

$$\frac{d[\vec{A} \times \vec{B}]}{ds} = \left[\vec{A} \times \frac{d\vec{B}}{ds}\right] + \left[\frac{d\vec{A}}{ds} \times \vec{B}\right]. \tag{1.34}$$

**Vector Operators**

There are three vector differential operators that are used extensively in physics when dealing with field quantities defined over a region of space:

The *gradient* of a scalar is a vector having the magnitude and direction of the greatest space rate of change of the scalar:

$$grad\ \phi = \hat{i}\frac{\partial \phi}{\partial x} + \hat{j}\frac{\partial \phi}{\partial y} + \hat{k}\frac{\partial \phi}{\partial z}. \tag{1.35}$$

The components of the gradient are the rates of change in each direction. The symbol $\nabla$ is commonly used to represent the gradient vector differential operator:

$$\nabla \equiv \hat{i}\frac{\partial}{\partial x} + \hat{j}\frac{\partial}{\partial y} + \hat{k}\frac{\partial}{\partial z}. \tag{1.36}$$

It can be applied to vectors as well as to scalars.

The *divergence* of a vector is a scalar obtained by taking the scalar product of the gradient operator and the vector:

$$div\ \vec{A} = \nabla \cdot \vec{A} = \frac{\partial A_i}{\partial x_i} = \frac{\partial A_x}{\partial x} + \frac{\partial A_y}{\partial y} + \frac{\partial A_z}{\partial z}. \tag{1.37}$$

It represents the net outward flow of a quantity from a differential volume.

The *curl* of a field vector is a vector giving the magnitude and direction of its *rotation*. It is obtained by taking the cross product of the gradient operator and the vector:

$$curl\ \vec{A} \equiv \nabla \times \vec{A} = \begin{vmatrix} \hat{i} & \hat{j} & \hat{k} \\ \frac{\partial}{\partial x} & \frac{\partial}{\partial y} & \frac{\partial}{\partial z} \\ A_x & A_y & A_z \end{vmatrix} = \hat{i}\left(\frac{\partial A_z}{\partial y} - \frac{\partial A_y}{\partial z}\right) + \ldots . \tag{1.38}$$

Since the curl of a vector is a measure of its rotation, vector fields having zero curl are termed *irrotational fields*.

**Scalar Potentials**

Many fluid flows, in acoustics as well as in fluid mechanics, are irrotational. Whenever the curl of a vector quantity is zero, it is possible to define that vector quantity in terms of the gradient of a *scalar potential*,

$$\vec{A} = \pm\, grad\, \phi\,, \tag{1.39}$$

where the sign is arbitrary, but is generally taken as negative. It can readily be shown that existence of a scalar potential implies irrotationality, since the curl of a gradient operator is always zero. Potentials are used frequently, since they allow irrotational vector fields to be treated in terms of scalar fields, thereby essentially replacing the three equations for the three vector components by a single equation.

In many instances the differential equation defining a scalar potential is of second order, involving the divergence of the gradient of the potential. This second-order differential operator is called the *Laplacian* and is represented by $\nabla^2$:

$$\nabla^2 \phi = div\, grad\, \phi = \nabla \cdot \nabla\phi = \frac{\partial^2 \phi}{\partial x^2} + \frac{\partial^2 \phi}{\partial y^2} + \frac{\partial^2 \phi}{\partial z^2} = \frac{\partial^2 \phi}{\partial x_i^2}\,. \tag{1.40}$$

The Laplacian operator plays a central role in equations of acoustics.

## Spherical Symmetry

Thus far the various vector operators have been described in cartesian coordinates. However, many problems of fluid mechanics and acoustics exhibit spherical symmetry and are better treated in spherical coordinates. Spherical coordinates involve a radial unit vector, $\hat{r}$, and two angular coordinates. When spherical symmetry exists, spatial derivatives with respect to all directions except the radial direction are zero, and the vector operators take on relatively simple forms:

$$\vec{A} = \hat{r} A_r(r)\,, \tag{1.41}$$

$$\nabla\phi = \frac{\partial\phi}{\partial r}\,, \tag{1.42}$$

$$\nabla \cdot \vec{A} = \frac{1}{r^2}\,\frac{\partial (r^2 A_r)}{\partial r} = \frac{\partial A_r}{\partial r} + \frac{2}{r} A_r\,, \tag{1.43}$$

$$\nabla^2\phi = \frac{1}{r^2}\,\frac{\partial}{\partial r}\left(r^2\,\frac{\partial\phi}{\partial r}\right) = \frac{1}{r}\,\frac{\partial^2 (r\phi)}{\partial r^2}\,. \tag{1.44}$$

## Line, Surface and Volume Integrals

*Line integrals* of a function are carried out between two points along a specified path. They are written

$$\int_A^B f ds\,,$$

where $ds$ is a differential segment of the specific path. If the quantity is a vector, then the line integral is the integral of the component of the vector in the direction of the segment, given by

$$\int_A^B \vec{f} \cdot \vec{ds} = \int_A^B \left(f_x dx + f_y dy + f_z dz\right) = \int_A^B f_i ds_i \ . \tag{1.45}$$

In general, line integrals depend upon the specific path chosen. However, for the important class of fields for which rotation is zero and for which a scalar potential exists, the integral is independent of path and dependent only on its end points:

$$\int_A^B \nabla\phi \cdot \vec{ds} = \int_A^B \left(\frac{\partial\phi}{\partial x} dx + \frac{\partial\phi}{\partial y} dy + \frac{\partial\phi}{\partial z} dz\right) = \int_A^B d\phi = \phi_B - \phi_A \ . \tag{1.46}$$

A *contour integral* is a line integral taken around the edges of a surface, returning to the starting point. The value of a contour integral is a measure of the rotation enclosed by the contour and is zero for irrotational fields.

Differential elements of surface are described by a magnitude and by the direction of the outward-drawn normal to the surface. The *surface integral* of a vector function is the integral of its normal component over the surface:

$$\int_S \vec{f} \cdot \vec{dS} = \int_S (\vec{f} \cdot \hat{n})\, dS = \int_S f_n dS \ . \tag{1.47}$$

The surface integral gives the flux of the quantity through the surface and is a scalar quantity.

*Volume integrals* are used to sum a quantity over a specified volume. They can be applied to vectors as well as to scalars. For example, the mass within a volume is given by the volume integral of density

$$m = \int_V \rho dV \ . \tag{1.48}$$

**Complex Quantities**

It is often useful to express a physical quantity as the real part of a complex quantity. This procedure is used extensively when dealing with sinusoids, since the projection on either axis of a uniformly-rotating two-dimensional vector is a sinusoid. A *complex number* may be written either as the sum of a real and an imaginary part or as a magnitude and phase angle, or argument,

$$\underline{A} = A_1 + iA_2 = Ae^{i\theta} \ , \tag{1.49}$$

where the *magnitude*, $A$, is given by

$$A \equiv |A| = \sqrt{A_1^2 + A_2^2} \ , \tag{1.50}$$

and the *argument*, $\theta$, by

$$\theta = \tan^{-1} \frac{A_2}{A_1} . \tag{1.51}$$

$A_1$ is called the *real component* and $A_2$ the *imaginary* one.

The *complex conjugate* of a complex number has the same amplitude but negative argument

$$\underline{A}^* \equiv A_1 - iA_2 = Ae^{-i\theta} , \tag{1.52}$$

from which an alternative expression for the amplitude is

$$A = \sqrt{\underline{A} \cdot \underline{A}^*} . \tag{1.53}$$

When using complex quantities in physical equations, it should be remembered that the physical quantities they represent are their real parts, sometimes written $RP(\underline{A})$. Often the $RP$ is omitted, since it is understood that physical quantities are real. Equations written between complex quantities are also valid equations between their real components. It is useful to think of $i$ as a 90° rotational operator:

$$i \equiv \sqrt{-1} = e^{i(\pi/2)} . \tag{1.54}$$

From this it also follows that $-1$, which is $i$ multiplied by itself, represents a rotation of 180°, or $\pi$ radians.

Interpretation of the real and imaginary parts of a complex number as projections of a vector on the real and imaginary axes leads to several relations between exponential and trigonometric functions. Thus, Eq. 1.49 can be written

$$\underline{A} = A_1 + iA_2 = A \cos\theta + iA \sin\theta = Ae^{i\theta} , \tag{1.55}$$

from which it follows that

$$e^{i\theta} = \cos\theta + i \sin\theta \tag{1.56}$$

and that

$$e^{-i\theta} = \cos(-\theta) + i \sin(-\theta) = \cos\theta - i \sin\theta . \tag{1.57}$$

By simultaneous solution of Eqs. 1.56 and 1.57,

$$\cos\theta = \frac{1}{2}\left(e^{i\theta} + e^{-i\theta}\right) \tag{1.58}$$

and

$$\sin\theta = \frac{1}{2i}\left(e^{i\theta} - e^{-i\theta}\right). \tag{1.59}$$

**Fourier Series**

Provided only that linearity can be assumed, any arbitrary function can be represented by an infinite series of functions of a prescribed set. Functions that are useful in mathematical analyses of physical problems include trigonometric functions, Bessel functions and Legendre polynomials. The Fourier method using trigonometric functions is the most popular. Trigonometric functions have the important property that all their derivatives are trigonometric functions, and that every even derivative is the same function.

If $f(x)$ is a continuous function defined in the interval $-L < x < L$, then $f(x)$ can in general be represented by

$$f(x) = \frac{a_o}{2} + \sum_{n=1}^{\infty}\left(a_n \cos\frac{n\pi x}{L} + b_n \sin\frac{n\pi x}{L}\right), \tag{1.60}$$

where the coefficients of the cosine and sine series satisfy the relationships:

$$a_n = \frac{1}{L}\int_{-L}^{L} f(x)\cos\left(\frac{n\pi x}{L}\right) dx \qquad n = 0,1,2,\ldots \tag{1.61}$$

and

$$b_n = \frac{1}{L}\int_{-L}^{L} f(x)\sin\left(\frac{n\pi x}{L}\right) dx \qquad n = 1,2,\ldots. \tag{1.62}$$

The coefficient $a_o$ calculated from Eq. 1.61 with $n = 0$ is twice the average value of $f(x)$ over the interval.

Another useful form of this series makes use of the relations between trigonometric functions and exponentials given in Eqs. 1.58 and 1.59 to replace the sine and cosine terms by a complex exponential,

$$f(x) = \sum_{n=-\infty}^{\infty} \underline{C}_n e^{i(n\pi x/L)}, \tag{1.63}$$

where $\underline{C}_n$ can be expressed in terms of $a_n$ and $b_n$ or calculated directly from

$$\underline{C}_n = \frac{1}{2L}\int_{-L}^{L} f(x)e^{-i(n\pi x/L)}\, dx \qquad n = 0,1,2,\ldots. \tag{1.64}$$

Normally the number of terms required to represent a given function over a restricted interval is fairly small, ten terms usually being sufficient.

**Fourier Integrals and Transforms**

To analyze continuous, non-periodic functions, it is necessary to let $L$ approach infinity. The number of important terms increases accordingly, and in the limit the sum becomes replaceable by an integral. The *Fourier integral* expression for a non-periodic function may be written

$$f(x) = \sum_{-\infty}^{\infty} \underline{F}(\eta) e^{i\eta x} \, d\eta \,, \tag{1.65}$$

where $\eta$ replaces $n\pi/L$ in Eq. 1.63 as $n$ and $L$ both approach infinity. The function $\underline{F}(\eta)$ is called the *Fourier transform* of $f(x)$ and is given by

$$\underline{F}(\eta) = \frac{1}{2\pi} \int_{-\infty}^{\infty} f(x)\, e^{-i\eta x} \, dx \,. \tag{1.66}$$

Fourier transforms are frequently used in acoustics in transferring from the time domain to spectral space. It is the validity of the Fourier transform concept that makes spectral analysis of complex signals so valuable.

## REFERENCES


Bartberger, C.L., *Lecture Notes on Underwater Acoustics*, U.S. Naval Air Development Center, Johnsville, Pa., 1965 (AD 468869).

Beranek, L.L. (Ed.), *Noise Reduction*, McGraw-Hill, New York, 1960 (Part I).

Beranek, L.L. (Ed.), *Noise and Vibration Control*, McGraw-Hill, New York, 1971 (Chapter 2).

Churchill, R.V., *Complex Variables and Applications*, 2nd Edit., McGraw-Hill, New York, 1960.

Churchill, R.V., *Fourier Series and Boundary Value Problems*, 2nd Edit., McGraw-Hill, New York, 1963.

Harris, C.M. (Ed.), *Handbook of Noise Control*, McGraw-Hill, New York, 1957.

Horton, C.W., Sr., *Signal Processing of Underwater Acoustic Waves*, U.S. Govt. Printing Office, Washington, 1969.

Kinsler, L.E. and Frey, A.R., *Fundamentals of Acoustics*, 2nd Edit., Wiley, New York, 1962 (Chapters 1 and 15).

Lighthill, M.J., *Introduction to Fourier Analysis and Generalized Functions*, Cambridge University Press, New York, 1964.

Morse, P.M. and Ingard, K.U., *Theoretical Acoustics*, McGraw-Hill, New York, 1968 (Chapter 1).

Urick, R.J., *Principles of Underwater Sound for Engineers*, McGraw-Hill, New York, 1967.

# CHAPTER 2

# SOUND WAVES IN LIQUIDS

## 2.1 Description of Waves

A *wave* is an energy-carrying disturbance moving through a distributed medium. Familiar examples include surface waves on water, waves in strings and electromagnetic (radio) waves. Sound energy is carried by longitudinal waves, which involve alternating compressions and rarefactions of the medium. Sound waves occur in gases, liquids and solids. Derivations of the pertinent equations are slightly different for the three types of media, although the basic nature of the wave motion is the same. Discussions and derivations given in this book are specific to liquids, but apply almost equally well to gases. The equations for sound waves in solids are more complex (see Officer, 1958).

Figure 2.1 illustrates the simplest example of wave motion, such as that on a string. A simple disturbance moves along the $x$-axis with wave speed $c$, maintaining its shape as it progresses. The most general function describing such a motion is of the form $f(x - ct)$, which is a solution of the second-order differential equation

$$\frac{\partial^2 f}{\partial x^2} - \frac{1}{c^2}\frac{\partial^2 f}{\partial t^2} = 0 , \qquad (2.1)$$

as can readily be shown by performing the indicated partial differentiations. This equation is the *wave equation* for a wave progressing in the $x$ direction.

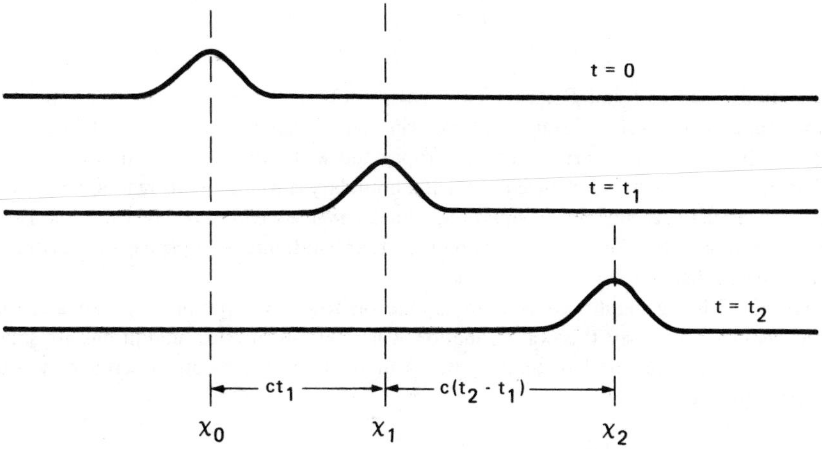


Fig. 2.1. A Simple Progressing Wave

**Plane Waves**

A general analytic expression for a plane wave in space is of the form $F(r - ct)$, where $r$ is distance traveled by the wave in the direction of propagation. In cartesian coordinates

$$F(r - ct) = F(n_x x + n_y y + n_z z - ct) , \tag{2.2}$$

where the various $n$'s are the three direction cosines, i.e., the three coordinate projections of a unit vector normal to a plane of constant phase. The direction cosines satisfy the relationship

$$n_x^2 + n_y^2 + n_z^2 = \left(\frac{x}{r}\right)^2 + \left(\frac{y}{r}\right)^2 + \left(\frac{z}{r}\right)^2 = 1 . \tag{2.3}$$

The function $F$ satisfies the generalized wave equation for disturbances in three-dimensional space,

$$\frac{\partial^2 F}{\partial x^2} + \frac{\partial^2 F}{\partial y^2} + \frac{\partial^2 F}{\partial z^2} - \frac{1}{c^2}\frac{\partial^2 F}{\partial t^2} = 0 , \tag{2.4}$$

which can also be expressed in terms of the Laplacian defined by Eq. 1.40,

$$\nabla^2 F - \frac{1}{c^2}\frac{\partial^2 F}{\partial t^2} = 0 . \tag{2.5}$$

This general form is applicable in numerous coordinate systems.

**Retarded Time**

Physically, functions such as $f$ and $F$ represent action at a distance retarded in time. Thus, a disturbance at point $x_o$ at time $t = 0$ in Fig. 2.1 is experienced at a remote point $x_2$ at later time $t_2 = (x_2 - x_o)/c$. Introducing retarded time as

$$t' \equiv t - \frac{r}{c} , \tag{2.6}$$

wave functions such as $f$ and $F$ can be expressed simply as functions of retarded time, $t'$. Equation 2.5 implies action at a distance retarded in time. Whenever action at all locations occurs simultaneously, disturbances are essentially propagated with infinite speed and the second term in Eq. 2.5 is zero. Thus, when a change occurs at a boundary, instantaneous reaction everywhere can be described mathematically by an equation, called *Laplace's equation*, in which the Laplacian is zero. An equation of the form of Eq. 2.5, on the other hand, implies a propagating disturbance for which action at a distance is retarded in time.

Equation 2.5 is a general wave equation applicable to many types of propagating disturbances. Acoustic disturbances obey this wave equation when certain physical conditions are satisfied. In Chapter 5 it will be shown that bending waves in rods and plates are described by a different differential equation.

**Harmonic Representation of Waves**

If amplitudes of waves are small enough so that linear relationships between stress and strain apply in the medium, then several waves may be superimposed, creating new waves. More important, any arbitrary disturbance may be decomposed into a number of component periodic waves. The simplest periodic waves are, of course, sinusoids associated with simple harmonic motion. A sinusoid propagating in the $x$ direction may be written

$$f(x - ct) = A_1 \cos\left(\omega t - \frac{\omega}{c}x\right) + A_2 \sin\left(\omega t - \frac{\omega}{c}x\right), \tag{2.7}$$

where $\omega \equiv 2\pi f$ is the angular frequency measured in radians per second. The angular frequency divided by the speed of wave propagation is essentially a spatial frequency. It is proportional to the number of wave cycles occurring in a unit distance, and is termed the *wave number*:

$$k \equiv \frac{\omega}{c} = \frac{2\pi f}{c} = \frac{2\pi}{\lambda}. \tag{2.8}$$

Wave number plays a role in space similar to that of angular frequency in the time domain.

The sinusoid of Eq. 2.7 may be expressed by a single cosine term:

$$f(x - ct) = \sqrt{A_1^2 + A_2^2}\cos\left(\omega t - kx - \tan^{-1}\frac{A_2}{A_1}\right). \tag{2.9}$$

Using the convention that the cosine is the real part of a complex exponential, as in Eq. 1.56, Eq. 2.9 can be written

$$f(x - ct) = RP\left(\underline{A}\, e^{i(\omega t - kx)}\right), \tag{2.10}$$

where the complex amplitude, $\underline{A}$, expresses the phase angle as well as magnitude of a rotating complex vector. In what follows, we will represent most sinusoids as complex quantities and omit $RP$, since "real part of" is always understood in physical equations.

The harmonic approach to wave phenomena is used almost universally. This is because it is consistent with spectral analysis, and because there are cases for which the effective wave speed, $c$, is a function of frequency and for which the general wave equation is therefore invalid.

**Helmholtz Equation**

When the solution of the wave equation is expressed by sinusoids, the equation itself takes a somewhat modified form. Since

$$\frac{\partial^2 F}{\partial t^2} = (i\omega)^2 F = -k^2 c^2 F, \tag{2.11}$$

Eq. 2.5 becomes

$$\nabla^2 F + k^2 F = 0. \tag{2.12}$$

This is the *Helmholtz equation*, and is a common form of the wave equation.

**Wave Vectors**

The wave number defined by Eq. 2.8 as a kind of spatial frequency is a scalar quantity, i.e., it is characterized by a number without any directional implications. However, position in space implies direction from an origin and is a vector. It is, therefore, quite useful to define a vector quantity for the spatial domain representing not only the magnitude of the wave number, but also the direction of propagation of the wave. In cartesian coordinates

$$\vec{k} \equiv \hat{\imath} k_x + \hat{\jmath} k_y + \hat{k} k_z = k\left(\hat{\imath} n_x + \hat{\jmath} n_y + \hat{k} n_z\right) , \tag{2.13}$$

where the various $n$'s are the direction cosines of a unit vector normal to the plane of constant phase, as previously discussed. Since the sum of the squares of the direction cosines is unity, it follows that

$$k^2 = k_x^2 + k_y^2 + k_z^2 . \tag{2.14}$$

Using the wave vector, the general expression for a plane harmonic wave in space may be written:

$$F(x,y,z,\omega,t) = \underline{A}\, e^{i(\omega t - \vec{k}\cdot\vec{r})} . \tag{2.15}$$

The significance of the wave vector can be illustrated in connection with the solution of the wave equation by the method of separation of variables. If the function $F$ is expressed as the product of three spatial functions and a time function,

$$F(x,y,z,\omega,t) = X(x,\omega) \cdot Y(y,\omega) \cdot Z(z,\omega)\, e^{i\omega t} , \tag{2.16}$$

then Eq. 2.12 becomes

$$\frac{1}{X}\frac{d^2X}{dx^2} + \frac{1}{Y}\frac{d^2Y}{dy^2} + \frac{1}{Z}\frac{d^2Z}{dz^2} + k_x^2 + k_y^2 + k_z^2 = 0 . \tag{2.17}$$

Treating this equation as three equations of the form

$$\frac{d^2X}{dx^2} + k_x^2 X = 0 , \tag{2.18}$$

it is clear that the components of the wave vector are the constants that separate the three-dimensional wave equation into three separate equations.

Just as waves can be analyzed in terms of their spectral components in the frequency domain, they can also be analyzed in terms of their wave-number spectra. The only difference is that the analysis involves all three coordinate directions and resolves into three wave-number spectra. Fourier transforms are consequently somewhat more complex.

Radar antennas and acoustic arrays that discriminate in direction can be treated as wave-vector filters, analogous to spectral filters that respond to a band of frequencies. Wave vectors are also quite useful when dealing with propagation between two media, since the boundary can be treated as a wave-vector transformer. Radiation problems invariably concern two media and so are often analyzed by means of wave vectors.

## 2.2 Wave Equation for Sound in Fluids

There are a number of possible approaches to the derivation of the differential equation for propagation of acoustic disturbances in a fluid medium. The approach which is taken here treats acoustics as small-signal, non-steady (a.c.) fluid mechanics. In this approach, differential equations governing sound propagation are derived from equations of fluid mechanics by treating acoustic signals as small fluctuating disturbances. Relations used are: the continuity equation, expressing conservation of mass; the equation of motion (law of conservation of momentum), which is the statement for fluids of Newton's second law; and the stress-strain relationship, or equation of state, for a fluid.

In one approach, the continuity and momentum equations are combined prior to making any special acoustic assumptions. This approach is taken in Chapter 3 in deriving a more general equation, from which the wave equation can be derived as a special case. In the present section, the acoustic wave equation is derived by making a number of restrictive assumptions and applying them to the continuity and momentum equations before their combination. This process is illuminating, since the wave equation is strictly valid for sound only when all of the assumptions given below are satisfied, and it is important to understand the roles of the assumptions.

### Assumptions

The physical assumptions used in deriving the acoustic wave equation from fluid mechanics are:

1) the fluid is isotropic, homogeneous and continuous;
2) the fluid cannot withstand static shear stresses in the manner of a solid;
3) viscous stresses are negligible;
4) there is no conduction or radiation of heat;
5) any chemical, electromagnetic or other external forces experienced by the fluid are negligible;
6) there are no local sources of sound;
7) the only steady motion of the medium is a uniform constant translation;
8) the stress-strain relationship is linear;
9) the relative compression of the medium is very small ($\Delta\rho << \rho_o$);
10) particle motions associated with sound waves are irrotational; and
11) spatial variations of the ambient pressure, density and temperature are relatively very small.

These assumptions are required in order to derive a simple equation. To the extent that they are not valid, additional terms occur in the final equation. Most of these additional terms may be treated as source terms, but some of them invalidate the wave solution.

The basic *acoustic assumption* is that physical quantities in fluid mechanics can be expressed as sums of steady-state, time-independent values plus fluctuating acoustic values. Thus, the static pressure is expressed by

$$p(x,y,z,t) = p_o(x,y,z) + p'(x,y,z,t) \;, \tag{2.19}$$

where

$$p_o = \frac{1}{T} \int_o^T p dt \qquad (2.20)$$

is the ambient value that exists when sound is absent and $p'$ is the acoustic component, the long-time average of which is zero. Similar expressions apply to density and to the components of velocity. However, the seventh assumption listed above, that of constant translational velocity, implies that the equations can be written for a coordinate system moving with the fluid, for which $\vec{v}_o = 0$.

**Equation of State**

The equation of state of a substance is a relationship between static pressure, density and temperature. At a fixed temperature, pressure may be expressed as a power expansion of density, as

$$p = p_o + a(\rho - \rho_o) + b(\rho - \rho_o)^2 + \ldots , \qquad (2.21)$$

where the coefficients $a$ and $b$, as well as $p_o$ and $\rho_o$, are functions of temperature. From the eighth and ninth assumptions, it follows that in linear acoustics higher order terms are negligible and that the acoustic pressure, $p'$, can be related to the acoustic component of the density, $\rho'$, by

$$p' = p - p_o \doteq a(\rho - \rho_o) = a\rho' , \qquad (2.22)$$

which is the equation of state for an acoustic disturbance. From the eleventh assumption, coefficient $a$ is assumed to be constant or, if varying, to be a slowly varying function of position.

**Equation of Continuity**

The continuity equation of fluid mechanics expresses conservation of mass. It can be derived by either of two approaches. In one approach, named after Lagrange, attention is focused on a particular mass of fluid as it moves through space. Continuity simply states that this mass must be constant:

$$\frac{Dm}{Dt} = \frac{D}{Dt} \int_V \rho dV = 0 . \qquad (2.23)$$

The special type of derivative represented by $D/Dt$ applies to a particle as it moves. It is called a *material derivative*, or *substantial*, and has all the mathematical attributes of a total derivative with respect to time. Since the particle moves through space, the material derivative can be expressed in terms of particle velocity, $\vec{v}$, and local partial derivatives by

$$\frac{D}{Dt} = \frac{\partial}{\partial t} + \frac{\partial x}{\partial t} \cdot \frac{\partial}{\partial x} + \frac{\partial y}{\partial t} \cdot \frac{\partial}{\partial y} + \frac{\partial z}{\partial t} \cdot \frac{\partial}{\partial z} \qquad (2.24a)$$

$$\frac{D}{Dt} = \frac{\partial}{\partial t} + (\vec{v} \cdot \nabla) = \frac{\partial}{\partial t} + v_i \frac{\partial}{\partial x_i} . \tag{2.24b}$$

Material derivatives can be applied to vector as well as scalar quantities.

As a particle moves through space, its density may change. Since its mass is constant, the volume it occupies must also change. The *transport theorem*, originally derived by Euler, relates the material derivative of an element of volume to the divergence of the velocity field:

$$\frac{D}{Dt} \int_V dV = \int_V div\, \vec{v}\, dV . \tag{2.25}$$

Using this relationship, Eq. 2.23 can be expanded:

$$\frac{Dm}{Dt} = \int_V \left( \frac{D\rho}{Dt} + \rho\, div\, \vec{v} \right) dV = 0 . \tag{2.26}$$

Since the volume is finite, it follows that the expression within the parentheses must be zero,

$$\frac{D\rho}{Dt} + \rho \left( \nabla \cdot \vec{v} \right) = 0 , \tag{2.27}$$

which is the Lagrangian form of the equation of continuity. Expanding the material derivative of the density by Eq. 2.24b yields a second form,

$$\frac{\partial \rho}{\partial t} + \vec{v} \cdot \nabla \rho + \rho \left( \nabla \cdot \vec{v} \right) = 0 , \tag{2.28}$$

which is the one used in deriving a continuity equation for acoustic disturbances.

The second method of deriving the continuity equation of fluid mechanics is named for Euler. In this approach, attention is focused on a fixed volume and the time-rate-of-change of mass within this volume is equated to the flux of mass into the volume through its surfaces:

$$\frac{\partial}{\partial t} \int_V \rho dV = \int_V \frac{\partial \rho}{\partial t} dV = - \int_S \rho \vec{v} \cdot \vec{dS} . \tag{2.29}$$

The surface integral can be expressed as a volume integral by invoking Gauss' divergence theorem,

$$\int_S \vec{A} \cdot \vec{dS} = \int_V div\, \vec{A}\, dV , \tag{2.30}$$

whereupon Eq. 2.29 becomes

$$\int_V \left( \frac{\partial \rho}{\partial t} + div\left(\rho \vec{v}\right) \right) dV = 0 \,, \tag{2.31}$$

and it follows that

$$\frac{\partial \rho}{\partial t} + div(\rho \vec{v}) = \frac{\partial \rho}{\partial t} + \nabla \cdot \rho \vec{v} = \frac{\partial \rho}{\partial t} + \frac{\partial (\rho v_i)}{\partial x_i} = 0 \,, \tag{2.32}$$

which is the Eulerian form of the continuity equation. When the divergence term is expanded, this result is identical to that of Eq. 2.28.

The acoustic form of the equation of continuity can be derived from Eq. 2.28 by expressing each physical variable as the sum of a time-independent average value and a fluctuating component, and taking a coordinate system moving with the fluid:

$$\frac{\partial \rho'}{\partial t} + \vec{v}' \cdot \nabla \left(\rho_o + \rho'\right) + \left(\rho_o + \rho'\right)\left(\nabla \cdot \vec{v}'\right) = 0 \,. \tag{2.33}$$

The gradient of $\rho_o$ is negligible by the eleventh assumption, and $\rho$ is negligible relative to $\rho_o$ in the third term by the ninth assumption, leaving

$$\frac{\partial \rho'}{\partial t} + \vec{v}' \cdot \nabla \rho' + \rho_o\left(\nabla \cdot \vec{v}'\right) = 0 \,. \tag{2.34}$$

The first and last terms exhibit linear dependencies on fluctuating quantities, while the middle term is quadratic. In the limit, for very small acoustic fluctuations, this term must become negligible relative to the other two. The final form of the linear acoustic continuity equation in a region free of acoustic sources is

$$\frac{\partial \rho'}{\partial t} + \rho_o\left(\nabla \cdot \vec{v}'\right) = \frac{\partial \rho'}{\partial t} + \rho_o \frac{\partial v_i'}{\partial x_i} = 0 \,. \tag{2.35}$$

**Equation of Motion**

The equation of motion for a fluid may be formulated directly from Newton's second law by equating the rate-of-change of momentum of a fluid particle to the sum of the forces acting on it. Forces which are considered in fluid mechanics include gravity, the gradient of pressure, viscous stresses and other unspecified external forces. However, in an acoustic derivation, by the first six assumptions, it is only necessary to consider forces associated with gravity and with the gradient of the pressure.

The gravitational force experienced by a particle is given by

$$\vec{F}_g = m\vec{g} = \int_V \rho\vec{g}\,dV = -\int_V \rho g \nabla z\, dV\,, \tag{2.36}$$

where the minus sign shows that gravity is a downward force, the $z$-axis being positive upward.

Pressure applies force normal to surfaces of a volume,

$$\vec{F}_p = -\int_S p\, d\vec{S}\,, \tag{2.37}$$

where the minus sign arises from the inward direction of pressure-generated forces and use of the outward normal in defining a vector surface element. Surface integrals can be transformed to volume integrals by use of Gauss' gradient theorem,

$$\int_S A\, d\vec{S} = \int_V \mathrm{grad}\, A\, dV\,, \tag{2.38}$$

and the net force caused by the gradient of the pressure becomes

$$\vec{F}_p = -\int_V \nabla p\, dV\,. \tag{2.39}$$

The momentum of a particle is the volume integral of the product of its density and velocity. Taking the material derivative, expanding it by means of Eq. 2.24 and using the transport theorem, Eq. 2.25, one obtains

$$\frac{DM}{Dt} = \frac{D}{Dt}\int_V (\rho\vec{v})dV = \int_V \left(\frac{D(\rho\vec{v})}{Dt} + (\rho\vec{v})(\nabla\cdot\vec{v})\right)dV$$

$$= \int_V \left(\rho\frac{D\vec{v}}{Dt} + \vec{v}\frac{D\rho}{Dt} + (\rho\vec{v})(\nabla\cdot\vec{v})\right)dV\,. \tag{2.40}$$

From the continuity equation as given by Eq. 2.27, the second and third terms are seen to add to zero leaving only the first term. Equating the rate-of-change of momentum to the sum of the forces,

$$\frac{dM}{dt} = \int_V \rho\frac{D\vec{v}}{Dt}\,dV = \vec{F}_g + \vec{F}_p = -\int_V (\rho g\nabla z + \nabla p)\,dV\,, \tag{2.41}$$

it follows that

$$\rho \frac{D\vec{v}}{Dt} = - \rho g \nabla z - \nabla p \, , \tag{2.42}$$

which is the Lagrangian form of the momentum equation in an ideal inviscid fluid. Expanding the material derivative by Eq. 2.24 yields

$$\rho \frac{\partial \vec{v}}{\partial t} = - \left( \rho g \nabla z + \nabla p + \rho (\vec{v} \cdot \nabla) \vec{v} \right), \tag{2.43}$$

which is a form useful for acoustic derivations.

As for continuity, the acoustic form of the momentum equation is obtained by replacing each physical variable by the sum of its steady and fluctuating components, and by taking a coordinate system moving with the fluid, so that $\vec{v}_o = 0$. When this is done, Eq. 2.43 becomes

$$(\rho_o + \rho') \frac{\partial v'}{\partial t} = - (\rho_o + \rho') g \nabla z - \nabla (p_o + p') - (\rho_o + \rho') (\vec{v}' \cdot \nabla) \vec{v}' \, . \tag{2.44}$$

Making the ninth assumption and retaining only linear terms,

$$\rho_o \frac{\partial \vec{v}'}{\partial t} = - \left( \rho_o g \nabla z + \nabla p_o + \nabla p' \right). \tag{2.45}$$

Since this equation is also valid in the absence of sound, the gradient of the ambient pressure cancels the gravitational term,

$$\nabla p_o = - \rho_o g \nabla z \, , \tag{2.46}$$

leaving

$$\rho_o \frac{\partial \vec{v}'}{\partial t} = - \nabla p' \, , \tag{2.47}$$

which is the acoustic conservation of momentum equation for an ideal fluid medium free of external sources.

It is in the next to the last step that derivations for liquids and gases may differ. The derivation given here is valid for all non-viscous fluids. However, when deriving the acoustic momentum equation for gases, it is common practice to ignore gravitational forces and to assume that the gradient of the ambient pressure is of second order. While valid for gases, this procedure is not valid in liquids. It is also common practice to assume that pressure fluctuations are small, an assumption that is often not valid in liquids and which is not made in the present derivation.

**Acoustic Wave Equation**

Equations 2.35, 2.47 and 2.22 for continuity, momentum and state can be combined to derive a second-order differential equation for acoustic quantities. Taking the partial derivative of

Eq. 2.35 with respect to time,

$$\frac{\partial^2 \rho'}{\partial t^2} + \frac{\partial}{\partial t}\left(\rho_o \nabla \cdot \vec{v}'\right) = \frac{\partial^2 \rho'}{\partial t^2} + \rho_o\left(\nabla \cdot \frac{\partial \vec{v}'}{\partial t}\right) = 0 , \qquad (2.48)$$

since the order of differentiation is immaterial. Taking the divergence of the momentum equation, Eq. 2.47, yields

$$\nabla \cdot \rho_o \frac{\partial \vec{v}'}{\partial t} \doteq \rho_o\left(\nabla \cdot \frac{\partial \vec{v}'}{\partial t}\right) = -\nabla^2 p' , \qquad (2.49)$$

where a term involving grad $\rho_o$ has been assumed to be of second order, in accordance with the eleventh assumption. Substituting Eq. 2.49 for the second term in Eq. 2.48,

$$\frac{\partial^2 \rho'}{\partial t^2} - \nabla^2 p' = 0 . \qquad (2.50)$$

The equation of state can now be used to eliminate either acoustic density or pressure. The results are similar. Thus, using Eq. 2.22 for $p'$ and assuming that spatial derivatives of $a$ are negligible,

$$\frac{\partial^2 \rho'}{\partial t^2} - a\nabla^2 \rho' = 0 . \qquad (2.51)$$

Dividing both terms by $-a$ yields a more common form,

$$\nabla^2 \rho' - \frac{1}{a}\frac{\partial^2 \rho'}{\partial t^2} = 0 , \qquad (2.52)$$

which we recognize as a wave equation, since it is similar to Eq. 2.5.

Comparing Eq. 2.52 to Eq. 2.5, it is apparent that the constant $a$ in Eq. 2.52 equals the square of the wave speed, $c$. Since the speed of sound is a property of the medium, it is represented by $c_o$. From Eq. 2.22, $c_o$ is a function of the compressibility of the medium,

$$c_o = \sqrt{a} = \sqrt{\frac{p'}{\rho'}} = \sqrt{\frac{dp}{d\rho}} = \sqrt{\frac{B}{\rho_o}} , \qquad (2.53)$$

where $B$ is the bulk modulus and expresses resistance to compression.

It is of interest to note that as the medium becomes more and more incompressible the speed of sound approaches infinity and the wave equation approaches Laplace's equation. Solutions of Laplace's equation are uniquely determined by boundary conditions: any changes in values at a boundary are felt immediately throughout the entire medium. In acoustics, changes at a boundary are experienced throughout a medium at later times. Thus, the fundamental distinction between acoustics and hydrodynamics is the delay of responses at a distance, delay being implied by the finiteness of the second term of the wave equation. Stated another way, Laplace's equation is valid when the largest dimensions involved in a problem are small compared to an acoustic wavelength. When physical dimensions become comparable to a wavelength, then compressibility can no longer be ignored and the wave equation must be used.

**Velocity Potential**

Wave equations of the same form as Eq. 2.52 can be derived for acoustic pressure, $p'$, and for each component of particle velocity, $\vec{v}'$. Since by the tenth assumption particle motions in sound waves are irrotational, it is also possible to define a scalar velocity potential by

$$\vec{v}' \equiv - \, grad \, \phi \; , \tag{2.54}$$

and to relate density and pressure fluctuations to this acoustic potential. Substituting for the velocity term in the acoustic momentum equation, Eq. 2.47 becomes

$$\rho_o \nabla \left( \frac{\partial \phi}{\partial t} \right) = \nabla p' \; , \tag{2.55}$$

from which it follows that

$$p' \equiv \rho_o \frac{\partial \phi}{\partial t} \; , \tag{2.56}$$

since by the very definition of a fluctuating component all constants of integration must be zero. From the equation of state, Eq. 2.53, the acoustic density is given by

$$\rho' = \frac{p'}{c_o^2} = \frac{\rho_o}{c_o^2} \frac{\partial \phi}{\partial t} \; . \tag{2.57}$$

Acoustic potential also satisfies the wave equation, as can be shown by substituting Eq. 2.57 for $\rho'$ and Eq. 2.54 for $\vec{v}'$ into the continuity equation, Eq. 2.35:

$$\frac{\partial}{\partial t} \left( \frac{\rho_o}{c_o^2} \frac{\partial \phi}{\partial t} \right) - \rho_o \nabla \cdot \nabla \phi = 0 \; . \tag{2.58}$$

Therefore,

$$\nabla^2 \phi - \frac{1}{c_o^2} \ddot{\phi} = 0 \; , \tag{2.59}$$

where each dot over $\phi$ represents a differentiation with respect to time.

**Harmonic Solutions**

The assumption of linearity made in deriving the acoustic wave equation makes it possible to treat any arbitrary disturbance as the sum of sinusoidal components, each of the form

$$\phi(\omega) = RP(\underline{\phi}) = RP(\Phi e^{i\omega t}) \; , \tag{2.60}$$

where the complex amplitude, $\Phi$, is a function of position in space as well as frequency and is found by solving the Helmholtz equation, Eq. 2.12:

$$\nabla^2 \underline{\Phi} + k^2 \underline{\Phi} = 0 \ . \tag{2.61}$$

Once the potential is known, the acoustic pressure and density can readily be found from

$$\underline{p}' = \rho_o \dot{\underline{\phi}} = i\omega\rho_o \underline{\phi} = ik\rho_o c_o \underline{\phi} \tag{2.62}$$

and

$$\underline{\rho}' = \frac{\rho_o}{c_o^2} \dot{\underline{\phi}} = i\omega \frac{\rho_o}{c_o^2} \underline{\phi} = ik \frac{\rho_o}{c_o^2} \underline{\phi} \ . \tag{2.63}$$

However, the particle velocity, being a function of the gradient of the potential, depends upon the particular spatial solution. Of the many possible solutions, the two most useful are for plane and spherical waves. Since most other waves can be treated as superpositions of either of these fundamental types, we will limit our discussions of solutions of Eq. 2.61 to plane and spherical waves.

## 2.3 Plane Sound Waves

### Acoustic Potential

The scalar potential describing a plane harmonic sound wave can be written

$$\underline{\phi} = \underline{\Phi}\, e^{i\omega t} = \underline{A}\, e^{i(\omega t - \vec{k} \cdot \vec{r})} = \underline{A}\, e^{i(\omega t - k_x x - k_y y - k_z z)} \ , \tag{2.64}$$

which can be verified either by carrying out the indicated differentiations and substituting the results into the Helmholtz equation or by direct comparison with the expressions given in Eqs. 2.15 and 2.16. The amplitude $\underline{A}$ is constant as the wave progresses.

### Particle Velocity

The particle velocity, $\vec{\underline{v}}'$, is related through Eq. 2.54 to the gradient of the scalar potential. In cartesian coordinates, for a plane wave

$$\vec{\underline{v}}' = -\nabla \underline{\phi} = -\left( \hat{\imath} \frac{\partial \underline{\phi}}{\partial x} + \hat{\jmath} \frac{\partial \underline{\phi}}{\partial y} + \hat{k} \frac{\partial \underline{\phi}}{\partial z} \right) = i \left( \hat{\imath} k_x \underline{\phi} + \hat{\jmath} k_y \underline{\phi} + \hat{k} k_z \underline{\phi} \right) = i\vec{k}\underline{\phi} \ , \tag{2.65}$$

which is a vector having the same direction as the wave vector and having an instantaneous value given by the real part of $ik\underline{\phi}$. Since the direction of propagation is usually obvious from geometrical considerations, it is common to deal with the acoustic particle speed and to write

$$\underline{v}' = ik\underline{\phi} \ . \tag{2.66}$$

Comparison of this expression with Eqs. 2.56 and 2.57 for acoustic pressure and density shows that for a plane wave the particle speed is in phase with both pressure and density fluctuations. This differs from hydrodynamics, for which velocity and pressure changes are often 180° out of phase.

The ratio of the particle velocity to the sound speed of the medium is essentially the *Mach number, M'*, of the acoustic particle motion. One would expect that second-order effects might become important if this Mach number approached unity. Actually, for plane waves the expression for acoustic Mach number is identical to that for the ratio of the fluctuating density to its steady-state value, as given by Eq. 2.63:

$$M' \equiv \frac{\underline{v}'}{c_o} = i\frac{k}{c_o}\underline{\phi} = \frac{\underline{\rho}'}{\rho_o} . \tag{2.67}$$

Since, by the ninth assumption, the density ratio is assumed to be very small when deriving the wave equation, it follows that acoustic Mach numbers are also small.

**Specific Acoustic Impedance**

The concept of mechanical impedance is often used when dealing with mechanical systems to express the ratio of a force to a velocity. A similar concept is used in acoustics when dealing with forces experienced by a radiating surface. Since by Eqs. 2.62 and 2.66 the acoustic pressure and particle speed in a wave are both proportional to acoustic potential, their ratio is a constant which is called the *specific acoustic impedance*. For a plane wave,

$$\underline{z}_a \equiv \frac{\underline{p}'}{\underline{v}'} = \frac{i\omega\rho_o\underline{\phi}}{ik\underline{\phi}} = \frac{\omega\rho_o}{k} = \rho_o c_o . \tag{2.68}$$

The quantity $\rho_o c_o$ is a property of the medium. It is called the *characteristic impedance* of the medium and is measured in units called *Rayls*, named after Lord Rayleigh. The value for water is close to $1.5 \times 10^6$ MKS Rayls, while the corresponding value for standard air is only 415. The difference is indicative of the relative compressibilities of the two media.

**Acoustic Intensity**

The fact that there is both particle motion and medium compression associated with a sound wave implies that there are both kinetic and potential energies in sound waves. However, it is possible in a standing wave to have kinetic and potential energies without any net flow of energy from one place to another. We are really more interested in the transfer of power by an acoustic disturbance than in the energy *per se*. The quantity which measures the transfer of acoustic power across a unit area is called the *acoustic intensity*, *I*. Intensity is the time-average power flow per unit area normal to the direction of travel of the wave and is given by

$$I \equiv \frac{1}{T}\int_0^T p'(t)v'(t)\,dt = \overline{p'(t)v'(t)} , \tag{2.69}$$

where $p'(t)$ and $v'(t)$ are instantaneous values of the pressure and the particle speed.

In a progressing plane wave, pressure and particle speed are in phase with each other. The speed can be expressed in terms of pressure by Eq. 2.68 and the intensity is given by

$$I = \frac{1}{T}\int_0^T p'(t) \cdot \frac{p'(t)}{\rho_o c_o}\,dt = \frac{\overline{p'^2}}{\rho_o c_o} . \tag{2.70}$$

One could also use Eq. 2.68 to substitute for the acoustic pressure, deriving an expression for intensity in terms of the rms particle speed,

$$I = \frac{1}{T}\int_0^T \rho_o c_o \mathrm{v}'(t) \cdot \mathrm{v}'(t)\, dt = \rho_o c_o \overline{\mathrm{v}'^2} \ . \qquad (2.71)$$

It also can be shown that the intensity of a plane wave is simply the product of the rms pressure and rms particle speed.

In a standing wave, pressures of the two waves are cumulative, but particle velocities cancel on average. Hence, Eq. 2.69 yields zero intensity for an ideal plane standing wave.

## 2.4 Spherical Waves

### Acoustic Potential

There are many instances in underwater acoustics when a source can be treated as a small pulsating spherical surface radiating sound in all directions. For this situation, the Laplacian is written in spherical coordinates for spherical symmetry by Eq. 1.44, and the Helmholtz equation becomes

$$\nabla^2 \underline{\phi} + k^2 \underline{\phi} = \frac{1}{r}\frac{\partial^2 (r\underline{\phi})}{\partial r^2} + k^2 \underline{\phi} = 0 \ . \qquad (2.72)$$

Multiplying through by $r$, one finds

$$\frac{\partial^2 (r\underline{\phi})}{\partial r^2} + k^2 (r\underline{\phi}) = 0 \ , \qquad (2.73)$$

which is of the same form as a one-dimensional Helmholtz equation, with $(r\underline{\phi})$ replacing $\underline{\phi}$ and $r$ replacing $x$. It follows that the solution is of the form

$$\underline{\phi} = \frac{A}{r} e^{i(\omega t - kr)} \ , \qquad (2.74)$$

showing that the magnitude of the potential decreases inversely with increasing distance from a source of spherical waves.

Since Eqs. 2.56 and 2.57 for acoustic pressure and density involve only time derivatives of the acoustic potential, these quantities bear the same relation to the potential as for plane waves, Eqs. 2.62 and 2.63. Their amplitudes therefore vary inversely with distance, in the same manner as the potential. Thus

$$P(r) = \frac{1}{r} P(1) \ . \qquad (2.75)$$

**Particle Velocity**

Equation 2.54 for particle velocity depends on spatial derivatives of the acoustic potential, and so depends on the shape of the wave front. For spherical waves,

$$\underline{\vec{v}}' = -\nabla \underline{\phi} = -\hat{r}\frac{\partial \underline{\phi}}{\partial r} = \hat{r}\left(\frac{\underline{\phi}}{r} + ik\underline{\phi}\right). \tag{2.76}$$

It follows that the particle speed can be expressed in either of two forms,

$$\underline{v}' = \frac{\underline{\phi}}{r}(1 + ikr) = ik\underline{\phi}\left(1 - \frac{i}{kr}\right), \tag{2.77}$$

from which it is clear that basically there are two distinct regimes. Close to a radiating source, in the *near field* given by $kr << 1$, the particle speed is dominated by the term that is in phase with the potential. Far from a source, in the *far field*, the particle speed is dominated by the term that is out of phase with the potential but in phase with the acoustic density and pressure. In the near field, particle speed varies inversely with the square of distance, since it drops off faster than the potential. In the far field, its dependence on distance is the same as that of the potential.

**Specific Acoustic Impedance**

Since the particle speed has both near- and far-field terms, the specific acoustic impedance is also a function of relative distance:

$$\underline{z}_a \equiv \frac{\underline{p}'}{\underline{v}'} = \frac{i\omega\rho_o\underline{\phi}}{ik\underline{\phi}\,(1 - (i/kr))} = \rho_o c_o \frac{(kr)^2 + ikr}{1 + (kr)^2}. \tag{2.78}$$

In the near field, $kr < 1$, the impedance is dominantly reactive, while in the far field it is basically resistive and for large $kr$ approaches the plane-wave value.

The resistive and reactive components form a complex number which can be expressed in exponential form,

$$\underline{z}_a = \rho_o c_o \frac{kr}{\sqrt{1 + (kr)^2}} \cdot \frac{kr + i}{\sqrt{1 + (kr)^2}}$$

$$= \rho_o c_o \cos\theta\,(\cos\theta + i\sin\theta) = \rho_o c_o \cos\theta\, e^{i\theta}, \tag{2.79}$$

where

$$\theta = \tan^{-1}\frac{1}{kr} = \frac{\pi}{2} - \tan^{-1} kr. \tag{2.80}$$

In the near field, $kr << 1$ and $\theta$ approaches $\pi/2$, from which it follows that

$$\underline{z}_a \doteq ikr\rho_o c_o \quad (kr << 1). \tag{2.81}$$

In the far field, on the other hand, $\theta$ approaches $0$ and Eq. 2.79 reduces to Eq. 2.68 for the impedance of a plane wave.

**Acoustic Intensity**

Equation 2.69 for acoustic intensity involves the product of instantaneous values of the acoustic pressure and particle speed. In complex notation, intensity is the time-average value of the product of the components of pressure and particle speed that are in phase with each other. Combining Eqs. 2.62 and 2.77, the particle speed of a spherical wave is related to its acoustic pressure by

$$\underline{v}' = \frac{\underline{p}'}{\rho_o c_o}\left(1 - \frac{i}{kr}\right). \tag{2.82}$$

The component in phase with the pressure is clearly the first term, which is independent of $kr$ and is therefore the same in the near field as in the far field. From Eqs. 2.69 and 2.82, the intensity of a spherical wave is

$$I = \frac{1}{T}\int_0^T p'(t) \cdot \frac{p'(t)}{\rho_o c_o}\, dt = \frac{\overline{p'^2}}{\rho_o c_o}. \tag{2.83}$$

This is the same as Eq. 2.70 for plane waves. If, instead of substituting for the particle speed, one were to substitute for the pressure, then from Eq. 2.79

$$\underline{p}' = \underline{v}' \frac{\rho_o c_o (kr)^2}{1 + (kr)^2}\left(1 + \frac{i}{kr}\right) = \underline{v}' \rho_o c_o \cos^2\theta \left(1 + \frac{i}{kr}\right), \tag{2.84}$$

and the intensity is

$$I = \frac{1}{T}\int_0^T v'(t) \cdot v'(t) \rho_o c_o \cos^2\theta \, dt = \rho_o c_o \overline{v'^2} \cos^2\theta , \tag{2.85}$$

which differs from the plane-wave expression by $\cos^2\theta$.

Because of the general validity of Eq. 2.83, pressure-sensitive instruments are better indicators of acoustic intensity than are velocity-sensitive ones. In water, because of the high impedance of the medium, almost all measurements are made with pressure-sensitive transducers and Eq. 2.83 is used to estimate the intensity. This procedure is valid when there is only one source and sound waves are progressing in only one direction. If waves emanate from more than one source, the particle velocities will have different directions and may even cancel. For example, a standing wave is formed when two equal waves are progressing in opposite directions. Such a wave carries no energy and has zero intensity, even though the rms pressure is finite.

**Ideal Transmission Loss**

Since the intensity of a spherical wave is proportional to the square of the pressure, and pressure according to Eq. 2.75 is inversely proportional to distance, it follows that the intensity from a simple source decays as the square of the distance. For this reason, ideal spherical sound propagation is often called *inverse-square spreading.*

As discussed in Chapter 1, a logarithmic quantity, transmission loss, is often used to express changes of acoustic intensity and pressure with distance. Substituting Eq. 2.75 into Eq. 1.20, which defines transmission loss, it follows that in an ideal, lossless medium transmission loss is given simply by

$$TL_i \equiv 20 \log \frac{p(1)}{p(r)} = 20 \log r \; , \tag{2.86}$$

and that in such an ideal medium sound pressure levels decrease by 6 dB for every doubling of distance.

Equation 2.86 for the transmission loss for spherical waves in an ideal medium is a direct consequence of the wave equation and of the assumptions made in deriving it. To the extent that these assumptions are not met, actual transmission loss will differ from ideal spherical spreading. *Transmission anomaly*, *TA*, is defined as the difference of the actual transmission loss from that predicted by spherical spreading:

$$TA \equiv TL - TL_i = TL - 20 \log r \; . \tag{2.87}$$

Anomaly is thus the dB measure of the cumulative effects of all of the ways in which the actual medium differs from the ideal medium assumed in the derivation of the wave equation. It is positive when the measured transmission loss exceeds the ideal value.

### Acoustic Power

The total power radiated by a source can be obtained by integrating the intensity over a spherical surface:

$$W_{ac} = \int_S I \, dS \doteq \int_S \frac{\overline{p'^2}}{\rho_o c_o} \, dS \; . \tag{2.88}$$

In the most general case, radiation does not occur uniformly and both $I$ and $p'$ are functions of angle as well as distance. In the case of an omnidirectional source,

$$W_{ac} = \frac{\overline{p'^2}}{\rho_o c_o} \cdot 4\pi r^2 \doteq 4\pi \frac{\overline{p'(1)^2}}{\rho_o c_o} \; , \tag{2.89}$$

showing that a consequence of the inverse-square law is constancy of acoustic power as a function of distance from a source.

It is because of the dependence of the acoustic power on $\rho_o c_o$ indicated by Eq. 2.88 that the acoustic power for a given acoustic pressure is so much lower in water than in air. Since the product of the density and speed of sound of water is approximately 3600 times as great as that of air, the same acoustic power produces acoustic pressure 60 times larger in water than in air.

**Damped Sound Waves**

The wave equation was derived under the assumption that viscosity, heat conduction and other dissipative phenomena are negligible. In actual sound transmission in the ocean these effects, while very small, are not zero. They may be taken into account by a perturbation approach in which the wave speed is treated as a complex quantity for which the dissipative out-of-phase component is very small compared to the real part:

$$\underline{c} = c(1 + i\eta) \qquad \eta << 1 . \tag{2.90}$$

The wave number is then also complex, and the expression for a spherical wave becomes

$$\underline{\phi} = \frac{A}{r} e^{i(\omega t - \underline{k}r)} = \frac{A}{r} e^{-k\eta r} e^{i(\omega t - kr)} . \tag{2.91}$$

This expression represents a spherical wave whose amplitude decays at a slightly greater rate than inversely with distance.

The effect of the real exponential term in Eq. 2.91 is to increase the transmission loss relative to the ideal value given by Eq. 2.86. Thus

$$TL = 20 \log \frac{re^{k\eta r}}{e^{k\eta}} \doteq 20 \log r + 20 \log e^{k\eta r} , \tag{2.92}$$

since $k\eta << 1$. The dissipative transmission anomaly is therefore

$$TA_{dis} = 20 \log e^{k\eta r} = (20)(0.4343)k\eta r = 8.686 k\eta r . \tag{2.93}$$

It is usual to write $TA = \alpha r$ where

$$\alpha = 8.686 k\eta \tag{2.94}$$

is the absorption coefficient in dB/m. The transmission loss in a slightly dissipative medium is thus

$$TL = TL_i + TA_{dis} = 20 \log r + \alpha r . \tag{2.95}$$

For this perturbation approach to the damping of sound waves to be valid, it is necessary that $\eta$ be a very small quantity indeed. Measurements in sea water show that $\eta$ increases with frequency, and that for frequencies under one megahertz it is smaller than $2 \times 10^{-5}$. Equation 2.91 is thus an excellent approximation for the effect of damping on spherical waves in water over the entire frequency range generally exploited by underwater sound devices and systems.

**Spherical Waves from Plane Waves**

In most problems spherical symmetry, with its inverse radial dependence of pressure and density, is easy to handle analytically. However, for some cases, such as the interaction of spherical waves with plane surfaces, spherical symmetry is a handicap. For such problems, it is useful to treat spherical waves as the superposition of an infinite number of plane waves. Brekhovskikh

(1960) has shown that

$$\frac{e^{ikr}}{r} = \frac{i}{2\pi} \iint_{-\infty}^{\infty} \frac{e^{i\left(k_x x + k_y y + k_z z\right)}}{k_z} dk_x dk_y \ , \tag{2.96}$$

where the integration is in wave-vector space. With this transformation spherical waves can be replaced with plane waves when that is desirable.

## 2.5 Transmission at Media Interfaces

### Snell's Law

In many instances sound waves created in one fluid medium are received in, or reflected by, a second medium. Problems involving planar boundaries are best treated by considering plane waves. As we have just noted, spherical waves can be decomposed into plane waves. If the second medium is a fluid, then the boundary is incapable of sustaining a stress, and the components of wave velocity parallel to the boundary must be the same in both media. It follows that the components of the wave vector parallel to a boundary surface are unchanged in crossing between the two media. This recognition of the constancy of the components of the wave vectors parallel to a boundary between two fluids leads directly to a derivation of *Snell's Law*.

Figure 2.2 represents the geometric picture of incident, reflected and transmitted rays at a

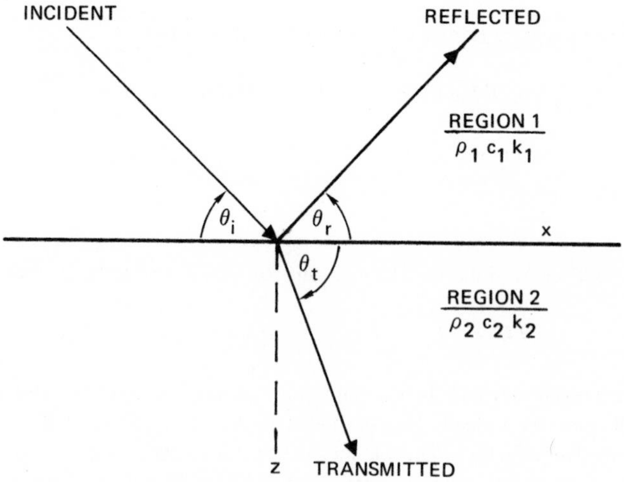


Fig. 2.2. Transmission at a Boundary between Two Fluid Media

boundary between two fluids. The parallel components of the three wave vectors are

$$k_{i_x} = k_1 \cos \theta_i \ , \tag{2.97}$$

$$k_{r_x} = k_1 \cos\theta_r \tag{2.98}$$

and

$$k_{t_x} = k_2 \cos\theta_t \,, \tag{2.99}$$

where $k_1 = \omega/c_1$ and $k_2 = \omega/c_2$, and angles are measured relative to the plane rather than to a normal as is more common in airborne acoustics. Since all three parallel components are equal, it follows that

$$\theta_r = \theta_i \tag{2.100}$$

and

$$\cos\theta_t = \frac{c_2}{c_1} \cos\theta_i \,. \tag{2.101}$$

This last relationship is Snell's law. It can be generalized to cases where sound speed is continuous, leading to the general statement that for any ray in a refractive medium the component of the wave vector parallel to the isovelocity surface is constant.

**Reflection from a Plane Boundary**

Equations 2.100 and 2.101 relate the angles of reflected and transmitted rays to the incident ray angle. Relationships between the amplitudes can be derived by recognizing that both the pressure and normal particle velocity must be continuous. Continuity of pressure requires that

$$P_i + P_r = P_t \,, \tag{2.102}$$

where the various $P$'s are amplitudes of the respective acoustic pressures. Continuity of the normal particle velocity leads to

$$P_i - P_r = \beta P_t \,, \tag{2.103}$$

where

$$\beta \equiv \frac{\rho_1 c_1}{\rho_2 c_2} \frac{\sin\theta_t}{\sin\theta_i} = \frac{\rho_1}{\rho_2} \frac{\tan\theta_t}{\tan\theta_i} \,. \tag{2.104}$$

Simultaneous solution of Eqs. 2.102 and 2.103 leads to a relation for the ratio of reflected pressure to incident pressure,

$$\alpha_r \equiv \frac{P_r}{P_i} = \frac{1-\beta}{1+\beta} \,, \tag{2.105}$$

which is valid if sin $\theta_t$ exists. When Eq. 101 is solved for sin $\theta_t$, it is found that

$$\sin \theta_t = \sqrt{1 - \left(\frac{c_2}{c_1}\right)^2 \cos^2 \theta_i} \,, \tag{2.106}$$

and that energy is transmitted into a medium with higher speed of sound only if the incident angle is greater than a *critical angle* defined by

$$\theta_c = \cos^{-1}\left(\frac{c_1}{c_2}\right) . \tag{2.107}$$

When grazing angles of incidence are less than the critical angle, all of the energy is reflected.

**Transmission through a Plane Boundary**

Simultaneous solution of Eqs. 2.102 and 2.103 for $P_t$ gives

$$\alpha_t \equiv \frac{P_t}{P_i} = \frac{2}{1 + \beta} \,, \tag{2.108}$$

provided, of course, that $\theta_i$ is greater than $\theta_c$. However, this equation for the pressure transmission ratio does not tell the whole story. Because the specific acoustic impedances of the two media differ, the relative sound power transmitted is not simply the square of the transmitted pressure ratio. Transmitted power can be calculated by subtracting reflected power from incident power, from which it follows that

$$\frac{W_t}{W_i} = 1 - \frac{W_r}{W_i} = 1 - \alpha_r^2 = \frac{4\beta}{(1 + \beta)^2} . \tag{2.109}$$

In treating transmission loss between two media, distinction needs to be made between pressure and power transmission losses. From Eq. 2.108 the pressure transmission loss is

$$TL \equiv 20 \log \frac{P_i}{P_t} = 20 \log \frac{1 + \beta}{2} \,, \tag{2.110}$$

while the power loss is

$$PTL \equiv 10 \log \frac{W_i}{W_t} = 10 \log \frac{(1 + \beta)^2}{4\beta} = TL - 10 \log \beta . \tag{2.111}$$

**Transmission from Air to Water**

Sometimes when calculating noise in water it is necessary to estimate contributions of sources in air. For example, one may wish to calculate the sound in water caused by aircraft flying overhead. The speed of sound in water is 4.35 times that of air. From Eq. 2.107, it follows that sound is transmitted from air into water only if the incident angle exceeds about 75°. The ratio of the specific acoustic impedances of the two media is 3600, from which

$$\beta \doteq 2.8 \times 10^{-4} \sin \theta_t \,. \tag{2.112}$$

The most efficient transmission of sound from air into water occurs near normal incidence, for which

$$\alpha_t = \frac{2}{1 + \beta} \doteq 2 \tag{2.113}$$

and

$$\frac{W_t}{W_i} = \frac{4\beta}{(1 + \beta)^2} \doteq 1.1 \times 10^{-3} \,. \tag{2.114}$$

The pressure level underneath the water surface is thus about 6 dB higher than its value in the air above the surface. However, the corresponding intensity and power levels are about 29.5 dB lower. It follows that, while airborne sources transmit very little acoustic power into water, they may be as detectable by pressure-sensitive transducers as by microphones.

Young (1973) has demonstrated that the entire sound field in water attributable to a source in air can be calculated with reasonable accuracy by locating a virtual source of strength 7 dB less than the actual source directly under the actual source at one-fifth its elevation, and assuming a dipole (cosine) radiation pattern with its maximum directly under the source.

**Transmission from Water into Air**

Detection of sources in water by instruments in air is a different matter. Again considering near-normal incidence,

$$\beta \doteq \frac{3600}{\sin \theta_i} \geqslant 3600 \,, \tag{2.115}$$

and the power transmission ratio is

$$\frac{W_t}{W_i} = \frac{4\beta}{(1 + \beta)^2} \doteq \frac{4}{\beta} \leqslant 1.1 \times 10^{-3} \,. \tag{2.116}$$

Thus the loss is at least 29.5 dB, the same as for transmission from air to water. However, the relative pressure level is much lower since, from Eq. 2.108, the pressure ratio is

$$\alpha_t = \frac{2}{1 + \beta} \leqslant \frac{2}{3601} = 5.5 \times 10^{-4} \,, \tag{2.117}$$

and it follows that the pressure transmission loss is at least 65 dB. Most noise sources in water are therefore virtually undetectable in air; only large high-power sources such as active sonars and explosions produce significant signals in the atmosphere.

To calculate the pressure field in air from a source in water, Young (1973) placed a virtual source at five times the actual source depth, of strength 52 dB less than the actual source level, and assumed a cosine-squared directional pattern. This calculation confirms the low levels in air indicated by Eq. 2.117.

## Reflection of Underwater Sound by Ocean Surfaces

The air-water interface at the ocean surface is an excellent reflector of underwater sound. From Eq. 2.105,

$$\alpha_r = -\frac{\beta - 1}{\beta + 1} \doteq -\left(1 - \frac{2}{\beta}\right) \doteq -0.9995 , \qquad (2.118)$$

showing that reflection occurs virtually without loss of amplitude and with a phase shift of 180°. Since the angle of reflection equals the angle of incidence, the effect of a free surface can be treated by considering negative image sources above the surface, as illustrated in Fig. 2.3. Often the geometrical situation is such that a receiver receives sound by both direct and reflected paths, resulting in complicated interference patterns. This subject is considered in more detail in Section 4.6.

The result given by Eq. 2.118 has been derived for a smooth plane surface. The actual ocean surface is of course quite rough, causing scattering of incident sound. Scattering may be thought to cause the image to dance around, or it may be considered to cause reflection loss and thus to reduce the amplitude of a fixed image. In any case, the effect increases with frequency, wave height and angle of incidence. A surface can be considered to be acoustically smooth and scattering loss to be negligible provided

$$\frac{h \sin \theta_i}{\lambda} < \frac{1}{4} , \qquad (2.119)$$

where $h$ is wave height. Thus, at 1 kHz, for which $\lambda = 1.5$m, at an angle of 10° the ocean is acoustically smooth for wave heights up to at least 2 m.

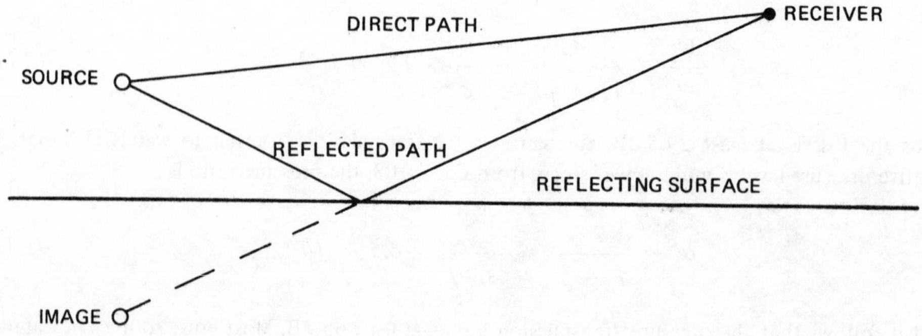


Fig. 2.3. Image Source for Reflection by Air-Water Interface

## 2.6 Finite-Amplitude Effects

In all of the discussions of sound waves in the present chapter, linearity has been assumed. Resolution of waves into independent harmonic components depends on this property. The derivation of the wave equation assumes linearity. Most phenomena in underwater acoustics can be completely understood in terms of linear acoustics. However, there are occasions when non-linear, finite-amplitude effects must be considered. The present brief exposition is intended merely to call attention to this aspect of acoustics and to present criteria which can be used to assess the possible significance of non-linear effects.

In linear acoustics, a fundamental assumption is that the particle velocity is small compared to the speed of sound. It follows that all parts of a wave travel at the same speed. Actually, this is not strictly true. The actual speed is a superposition of the local sound speed and the local particle velocity, both of which may vary with place in the wave. Thus, locally,

$$\frac{dx}{dt} = c + v' = c_o + \rho_o c_o \left(\frac{dc}{dp}\right) v' + v' . \tag{2.120}$$

The occurrence of non-linear effects is thus primarily attributable to the finite amplitude of the particle speed relative to that of sound, and secondarily to the fact that the speed of sound is itself not a constant. Beyer (1960) showed that the degree of non-linearity is controlled by the parameter

$$\frac{1}{c_o}\left|\frac{dx}{dt}\right|_{max} - 1 = \left(1 + \rho_o c_o \frac{dc}{dp}\right) M' = LM' , \tag{2.121}$$

where $M'$ is the acoustic Mach number of the wave at its peak. For a gas, $L$ can be shown to be related to the ratio of the specific heats, and to be equal to about 1.2 in air. For water, the value is about 3.5. Based on the larger value of $L$, one might expect greater non-linear effects in water than in air. However, the acoustic Mach number is invariably much less in water than in air.

Non-linear effects are also strongly frequency dependent, since the effects cumulate as the wave travels a number of wavelengths. A parameter governing non-linearity is the stretched range variable, $\sigma$, defined by

$$\sigma \equiv LM'kr_o \ln \frac{r}{r_o} , \tag{2.122}$$

where $r_o$ is a reference distance, usually about one meter. Expressing the acoustic Mach number in terms of the peak acoustic pressure,

$$\sigma = L\omega \frac{P(r_o) \cdot r_o}{\rho_o c_o^{3}} \ln \frac{r}{r_o} . \tag{2.123}$$

Distortion of the wave is negligible as long as $\sigma$ is less than about 0.15. It follows that non-linear effects can be completely ignored in sea water provided that the product of source pressure level and frequency do not exceed 30 kilohertz-atmospheres.

The only sources which approach non-linearity in normal sea water are large active sonars and explosions. However, if the medium contains quantities of bubbles, as in a zone of cavitation, $L$ may be significantly higher than normal and $c_o$ significantly lower, resulting in non-linear effects at much lower sound pressures. Thus, harmonic distortion, intermodulation products and increased absorption can all be expected to occur when the compressibility of a liquid is significantly increased due to the presence of bubbles.

## REFERENCES


Bartberger, C.L., *Lecture Notes on Underwater Acoustics*, U.S. Naval Air Development Center, Johnsville, Pa., 1965 (AD 468869) (pp. 5-176).

Beyer, R.T., Parameter of nonlinearity in fluids, *J.A.S.A., 32*, 719-721, 1960.

Beyer, R.T., *Nonlinear Acoustics*, Naval Sea Systems Command, Washington, 1974 (Chapter 3).

Blackstock, D.T., Propagation of plane sound waves of finite amplitude in nondissipative fluids, *J.A.S.A., 34*, 9-30, 1962.

Blackstock, D.T., "Nonlinear Acoustics (Theoretical)," Chapter 3n of *American Institute of Physics Handbook*, 3rd Edit., McGraw-Hill, New York, 1972.

Brekhovskikh, L.M., *Waves in Layered Media*, Academic Press, New York, 1960.

Eckart, C., The scattering of sound from the sea surface, *J.A.S.A., 32*, 1547-1551, 1960.

Fortuin, L., Survey of literature on reflection and scattering of sound waves at the sea surface, *J.A.S.A., 47*, 1209-1228, 1970; also, *SACLANT ASW Res. Centre Rept. 138*, 1969.

Hunt, F.V., "Propagation of Sound in Fluids," Chapter 3c of *American Institute of Physics Handbook*, McGraw-Hill, New York, 1957.

Kinsler, L.E. and Frey, A.R., *Fundamentals of Acoustics*, 2nd Edit., Wiley, New York, 1962 (Chapters 5, 6, 7 and 9).

Lamb, Sir Horace, *Hydrodynamics*, 6th Edit., Cambridge University Press, 1932; Dover, New York, 1945 (Chapter 1).

Lindsay, R.B., *Mechanical Radiation*, McGraw-Hill, New York, 1960 (Chapters 1, 2, 3 and 9).

Medwin, H. "Scattering from the Sea Surface," Chapter 3 of *Underwater Acoustics*, R.W.B. Stephens (Ed.), Wiley-Interscience, London, 1970 (pp. 57-89).

Morse, P.M., *Vibration and Sound*, 2nd Edit., McGraw-Hill, New York, 1948 (Sections 22, 25 and 27).

Morse, P.M. and Ingard, K.U., *Theoretical Acoustics*, McGraw-Hill, New York, 1968 (Chapter 6).

Naugol'nykh, K.A., "Absorption of Finite-Amplitude Waves," Part I of *High-Intensity Ultrasonic Fields*, L.D. Rozenberg (Ed.), Plenum Press, New York, 1971.

Officer, C.B., *Introduction to the Theory of Sound Transmission*, McGraw-Hill, New York, 1958 (Chapter 1).

Rayleigh, Lord, *Theory of Sound*, Vol. II, 2nd Edit., London, 1896; Dover, New York, 1945.

Young, R.W., Sound pressure in water from a source in air and vice versa. *J.A.S.A., 53*, 1708-1716, 1973.

## CHAPTER 3

# ACOUSTIC RADIATION FUNDAMENTALS

## 3.1 General Characterization of Noise Sources

Sound is generated in a fluid medium by any process that causes a non-steady pressure field to occur in that medium. Physical processes that can cause unsteady pressures include the pulsation or vibration of a boundary surface of the medium, the action of a non-steady force on the fluid, turbulent motions in the fluid, and oscillatory temperatures.* Each noise source can be characterized according to its dominant mechanism.

### Monopoles, Dipoles and Quadrupoles

Each basic physical mechanism that generates acoustic pressure fields corresponds mathematically to a dominant order of multipole. Thus, volume or mass fluctuations give rise to dominant simple sources, i.e., to zero-order poles called *monopoles*. Examples are pulsating bubbles, pistons in baffles and cavitation. Monopoles are essentially omnidirectional, although directional radiation patterns can be generated by forming arrays of monopoles. Fluctuating forces and vibratory motions of unbaffled rigid bodies are associated with *dipoles* and have cosine directional patterns. Turbulent fluid motions involve distortion without net volume changes or net forces and radiate as *quadrupoles*. Monopoles and dipoles occur only at fluid boundaries, but it is now recognized that quadrupoles can occur within the fluid itself, away from fluid boundaries, in regions of free turbulence where they are associated with fluctuating turbulent shear stresses. Figure 3.1 summarizes the basic physical characteristics of the three lowest order multipole sources.

### Radiation Impedance

If a source were a perfectly efficient radiator of sound, the entire motion would be converted into a radiating pressure field. Actual sources create a hydrodynamic non-radiating field as well as an acoustic field. Local pressures associated with the hydrodynamic motion are 90° out of phase with the acoustic component. These concepts are embodied in the radiation impedance

$$\underline{Z}_r = R_r + iX_r \,, \tag{3.1}$$

so defined that the resistance is proportional to the acoustic power and the reactance measures the sloshing hydrodynamic motion. Usually one can find a mean velocity associated with a noise source, in which case acoustic resistance is related to acoustic power by

---

*Thermal sources of sound are not generally considered when dealing with noise in liquids, although recent experiments with laser beams in water have produced sound by this mechanism.

$$R_r = \frac{W_{ac}}{\overline{U^2}} . \tag{3.2}$$

Radiation reactance is related to hydrodynamic reactive power by a similar relationship.

Radiation impedance measures the reaction of the medium on a source. As such, it is generally proportional to the impedance of the medium, $\rho_o c_o$, and to the area of the source, $S_o$. The *specific radiation resistance* is the non-dimensional normalized form of the radiation resistance defined by

$$\sigma_r \equiv \frac{R_r}{\rho_o c_o S_o} = \frac{W_{ac}}{\rho_o c_o S_o \overline{U^2}} , \tag{3.3}$$

and the *specific radiation reactance*, $\sigma_x$, is the corresponding non-dimensional form of the radiation reactance.

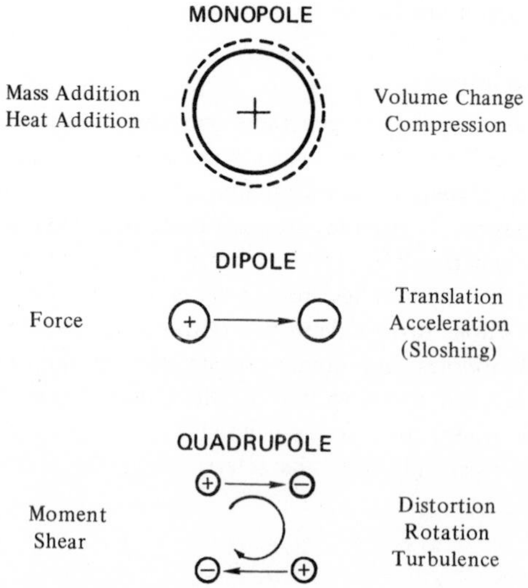


Fig. 3.1. Types of Sound Sources

## Radiation Efficiency

The *radiation efficiency* introduced in Chapter 1 by Eq. 1.4 is the ratio of acoustic power to the total power involved in the acoustic and hydrodynamic fluid motions. Thus,

$$\eta_{rad} \equiv \frac{W_{ac}}{W_{ac} + W_{slosh}} = \frac{R_r}{|\underline{Z}_r|} = \frac{R_r}{\sqrt{R_r^2 + X_r^2}} = \frac{\sigma_r}{\sqrt{\sigma_r^2 + \sigma_x^2}} . \tag{3.4}$$

Some authors prefer to call this the *radiation loss factor*, using the term *radiation efficiency* for the non-dimensional radiation resistance defined by Eq. 3.3.

The radiation efficiency of a multipole is dependent on the order of the pole and the ratio of the size of the radiator to a wavelength. For radiators which are small compared to the wavelength

$$\eta_{rad} \sim \left(\frac{a}{\lambda}\right)^{2m+1} \sim (ka)^{2m+1} , \tag{3.5}$$

where $m$ is the order of the pole, being zero for a monopole, one for a dipole and two for a quadrupole. Since many sources in liquids are characterized by having $ka$ small compared to unity, it follows that the lower the order of the source the more efficient it is as an acoustic radiator. When monopoles exist, they generally dominate. Lacking monopoles, dipoles are most important. It will be shown later in this chapter that quadrupole radiation is seldom significant in liquids.

## 3.2 General Equation for Sound Generation

The roles of fluctuating mass and force as source terms in acoustics were understood by Stokes and Rayleigh in the 19th century, but it was not until the middle of the 20th century that Lighthill (1952) recognized that turbulent shear stresses could also act as sources of sound. Lighthill realized that sounds from jet aircraft could not be explained in terms of simple mass or force sources and looked to the fluctuating fluid flow as the source of this sound. The derivation of Lighthill's differential equation is more straightforward than that given in Section 2.2 for the usual wave equation in that some of the assumptions made in deriving the wave equation are not needed. Lighthill's equation can be derived simply by combining the continuity and momentum equations without assumptions concerning linearity or steadiness or irrotationality of the fluid flow. The resultant equation can be interpreted as a wave equation with source terms. The same procedure can be used to derive a general equation for sound generation by volume and force as well as shear-stress sources.

### Derivation

In deriving a general differential equation for sound generation we start with the continuity and momentum equations of fluid mechanics written for regions that include mass and force source terms. These are then combined to form a single equation prior to making the acoustic assumption. Upon making the acoustic assumption, and after some manipulation, a single differential equation is obtained which has the form of a wave equation on the left, but with a number of terms on the right which can be interpreted as source terms. In carrying out this derivation, it is convenient to use the double-subscript tensor notation described in Section 1.5. In this notation, the continuity equation, Eq. 2.32, in a region containing sources is

$$\frac{D\rho}{Dt} + \rho\,(\nabla \cdot \vec{v}) = \frac{\partial \rho}{\partial t} + \frac{\partial(\rho v_i)}{\partial x_i} = q , \tag{3.6}$$

where $q$ is the rate at which new mass is created per unit volume. This equation differs from Eqs. 2.27 and 2.32 only in the addition of the source term.

It is the momentum equation that takes on a different form in a region containing sources. Eq. 2.40 for the rate-of-change of momentum may be written

$$\frac{DM}{Dt} = \int_V \left( \frac{D(\rho v_i)}{Dt} + \rho v_i \frac{\partial v_j}{\partial x_j} \right) dV = \int_V \left( \frac{\partial(\rho v_i)}{\partial t} + v_j \frac{\partial(\rho v_i)}{\partial x_j} + \rho v_i \frac{\partial v_j}{\partial x_j} \right) dV . \tag{3.7}$$

The second and third terms can readily be combined into a single term. Equating the time-rate-of-change of momentum to the sum of the forces, Eq. 2.43 is replaced by

$$\frac{\partial(\rho v_i)}{\partial t} + \frac{\partial(\rho v_i v_j)}{\partial x_j} = - \frac{\partial p}{\partial x_i} - \rho g \frac{\partial z}{\partial x_i} + f_i , \tag{3.8}$$

where $f_i$ represents the net force per unit volume exerted by any external mechanical forces that may be acting on the fluid. In this form, viscous stresses are not included. Lighthill chose to include viscous stresses, even though they are negligible in all practical calculations of fluid-dynamic noise. He replaced the pressure, $p$, by a stress tensor, $p_{ij}$, which includes both the normal stresses and the viscous shear stresses. In tensor notation, the complete momentum equation may be written

$$\frac{\partial(\rho v_i)}{\partial t} = - \frac{\partial p_{ij}}{\partial x_j} - \rho g_i - \frac{\partial(\rho v_i v_j)}{\partial x_j} + f_i , \tag{3.9}$$

where $g_i = -g \; grad \; z$.

A single second-order differential equation can now be derived by taking the partial derivative of Eq. 3.6 with respect to time,

$$\frac{\partial^2 \rho}{\partial t^2} + \frac{\partial^2(\rho v_i)}{\partial t \partial x_i} = \frac{\partial q}{\partial t} , \tag{3.10}$$

and the divergence of Eq. 3.9,

$$\frac{\partial^2(\rho v_i)}{\partial x_i \partial t} = - \frac{\partial^2 p_{ij}}{\partial x_i \partial x_j} + \frac{\partial(\rho g_i)}{\partial x_i} + \frac{\partial f_i}{\partial x_i} - \frac{\partial^2(\rho v_i v_j)}{\partial x_i \partial x_j} . \tag{3.11}$$

Subtracting

$$c_o^2 \frac{\partial^2 \rho}{\partial x_i^2} = \delta_{ij} c_o^2 \frac{\partial^2 \rho}{\partial x_i \partial x_j} = \frac{\partial^2(c_o^2 \rho \delta_{ij})}{\partial x_i \partial x_j} \tag{3.12}$$

from both sides of Eq. 3.10 and then combining with Eq. 3.11, one obtains

$$\frac{\partial^2 \rho}{\partial t^2} - c_o^2 \frac{\partial^2 \rho}{\partial x_i^2} = \frac{\partial q}{\partial t} - \frac{\partial(\rho g_i)}{\partial x_i} - \frac{\partial f_i}{\partial x_i} + \frac{\partial^2(p_{ij} + \rho v_i v_j - c_o^2 \rho \delta_{ij})}{\partial x_i \partial x_j} . \tag{3.13}$$

Lighthill recognized that the last term of Eq. 3.13 represents several types of stresses. He combined these stresses into a single stress tensor, writing

$$\tau_{ij} \equiv \rho v_i v_j + p_{ij} - c_o^2 \rho \delta_{ij} \; . \qquad (3.14)$$

Since the gravitational force is conservative, its divergence is zero, and

$$\frac{\partial^2 \rho}{\partial t^2} - c_o^2 \frac{\partial^2 \rho}{\partial x_i^2} = \frac{\partial q}{\partial t} - g_i \frac{\partial \rho}{\partial x_i} - \frac{\partial f_i}{\partial x_i} + \frac{\partial^2 \tau_{ij}}{\partial x_i \partial x_j} \; . \qquad (3.15)$$

Equation 3.15 applies to instantaneous values of the physical quantities, which are the sums of the steady-state values and fluctuating components. Making the acoustic assumption for each quantity, as in Eq. 2.19, subtracting the equation that applies when there are no fluctuating components, and neglecting a residual gravitational term, one obtains a differential equation for the fluctuating components:

$$\frac{\partial^2 \rho'}{\partial t^2} - c_o^2 \frac{\partial^2 \rho'}{\partial x_i^2} = \frac{\partial q'}{\partial t} - \frac{\partial f_i'}{\partial x_i} + \frac{\partial^2 \tau_{ij}}{\partial x_i \partial x_j} \; . \qquad (3.16)$$

This generalization of Lighthill's equation includes mass flux and force sources as well as the stresses which he originally considered.

As discussed in Chapter 1, underwater acoustics usually deals with acoustic pressures rather than with fluctuating densities. Equation 3.16 can be transformed into a similar equation for acoustic pressure only by making assumptions that the stress-strain relationship is linear and that spatial variations of ambient quantities are negligible (assumptions 8 and 11 in Section 2.2). Thus, using Eq. 2.22 to relate the acoustic pressure to the fluctuating density and assuming $\nabla a$ to be negligible,

$$\nabla^2 p' - \frac{1}{c_o^2} \ddot{p}' = - \dot{q}' + \nabla \cdot \vec{f}' - \frac{\partial^2 \tau_{ij}}{\partial x_i \partial x_j} \; . \qquad (3.17)$$

This form is particularly useful when dealing with mass and force sources in water and is used frequently in the present volume.

### Interpretation

The wave equation, Eq. 2.52, can be derived directly from Eqs. 3.16 or 3.17 by assuming that there are no fluctuating mass inputs, that no fluctuating external forces are being experienced, and that the unsteady stress tensor is zero. In other words, these equations reduce to the wave equation in regions free of acoustic sources. The three terms on the right therefore represent the dominant types of sources of acoustic radiation. The first term on the right, involving unsteady mass flow into the fluid, acts basically as a monopole. The second term, the divergence of the unsteady forces applied at some boundary, is of dipole nature. It was these two types of sources which were considered by Stokes and Rayleigh. The last term, involving turbulent stresses in the fluid itself, is the term which Lighthill derived and showed to be of quadrupole nature.

In his classic article, Lighthill (1952) noted that there are three ways in which kinetic energy can be converted into acoustic energy:

1. by forcing the mass in a fixed region of space to fluctuate, represented by $\dot{q}'$;
2. by forcing the momentum in a fixed region to vary, i.e., by exerting a fluctuating external force on it, represented by *div* $f'$; or

3. by forcing the rates of momentum flux across fixed surfaces in space to vary, as by turbulent shear stresses in space.

The first two require boundaries, but the last can occur in open regions away from boundaries. Lighthill also recognized that the efficiencies of the terms as sources decreases with increasing dependence on spatial derivatives. One can understand this when it is recognized that for functions of the form $f(x - ct)$, which represent waves, a derivative with respect to time is of order of magnitude $c$ greater than a spatial derivative. It follows then that, other factors being equal, the oscillating force term is small with respect to the mass flux term, and the shear term is the smallest. Lighthill's contribution was his pointing out that the lowest order source that could exist away from boundaries is of quadrupole nature, becoming efficient when fluctuating fluid velocities approach the speed of sound.

## 3.3 General Spherical Sources

Equation 3.17 indicates the nature of the common source terms found in acoustics, but its solution for a pressure field is often quite difficult. Solutions for many common sources are obtained by solving the source-free wave equation with appropriate symmetry and then matching the expression for particle velocity at the boundary to the vibratory velocity of the source, under the assumption that continuity of material requires that a fluid and its boundaries move in synchronism.

As indicated in Chapter 2, many sources exhibit spherical symmetry. In fact, it is possible to calculate the radiation field of any arbitrarily shaped source by superposition of the fields of small sources having spherical symmetry. By small sources, we mean sources small compared to a wavelength, i.e., sources having $ka << 1$, where $k$ is the wave number and $a$ is a characteristic dimension. Stated another way, the sound field from any arbitrary source can be calculated in terms of a superposition of elementary multipoles, provided only that the assumption of linearity is valid.

The basic properties of multipoles can be derived by considering the general problem of radiation from a small sphere whose surface vibrates in an infinite number of symmetrical modes. The general solution involves Legendre functions and spherical Bessel functions.* However, it can be shown that provided $ka << 1$ the radiation resistance and reactance are relatively simple functions of $ka$,

$$\sigma_{r_m} = \frac{(ka)^{2m+2}}{(2m+1)(m+1)^2\,(1 \cdot 3 \cdot \cdot \cdot (2m-1))^2} \tag{3.18}$$

$$\sigma_{x_m} = \frac{ka}{(2m+1)(m+1)}\,, \tag{3.19}$$

where $m$ is the order of the multipole, starting with zero for a monopole. Since for small $ka$ the reactance is large compared to the resistance, it follows that the radiation efficiency, Eq. 3.4, is given simply by

*See Morse (1948), Section 27, or Morse and Ingard (1968), Section 7.2.

$$\eta_{rad} \doteq \frac{\sigma_r}{\sigma_x} = \frac{(ka)^{2m+1}}{(m+1)\left(1 \cdot 3 \cdot 5 \cdot \cdots \cdot (2m-1)\right)^2}, \tag{3.20}$$

which is of the same form as Eq. 3.5 but includes values for the constants of proportionality.

## 3.4 Hydrodynamic Sources

### Radiation Efficiencies

Many of the important sources that govern the noises of ships, submarines and torpedoes are hydrodynamic in nature, i.e., they are related in some way to the movement of a fluid past a vehicle or inside a conduit. These hydrodynamic sources of sound can each be classified in accordance with a major noise-producing mechanism: volume change (monopole), oscillating force (dipole), vibratory motions of small bodies (dipole), or free turbulence (quadrupole). The order of the multipole determines the Mach number dependence of the radiation process, and hence the order of magnitude of the radiation efficiency. Equation 3.20 gives the radiation efficiency in terms of the parameter *ka*. When a flow speed, $U_o$, exists, *ka* can be rewritten as a product of a dimensionless frequency and the Mach number:

$$ka = \frac{\omega a}{c_o} = \left(\frac{\omega a}{U_o}\right)\left(\frac{U_o}{c_o}\right) = \left(\frac{\omega a}{U_o}\right) M . \tag{3.21}$$

Using this form of *ka*, the radiation efficiencies of monopoles, dipoles and quadrupoles are given by the following:

$$\eta_{rad} = ka = \left(\frac{\omega a}{U_o}\right) M \quad (monopole) , \tag{3.22}$$

$$\eta_{rad} = \frac{1}{2}(ka)^3 = \frac{1}{2}\left(\frac{\omega a}{U_o}\right)^3 M^3 \quad (dipole) \tag{3.23}$$

and

$$\eta_{rad} = \frac{1}{27}(ka)^5 = \frac{1}{27}\left(\frac{\omega a}{U_o}\right)^5 M^5 \quad (quadrupole) . \tag{3.24}$$

These equations show increasing dependence on Mach number as the order of the multipole increases. The quantity in parentheses is a dimensionless frequency, which is usually of the order of unity.

### Fluctuating-Volume Acoustic Sources

In situations for which the source of sound is associated with fluctuations of the total mass of fluid, Eq. 3.17 for acoustic pressure reduces to

$$\nabla^2 p' - \frac{1}{c_o^2}\ddot{p}' = -\dot{q} . \tag{3.25}$$

Since matter is not created within the fluid itself, any fluctuations of mass must occur at boundaries of the fluid region. Within the fluid itself there are no sources, the wave equation solution is valid, and the term on the right simply controls the amplitude of the acoustic signal. Provided the source is small compared to an acoustic wavelength, the solution of Eq. 3.25 is simply

$$p'(r,t) = \frac{\dot{Q}(t - r/c_o)}{4\pi r} = \frac{\dot{Q}(t')}{4\pi r} , \qquad (3.26)$$

where $t'$ is retarded time (Eq. 2.6) and

$$Q \equiv \int_V q\, dV = \frac{d}{dt}(\rho_o V) . \qquad (3.27)$$

In liquids, density fluctuations are negligible, and Eq. 3.26 reduces to

$$p'(r,t) = \frac{\rho_o \ddot{V}(t')}{4\pi r} . \qquad (3.28)$$

This is the most general form for sound radiation from a small fluctuating-volume (monopole) noise source. The strength of such a source is proportional to the product of fluid density and volume acceleration.

When they occur, fluctuating-volume noise sources radiate the highest levels found in hydroacoustics. This is because of the first-order dependence of the radiation efficiency on Mach number. Cavitation is an important source of monopole radiation in liquids. Pistons located in the boundaries also radiate as volume sources, as do pulsating pipe exhausts and certain tank resonances. Because of their prime importance, four chapters are devoted to volume noise sources.

**Fluctuating-Force Sources**

Any rigid surface acted on by a non-steady force will radiate sound. The reason is that there must be a fluctuating pressure field associated with any fluctuating force, and fluctuating pressure fields in a compressible medium radiate sound. The differential equation for sound generated by fluctuating forces is

$$\nabla^2 p' - \frac{1}{c_o^2}\ddot{p}' = \frac{\partial f_i'}{\partial x_i} = \nabla \cdot \vec{f}' . \qquad (3.29)$$

In the absence of electromagnetic or chemical body forces, all forces are experienced at fluid boundaries and the solution of Eq. 3.29 for a concentrated force is

$$p'(\vec{r},t) = \frac{1}{4\pi r} \nabla \cdot \vec{F}(t') , \qquad (3.30)$$

where $F(t')$ is the total fluctuating force. Relative to retarded time, the divergence of a function and its time derivative are of the same form and differ only by the speed of sound. In terms of the time derivative,

$$p'(\vec{r},t) = \frac{\dot{\vec{F}} \cdot \hat{r}}{4\pi r c_o} = \frac{\dot{F}(t')}{4\pi r c_o} \cos\theta \ , \qquad (3.31)$$

where $\theta$ is the angle between the force vector and the direction to the field point for which the pressure is being calculated. The $\cos\theta$ term represents a dipole pressure pattern.

Since it is virtually impossible to produce a steady force without also producing a fluctuating component, sound having dipole characteristics is invariably generated as a by-product of a useful force. From Eq. 3.23, the radiation efficiency of such a dipole source is proportional to the third power of the Mach number. Of the many fluctuating-force noise sources, those associated with propellers are usually dominant because the highest flow speeds occur at propeller blade-tip sections. The local flow speed at a propeller tip is the vector sum of the forward and rotational speed components. This tip speed is generally about three times the forward speed, resulting through third-power dependence on Mach number in dominance of the propeller tip sections relative to other parts of the vessel that experience only the forward speed. Fluctuating-force noises are quite important in underwater acoustics and are discussed in more detail in Chapter 9.

### Turbulence Noise

Fluctuating-volume and -force noise sources generally occur at fluid boundaries. However, the source term in Lighthill's equation includes a component associated with hydrodynamic motions of the fluid itself. The non-steady stress tensor may be written

$$\tau'_{ij} \doteq (\rho v_i v_j)' + (p'_{ij} - p'\delta_{ij}) + (p' - c_o^2 \rho')\delta_{ij} \ . \qquad (3.32)$$

The first term represents fluctuating shear stresses associated with turbulent fluid motions, the second accounts for viscous stresses, and the third represents heat conduction and/or nonlinearity. At the Reynolds and Mach numbers of liquid flows, only the first term representing turbulence is important. To a first order,

$$\tau'_{ij} \doteq 2\rho_o U u'_i \ , \qquad (3.33)$$

where $u$'s have been used rather than v's to indicate that all fluctuating as well as steady velocities in the stress tensor refer to hydrodynamic quantities rather than acoustic ones.

By analogy with Eqs. 3.26 and 3.30, and assuming Eq. 3.33, the sound generated by turbulence is given by

$$p'(\vec{r},t) \doteq \frac{\rho_o U}{2\pi r} \frac{\partial^2}{\partial x_i \partial x_j} \int_V u'_i(t')\, dV \ , \qquad (3.34)$$

where differences in retarded time must be considered unless the source region is small compared to a wavelength. The two spatial derivatives imply a basic quadrupole nature of this sound.

The radiation efficiency of fluid turbulence can be estimated from Eq. 3.24, using hydrodynamic relations for cold jets. The source radius, $a$, can be assumed to be equal to one half the scale length, $\ell$, of the largest turbulent eddies; hence

$$\eta_{rad} \doteq \frac{1}{27}(ka)^5 \doteq \frac{1}{27}\left(\frac{1}{2}\right)^5\left(\frac{\omega\ell}{U_o}\right)^5 M^5 , \qquad (3.35)$$

where $U_o$ is the flow speed used in calculating the Mach number. Experiments with cold jets reveal that $\omega\ell \doteq U_o$, so that

$$\eta_{rad} \doteq \left(\frac{1}{27}\right)\left(\frac{1}{2}\right)^5 M^5 \doteq 1.1 \times 10^{-3} M^5 . \qquad (3.36)$$

Since about one sixth of the fluid mechanical power in a wake or jet occurs as vibratory power of the turbulence, it follows that

$$\eta_{ac} \doteq 2 \times 10^{-4} M^5 , \qquad (3.37)$$

which result is in good agreement with measurements of the noise powers of cold subsonic jets.

**Noise from Wake Turbulence**

When a body is propelled through water, a significant fraction of the total power is converted into wake turbulence, which eventually decays into heat. One might expect this turbulence to be a major source of sound, as it is in the case of a jet aircraft. However, the noises emitted by wake turbulence in water are entirely negligible provided there are no bubbles present.

It is clear from Eq. 3.37 why turbulence noise is of such importance in air and of so little importance in water. The difference is the Mach number. Jets in air often have Mach numbers in the vicinity of unity or even higher. In water, a 60-knot vehicle would have a Mach number of only 0.02. Only about one part in $10^{12}$ of its power would be radiated from the free turbulence of its wake. It is because of the low Mach number that quadrupole sources can be considered completely negligible in hydroacoustics, monopoles and dipoles at the boundaries always being dominant.

Sometimes noise does radiate from the wake of a vessel, but this noise is attributable to entrained air bubbles. Crighton and Ffowcs Williams (1969) have shown that monopole radiation resulting from the volumetric response of wake bubbles to turbulent pressure fluctuations overwhelms the quadrupole radiation by as much as 50 dB for a 1% concentration of air.

**Flow Noise**

Another way that fluid turbulence can be an important source of noise in liquids involves interaction with a boundary. Thus, the fluctuating pressures associated with a turbulent boundary layer excite flexural vibrations of the solid, and these vibrations then radiate sound. This flow noise occurs whenever fluids flow over non-rigid bodies or inside pipes and tubes. It is an especially important source of sonar self-noise.

Flexural wave radiation is a monopole process, and the efficiency of excitation of flexural waves by the fluctuating turbulent pressures is also proportional to the first power of the Mach number. Consequently, acoustic efficiencies for flow noise are proportional to the square of the Mach number. This topic has received a great deal of attention in the literature during the past 20 years, and a summary is given in Section 6.6.

Turbulence can also give rise to transducer self-noise when a receiver is placed in a turbulent stream. Pressure fluctuations associated with turbulence velocities cause *pseudo sound*, which though non-acoustic can be a dominant source of interference if the receiver is not protected from the flow by a dome.

## 3.5 Sources in Motion

In the previous section, radiation efficiencies of various hydrodynamic noise sources were related to Mach number, in the low Mach number limit. Although the noise was assumed to be a function of the mean flow speed, the calculation of the radiation itself assumed the source to be essentially at rest in the fluid medium. Steady motion of a source in a medium, and/or motion of a receiver relative to the medium, can affect received sound both as to its apparent frequency and its magnitude and oscillatory motions of constant masses and steady forces can create additional sound sources.

### Doppler Shift

The most obvious effect of source motion relative to a receiver is a change of frequency known as the *Doppler shift*. The frequency received, $f_a$, is related to that radiated, $f_s$, by

$$f_a = \frac{f_s}{1 - M_S \cos\theta}, \tag{3.38}$$

where $M_S$ is the convection Mach number of the source and $\theta$ is the angle between the motion vector and the direction toward the receiver. For small Mach numbers

$$f_a \doteq f_s(1 + M_S \cos\theta), \tag{3.39}$$

which is the expression generally found in elementary texts.

If the receiver is in motion toward the source, then the apparent frequency will also be altered:

$$f_a = f_s(1 + M_R \cos\theta). \tag{3.40}$$

Thus, for low Mach numbers motion of the receiver is equivalent to motion of the source.

### Effect of Steady Motion on Level

Not only is the received frequency altered by steady motion of a source or receiver, but also the received signal is altered in strength from that calculated for a stationary situation. Lowson (1965) has shown that calculated values for both monopole and dipole type sources are modified by $(1 - M\cos\theta)^{-2}$, and that for quadrupoles the exponent changes from $-2$ to $-3$. Since this effect becomes significant only when relative Mach numbers exceed about 0.1, it is generally not included in underwater sound calculations.

### Periodic Motions

The source terms in Eqs. 3.16 and 3.17 are expressed as partial derivatives and are calculated for volume elements fixed in the chosen coordinate system, in the Eulerian sense. There are therefore two distinct physical ways in which acoustic source terms can arise. One of these is fluctuations of mass, force and stress at positions fixed in a coordinate system. The other is oscillations of non-fluctuating quantities in position. Stated another way, both time and space changes of mass, force and stress produce acoustic disturbances. Of the two, fluctuations with time are generally more important than oscillations of position, especially in underwater acoustics. The reason is that motions in space must occur at speeds comparable to the speed of sound to be effective as sound radiators. It can be shown that a constant mass experiencing oscillatory motion radiates with the same directional pattern and Mach number dependence of radiation efficiency as a dipole, while a constant force executing periodic motion radiates as a quadrupole. Each is one order multipole higher than for the corresponding fluctuating quantity.

For many years, explanations of tonal radiation from rotating propellers were based on the periodic motion of steady forces, as originally derived by Gutin (1936). Gutin's results exhibit a very strong Mach number dependence and predict strong tones only at high Mach numbers. However, as discussed in Chapter 1, it is impossible to produce steady mechanical forces free of vibratory values. It is now recognized that even in air fluctuating forces are usually dominant sources of tonal radiation. In water, periodic motions of steady forces are never important, and Gutin's analysis is therefore omitted from this volume.

## REFERENCES


Blokhintsev, D.I., *Acoustics of Nonhomogeneous Moving Media* (in Russian), Leningrad, 1946; translated in *N.A.C.A. Tech. Memo. 1399*, 1956.

Crighton, D.G. and Ffowcs Williams, J.E., Sound generation by turbulent two-phase flow, *J. Fluid Mech., 36*, 585-603, 1969.

Curle, N., The influence of solid boundaries upon aerodynamic sound, *Proc. Royal Soc. (London), A231*, 505-514, 1955.

Dyer, I., "Aerodynamic Noise," *Proceedings Symposium on Engineering Applications of Random Function Theory and Probability*, Purdue University, Nov. 1960 (pp. 204-230).

Fitzpatrick, H.M. and Lee, R., Measurements of Noise Radiated by Subsonic Air Jets, *D.T.M.B. Rept. 835*, 1952.

Fitzpatrick, H.M. and Strasberg, M., "Hydrodynamic Sources of Sound," Paper 10 of *Symposium on Naval Hydrodynamics*, Nat. Acad. of Sciences, Nat. Res. Council Publication 515, Washington, D.C., 1956; also *D.T.M.B. Rept. 1269*, 1959.

Goldstein, M., Unified approach to aerodynamic sound generation in the presence of solid boundaries, *J.A.S.A., 56*, 497-509, 1974.

Gutin, L.Ya., On the sound field of a rotating propeller, *J. Tech. Phys. (USSR), 6*, 899-909, 1936; translated in *N.A.C.A. Tech. Memo 1195*, 1948.

Lee, R., Free Field Measurements of Sound Radiated by Subsonic Air Jets, *D.T.M.B. Rept. 868*, 1953.

Lighthill, M.J., On sound generated aerodynamically, *Proc. Royal Soc. (London), A211*, 564-587, 1951; *A222*, 1-32, 1954.

Lighthill, M.J., Sound generated aerodynamically (The Bakerian Lecture, 1961), *Proc. Royal Soc. (London), A267*, 147-182, 1962.

Lowson, M.V., The sound field for singularities in motion, *Proc. Royal Soc. (London), A286*, 559-572, 1965.

Mangiarotty, R.A. and Turner, B.A., Wave radiation Doppler effect correction for motion of a source, observer and the surrounding medium, *J. Sound and Vibr., 6*, 110-116, 1967.

Morfey, C.L., The sound field of sources in motion, *J. Sound and Vibr., 23*, 291-5, 1972.

Morse, P.M. and Ingard, K.U., *Theoretical Acoustics*, McGraw-Hill, New York, 1968 (Chapters 7 and 11).

Richards, E.J. and Mead, D.J. (Ed.), *Noise and Acoustic Fatigue in Aeronautics*, Wiley, London, 1968 (Chapters 1, 5 and 7).

# CHAPTER 4

# RADIATION BY FLUCTUATING-VOLUME (MONOPOLE) SOURCES

As discussed in Chapter 3, motions of boundaries that cause fluctuations of fluid volume are the most efficient radiators of sound. The basic fluctuating-volume source is a small, pulsating spherical surface, called a *monopole*, which radiates sound uniformly in all directions. Monopoles are defined as spherical sources whose dimensions are small compared to an acoustic wavelength. Larger fluctuating-volume sources can be considered to be composed of many monopoles, and their pressure fields can be found by superposition of monopole fields.

The approach taken in the present chapter is to develop the equations for a uniformly pulsating sphere of arbitrary size, and then to obtain the properties of monopoles by taking the limit as size becomes very small. The equations derived for pulsating spheres are then applied to air bubbles pulsating in liquids, and those for monopoles used to calculate pressure fields of linear arrays, pistons and hull openings. Brief consideration is also given to several approaches for the calculation of radiation fields of arbitrary vibrating surfaces. The final section is an overview of hull radiation. Two other important practical examples of fluctuating-volume sources, namely plate bending waves and cavitation, are treated in later chapters.

## 4.1 Uniformly Pulsating Spherical Source

As an introduction to monopoles, it is useful to consider radiation from uniformly pulsating spherical sources of arbitrary size. Monopole radiation is then simply the limit as size approaches zero. The methodology used is similar to that employed in most fundamental radiation problems. An expression for the acoustic particle velocity in a fluid medium is matched to the normal surface vibratory velocity of a solid boundary, and the acoustic pressure is then found from the acoustic impedance.

Consider a spherical cavity having a mean radius $a_o$ experiencing a uniform, small harmonic fluctuation of its volume. This volume fluctuation causes a rate-of-change of fluid in the medium, i.e., a mass flux, $Q$, which can be expressed by

$$Q(t) \equiv \rho_o \dot{V}(t) = Q_o \cos \omega t = RP\left[Q_o \, e^{i\omega t}\right] . \tag{4.1}$$

By assuming that the relative change of volume of the sphere is small, one can write the flux in terms of the product of the area and radial velocity of the surface,

$$Q(t) \doteq \rho_o \left(4\pi a_o^2\right) \dot{a} = \rho_o S_o u . \tag{4.2}$$

It follows that the instantaneous surface velocity can be expressed by

$$\underline{u} = u_o e^{i\omega t} = \frac{Q_o}{4\pi a_o^2 \rho_o} e^{i\omega t} . \tag{4.3}$$

Since the fluid is everywhere in contact with the vibrating surface, the acoustic particle speed, $v'(a_o)$, must equal the surface vibratory speed, $u$. With this relation, the acoustic pressure at the surface of the sphere can be calculated by multiplying the vibratory speed, $u$, by the specific acoustic impedance evaluated at the surface. From Eqs. 2.78 and 2.79, it follows that

$$\underline{p}'(a_o) = \underline{z}_a(a_o)\underline{v}'(a_o) = \rho_o c_o \frac{(ka_o)^2 + i(ka_o)}{1 + (ka_o)^2} \underline{u}$$

$$= \frac{\omega Q_o}{4\pi a_o} \frac{1}{\sqrt{1 + (ka_o)^2}} e^{i(\omega t + \theta_a)} , \tag{4.4}$$

where $\theta_a$ is the phase angle between the pressure and the velocity on the surface of the sphere, as defined by Eq. 2.80, and as given by

$$\theta_a \equiv \tan^{-1}\left(\frac{1}{ka_o}\right) . \tag{4.5}$$

It follows that the pressure at distance $r$ from the center of the sphere is

$$\underline{p}'(r) = \frac{a_o}{r} \underline{p}'(a_o) e^{-ik(r - a_o)}$$

$$= \frac{\omega Q_o}{4\pi r} \frac{e^{i(\theta_a + ka_o)}}{\sqrt{1 + (ka_o)^2}} e^{i(\omega t - kr)} . \tag{4.6}$$

This expression has a form typical of that for the radiated acoustic pressure of many different types of sources. The first term is independent of the relative size and shape of the source and includes the first-power dependence on distance from the origin typical of spherical spreading. The second term involves $ka_o$ and expresses something about the size and/or shape of the specific radiator, in this case the size relative to an acoustic wavelength. The final, exponential, term represents a propagating harmonic disturbance.

## Intensity and Power

The intensity and power of a spherical source can be calculated from the pressure, using expressions derived in Section 2.4. The intensity is

$$I = \frac{\overline{p'^2}}{\rho_o c_o} = \frac{\omega^2 Q_o^2}{32\pi^2 r^2 \rho_o c_o} \cdot \frac{1}{1 + (ka_o)^2} , \tag{4.7}$$

and the total radiated power is

$$W_{ac} = \int_S I\,dS = 4\pi r^2 I = \frac{\omega^2 Q_o^2}{8\pi\rho_o c_o} \cdot \frac{1}{1 + (ka_o)^2} . \tag{4.8}$$

**Radiation Impedance**

As indicated in Section 3.1, acoustic power can also be expressed as the product of the radiation resistance and the mean-square surface velocity. From Eqs. 3.3, 4.3 and 4.8 it follows that the specific radiation resistance is given by

$$\sigma_r \equiv \frac{R_r}{\rho_o c_o S_o} = \frac{W_{ac}}{\rho_o c_o S_o \overline{u^2}} = \frac{(ka_o)^2}{1 + (ka_o)^2} . \tag{4.9}$$

As shown in Fig. 4.1, this factor is proportional to the square of $ka_o$ for small values and approaches unity in the limit of large $ka_o$. The specific radiation reactance is given by the imaginary term in Eq. 4.4 as

$$\sigma_x \equiv \frac{X_r}{\rho_o c_o S_o} = \frac{ka_o}{1 + (ka_o)^2} , \tag{4.10}$$

which function is also plotted in Fig. 4.1.

The total radiation impedance is the ratio of the force exerted on the surface of the uniformly vibrating sphere to the surface velocity. It is simply the surface area multiplied by the specific

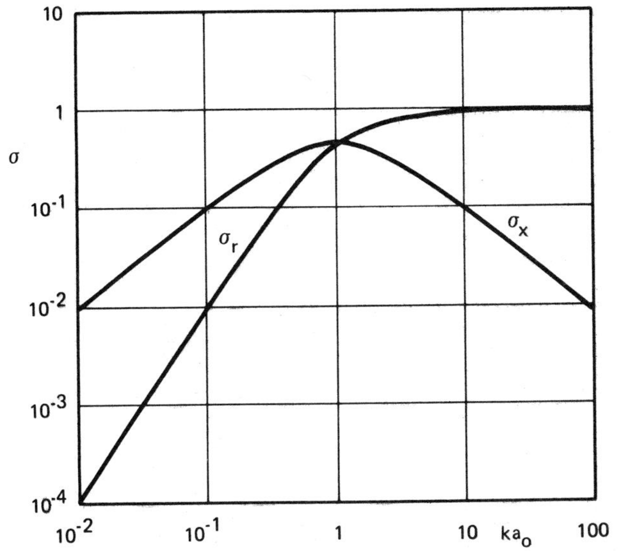


Fig. 4.1. Specific Radiation Impedance for Uniformly Pulsating Sphere

acoustic impedance evaluated at the surface,

$$\underline{Z}_r = S_o \underline{z}_a(a) = \rho_o c_o S_o \frac{(ka_o)^2 + i(ka_o)}{1 + (ka_o)^2} . \quad (4.11)$$

**Radiation Efficiency**

The radiation efficiency, defined by Eqs. 1.4 and 3.4, is

$$\eta_{rad} = \frac{R_r}{\sqrt{R_r^2 + X_r^2}} = \frac{\sigma_r}{\sqrt{\sigma_r^2 + \sigma_x^2}} = \frac{ka_o}{\sqrt{1 + (ka_o)^2}} . \quad (4.12)$$

As shown in Fig. 4.2, the radiation efficiency is a linear function of $ka_o$ for small spheres and approaches unity for large ones. The first-power dependence of the radiation efficiency on $ka_o$ is a characteristic of small, fluctuating-volume sources, as discussed in Chapter 3.

**Entrained Mass**

The reactive component of the radiation impedance is that of the mass of the fluid participating in the motion, i.e., the mass entrained by the motion of the spherical surface. The *entrained mass* can be calculated by dividing the reactance by the angular frequency, $\omega$, giving

$$m_e = \frac{X_r}{\omega} = \frac{\rho_o S_o a_o}{1 + (ka_o)^2} = \frac{3}{1 + (ka_o)^2}\left(\frac{4}{3}\pi a_o^3 \rho_o\right) = \frac{3\rho_o V_o}{1 + (ka_o)^2} . \quad (4.13)$$

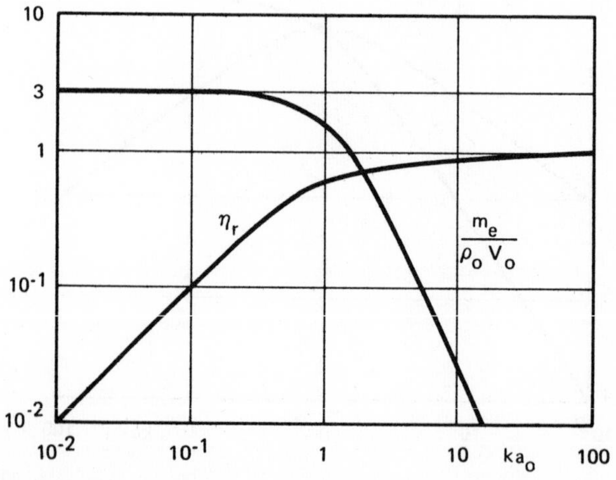


Fig. 4.2. Radiation Efficiency and Relative Entrained Mass for Spherical Sources

Thus, for small values of $ka_o$ the entrained mass is three times the mass of the displaced fluid, while for large values it approaches zero. The relative entrained mass is also plotted in Fig. 4.2.

## 4.2 Monopole Radiation

The general expressions presented in the previous section for spherical sources of arbitrary size are directly usable whenever a spherical radiator can be treated as pulsating uniformly, such as in the case of pulsating bubbles, treated in Section 4.3. However, it is more useful to consider spherical sources that are small compared to an acoustic wavelength. Monopoles are characterized by $ka << 1$. With this stipulation, the phase angle $\theta_a$ between the pressure and the velocity at the surface becomes

$$\theta_a = tan^{-1}\left(\frac{1}{ka_o}\right) \doteq \frac{\pi}{2} - ka_o \, , \qquad (4.14)$$

and the second term in Eq. 4.6 reduces to $i$. The radiated pressure at distance $r$ from the center of the source is then

$$\underline{p}'(r) = i\,\frac{\omega Q_o}{4\pi r}\,e^{i(\omega t - kr)} \, . \qquad (4.15)$$

The intensity is given by

$$I(r) = \frac{\overline{p^2}}{\rho_o c_o} = \frac{\omega^2 Q_o^2}{32\pi^2 r^2 \rho_o c_o} \, , \qquad (4.16)$$

and the total power radiated is

$$W_{ac} = \frac{\omega^2 Q_o^2}{8\pi \rho_o c_o} \, . \qquad (4.17)$$

The specific radiation resistance and reactance given by Eqs. 4.9 and 4.10 reduce to

$$\sigma_r = (ka_o)^2 \qquad (4.18)$$

and

$$\sigma_x = ka_o \, , \qquad (4.18)$$

from which it follows that the radiation efficiency for a monopole is

$$\eta_{rad} = ka_o \, . \qquad (4.20)$$

From Eq. 4.13, the mass entrained by a monopole is three times the mass of the displaced fluid.

These same results could have been derived by starting with Eq. 3.28 for the acoustic pressure associated with volume acceleration. Assuming an harmonic oscillation, Eq. 3.28 leads to

$$p'(r) = \frac{\rho_o \ddot{V}}{4\pi r} = \frac{\dot{Q}(t')}{4\pi r} = \frac{i\omega Q_o}{4\pi r} e^{i\omega(t - r/c_o)} , \tag{4.21}$$

which result is equivalent to that of Eq. 4.15. The expressions for intensity and power follow directly. The specific radiation resistance is then calculated from Eq. 3.3, giving

$$\sigma_r = \frac{W_{ac}}{\rho_o c_o S_o \overline{u^2}} = (ka_o)^2 . \tag{4.22}$$

Since the radiation efficiency of a monopole was derived for a general spherical multipole of zero order, Eq. 3.22, and shown to be equal to $ka_o$, it follows that the reactance ratio is

$$\sigma_x = \frac{\sigma_r}{\eta_{rad}} = \frac{(ka_o)^2}{ka_o} = ka_o = \frac{\omega a_o}{c_o} , \tag{4.23}$$

leading to the conclusion that the reactance is equal to three times that of the mass of the displaced fluid,

$$X_r = \rho_o c_o S_o \sigma_x = \rho_o \omega 4\pi a_o^3 = 3\omega \rho_o V_o , \tag{4.24}$$

in full agreement with the result obtained by letting $ka_o$ approach zero in Eq. 4.13.

## 4.3 Sounds from Gas Bubbles in Liquids

It is not uncommon to find gas bubbles present in the ocean, in streams and in pipe flows. Minnaert (1933) concluded that the almost musical sounds of running water are caused by air bubbles oscillating at their natural frequencies and radiating as monopoles. Sounds are also radiated when bubbles flow into regions of varying hydrodynamic pressure. Examples of this are bubbles entrained near the bow of a ship when acted on by the pressure field of that ship and when passing through its propeller, and bubbles flowing through a constriction in a pipe or around a pipe bend. Sound is also generated when bubbles form, collapse, divide or coalesce. The sounds radiated by these phenomena can be estimated by using a differential equation for bubble wall motion to find the volume acceleration and then using Eq. 4.21 to calculate the sound pressure. While changes of shape invariably accompany volume pulsations, Strasberg (1956) has shown that any sound radiated by such changes is negligible and that valid estimates of sound radiation can be made by considering only volume effects.

### Linear Bubble Pulsations

Volume pulsations of a gas bubble in a liquid can be treated as a mass-spring system in which the mass of entrained liquid provides inertia, and adiabatic compression of the gas acts as a spring. Resistance to the motion is caused by liquid viscosity, thermal losses in the gas and radiation of sound energy. Differential equations for bubble motions can be derived by equating the sum of the forces acting at the bubble surface to the rate-of-change of momentum of the entrained liquid. Such equations usually include surface-tension forces and several non-linear terms. However, a linear second-order differential equation can be used to analyze relatively small pulsations of gas-filled bubbles. Strasberg (1956) has written this equation in terms of the bubble volume, $V$, as

$$m_e \ddot{V} + R\dot{V} + K(V(t) - V_o) = S_o^2(p_o - p(t)) \,, \qquad (4.25)$$

where $m_e$ is the entrained mass, as given by Eq. 4.13, $K$ is the spring constant of the compressed gas inside the bubble and $R$ is a coefficient of resistance. Subscripts zero refer to equilibrium values of the static pressure, $p$, and the bubble volume, $V$. The spring constant can be derived from thermodynamic relations for a nearly spherical volume,

$$K \equiv -\frac{dF}{da} = -S\frac{dp}{da} \doteq -S_o^2\frac{dp}{dV} \,. \qquad (4.26)$$

For an adiabatic process, for which $pV^\gamma$ = constant, the spring constant is given by

$$K = \gamma S_o^2 \frac{p_o}{V_o} = \frac{3\gamma S_o p_o}{a_o} \,, \qquad (4.27)$$

where $\gamma$ is the ratio of the specific heats of the gas inside the bubble.

*Second-order linear differential equations* of the form of Eq. 4.25 are quite common in mechanics as well as in other branches of physics, and their solutions are well known. The complete solution is composed of two parts: that of the homogeneous equation for which the applied force is set equal to zero, and a solution having the same form as the applied force. The solution of the homogeneous equation describes the motion when the system is acted on by a transient disturbance and allowed to respond freely. The nature of the solution depends on the relative amount of damping. Bubbles are generally lightly damped and the applicable solution is that of a damped oscillation, of the form

$$\underline{V} = V_o + \underline{A}e^{-\alpha t}\, e^{i\omega_o t} \,, \qquad (4.28)$$

where $\underline{A}$ is the amplitude of the motion as determined by initial values of the volume and its time derivative, and $\alpha$ is a *dissipation coefficient* given by

$$\alpha = \frac{R}{2m_e} \,. \qquad (4.29)$$

The ratio of the resistance coefficient to the inertial reactance of the entrained mass at the frequency of oscillation is called the *loss factor*, $\eta$, and is related to the dissipation coefficient by

$$\eta \equiv \frac{R}{\omega_o m_e} = 2\frac{\alpha}{\omega_o} \,. \qquad (4.30)$$

In most instances, the loss factor is less than unity, and Eq. 4.28 then represents an exponentially damped oscillation having a rate of decay that is slow compared to the period of oscillation, as depicted in Fig. 4.3. The period between maxima is simply the reciprocal of the frequency,

$$T_o = \frac{1}{f_o} = \frac{2\pi}{\omega_o} \,, \qquad (4.31)$$

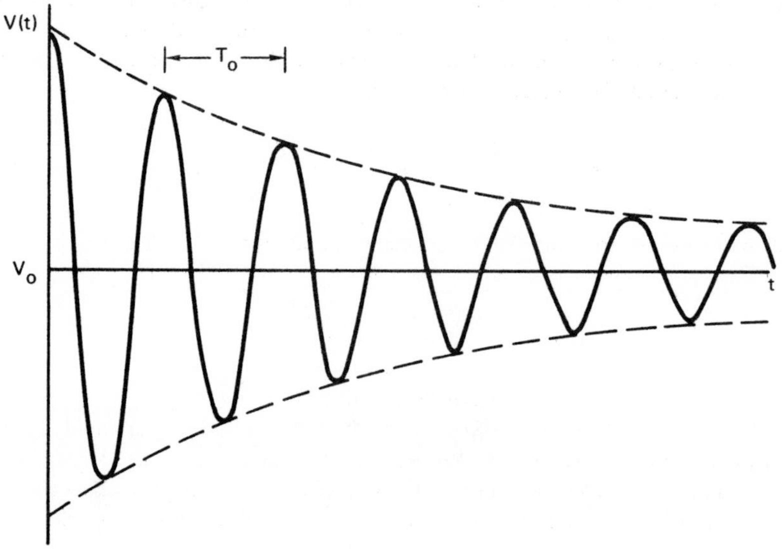


Fig. 4.3. Damped Oscillation of a Gas Bubble

and the relative decay in one period is the *logarithmic decrement*, $\delta$, given by

$$\delta \equiv ln \frac{1}{e^{-\alpha T_o}} = \alpha T_o = \frac{2\pi\alpha}{\omega_o} = \pi\eta . \tag{4.32}$$

Since the mechanical energy of a vibrating system is proportional to the square of the amplitude of its vibration, it follows that for a lightly damped system the relative energy lost in one vibrational period is $2\delta$, or $2\pi\eta$.

The complex amplitude, $\underline{A}$, of the motion is an involved function of the initial volume displacement, $\Delta V(0)$, and the initial volume velocity, $\dot{V}(0)$. Its magnitude is given by

$$A = \Delta V(0) \sqrt{1 + \frac{\eta}{\omega_o} \frac{\dot{V}(0)}{\Delta V(0)} + \left( \frac{1}{\omega_o} \frac{\dot{V}(0)}{\Delta V(0)} \right)^2} , \tag{4.33}$$

and its phase angle, $\phi$, by

$$\phi = - \tan^{-1}\left( \frac{\eta}{2} + \frac{\dot{V}(0)}{\omega_o \Delta V(0)} \right) . \tag{4.34}$$

In most situations the initial velocity is small; hence the magnitude $A$ equals the initial displacement, $\Delta V(0)$, and the phase angle $\phi$ reduces to $- \eta/2$.

**Frequency of Bubble Oscillation**

An expression for the resonance frequencies of gas bubbles in liquids was first derived by Minnaert (1933). He assumed that damping is negligible and that the bubble diameter is small compared to the wavelength. Thus, ignoring damping,

$$\ddot{V} = -\omega_o^2 (V - V_o) , \tag{4.35}$$

and the homogeneous form of Eq. 4.28 becomes

$$(-\omega_o^2 m_e + K)(V - V_o) = 0 , \tag{4.36}$$

from which

$$f_o \equiv \frac{\omega_o}{2\pi} \doteq \frac{1}{2\pi}\sqrt{\frac{K}{m_e}} = \frac{1}{2\pi}\sqrt{\frac{3\gamma S_o p_o}{3\rho_o V_o a_o}} = \frac{1}{2\pi a_o}\sqrt{\frac{3\gamma p_o}{\rho_o}} . \tag{4.37}$$

Minnaert's experiments with gas bubbles in water appeared to confirm this expression and to justify his assumptions. When damping is included, the resonance frequency is modified slightly, the more complete expression being

$$f_o = \frac{1}{2\pi}\sqrt{\frac{K}{m_e} - \alpha^2} \doteq \frac{1}{2\pi}\sqrt{\frac{K}{m_e}}\left(1 - \frac{\eta^2}{8}\right) . \tag{4.38}$$

Thus, the effect of damping on the resonance frequency is less than 1% if $\eta < 0.3$, which condition is invariably satisfied in low-viscosity liquids such as water.

In deriving Eq. 4.37, Minnaert assumed that the entrained mass equals three times the displaced mass, which follows from Eq. 4.13 provided $(ka_o)^2 << 1$. Combining Eqs. 4.13 and 4.37,

$$ka_o = \frac{\omega_o a_o}{c_o} = \sqrt{\frac{3\gamma p_o}{\rho_o c_o^2}}\sqrt{1 + (ka_o)^2} . \tag{4.39}$$

For air bubbles in water at pressures up to several hundred atmospheres, this reduces to

$$ka_o \doteq 0.0136\sqrt{P_A} , \tag{4.40}$$

where $P_A$ is the static pressure in atmospheres. The assumption is therefore verified for static pressures up to 100 atm. Under this condition, Eq. 4.37 yields

$$f_o \doteq \frac{3.28}{a_o}\sqrt{P_A} \quad Hz \tag{4.41}$$

for the resonance frequency of an air bubble in water. Thus, an air bubble having a radius of 1 mm in water at 1 atm. would have a resonance frequency of about 3.3 kHz.

Equations 4.37 and 4.41 for the natural frequencies of bubbles are accurate for bubbles that are neither too small nor too large. If bubbles are smaller than about $3 \times 10^{-3}$ cm in diameter, surface tension and viscosity raise the frequency, while bubbles larger than 1 cm tend to take shapes so far removed from spherical that the assumptions made in deriving Eqs. 4.13 and 4.27 are not valid. Strasberg (1953) has shown that the resonance frequency of a prolate spheroid having a 2:1 ratio of its axes is 2% higher than that calculated by Eq. 4.37. The effects of nearby boundaries on bubble pulsations, which are more serious, are beyond the scope of the present volume.

**Damping Mechanisms**

As indicated above, damping has only a secondary effect on bubble resonance frequencies, but it controls the rate of decay of bubble pulsations set into motion by transient disturbances. A number of investigators have made theoretical calculations and experimental measurements of bubble damping. In a survey of this subject, Devin (1959) listed three dominant mechanisms:

1) sound radiation,
2) thermal losses in the gas, and
3) viscous losses in the liquid.

Of these, only sound radiation is independent of bubble size. Both thermal and viscous losses increase with decreasing bubble size.

For a bubble containing an ideal gas pulsating in an ideal, lossless liquid, the only loss mechanism would be the radiation of sound itself. The loss factor, $\eta$, of the vibratory motion would then equal the radiation efficiency of a vibrating sphere, as given by Eq. 4.12. Combining with Eq. 4.39, the loss factor would be given by

$$\eta \doteq \eta_{rad} = \frac{ka_o}{\sqrt{1 + (ka_o)^2}} = \sqrt{\frac{3\gamma p_o}{\rho_o c_o^2}} , \qquad (4.42)$$

which for air bubbles in water is

$$\eta \doteq \eta_{rad} = 0.0136 \sqrt{P_A} . \qquad (4.43)$$

Devin and others have shown that, for most air bubbles in water at atmospheric pressure, thermal damping equals or exceeds radiation damping, becoming as much as an order of magnitude greater for bubbles having diameters of less than $10^{-2}$ cm. Viscous losses are not important in water, but are usually dominant in oil. Measurements of damping factors made by different investigators are not in complete agreement. Figure 4.4 presents approximate values, based on the summary of results published by Devin (1959).

**Sound Radiation**

The sound radiated by a gas bubble excited into resonant vibration can be calculated using equations developed in Sections 4.1 and 4.2. Most of these equations are expressed in terms of the mass flux, $Q$, which equals the volume velocity, $\dot{V}$, multiplied by the fluid density. Taking the time derivative of the bubble volume, as given in Eq. 4.28, and assuming the loss factor, $\eta$, to be small compared to unity, it follows that

$$\underline{Q}(t') \equiv \rho_o \underline{\dot{V}}(t') = i\omega_o \rho_o A e^{i(\phi + \eta/2)} e^{-(\eta/2)\omega_o t'} e^{i\omega_o t'} , \qquad (4.44)$$

where $t'$ is retarded time as defined by Eq. 2.6. In most cases the transient disturbance can be assumed to have created a difference, $\Delta V$, between the initial volume and the equilibrium value,

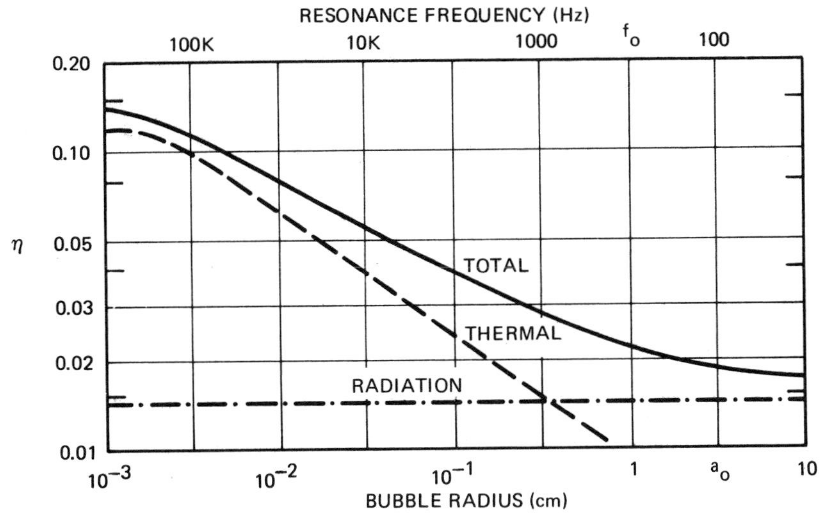


Fig. 4.4. Damping of Resonant Air Bubbles at Atmospheric Pressure, after Devin (1959)

and $\dot{V}(0)$ can be assumed to be zero. In these cases, Eq. 4.44 for the mass flux reduces to

$$\underline{Q}(t') = i\omega_o \rho_o \Delta V\, e^{-(\eta/2)\omega_o t'}\, e^{i\omega_o t'} . \tag{4.45}$$

It follows from Eq. 4.15 that the acoustic pressure at distance $r$ is given by

$$\underline{p}'(r,t) = i\,\frac{\omega Q_o(t')}{4\pi r}\, e^{i(\omega t - kr)} \doteq -\,\frac{\rho_o \omega_o^2 \Delta V}{4\pi r}\, e^{-(\eta/2)(\omega_o t - k_o r)}\, e^{i(\omega_o t - k_o r)} , \tag{4.46}$$

where the minus sign implies that an oversize bubble will initially contract, thereby creating a rarefaction. The amplitude of the acoustic pressure can be expressed as a function of the static pressure, bubble dimensions and ratio of specific heats by using Eq. 4.37 for the resonant frequency. The resultant expression,

$$\left| \underline{p}'(r,t) \right| = \frac{\gamma p_o}{r/a_o}\, \frac{\Delta V}{V_o}\, e^{-(\eta/2)(\omega_o t - k_o r)} , \tag{4.47}$$

shows that, other factors being equal, the peak pressure increases linearly with bubble diameter.

It is of interest to calculate the total energy radiated by a bubble given an initial volume displacement. From Eqs. 4.17 and 4.45, the instantaneous power is

$$W_{ac} = \frac{\omega^2 Q_o^2}{8\pi \rho_o c_o} = \frac{\rho_o \omega_o^4 (\Delta V)^2}{8\pi c_o}\, e^{-\eta \omega_o t'} . \tag{4.48}$$

Integrating from the time of the disturbance,

$$E_{ac} = \int_0^{\infty} W_{ac} dt' = \frac{\rho_o \omega_o^3 (\Delta V)^2}{8\pi c_o \eta} . \tag{4.49}$$

Using Eq. 4.37 for the resonance frequency and utilizing Eq. 4.20 for the radiation efficiency, the total energy radiated during the entire decay period is

$$E_{ac} = \frac{\gamma p_o (\Delta V)^2}{2V_o} \frac{\eta_{rad}}{\eta} = \frac{1}{2} \Delta p \Delta V \frac{\eta_{rad}}{\eta} , \tag{4.50}$$

where $\Delta p$ is the magnitude of pressure change associated with volume change $\Delta V$ for an adiabatic expansion of a constant amount of gas.

The above equations have been derived for a constant-mass gas bubble and apply to such cases as a bubble set into oscillation by passage through a pressure jump, as in a pump, or to a bubble acted on by a pressure pulse. Strasberg (1956) has shown that the result is essentially the same when a bubble is formed at a nozzle, $\Delta p$ being the excess pressure of the gas supply forming the bubbles, and $\Delta V$ being the final volume of each bubble. Sound is also emitted when bubbles split or coalesce. In this case, the pressure difference causing the volume change is the difference between the surface tension pressures of the two sizes of bubbles.

Most practical examples of bubble noise involve many bubbles. Since the sounds add incoherently, the acoustic power is simply $N$ times the radiated energy per bubble, where $N$ is the number of bubbles experiencing the pressure jump or volume change each second. Thus, the sound radiated by a gas jet in water should be primarily controlled by the flow rate and not influenced significantly by the size of the orifice. This result has been verified by Mühle and Heckl (1971), who measured the sound when gas jets discharge into still water. However, measurements by Gavigan, Watson and King (1974) in a water tunnel have shown that when gas discharges into a moving turbulent flow the orifice size is a critical parameter. Apparently bubble breakup and collapse can be a dominant noise-generating mechanism in a turbulent flow.

## 4.4 Sounds from Splashes

Splashes associated with the impact of water droplets on the ocean surface are a major source of underwater noise. The droplets are generally created by breaking waves, but are also caused by rain and by the breaking of surface ship bow waves. While numerous photographs of the resultant spatter have been published, very little attention has been given in the literature to underwater noise aspects. The only thorough study of this subject known to the author is that of Franz (1959).

### Franz's Measurements

Franz measured the underwater noise produced by the impacts of single drops as well as that from sprays of droplets. He found that two distinct noise mechanisms account for the sound, and that both radiate with cosine directional patterns typical of near-surface sources. A sharp pulse is radiated by the actual impact of a water drop on the surface, and this is followed by sounds emitted by bubble volume pulsations. Impact sounds are proportional to the kinetic energy and cube of the Mach number of the impacting body, but bubble sounds are quite erratic and do not vary consistently with droplet size or velocity. Franz was able to separate the two types of sounds and to measure their spectra individually.

The spectra radiated by the impact phase of splashing water droplets were found to cover a wide frequency band and to vary consistently with drop size and impact speed. Figure 4.5 summarizes Franz's results for this type of sound. It can be seen that a broad peak is centered at a dimensionless frequency close to unity, decreasing at a rate approaching 5 dB/octave at the higher frequencies. For drops of a given size, the sound radiated increases by 13 to 17 dB for a factor of 2 increase of the impact velocity.

Sounds from bubble pulsations were found to be more nearly sinusoidal, producing spectra with relatively sharp peaks, generally between 500 Hz and 10 kHz. Franz found that bubble sounds usually dominate in the octave for which they are strongest, with impact sounds controlling the spectrum at the other frequencies, as illustrated in Fig. 4.6.

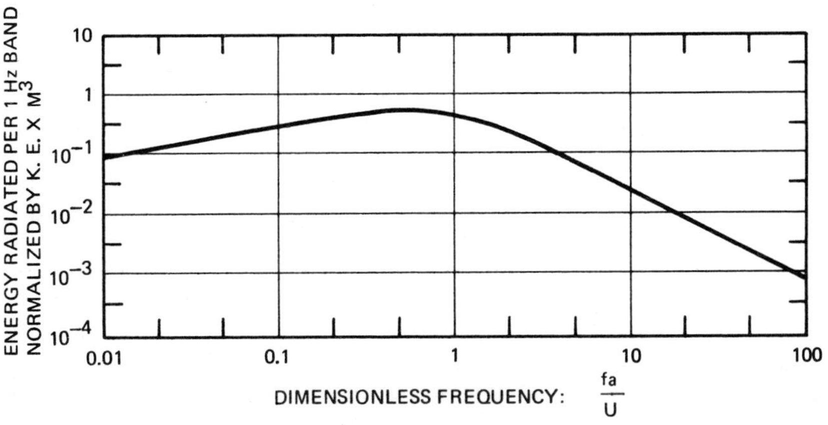


Fig. 4.5. Spectra of Sounds From Surface Impacts, as measured by Franz (1959)

### Wind-Generated Ambient Sea Noise

Splash noise from breaking waves is a major source of underwater ambient noise, generally dominating measured spectra above 300 Hz and sometimes being dominant to as low as 20 Hz. Noise levels measured during World War II, mostly above 500 Hz, were almost invariably controlled by the degree of agitation of the sea surface as described either by wind speed or sea state. The famous summary curves published by Knudsen, Alford and Emling (1944, 1948) and reproduced in Fig. 4.7 have a constant – 5 dB/octave slope extending from 100 Hz to over 30 kHz. However, measurements made following the end of WWII revealed that levels below about 200 Hz are often independent of sea state and that extrapolation of the Knudsen curves below 500 Hz is erroneous. It was found that the spectral shape of the sea agitation contribution to ambient noise is quite similar to that reported by Franz for splash noise (as depicted in Fig. 4.5) with the peak frequency occurring between 300 and 600 Hz.

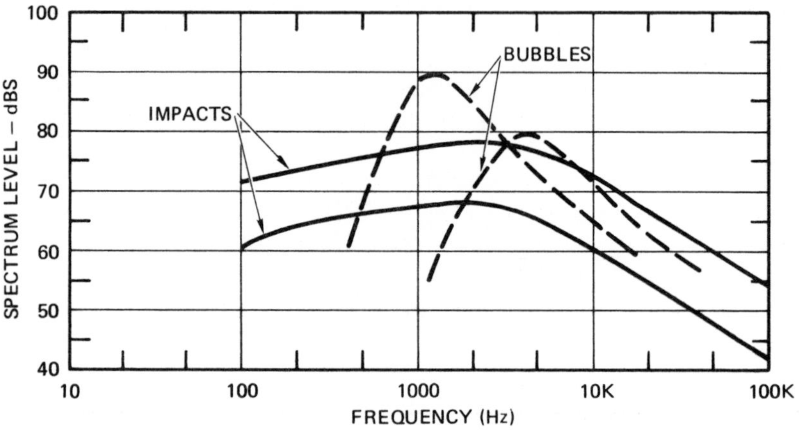


Fig. 4.6. Sounds From Splashes, after Franz (1959)

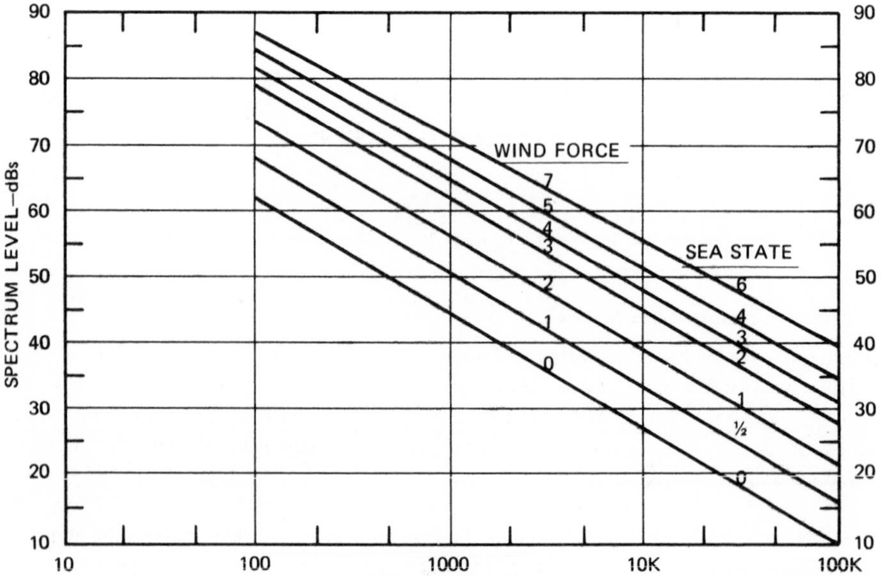


Fig. 4.7. Knudsen Average Ambient Spectra (1944)

In a comprehensive summary paper, Wenz (1962) attributed the wind-independent noise at low frequencies to distant shipping, which source is discussed in Chapter 8. Measurements made at low frequencies in remote regions free of shipping show spectra that are practically flat from 20 to 500 Hz, decreasing above this frequency at a rate of about 5 dB/octave. Figure 4.8 summarizes a number of these modern measurements of wind-generated deep-water ambient noise. As indicated in this figure, deep-water levels above 1 kHz are somewhat lower than those reported for the same wind speed by Knudsen et al. On the other hand, Piggott (1964) and others have reported shallow-water levels higher than the Knudsen values, and a trend to lower levels in deeper water was also found by Perrone (1970). Apparently the curves developed from WWII data apply to medium water depths of the order of 100 fathoms. In any case, the important feature shown by the curves in Fig. 4.8 is the peaks at about 400 Hz with slight decreases below this frequency. This results in levels as much as 15 to 25 dB below Knudsen extrapolated values for frequencies below 100 Hz.

**Rain Noise**

The spectra generated by breaking waves are typical of what would be expected from Franz's results for droplet impact speeds of the order of only a few meters per second. Raindrops fall at higher speeds and so produce spectra with higher peak frequencies as well as higher levels. Figure 4.9 shows several typical rain-generated ambient noise spectra, as measured by Heindsman et al (1955) and Bom (1969) for several rain rates. At 10 kHz the levels are as much as 20 to 30 dB higher than those typical of breaking waves.

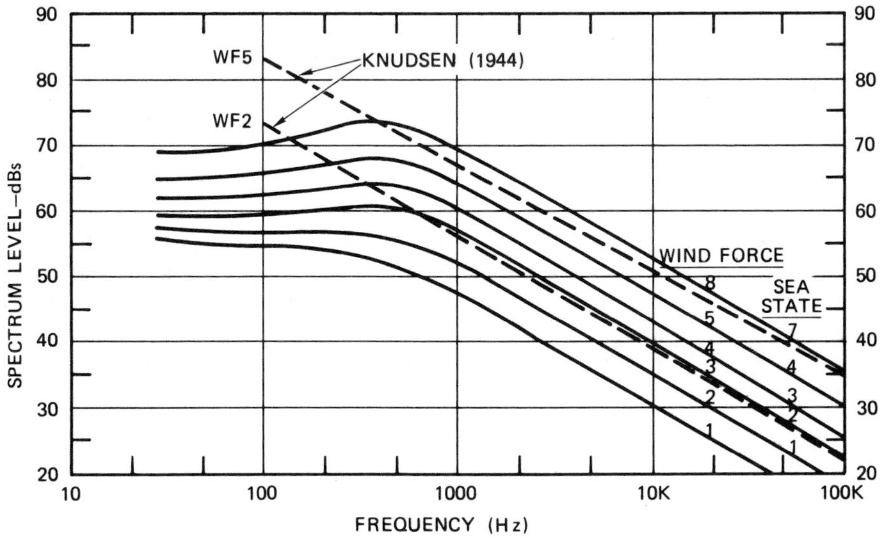


Fig. 4.8. Wind-Generated, Deep-Water Ambient Noise Spectra

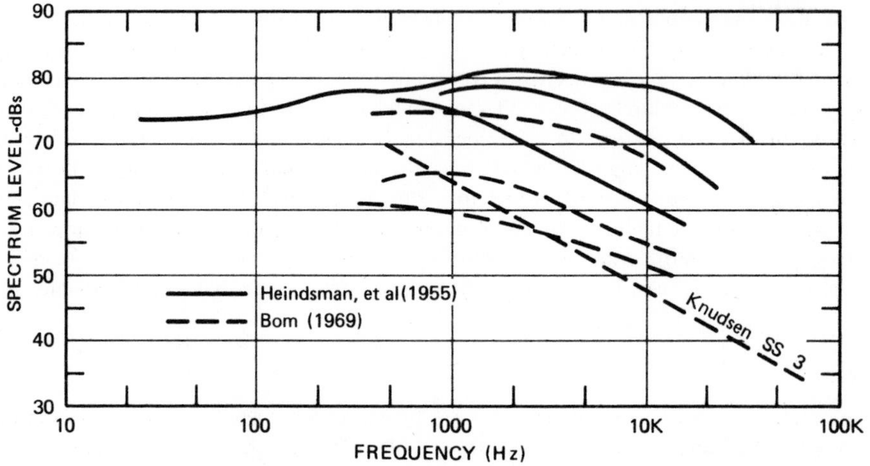


Fig. 4.9. Examples of Measured Rain Noise in Shallow Water

## 4.5 Radiation by Two Equal Monopoles

Many practical fluctuating-volume noise sources have dimensions that are large compared to a wavelength. The sound fields resulting from such sources can in principle be calculated by dividing their surfaces into a large number of small sources and then summing all the individual sound fields, being careful to retain phase information. Such calculations are often quite laborious and usually require high-powered computers. The topic of the present section is radiation from two equal monopoles separated by an arbitrary distance, which is the simplest example illustrative of the calculation for a large radiator.

### General Equation for Pressure Field

Consider two equal monopoles radiating at exactly the same frequency and separated by distance $d$, as depicted in Fig. 4.10. Their midpoint is taken as origin. The field point, $P$, at which the pressure is to be calculated is located at distance $r$ from the origin that may or may not be large compared to their separation. The $x$ axis is taken to be perpendicular to their connecting line, and $\theta$ is the angle of the field point relative to this axis. The distances $r_1$ and $r_2$ of the individual sources from the field point are given by

$$r_1^2 = r^2 \cos^2\theta + \left(r \sin\theta - \frac{d}{2}\right)^2$$

$$= r^2 + \left(\frac{d}{2}\right)^2 - rd \sin\theta \quad , \qquad (4.51)$$

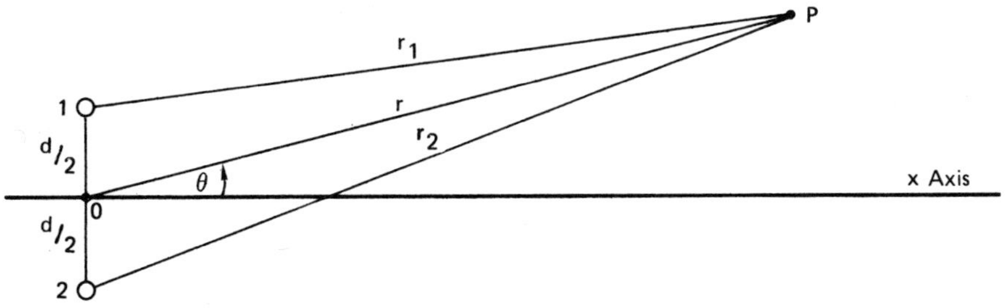


Fig. 4.10. Geometric Representation of Two Monopoles

and

$$r_2^2 = r^2 \cos^2 \theta + \left(r \sin \theta + \frac{d}{2}\right)^2$$

$$= r^2 + \left(\frac{d}{2}\right)^2 + rd \sin \theta \tag{4.52}$$

It is useful to express these distances in terms of the *rms distance*, $r$, defined by

$$\bar{r} \equiv \sqrt{\overline{r^2}} = \sqrt{\frac{r_1^2 + r_2^2}{2}} = \sqrt{r^2 + \left(\frac{d}{2}\right)^2} , \tag{4.53}$$

and a dimensionless parameter, $\beta$, defined by

$$\beta \equiv \frac{rd}{r_1^2 + r_2^2} \sin \theta = \frac{rd}{2\bar{r}^2} \sin \theta . \tag{4.54}$$

The expressions for the distances $r_1$ and $r_2$ can then be written

$$r_1 = \bar{r} \sqrt{1 - \frac{rd}{\bar{r}^2} \sin \theta} = \bar{r}\sqrt{1 - 2\beta} , \tag{4.55}$$

and

$$r_2 = \bar{r} \sqrt{1 + \frac{rd}{\bar{r}^2} \sin \theta} = \bar{r}\sqrt{1 + 2\beta} . \tag{4.56}$$

The acoustic pressure at the field point is simply the sum of the individual monopole pressure fields as given by Eq. 4.15, namely

$$\underline{p}' = \frac{i\omega Q_o}{4\pi r_1} e^{i(\omega t - kr_1)} + \frac{i\omega Q_o}{4\pi r_2} e^{i(\omega t - kr_2 - \psi)}, \tag{4.57}$$

where $\psi$ is the phase angle of the second source relative to the first. It is useful to calculate this resultant pressure field in terms of that which would exist at distance $\bar{r}$ from a single source located at the origin and radiating with the average phase angle. Defining such a reference pressure by

$$\underline{p}'_o \equiv \frac{i\omega Q_o}{4\pi \bar{r}} e^{i(\omega t - k\bar{r} - \psi/2)}, \tag{4.58}$$

Eq. 4.57 for the pressure field of the two sources becomes

$$\underline{p}' = \underline{p}'_o \left[ \frac{e^{ik\bar{r}(1 - \sqrt{1 - 2\beta})}}{\sqrt{1 - 2\beta}} e^{i(\psi/2)} + \frac{e^{ik\bar{r}(1 - \sqrt{1 + 2\beta})}}{\sqrt{1 + 2\beta}} e^{-i(\psi/2)} \right]. \tag{4.59}$$

This result is valid throughout the pressure field. Except in the immediate vicinity of each source, the parameter $\beta$ is less than 0.2. With this condition, the square roots in Eq. 4.59 can each be expanded as a power series. Retaining only the linear terms, one obtains an approximate expression for the pressure,

$$\underline{p}' \doteq \underline{p}'_o \left[ \frac{e^{i(\beta k\bar{r} + (\psi/2))}}{1 - \beta} + \frac{e^{-i(\beta k\bar{r} + (\psi/2))}}{1 + \beta} \right], \tag{4.60}$$

which is valid throughout most of the field.

### Far-Field Pressure Pattern

Most often interest is limited to the far field that exists at distances large compared to the separation between the sources. At these long ranges all distances can be assumed to be equal, and the parameter $\beta$ is small compared to unity. Substituting for $\beta$ from Eq. 4.54, Eq. 4.60 reduces to

$$\underline{p}' \doteq \underline{p}'_o \left[ e^{i((kd/2)\sin\theta + (\psi/2))} + e^{-i((kd/2)\sin\theta + (\psi/2))} \right]. \tag{4.61}$$

From Eq. 1.58, the sum of the two exponential terms can be replaced by a trigonometric function, leading to

$$\underline{p}' = 2\underline{p}'_o \cos\left( \frac{kd}{2} \sin\theta + \frac{\psi}{2} \right), \tag{4.62}$$

and to the alternative form

$$\underline{p}' = \underline{p}'_o \frac{\sin(kd \sin\theta + \psi)}{\sin\left( \frac{kd}{2} \sin\theta + \frac{\psi}{2} \right)}. \tag{4.63}$$

The pressure patterns described by these two equivalent expressions have maxima whenever the argument of the cosine is zero or a multiple of $\pi$, that for zero being called the *principal maximum* and the others being secondary maxima. The angle, $\theta_o$, of the principal maximum is related to the phase shift by

$$\theta_o = -\sin^{-1}\frac{\psi}{kd} \, . \qquad (4.64)$$

Expressing the phase difference, $\psi$, in terms of this angle, Eq. 4.62 for the pressure field can be written

$$\underline{p}' = 2\underline{p}'_o \cos\frac{kd}{2}(\sin\theta - \sin\theta_o) \, . \qquad (4.65)$$

**Directivity Function**

When calculating or measuring the far-field radiated pressure field of any large source, it is customary to express the result in terms of the pressure in the direction of the principal maximum multiplied by the normalized pressure pattern, or *directivity function*, $D(\theta)$, defined by

$$D(\theta) \equiv \frac{|p'(\theta)|}{|p'(\theta_o)|} = \frac{p(\theta)}{p(\theta_o)} \, , \qquad (4.66)$$

where the $p$'s in the second form represent rms pressures. In the case of two equal monopoles, the directivity function is the cosine expression of Eqs. 4.62 and 4.65. Usually the directivity function is expressed in decibels by taking 20 times the logarithm of the pressure ratio of Eq. 4.66.

**Electrical Steering**

Phase differences between radiators are often introduced electricially by means of time delay. The phase angle at any frequency is related to the *time delay*, $\tau$, by

$$\psi = \omega\tau \, , \qquad (4.67)$$

from which it follows that the angle of the principal maximum,

$$\theta_o = -\sin^{-1}\frac{\omega\tau}{kd} = -\sin^{-1}\frac{c_o\tau}{d} \, , \qquad (4.68)$$

is independent of frequency. Thus $\theta_o$ is the angle whose sine is the ratio of the time delay, $\tau$, to the time for an acoustic wave to travel between the two sources. This frequency independence of the peak angle is the reason that electrical steering is so popular.

**Two Equal In-Phase Sources**

If two sources are in phase, then $\psi = 0$ and Eqs. 4.62 and 4.65 reduce to

$$\underline{p}' = 2\underline{p}_o' \cos\left(\frac{kd}{2} \sin\theta\right), \tag{4.69}$$

which has a maximum for $\theta = 0$ equal to the in-phase sum of the two pressures, and a directivity function given by

$$D(\theta) = \left| \cos\left(\frac{kd}{2} \sin\theta\right) \right| . \tag{4.70}$$

This function is plotted in Fig. 4.11 for three values of the parameter $kd$. Secondary maxima occur when $kd$ is greater than $2\pi$. For values of $kd$ less than unity, the radiation pattern is practically nondirectional.

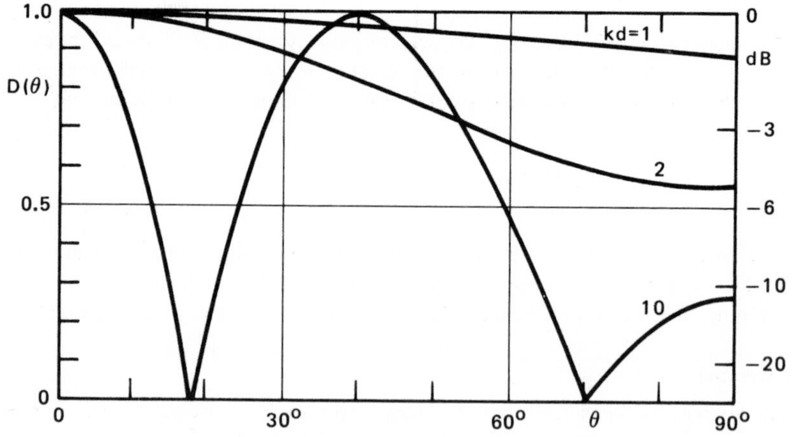


Fig. 4.11. Radiation Pattern for Two Equal In-Phase Monopole Sources

### Out-of-Phase Sources

An important special case of two equal sources is that for which the two sources are exactly out of phase with each other. Setting $\psi = \pi$ in Eq. 4.60 leads to

$$\underline{p}' = i\underline{p}_o' \left[ \frac{e^{i\beta k\bar{r}}}{1 - \beta} - \frac{e^{-i\beta k\bar{r}}}{1 + \beta} \right], \tag{4.71}$$

where the reference pressure, $\underline{p}_o'$, is now

$$\underline{p}_o' = \frac{\omega Q_o}{4\pi\bar{r}} e^{i(\omega t - k\bar{r})} . \tag{4.72}$$

By algebraic manipulation and the use of Eq. 1.59 relating the exponentials to a trigonometric function, Eq. 4.71 can be written in the form

$$\underline{p}' \doteq -\frac{\omega Q_o}{2\pi\bar{r}} e^{i(\omega t - k\bar{r})} \left[\sin(\beta k\bar{r}) - i\beta\cos(\beta k\bar{r})\right], \qquad (4.73)$$

provided that $\beta < 0.2$.

The approximate expression for the instantaneous pressure for two equal out-of-phase sources given by Eq. 4.73 retains phase information. Of more general interest is the magnitude, $P$, of the pressure and its relation to that of a single monopole. From Eqs. 4.53 and 4.73,

$$P = \frac{\omega Q_o}{4\pi r} \frac{2}{\sqrt{1 + \left(\frac{d}{2r}\right)^2}} \sqrt{\sin^2(\beta k\bar{r}) + \beta^2\cos^2(\beta k\bar{r})}, \qquad (4.74)$$

where the first term is the magnitude of the pressure from a monopole at the origin. The cosine term is negligible except when the sine term is near zero. The pressure is seen to go through alternate maxima and minima. In the far field, maxima equal to twice the pressure from a single monopole occur whenever $\beta k\bar{r}$ is an odd multiple of $\pi/2$. Minima equal to $2\beta$ times the monopole value occur when $\beta k\bar{r}$ is a multiple of $\pi$.

**Dipoles**

A *dipole* consists of two equal out-of-phase radiators whose separation is very small compared to both wavelength and distance to the field point. With this condition both $\beta$ and $\beta kr$ are very small compared to unity and Eq. 4.73 becomes

$$\underline{p}' \doteq -\frac{\omega Q_o}{4\pi r} e^{i(\omega t - kr)} \left[kd\left(1 - \frac{i}{kr}\right)\sin\theta\right]. \qquad (4.75)$$

In the far field, $kr >> 1$. Dropping the out-of-phase component, Eq. 4.75 then reduces to

$$\underline{p}' = -\frac{\omega^2 Q_o d \sin\theta}{4\pi r c_o} e^{i(\omega t - kr)}. \qquad (4.76)$$

The product of the separation, $d$, and the source flux magnitude, $Q_o$, is the *dipole strength*, $D_o$.

The most characteristic aspect of dipole radiation, making it readily recognizable, is the dependence of pressure magnitude on $\sin\theta$. Thus, the directivity function of a dipole is

$$D(\theta) = \sin\theta = \cos\left(\frac{\pi}{2} - \theta\right). \qquad (4.77)$$

The intensity at an angle $\theta$ is

$$I(\theta) = \frac{\overline{p'^2}}{\rho_o c_o} = \frac{\omega^4 D_o^2}{32\pi^2 r^2 \rho_o c_o^3} \sin^2\theta, \qquad (4.78)$$

and the total power radiated is

$$W_{ac} = 2\pi r^2 \int_0^{\pi} I(\theta) \cos\theta \, d\theta = \frac{\omega^4 D_o^2}{24\pi\rho_o c_o^3} . \qquad (4.79)$$

Dipole radiation is of fundamental importance and will be discussed further in Section 9.1.

## 4.6 Near-Surface Sources

The surface of the ocean is a nearly perfect reflector of sound. As discussed in Section 2.5, radiation from a source near a surface can be analyzed in terms of direct radiation from the source itself and from a negative image source located above the surface, as shown in Fig. 2.3. The strength of the image source is proportional to the specular reflection coefficient, $\alpha_r$, of the surface and so is a function of its roughness (see Eq. 2.119). The complete radiation pattern is that of two equal out-of-phase monopoles each having a source strength given by that of the image source, plus the field of a monopole of strength equal to their difference.

**Surface Image**

Figure 4.12 shows the geometrical situation for a source located at a depth $h_S$ below the ocean surface, with a receiver at depth $h_R$ at a horizontal distance $r_H$ from the source. The distances and angles used in the analysis in Section 4.5 are also shown. The rms distance, $\bar{r}$, is given by

$$\bar{r} = \sqrt{r^2 + \frac{d}{2}^2} = \sqrt{r_H^2 + h_S^2 + h_R^2} , \qquad (4.80)$$

and the parameter $\beta$, which is given by

$$\beta = \frac{rd}{2\bar{r}^2} \sin\theta = \frac{h_S h_R}{\bar{r}^2} , \qquad (4.81)$$

is seen to be symmetric with respect to source and receiver depths. The direct distance, $r_1$, between source and receiver is given by

$$r_1 = \sqrt{r_H^2 + (h_R - h_S)^2} = \bar{r}\sqrt{1 - 2\beta} . \qquad (4.82)$$

When the horizontal range is at least twice the source or receiver depth, then $\beta$ will be less than 0.2 and Eqs. 4.73 and 4.74 can be used to calculate the image contribution. Assuming that the surface is a perfect reflector, the pressure amplitude at the receiver can be approximated by

$$P \doteq \frac{\omega Q_o}{4\pi r_1} 2\sqrt{1 - 2\beta}\sqrt{\sin^2(\beta k\bar{r}) + \beta^2} , \qquad (4.83)$$

where the first term is the pressure that would be measured at the receiver if source and receiver were both far from a reflecting surface relative to the distance between them. The remaining terms represent the effect of surface reflection on the received signal.

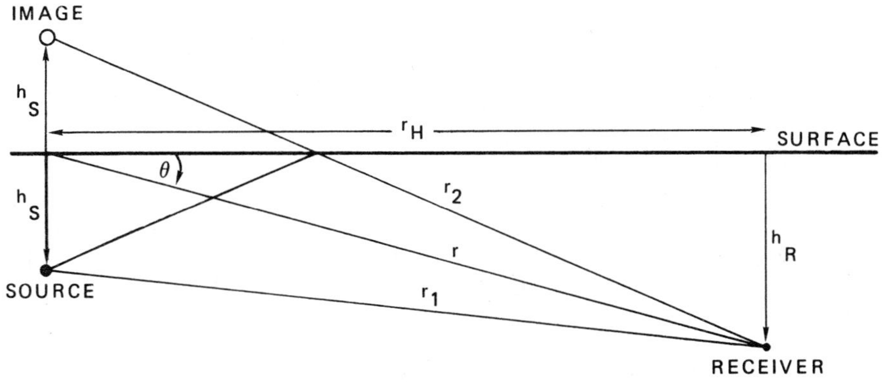


Fig. 4.12. Source and Receiver Near Sea Surface

The effect of a free surface on the received pressure is seen to depend on the values of $\beta$ and $\beta k\bar{r}$ and therefore on three dimensionless parameters, $h_S/h_R$, $h_R/r_H$ and $kh_S$, of which two are defined by the geometry and the third is dependent on frequency.

**Interference Patterns**

If the source depth is large compared to a wavelength, then $\beta kr$ may exceed $\pi$ at close-in distances. In this *near field*, the pressure oscillates rather wildly, between a maximum of almost two times that in an ideal medium and a minimum given by the second term of Eq. 4.83, i.e.,

$$2\beta\sqrt{1 - 2\beta} < \frac{P}{P_i} < 2\sqrt{1 - 2\beta} \; . \tag{4.84}$$

An example of the resultant interference pattern is shown in Fig. 4.13 as range is increased for fixed source and receiver depths. Similar patterns are obtained by fixing the horizontal distance and changing either source or receiver depths. Varying the frequency changes the number of maxima and minima and also the distances at which they occur.

The region of oscillation is bounded by $\beta k\bar{r}$ equal to $\pi/2$. This occurs where the geometry is such that

$$\frac{h_R}{r_H} \doteq \sin\theta = \frac{\lambda}{4h_S} \; . \tag{4.85}$$

For angles less than this, i.e., for shallower receiver depths or greater horizontal ranges, the relative level decreases continuously. In the example given in Fig. 4.13 this occurs at a relative range of 20. Beyond a relative range of 60, the level received in the presence of a surface is everywhere less than the free-field value, the discrepancy increasing at a rate of 6 dB per double distance. Thus, when

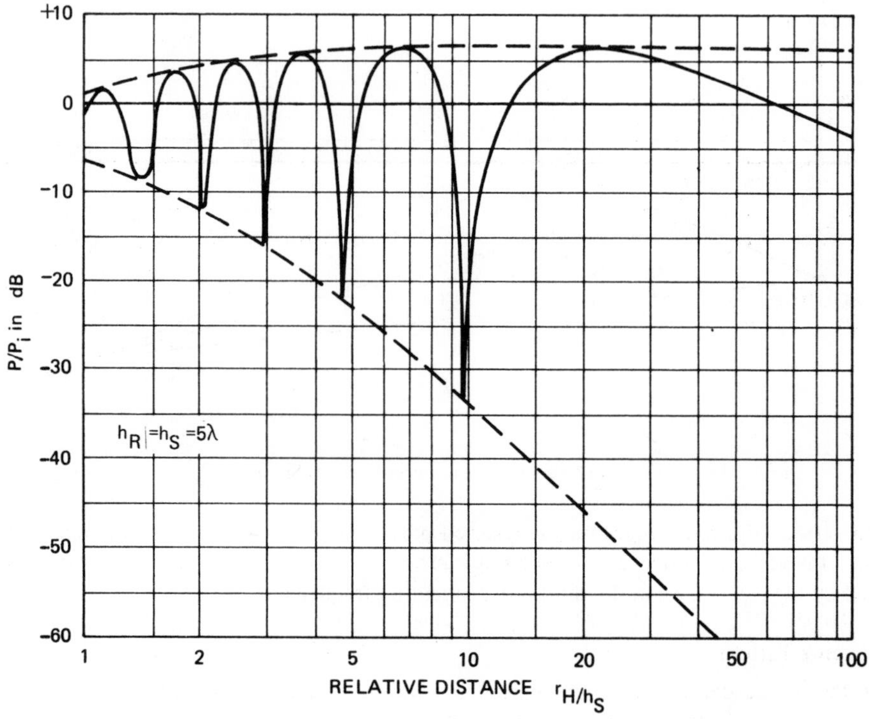


Fig. 4.13. Example of Image Interference

source and receiver are close to the surface, the far-field pressure decreases at a rate of 12 dB per double distance, twice that normally attributable to spherical spreading in an unbounded medium.

The effect at long ranges is appreciably reduced if the surface is rough and only part of the signal is specularly reflected. It can be shown that, when the surface is not perfectly reflecting, the inequality of Eq. 4.84 should be supplemented by another,

$$1 - |\alpha_r| < \frac{P}{P_i} < 1 + |\alpha_r| \;, \tag{4.86}$$

where $\alpha_r$ is the pressure reflection coefficient defined in Section 2.5. Thus, if the reflection coefficient were only 0.9, the anomaly would be limited to 20 dB, and several of the minima in Fig. 4.13 would not be so severe.

Underwater sound pressure fields are affected by surface image interference in many practical situations. Thus, it is not unusual to find interference minima and maxima out to distances of 3 to 5 km from a source. The effects are strongest in the middle frequencies of 300 to 3000 Hz. Above these frequencies, roughness of the surface often tends to wipe out the coherence between source and image, and the received intensity is nearly twice that for the direct path alone. At lower frequencies, bottom reflections can act to fill in the interference minima.

### Effects on Noise Measurements

Measurements of free-field underwater source strengths are often contaminated by free-surface image interference effects. In theory, image interference can be calculated and measured pressures corrected to free-field values. However, as illustrated by Fig. 4.13, the effect is very sensitive to exact values of the parameters. One seldom knows depths or distances with the precision required. One way of avoiding this problem is to average over several cycles of the interference pattern, either by varying the horizontal range during the measurement or by averaging readings of several receivers at a number of depths. When the decibel average of a number of measurements randomly scattered over several interference cycles is taken, the result is generally within ± 0.5 dB of the free-field value. When it is not possible to cover several interference cycles, another approach is to find a maximum of the interference pattern and to estimate the free-field value by subtracting 5 dB from the measured pressure.

Free-field source strengths cannot readily be measured when sources are within a quarter wavelength of the surface. In such cases the surface acts to modify the radiation pattern to that of a dipole, the strength of which is proportional to the product of the monopole strength and distance below the surface of the source. When making low-frequency measurements of such near-surface sources, it is not necessary to know the source depth if what is desired is the dipole source strength. One need merely compute $\sin\theta$ from

$$\sin\theta = \frac{h_R}{\sqrt{r_H^2 + h_R^2}}\,, \tag{4.87}$$

and correct the measured pressures by this amount. However, if the monopole source strength is to be calculated, then the effective source depth must also be ascertained. This is feasible for relatively small sources but quite difficult for large, distributed sources such as surface ships. If a source depth is assumed, then the complete measurement should specify this depth as well as the monopole source level, since any user of the data will need to know the effective source depth in order to calculate the sound field at a distance.

## 4.7 Linear Arrays

As an introduction to consideration of distributed sound sources such as pistons it is instructive to develop expressions for the pressure fields of linear arrays of monopoles.

### Arrays of Equally-Spaced Monopoles

The expressions derived in Section 4.5 for the pressure field of two equal monopoles can be generalized to any number of equally-spaced sources in a line either by summing the individual contributions from all $N$ elements of an array or by a process of extrapolation from results for a small number of elements. The second method will be developed here.

From Eqs. 4.62, 4.63 and 4.65, the far-field pressure for a two-element array (*two-pole*) can be written

$$\underline{p}'(2) = 2\underline{p}'_o \cos\phi = 2\underline{p}'_o \frac{\sin 2\phi}{2\sin\phi} , \tag{4.88}$$

where

$$\phi \equiv \frac{1}{2}(kd \sin\theta + \psi) = \frac{kd}{2}(\sin\theta - \sin\theta_o) . \tag{4.89}$$

The pressure field for a two-pole is therefore that of a source having peak strength equal to their sum and a directional pattern calculable from

$$D_2(\theta) = \frac{\sin 2\phi}{2\sin\phi} . \tag{4.90}$$

As illustrated by Fig. 4.14, arrays of three, four and five elements can be treated as the sums of monopoles and two-poles all of which have the same origin. Thus, the pressure field of the three-element array of Fig. 4.14b can be expressed as the sum of a monopole and a two-pole, the latter having separation $2d$, as

$$\underline{p}'(3) = \underline{p}'_o(1 + 2\cos 2\phi) = \underline{p}'_o(3 - 4\sin^2\phi) = 3\underline{p}'_o \frac{\sin 3\phi}{3\sin\phi} . \tag{4.91}$$

A four-element array can be treated as the sum of two two-poles, one with separation $d$ and the other with separation $3d$. The resultant pressure is

$$\underline{p}'(4) = \underline{p}'_o(2\cos\phi + 2\cos 3\phi) + \underline{p}'_o(8\cos^3\phi - 4\cos\phi) = 4\underline{p}'_o \frac{\sin 4\phi}{4\sin\phi} . \tag{4.92}$$

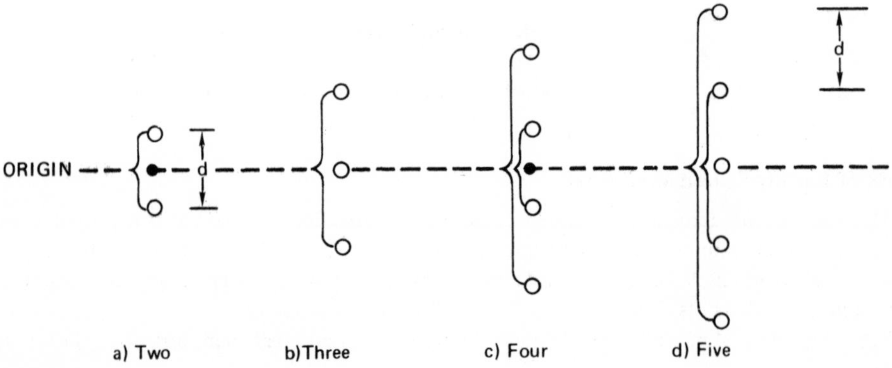


Fig. 4.14. Linear Arrays of up to Five Elements

A similar expression can be derived for a five-element array by summing the fields of a three-element array and a two-pole having a separation between elements of *4d*, as illustrated in Fig. 4.14d. The resultant pressure field is identical to the final form of Eq. 4.92 except that the three 4's are replaced by 5's. Since all of these results are of the same form, it is reasonable to generalize Eq. 4.92 to an *N*-element array, obtaining

$$\underline{p}'(N) = N\underline{p}'_o \frac{\sin N\phi}{N \sin \phi} , \qquad (4.93)$$

which in terms of separation, wave number and steering angle is

$$\underline{p}'(N) = N\underline{p}'_o \frac{\sin\left[\frac{Nkd}{2}(\sin\theta - \sin\theta_o)\right]}{N\sin\left[\frac{kd}{2}(\sin\theta - \sin\theta_o)\right]} . \qquad (4.94)$$

The quantity *Nd* is the effective length, $L'$, of the array, given by the actual length, *L*, plus one separation, *d*. If we think of each monopole source as the kernel of a line element of length *d* centered on the source, then $L'$ is the total length of all of these line elements. The product $N\underline{p}'_o$ is the pressure field that would result if all *N* of the monopoles were concentrated at the origin. The expression for the rms pressure field of an *N*-element array is thus

$$p(N) = Np_o D(\theta) , \qquad (4.95)$$

where

$$D(\theta) = \left| \frac{\sin\left[\frac{kL'}{2}(\sin\theta - \sin\theta_o)\right]}{N\sin\left[\frac{kd}{2}(\sin\theta - \sin\theta_o)\right]} \right| . \qquad (4.96)$$

We will return to this expression after first considering the special case of radiation from a continuous line.

**Continuous Line Radiators**

While few actual line radiators are continuous, many arrays approximate this condition and it is therefore useful to compute the directivity function for a continuous line. Consider the continuous line radiator sketched in Fig. 4.15. The field point *P* is considered to be in the far field, i.e., $r >> L$. The pressure at *P* due to the element *dy* located *y* distance from the center of the line, taken to be the origin, can be expressed

$$d\underline{p}' = d\underline{p}'_o \, e^{ik(r - r')} \doteq \frac{\underline{p}'_o}{L} e^{iky \sin\theta} dy . \qquad (4.97)$$

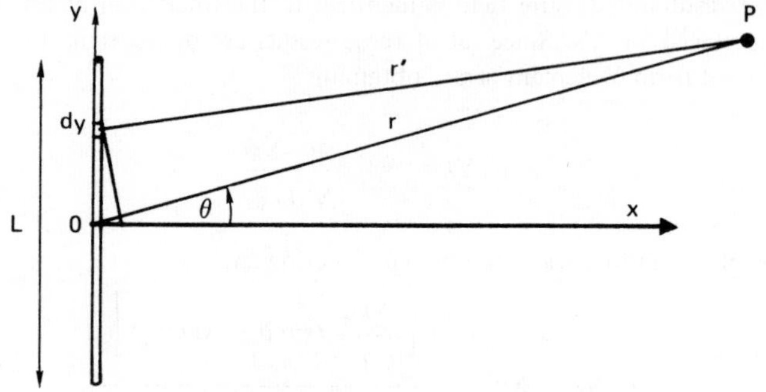


Fig. 4.15. A Continuous Line Radiator

The total pressure at $P$ is the integral of this expression over the length, as given by

$$\underline{p}' = \underline{p}'_o \frac{1}{L} \int_{-L/2}^{L/2} e^{iky \sin\theta} dy$$

$$= \frac{\underline{p}'_o}{ik \frac{L}{2} \sin\theta} \left[ e^{ik(L/2)\sin\theta} - e^{-ik(L/2)\sin\theta} \right] = \underline{p}'_o \frac{\sin\left(\frac{kL}{2}\sin\theta\right)}{\frac{kL}{2}\sin\theta} . \qquad (4.98)$$

The directivity function for a continuous line array is therefore

$$D(\theta) = \left| \frac{\sin\left(\frac{kL}{2}\sin\theta\right)}{\frac{kL}{2}\sin\theta} \right| = \left| \frac{\sin\overline{a}}{\overline{a}} \right| , \qquad (4.99)$$

where $\overline{a}$ represents the denominator. This same expression can be derived by treating a continuous line radiator as an $N$-element array in the limit as $N$ becomes very large and $d$ becomes very small. In this limit, $L' \to L$, $\sin\phi \to \phi$ and $N\phi \to \overline{a}$. Equation 4.96 then reduces to Eq. 4.99, provided $\theta_o$ is taken to be zero.

The directivity function for a continuous line radiator is plotted in Fig. 4.16, for values of $\overline{a}$ up to $6\pi$. The minor peaks are called *side lobes*. The first side lobe, at $\overline{a} = 3\pi/2$, is down 13.5 dB from the main lobe. The second one, at $\overline{a} = 5\pi/2$, is down 19 dB, and all the others are more than 20 dB below the peak of the pattern. The total width of the main beam is twice that of the side lobes.

Returning to an array of $N$ equally-spaced monopoles, Eq. 4.96 for the directivity function can be written in the form

$$D(\theta) = \left| \frac{\sin \bar{a}}{N \sin \phi} \right| = \left| \frac{\sin \bar{a}}{N\phi} \cdot \frac{\phi}{\sin \phi} \right| = \left| \frac{\sin \bar{a}}{\bar{a}} \right| \div \left| \frac{\sin \phi}{\phi} \right| = \frac{D(L', \theta)}{D(d, \theta)} , \qquad (4.100)$$

since $\bar{a} = N\phi$. Thus, the directivity function of an $N$-element array can be calculated by dividing the directivity function for a continuous line of length $L' = L + d$ by that for a line of length $d$. As long as $\phi$ is small, the pattern of the finite-element array is very similar to that for the continuous array. However, when $\phi$ exceeds about $\pi/4$, side-lobe response of the $N$-element array becomes larger, and, when $\phi = \pm \pi$ or any multiple thereof, the response equals that of the main lobe. The lowest frequency for which this can happen is that for which

$$\phi = \frac{\pi d}{\lambda} (\sin \theta - \sin \theta_o) = \pi . \qquad (4.101)$$

For an array steered broadside, this occurs when the separation between the elements equals a wavelength. If the array is steered to end fire, the second major lobe will first appear for an element spacing of only half a wavelength.

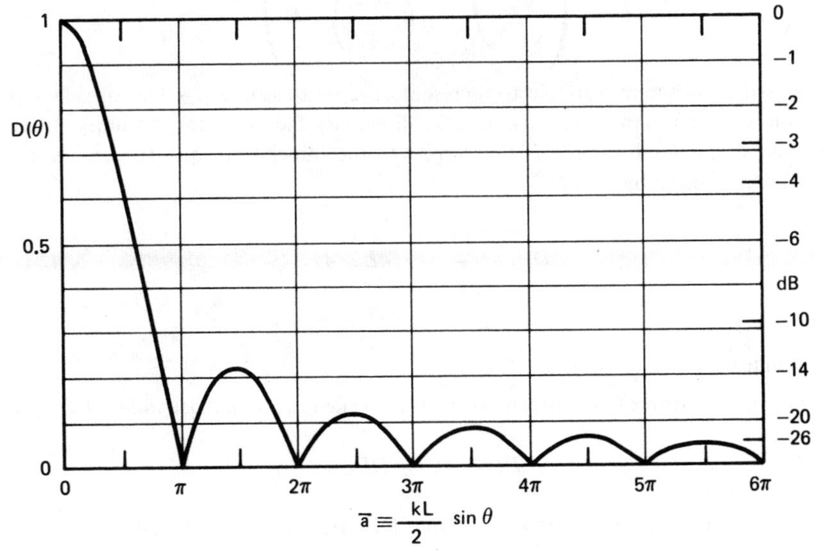


Fig. 4.16. Radiation Pattern of a Continuous Line Array

**Directivity Factor**

An important measure of the directional characteristics of any radiator is the ratio of the total power radiated to that which would have been radiated if all its strength were concentrated at the origin. This ratio of the average intensity to the intensity at the peak of the main lobe is always less than unity. Its reciprocal is the *directivity factor*, *DF*, defined by

$$DF \equiv \frac{I(\theta_o)}{\overline{I}} = \frac{4\pi r^2}{\iint_S D^2(\theta)\, dS} . \tag{4.102}$$

A surface element, $dS$, on a sphere can be expressed by

$$dS = 2\pi r \cos\theta \; r\, d\theta = 2\pi r^2\, d(\sin\theta) , \tag{4.103}$$

whence Eq. 4.102 for the directivity factor can be written

$$DF = \frac{2}{\int_{-1}^{1} D^2(\theta)\, d(\sin\theta)} . \tag{4.104}$$

The directivity factor of a continuous line array steered broadside is

$$DF = \left( \frac{2}{kL} \int_0^{\frac{kL}{2}} \left( \frac{\sin \overline{a}}{\overline{a}} \right)^2 d\overline{a} \right)^{-1} , \tag{4.105}$$

where $\overline{a}$ is used as a dummy variable to represent $kL/2 \sin\theta$, as in Eq. 4.99. For values of $kL < 2$, the radiation is almost omnidirectional and the directivity factor is close to unity. Directionality only becomes dominant for $kL > 4$. For large $kL$, the integral in Eq. 4.105 equals $\pi/2$ and the directivity factor is given by

$$DF \doteq \frac{kL}{\pi} \qquad (kL > 4) . \tag{4.106}$$

**Directivity Index**

The logarithmic form of the directivity factor is called the *directivity index*, *DI*, as defined by

$$DI \equiv 10 \log DF . \tag{4.107}$$

To a close approximation, the *DI* of a continuous line array, plotted in Fig. 4.17, can be estimated from

$$DI \doteq 10 \log \frac{kL}{\pi} = 10 \log \frac{2L}{\lambda} . \tag{4.108}$$

The directional pattern of an $N$-element array is essentially the same as that for a continuous line for frequencies such that the element spacing is less than a half wavelength. For these frequencies, the *DF* and *DI* are given by Eqs. 4.106 and 4.108 with $L'$ replacing $L$. For much higher frequencies for which the separation is large compared to a wavelength, the directivity function is given by that for a continuous line of length $L'$ divided by that for a line of length $d$, and

$$DF \doteq \frac{DF(L')}{DF(d)} = \frac{\frac{kL'}{\pi}}{\frac{kd}{\pi}} = \frac{Nd}{d} = N \qquad (d > \lambda) \ . \tag{4.109}$$

The directivity index is then

$$DI \doteq 10 \log N \ . \tag{4.110}$$

Thus, the directivity index of an $N$-element array is similar to that for a continuous line up to the frequency at which this equals 10 log N. For somewhat higher frequencies, the value stabilizes at 10 log N. This behavior is illustrated in Fig. 4.17 for a 20-element array.

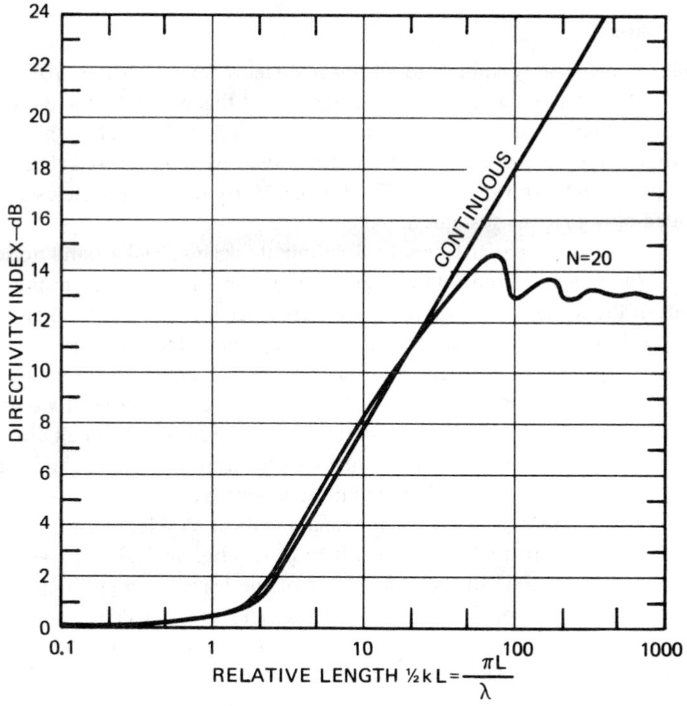


Fig. 4.17. Directivity Index of Line Arrays

**Arrays of Directional Sources**

The expressions derived thus far apply to arrays of omnidirectional sources. In later chapters we will deal with directive sources, which in some instances may be arranged in an array. If all of the elements of an array of directive sources have the same directivity pattern, then the directivity function of the array is simply the product of the directivity functions of the individual elements and that of an array of omnidirectional sources. Thus, the pattern for an array having an even number of elements, $N$, can be calculated as a two-pole consisting of directional elements each being formed by a sub-array of $N/2$ elements. Multiplying Eq. 4.88, for a two-element array in which $(N/2)d$ replaces $d$, by Eq. 4.94, for the directivity of a sub-array of $N/2$ elements, one obtains

$$D_2\left(\frac{N}{2}\right) = \frac{\sin N\phi}{2\sin\frac{N}{2}\phi} \cdot \frac{\sin\frac{N}{2}\phi}{\frac{N}{2}\sin\phi} = \frac{\sin N\phi}{N\sin\phi}, \qquad (4.111)$$

which is the same as the directivity function for an array of $N$ omnidirectional monopoles. Many practical applications follow from the fact that array calculations for omnidirectional sources can be readily extended to arrays of directional sources.

**Arrays as Spatial Filters**

The principle of reciprocity applies to all linear systems for which the differential equations are symmetric in the spatial variables. As a consequence of this principle, the directional response pattern of a configuration of receivers to incoming plane waves is identical to the radiation pattern of the same configuration of sources. All of the directional patterns derived thus far for radiating monopoles, two-poles and arrays are equally applicable to receiving systems having the same geometry, provided only that the systems are linear.

Passive arrays are used as spatial filters to discriminate against background noise coming from many directions. When sound from a target comes in at the angle of peak response of the main beam, the output of the receiving array will have a higher signal-to-noise ratio than that of a single, omnidirectional receiver by an amount that is the array signal-to-noise gain, usually called the *array gain*. It has been common practice to assume that the dB array gain of an array as a receiver equals its directivity index as a radiator. However, this is not usually true. It would be the case if the background noise were isotropic, i.e., arriving with equal intensity from all directions, but this does not generally occur. The assumption that the passive array gain equals the active directivity index is only valid to the extent that background noise is isotropic.

A number of writers have noted that the mathematical development of array directivity patterns is virtually identical to that for linear filters in spectral analysis. The angular frequency, $\omega$, of spectral theory corresponds to the component of the wave number along the array, i.e., to $k \sin\theta$. Time is analogous to position along the array, and spectral density is analogous to the radiation function. A continuous line array of length $L$ is a spatial analog of a square pulse. Discrete elements correspond to sampling. If the sampling is frequent enough, i.e., if elements are closer than a half wavelength, then the result is virtually unchanged from continuous coverage. If the sampling rate is not sufficient, i.e., if the elements are far apart relative to $\lambda$, then extraneous peaks occur.

Just as sampling functions for spectral filters can be designed to achieve specific spectral density functions, so also can linear arrays be designed to achieve desired main-lobe shaping and/or side-lobe reduction. The amplitudes and phases of the individual elements must be controlled in accordance with weighting functions, which functions may be derived from radiation theory or may be taken directly from the signal processing literature. This analogy between signal processing and array spatial filtering is developed more completely in several of the references listed at the end of this chapter.

## 4.8 Radiation from Rigid Pistons

In the preceding section we dealt with linear arrays of monopoles. However, most radiators of underwater sound occur as surfaces rather than lines. The treatment of surface radiators is essentially the same as that for lines, except that the resultant mathematical functions are usually more complex. In dealing with planar surfaces it is useful to replace the omnidirectional monopole used in array calculations with an elementary piston radiator that radiates sound in only one direction. The radiation pattern of an extended surface is then calculated by integration of the fields of these elementary pistons.

### Elementary Piston Radiator

The elementary piston radiator is closely related to the simple pulsating sphere, as can be seen from Fig. 4.18. Since a pulsating sphere radiates sound uniformly in all directions, the placement of a mathematical plane dividing it into two hemispheres has no effect on its field. We may then drop one side, without altering the sound field on the other side, provided we retain the same surface velocity. (Keeping the same flux would involve double the velocity and would produce

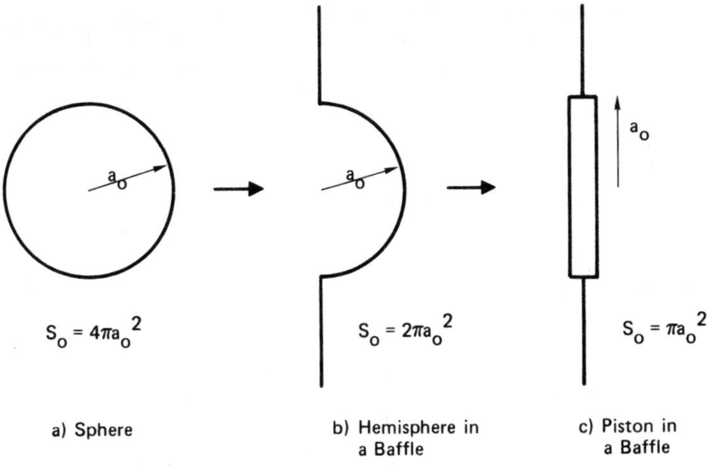


Fig. 4.18. Transformation from Pulsating Sphere to Piston in a Baffle

double the pressure.) It is then a simple step to change from a hemispherical source on a baffle to an equivalent vibrating piston. Since the area is half as great, the same surface velocity produces only half as much oscillating mass flux and half as much sound pressure. It follows that Eq. 4.15 for the pressure field of a monopole can be replaced for an elementary piston by

$$d\underline{p}'(r) = i\,\frac{\omega\rho_o \underline{u}_o}{2\pi r}\,e^{i(\omega t - kr)}\,dS\ . \qquad (4.112)$$

In principle, the pressure from any planar source can be calculated by integrating Eq. 4.112 over the surface of the source, taking into account any phase differences between elements.

### Circular Piston in a Baffle

The integration of Eq. 4.112 over the area of a uniformly vibrating circular piston is quite similar to the integration carried out in Eq. 4.98 for a continuous line array. Defining $\overline{p}$ as the pressure that would be radiated by a small piston having the same mass flux, the pressure is given by the integral

$$\underline{p}' = \overline{p}\int_S \frac{e^{ik(r - r')}}{r'/r}\,dS\ , \qquad (4.113)$$

where $r'$ is the exact distance from the element to the field point and $r$ is the nominal distance from the center, as depicted in Fig. 4.12 for a line. The integration is carried out in a number of texts, and the far-field result may be written

$$\underline{p}' = \overline{p}\left[\frac{2J_1(ka_o \sin\theta)}{ka_o \sin\theta}\right]. \qquad (4.114)$$

The expression in brackets is the pressure pattern of a circular piston in a baffle. It is seen to be similar in form to the *sin x/x* function that was found for linear arrays. $J_1(x)$ is the Bessel function of the first order, defined by the series

$$J_1(x) \equiv \frac{1}{2}\left(x - \frac{x^3}{2\cdot 4} + \frac{x^5}{2\cdot 4\cdot 4\cdot 6} - \frac{x^7}{2\cdot 4\cdot 4\cdot 6\cdot 6\cdot 8} + \ldots\right). \qquad (4.115)$$

Setting the denominator of Eq. 4.114 equal to $\overline{a}$, as was done in Eq. 4.99, the directivity function of a circular piston is

$$D(\theta) = \left|\frac{2J_1(ka_o \sin\theta)}{ka_o \sin\theta}\right| = \left|\frac{2J_1(\overline{a})}{\overline{a}}\right|, \qquad (4.116)$$

which function approaches unity for small $\overline{a}$, corresponding to omnidirectional radiation in one hemisphere. For large values of $\overline{a}$,

$$D(\theta) \rightarrow \left| 1.6 \frac{\sin(\bar{a} - 0.7)}{\bar{a}^{3/2}} \right| \quad (\bar{a} > 5) \ . \qquad (4.117)$$

For medium values, it behaves in a manner similar to that for a line array, as shown in Fig. 4.16, except that the first null occurs at $1.2\pi$, the second at $2.2\pi$, etc.

Many practical sound sources radiate as pistons having values of $ka_o < 2$, for which the directivity function can be expressed as the first three terms of a power series, as

$$D(\theta) = 1 - \frac{(ka_o \sin\theta)^2}{8} + \frac{(ka_o \sin\theta)^4}{192} \quad (a < 2) \ . \qquad (4.118)$$

Half of the total power radiated is contained in a cone defined by $ka_o \sin\theta \doteq 1.6$.

**Near Field of a Piston Radiator**

The expression in Eq. 4.114 for the radiated pressure of a piston source was derived under the assumption that the difference between $r'$ and $r$ is small compared to either distance. In practice, this expression for pressure agrees well with measurements for distances that satisfy the relationship

$$(kr) > (ka_o)^2 \ , \qquad (4.119)$$

which inequality defines the *far field*. The *near field* is quite complicated, often involving interference minima and maxima. However, for pistons having $ka_o < \pi$ there are no interference patterns and the intensity and pressure fields are continuous.

Close to the surface of a piston source, i.e., when $r < a_o$, the pressure on the axis is

$$\underline{p}'(r < a_o) \doteq 2\rho_o c_o u_o e^{i\omega t} \sin\left(\frac{ka_o}{2}\right) ; \qquad (4.120)$$

hence, the on-axis pressure at a large distance $r$ is related to the near-field pressure by

$$\frac{\underline{p}'(r > a_o)}{\underline{p}'(r < a_o)} \doteq i \frac{\left(\frac{ka_o}{2}\right)^2 e^{-ikr}}{(kr) \sin\left(\frac{ka_o}{2}\right)} \ . \qquad (4.121)$$

For the small values of $ka_o$ that are often found when dealing with ship radiation, the sine term in Eq. 4.121 can be replaced by its argument, and the rms pressure in the far field is then related to its near-field value by

$$\underline{p}(r > a_o) \doteq \underline{p}(r < a_o) \frac{a_o}{2r} \quad (ka_o < 1) \ . \qquad (4.122)$$

A practical consequence of Eq. 4.122 is that, for values of $ka_o$ typical of many radiations from ship hulls, pressure measurements made close to the hull are representative of far-field values. This experience is contrary to that of the transducer community, since most transducers are highly directional devices that operate at high values of $ka_o$ for which the near field is very complicated.

### Radiation Impedance and Efficiency

Pressure is not constant over the surface of a piston. Values given by Eq. 4.120 apply only near centers of pistons. To find the reaction force experienced by a piston due to its motion, one must find the average pressure over the entire piston surface. The general expression involves two types of Bessel functions. The resultant values for the specific radiation resistance and reactance are plotted in Fig. 4.19. For pistons satisfying the requirement that $ka_o < 1$, the specific radiation resistance is

$$\sigma_r = 1 - \frac{J_1(2ka_o)}{ka_o} \doteq \frac{(ka_o)^2}{2}\left[1 - \frac{(ka_o)^2}{6}\right], \quad (4.123)$$

and the reactance is

$$\sigma_x \doteq \frac{8}{3\pi}(ka_o)\left[1 - \frac{(2ka_o)^2}{15}\right]. \quad (4.124)$$

It follows that for small values of $ka_o$ the radiation efficiency is proportional to the first power of $ka_o$,

$$\eta_{rad} \doteq \frac{3\pi}{16} ka_o \qquad \left(ka_o < \frac{1}{2}\right), \quad (4.125)$$

as one would expect for a monopole type of radiation.

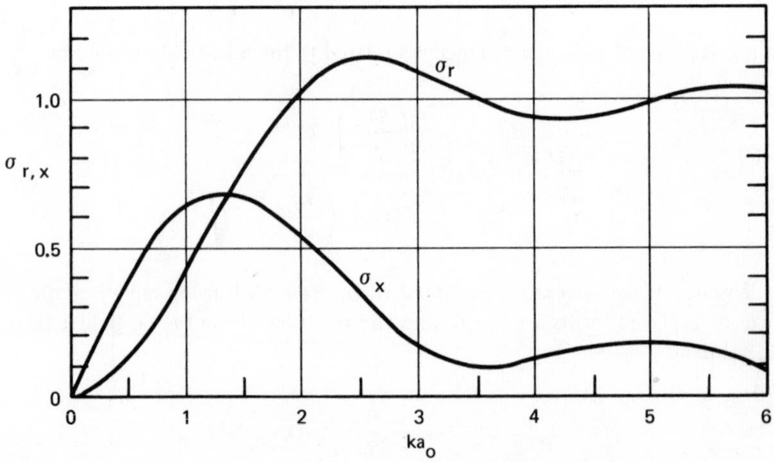


Fig. 4.19. Specific Impedances of Circular Pistons

**Directivity Factor and Index**

The directivity factor for a piston radiator is calculated by substituting the directivity function, $D(\theta)$, given by Eq. 4.116, into Eq. 4.102 and carrying out the integration. The result is

$$DF \equiv \frac{I(0)}{\bar{I}} = \frac{(ka_o)^2}{1 - \dfrac{J_1(2ka_o)}{2ka_o}} = \frac{(ka_o)^2}{\sigma_r} \quad . \qquad (4.126)$$

For values of $ka_o$ up to about 1, $DF \doteq 2$, representing essentially omnidirectional radiation in one hemisphere and zero radiation in the other. For $ka_o \geqslant 2$, $\sigma_r$ is close to unity, as shown in Fig. 4.19, and

$$DF \doteq (ka_o)^2 \qquad (ka_o \geqslant 2) \quad . \qquad (4.127)$$

The directivity index of a piston radiator is therefore 3 dB at low frequencies and is given by

$$DI = 20 \log ka_o = 20 \log \frac{2\pi a_o}{\lambda} \qquad (4.128)$$

at high frequencies.

**Pistons of Other Shapes**

The above development applies only to circular pistons. Many ship radiating surfaces are more nearly rectangular. For rectangular pistons of dimensions $2a \times 2b$ the directivity function is the product of two $\sin \bar{a}/\bar{a}$ functions, one for each dimension. Molloy (1948) calculated the directivity index and found that at high frequencies it can be estimated from

$$DI \doteq 1.2 + 10 \log ka + 10 \log kb \quad . \qquad (4.129)$$

Stenzel (1939) has shown that for many different shapes the main beam pattern is represented by

$$D(\theta) \doteq 1 - \frac{1}{2} k^2 L_x \sin^2 \theta \quad , \qquad (4.130)$$

where $L_x$ is the area moment of inertia about an axis perpendicular to the direction of the pattern. $L_x$ equals $(a/2)^2$ for a solid circle, $(a^2/2)$ for a ring, and $(a^2/3)$ for a square piston having sides of length $2a$. Since acoustic calculations usually need not be very precise, it follows that equations for circular pistons can be used, provided the aspect ratio of the radiator is close to unity.

**Planar Arrays**

It has been demonstrated that the directivity patterns of continuous line radiators are similar to those for linear arrays having their elements closer than a half wavelength. In the same way planar arrays of discrete radiators have radiation patterns similar to those of pistons. Directivity indices of planar arrays of pistons are given by Eq. 4.129 up to a limit 3 dB higher than 10 log N, the limit that applies for unbaffled omnidirectional sources.

**Pistons in Non-Rigid Baffles**

In the discussion thus far it has been assumed that the baffle is rigid. This is almost always a good approximation in air, but not as true in water. Feit and Duncan (1968) have considered the effect of finite baffle impedance on piston radiation impedance and found that both the resistance and reactance are reduced for $ka_o < 1$. For $ka_o$ up to about one half, they found that Eq. 4.123 can be replaced by

$$\sigma_r = \frac{(ka_o)^2}{2}\left[1 - \frac{\gamma_b}{ka}\tan^{-1}\left(\frac{ka_o}{\gamma_b}\right)\right] , \tag{4.131}$$

where

$$\gamma_b \equiv \frac{\rho_o a_o}{\mu_b'} , \tag{4.132}$$

and $\mu_b'$ is the mass area density of the baffle. Taking $h$ to be the baffle thickness,

$$\frac{\gamma_b}{ka_o} = \left(\frac{\rho_o a_o}{\rho_b h}\right)\left(\frac{c_o}{\omega a_o}\right) = \frac{\rho_o c_o}{\omega \rho_b h} , \tag{4.133}$$

where $\rho_b$ is the density of the baffle material and $\omega\rho_b h$ is the baffle mass reactance per unit area. It is apparent that for a given baffle the effect of finite baffle impedance is pronounced at low frequencies, and that at high frequencies the baffle appears to be rigid. It is essentially a question of the relative impedances of the medium and the baffle.

**Unbaffled and Partially Baffled Pistons**

The importance of the baffle to piston radiation can be appreciated by considering unbaffled and partially baffled pistons. Morse and Ingard (1968) show that the pressure pattern at large distances from a free-floating, vibrating disk is equal to that of a piston in a baffle multiplied by $\cos\theta$. At high frequencies, for which $ka_o >> 1$, the extra $\cos\theta$ has little effect and the pattern ahead of the disk is unchanged. Since radiation occurs behind the disk equal to that in front, though out of phase by 180°, the radiation resistance at high frequencies is double that for a baffled piston.

At low frequencies, for $ka_o < 1$, the $\cos\theta$ term dominates the radiation pattern of the free disk, and it radiates as a dipole. In the limit, for small $ka_o$, the radiation efficiency is given by

$$\eta_{rad} \doteq \frac{1}{2}(ka_o)^3 , \tag{4.134}$$

and unbaffled disks are seen to be much less efficient as radiators of sound than are pistons in infinite baffles.

The question of baffle size required to achieve much of the effect of an infinite baffle was examined by Crane (1967). He carried out calculations for circular pistons of radius $a_o$ in circular baffles of radius $r_b$, and found that the radiation impedance is virtually equal to that for an infinite baffle provided $kr_b > \pi$, i.e., that the baffle diameter is greater than a wavelength.

### Pistons on Non-Planar Baffles

In practical marine acoustics, piston-like radiating surfaces occur on finite curved bodies rather than in plane baffles. While the general case has not been treated mathematically, examples of pistons in rigid cylinders and spheres have been treated in the literature. The calculations involve Legendre and Bessel functions of various orders and are quite complex.

Morse (1948) considered a piston of radius $a_o = a \sin \phi_o$ in a sphere of radius $a$. He found that the equivalent source strength is somewhat greater than that for a piston in a plane baffle, and that for moderate angles, up to 60°,

$$Q_{eq} \doteq \frac{1}{\cos^2 \frac{\phi_o}{2}} Q \, . \tag{4.135}$$

His calculations also show that a change from plane to spherical baffle makes a large change in the angular distribution of the radiated sound pressure, but has relatively little effect on the average radiation impedance load of the piston.

Laird and Cohen (1952) were the first to solve the problem for pistons on cylinders, but did not report any simple relation to piston radiation in planar baffles. Greenspon and Sherman (1964) found that, for a piston set in a cylinder, the pressure distribution along the generator agrees well with that for a plane, while around the periphery it is in excellent agreement with that for a sphere. In all cases, the pressure distribution depends on both the *ka* of the piston itself and that of the curved body, while total radiated power and average intensity are much the same as those for a piston in a plane.

### Effect of Flow on Piston Radiation

Since ships are usually in motion, it is pertinent to investigate any effects which flow past a piston might have on its radiation. Chetaev (1956) calculated the acoustic impedance of a square piston in an infinite baffle radiating into a moving medium. He found negligible effects on both the resistive and reactive components provided the product of $ka_o$ and the Mach number, $M$, is small compared to unity. Thus, for speeds found in water, the effect should only be noticeable at very high frequencies.

## 4.9 Radiation from Hull Openings

Usually when dealing with pistons as sound sources one thinks in terms of oscillating rigid plates. At low frequencies, however, pulsating fluid motions in hole openings also generate sound by the same mechanism. This can be understood by thinking of a rigid piston as a device that causes the fluid in front of it to move back and forth, thereby radiating sound. The same oscillating motion can occur in an opening due to pressure pulsations in a tank or pipe. In ship systems, such pulsations occur in hull openings such as those connected with seawater piping systems and tanks, as well as propulsion system exhausts.

**Radiation from Pipe Ends**

The inlet and discharge lines of seawater pumps may be treated as open-ended pipes in essentially infinite baffles. Morse (1948) has shown that the radiation from an opening in a wall is the same as that from a massless piston set in the wall and having the same mass flux. The expressions given in the previous section for piston radiation therefore apply unaltered to pipe endings. The problem reduces to finding the mass flux, $Q$.

In the case of piping systems it is common practice to measure the rms oscillating pressure, $\bar{p}_i$, inside the pipe. If this is measured within an eighth of a wavelength of the opening, then the rms fluctuating fluid velocity, $\bar{u}$, is related to it through the impedance of the opening, as

$$\bar{u} \doteq \frac{\bar{p}_i S}{|Z_r|} = \frac{\bar{p}_i S}{\sqrt{R_r^2 + X_r^2}} = \frac{\bar{p}_i}{\rho_o c_o \sqrt{\sigma_r^2 + \sigma_x^2}} \tag{4.136}$$

The components of the radiation impedance are given in Fig. 4.19 and by Eqs. 4.123 and 4.124.

The assumption of constant velocity, $\bar{u}$, across the mouth of the opening is valid only for low frequencies for which the pipe diameter is small compared to a wavelength. For $ka_o < 1/2$, Eq. 4.136 reduces to

$$\bar{u} \doteq \frac{\bar{p}_i}{\rho_o c_o \sigma_x \sqrt{1 + \left(\frac{\sigma_r}{\sigma_x}\right)^2}} \doteq \frac{3\pi \bar{p}_i}{8 \rho_o c_o k a_o} , \tag{4.137}$$

from which the rms radiated sound pressure is

$$p(r) \doteq \frac{3\pi}{16} \frac{a_o}{r} \bar{p}_i D(\theta) . \tag{4.138}$$

The directivity function, $D(\theta)$, is the approximate expression given by Eq. 4.118. At low frequencies the power radiated is

$$W_{ac} = \eta_{ac} \bar{p}_i \bar{u} S_o \doteq \frac{1}{2} \left(\frac{3\pi}{8}\right)^2 \frac{\bar{p}_i^2 S_o}{\rho_o c_o} , \tag{4.139}$$

showing that the power for a given pipe pulsation pressure is proportional to the area of the opening but is independent of $ka_o$.

**Radiation from Tank Resonances**

When they occur, flow-excited cavity resonances of ship and submarine tanks produce very strong tonal components. All open-mouth cavities have resonant frequencies. The fluid in the opening moving in and out provides the mass, while compressibility of the cavity volume acts as the spring. In air, i.e., in *Helmholtz resonators*, compressibility is provided by the gas in the resonator. In liquids, which are virtually incompressible, flexibility of the tank walls provides the spring action. Sometimes tanks are only partially filled with liquid, in which case the gas volume is the compressible member.

Cavity resonances can be excited in a number of ways, but by far the most important is flow excitation. As discussed in Chapter 9, all wake flows are unstable, shedding vortices at frequencies controlled by flow speed and body dimensions. Such vortices occur in cavity openings when fluid flows past the cavity mouth. When the vortex shedding frequency approaches the resonance frequency of the cavity, the cavity begins to pulsate, strengthening the vortices and further increasing the pulsation velocity. The amplitude builds up until it is limited by non-linear effects. Not only does such a flow-excited resonance radiate a very strong tonal component, but also pressures inside the tank may be sufficient to cause fatigue cracking of the tank plates.

When flow-excited tank resonances are found in marine vehicles, they are readily corrected. Redesign of the cavity opening to change the vortex excitation frequency is one cure. Another is addition of reinforcing beams to the tank plates to decrease their flexibility and thereby increase the resonance frequency. Also, flow diverters can be introduced ahead of the tank opening, causing the flow to avoid the opening and thereby reducing both the strengths and frequencies of the vortices.

### Radiation from Exhaust Pipes

Pulsating exhaust flows from tail pipes of torpedoes and other underwater exhaust systems also radiate as monopoles. Even though unflanged, such open-ended pipes radiate as though baffled, with the pipe wall providing the baffle. At low frequencies sound is radiated equally in all directions. The radiation reactance is about 30% less, and the pressure about 1.5 dB lower, than that for an opening in a flat surface.

Ffowcs Williams (1969) and Plett and Summerfield (1974) have shown that even for jet engines in air, monopole sources dominate at low Mach numbers. Westervelt and McQuillin (1957) reported that at low frequencies sounds from pulse jets are controlled by volume pulsations. At higher frequencies, dipole and quadrupole radiations are observed. Marine vehicle exhaust systems are similar in many ways to low Mach number pulse jets; monopole radiation can therefore be expected to dominate.

## 4.10 Radiation from Arbitrary Bodies

While many practical sound sources can be understood in terms of the relatively simple configurations discussed earlier in this chapter, there are other types of radiators which are more complicated. Numerous papers have been published dealing with one or more specific configurations. The present section deals briefly with several methods that are used in calculating the sound fields radiated by arbitrary bodies, and the next section discusses their application to hull radiation problems.

### Integral Equation Methods

Solutions of Helmholtz's equation, Eq. 2.61, for acoustic fields radiated by arbitrary bodies can be expressed in terms of integrals over their surfaces. The approach used parallels that originally developed for solving Laplace's equation when presented with a set of arbitrary boundary conditions.* The fact that acoustics formulations deal with retarded time and must retain phase information makes acoustics problems somewhat more difficult than the usual boundary-value problems of potential theory. Were it not for the availability of high-speed computers, this approach would have little appeal.

*See, for example, Kellogg (1953).

Most integral methods start with the *Helmholtz integral equation*, derived by applying Green's theorem to acoustic potentials. In its most common form, the radiated pressure is expressed as a sum of two integrals:

$$\underline{p}'(r) = \int_S \frac{e^{-ikr}}{4\pi r} \left.\frac{\partial p'}{\partial n}\right|_S dS - \int_S p'(S) \frac{\partial}{\partial n}\left(\frac{e^{-ikr}}{4\pi r}\right) dS \,. \tag{4.140}$$

Solution of this equation requires knowledge of the pressure distribution and of its normal derivative, both evaluated just outside the surface. From Eq. 2.47, the normal pressure gradient at a surface is related to the surface velocity, $u$, by

$$\left.\frac{\partial p'}{\partial n}\right|_S = \rho_o \frac{\partial u}{\partial t} = i\omega\rho_o u = i\omega_o c_o k u \,. \tag{4.141}$$

The first integral therefore expresses the monopole field of the surface velocity distribution, while the second can be interpreted as the dipole field of the surface pressures. If both surface velocity and pressure distributions are given, then Eq. 4.140 can be used directly. However, usually only one of these is known and equations must be found to relate the unknown quantity to the known one. In solving these supplementary integral equations, difficulties in the form of indeterminacies occur at certain wave numbers. Chertock (1964, 1970 and 1971) has developed several practical computational procedures for overcoming these problems. Other methods for using integral equations have been published by Copley (1967, 1968) and Schenck (1968).

The most successful applications of integral methods have been in calculating the fields of large complex transducers and of cylindrical shells. Readers interested in further discussion of this subject are referred to the articles and reports listed at the end of this chapter, especially Chertock's (1971) overview.

### Spheroidal Wave Functions

Many radiators for which sound fields are desired are cigar-shaped. Rather than carry out the integrals of Eq. 4.140, it is more appropriate to express the sound fields of such bodies in terms of known mathematical functions, of which prolate spheroidal functions are the most useful. In this approach, the geometric outline of the body is fitted as well as possible by a prolate spheroid, and the surface velocity distribution is expressed by a finite series of spheroidal surface functions, as given by Morse and Feshbach (1953). The radiated field is then given by a series of spheroidal wave functions, in much the same manner as in the treatment of a general spherical radiator discussed in Section 3.3. Chertock (1961) developed expressions for the pressure field, radiation impedances and directivity factors for spheroidal modes, and applied these results to consideration of rigid-body and "accordion-like" vibrations of thin prolate spheroids. The usefulness of this approach depends both on the degree of fit of the actual body by a spheroid and the number of terms required to match the surface velocity distribution. It is therefore most useful when treating bodies of revolution at low frequencies.

### Slender Body Theory

A weakness of the spheroidal function method is that it assumes bow-stern symmetry. Pond

(1966) overcame this difficulty by representing relatively thin bodies of revolution by distributions of monopoles and dipoles on the body axis. The strengths of the sources are adjusted to produce streamlines that coincide with the hydrodynamic flow over the body. Pond found that bow-stern assymmetries introduce a number of important terms that are not part of a symmetric analysis. Chertock (1964) noted that at low frequencies the far-field radiation pattern is symmetric even though the body itself is not. Thus, the longitudinal *accordion* mode, which radiates strongly along the axis of the body, radiates sound almost equally in the bow and stern directions.

Chertock (1975) has developed a relatively simple method for calculating the radiation fields of slender bodies at very low frequencies. He assumed that the acoustic wavelength is larger than any distance along the body in which the motion changes appreciably. This implies that the fluid can be treated as incompressible when relating the surface velocity and pressure distributions. In fact, the local surface pressure is then simply the fluid density times the local surface acceleration. Chertock has successfully applied this method to the calculation of low-frequency fields of a number of ship-like structures.

**Radiation from Cylinders**

Slender body methods are most useful at the lowest frequencies. At somewhat higher frequencies, sound radiation from marine vehicles often has characteristics that are similar to those found when treating radiation from cylinders. In this medium frequency range, shell resonances play an important role, and much of the literature relating to cylinders is concerned with these resonances. The subject has offered considerable challenge to theoreticians and most of the papers are highly mathematical. Heckl (1962) summarized the results for finite cylindrical shells in air. He noted that while ring stiffness controls at low frequencies, the results are in good agreement with flat-plate calculations when the circumference of the cylinder exceeds the wavelength of longitudinal waves in the shell.

Junger (1975) pointed out that submergence of a structure in a liquid changes the nature of the problem. In air, the vibration can be calculated as for a vacuum and the radiation then derived from the vibrational pattern by any of a number of acoustic methods. In a liquid, on the other hand, motion of the fluid must be included in dealing with the structure, i.e., one is dealing with a coupled structural-acoustics problem. Junger (1952) has solved the coupled equations for thin, elastic cylindrical shells, finding as much as a 50% change in some resonances. He extended this approach in 1954 to cylinders with reinforcing rings and bulkheads. Different methods of solving the same problems have been developed by Warburton (1961) and by Bleich and Baron (1954, 1965).

It is the author's experience that most of the acoustic characteristics of radiating underwater systems can be understood without resort to detailed analyses of cylindrical structures. Furthermore, the mathematical complexity of these analyses tends to hide some of the basic physics. For these reasons, no details on this subject are given in the present volume. Readers who wish to pursue this subject further may do so by reading some of the articles already mentioned, as well as several others listed at the end of the chapter.

**Finite-Element Methods**

The finite-element approach to structural-acoustics problems has gained increasing favor as industry has developed larger and faster digital computers. In this approach one divides the structure into a large number of relatively simple sections so chosen that their independent vibrational and radiational characteristics are known. A series of coupled equations is written and the resultant matrix solved on a high-power computer. The larger the number of equations, the better the results. An application of this method to hull vibrations has been published by Greenspon (1963). MacNeal (1962) has written on the analogy of mechanical and electrical finite elements and the use of electric circuit theory to analyze complex structures. Before the development of high-speed digital computers, vibration problems were often solved by means of finite elements and their electric analogs.

## 4.11 Radiation from Hulls

The hulls of most marine vehicles are extremely complicated structures that can be excited into vibration, and consequently radiate sound, over a wide range of frequencies. In later chapters we will discuss a number of hydrodynamic and mechanical forces that cover the entire spectrum from as low as 1 Hz to as high as 20 kHz. Calculation of the resultant hull vibration and radiation by any single method seems virtually impossible. Most of the more important characteristics of hull vibrational response and radiation can be understood by dividing the spectrum into a few distinctive frequency regimes, treating each regime by relatively simple physical models.

### Definition of Frequency Regimes

Parameters that are most useful in dividing the spectrum into frequency regimes are ratios of the acoustic wavelength to various hull dimensions. Pertinent dimensions are overall length, diameter or width, lengths of compartments, frame spacings and plate thicknesses. The author has found it useful to think in terms of the three basic frequency ranges summarized by Fig. 4.20.

| | | |
|---|---|---|
| $> 20$ kHz | | |
| | HF | Small section vibrates, extending only a few frames.<br>Ribbed flat plate.<br>Curvature adds stiffness at low-freq. end. |
| $\lambda \doteq R$ | | |
| | MF | Compartments vibrate.<br>Resonances important.<br>Cylindrical shell in a rigid cylindrical baffle. |
| $\lambda \doteq L/2$ | | |
| | LF | Whole hull involved.<br>Rigid-body translation and rotation.<br>Beam flexural vibrations (whipping).<br>Accordion modes. |
| $\sim 1$ Hz | | |

L = vehicle length R = effective cross-sectional radius

Fig. 4.20. Frequency Regimes for Hull Vibrations and Radiation

**Low Frequencies**

The *low-frequency* (LF) regime extends from 1 Hz up to the frequency for which the acoustic wavelength equals half the vehicle length. For a vehicle 150 m long, this includes all frequencies up to about 20 Hz. In this regime, the entire hull participates in the motion and applicable models must represent the whole body. Three distinct types of motion may occur at low frequencies, each of which radiates sound with different characteristics. The body may experience rigid-body motion in which it retains its exact shape and either vibrates in position in response to an external alternating force or rotates about an axis. The second type is beam-like flexural bending vibrations, sometimes called *whipping* motions. Finally, there may occur dominantly longitudinal vibrations in which the two ends move out of phase in an accordion-like motion. Expansion and contraction, i.e., breathing, motions of the hull sections are associated with the latter type of vibration.

Low-frequency motions of surface ships are important to naval architects because they are sometimes strong enough to cause damage and because they can be very unpleasant to experience. However, acoustic radiation from these motions is generally negligible. The reason is that the ocean surface acts to reduce the sound by providing negative image sources within a half wave-length of the hull sources, thus partially cancelling them. Thus, any near-surface oscillating-volume source radiates as a dipole, while dipole sources radiate as quadrupoles. Also, as will be discussed in Chapter 8, direct radiation by propeller cavitation generally dominates in this frequency region. Low-frequency radiation is much more important for submerged vehicles, for which image cancellation is much reduced and for which propeller cavitation may be absent.

Methods for calculating low-frequency sounds from submerged bodies were discussed in the previous section. Additional material pertinent to flexural vibrations of hulls and the attendant radiation is presented in the next chapter.

**Medium Frequencies**

The *medium-frequency* (MF) region of the spectrum applies between the LF region and the frequency for which the acoustic wavelength equals the effective radius of the cross section. Thus, for a circular hull 10 m in diameter, this covers frequencies up to about 300 Hz. In this regime, response to excitation is usually limited to one compartment; the remainder of the hull acts as a baffle.

Individual hull resonances play a major role in the response of the hull to exciting forces and are therefore important in acoustic calculations for the MF range. Resonance frequencies can be estimated from results for cylinders, but are best calculated by finite-element methods. In many ways the decade of frequency covered by this regime is the most difficult part of the spectrum for vibration and acoustics calculations. Slight alterations in the structure that change a resonance frequency by only a few percent result in entirely different responses to specific forcing frequencies. The role of resonances in this frequency regime is clearly indicated in hull structural and acoustic measurements, such as those reported by Donaldson (1968).

**High Frequencies**

In the *high-frequency* (HF) region, each exciting force causes only a small area to vibrate and the remainder of the hull is effectively an infinite baffle. Radiation in this frequency region can be treated in terms of plate theory. This topic is covered in Chapter 6, where it is shown that ribs play a much more important role than plate curvature. In this frequency regime, the densities of resonances are of greater interest than are their exact frequencies. In fact, sufficient numbers of resonances occur to enable application of statistical energy methods. In this regime, sound radiation is controlled by plate thicknesses and frame spacings, and the results are only slightly influenced by the overall shape of the hull.

Excitation forces at high frequencies sometimes occur at a single point, such as at a machine foundation. Sometimes they are distributed over wide areas, as in the case of boundary layer turbulence. Both situations are discussed in Chapter 6.

## REFERENCES


### Sections 4.1 and 4.2

Junger, M.C. and Feit, D., *Sound, Structures and Their Interaction*, M.I.T. Press, Cambridge, Mass., 1972 (Sections 2.6 and 2.7).

Kinsler, L.E. and Frey, A.R., *Fundamentals of Acoustics*, 2nd Edit., Wiley, New York, 1962 (Section 7.7).

Lindsay, R.B., *Mechanical Radiation*, McGraw-Hill, New York, 1960 (Section 3.5).

Morse, P.M., *Vibration and Sound*, 2nd Edit., McGraw-Hill, New York, 1948 (Section 27).

Morse, P.M. and Ingard, K.U., *Theoretical Acoustics*, McGraw-Hill, New York, 1968 (Section 7.1).

Rayleigh, Lord, *Theory of Sound*, Vol. II, 2nd Edit., London, 1896; Dover, New York, 1945.

Rschevkin, S.N., *Theory of Sound*, Pergamon Press, Oxford, 1963 (Chapter 4).

### Section 4.3

Brooke-Benjamin, T., "Surface Effects in Non-Spherical Motions of Small Cavities," in *Cavitation in Real Liquids*, R. Davies (Ed.), Elsevier, Amsterdam, 1964 (pp. 164-180).

Devin, C., Jr., Survey of thermal, radiation and viscous damping of pulsating air bubbles in water, *J.A.S.A.*, *31*, 1654-1667, 1959.

Fitzpatrick, H.M. and Strasberg, M., "Hydrodynamic Sources of Noise," Paper 10 of *Symposium on Naval Hydrodynamics*, Nat. Acad. of Sciences, Nat. Res. Council Publication 515, Washington, D.C., 1956; also *D.T.M.B. Rept. 1269*, 1959.

Gavigan, J.J., Watson, E.E. and King, W.R., III, Noise generation by gas jets in a turbulent wake, *J.A.S.A.*, *56*, 1094-1099, 1974.

Kapustina, O.A., "Gas Bubbles in Liquids," Chapter 1, Part 4 of *Physical Principles of Ultrasonic Technology*, Vol. I, L.D. Rozenberg (Ed.), Plenum Press, New York, 1973 (pp. 382-390).

Lauterborn, W., Resonance frequencies of gas bubbles in liquids, *Acustica*, *20*, 14-20, 1968; *23*, 73-81, 1970 (in German).

Meyer, E. and Tamm, K., Resonant vibrations and damping of gas bubbles in liquids, *Akust. Zeit.*, *4*, 145, 1939; *D.T.M.B. Trans. 109*.

Meyer, E., "Air Bubbles in Water," Chapter 5 of *Technical Aspects of Sound*, Vol. II, E.G. Richardson (Ed.), Elsevier, Amsterdam, 1957.

Minnaert, M., On musical air bubbles and the sounds of running water, *Phil. Mag.*, *16*, 235-248, 1933.

Mühle, C. and Heckl, M., Sound Radiation by Submerged Exhaust, *Müller-BBN Rept. 2605*, 1971, translated from German in *NAVSHIPS Trans. 1321*, 1972.

Shima, A., The Natural Frequency of a Bubble Oscillating in a Viscous Compressible Liquid, *A.S.M.E.* Paper 69-WA/FE-1, 1969.

Shima, A., The natural frequencies of two spherical bubbles oscillating in water, *J. Basic Engin.*, *93*, 426-432, 1971.

Strasberg, M., Pulsation frequency of nonspherical gas bubbles in liquids, *J.A.S.A.*, *25*, 536-537, 1953.

Strasberg, M., Gas bubbles as sources of sound in liquids, *J.A.S.A.*, *28*, 20-26, 1956; also *D.T.M.B. Rept. 1042*, April 1956.

Victor, A.S., A Study of the Damping and Stability of a Pulsating Spherical Bubble in a Flowing Fluid, *U.S.N. Mine Defense Lab. Rept. 329*, April 1967.

Vorotnikova, M.I. and Soloukin, R.I., A calculation of the pulsations of gas bubbles in an incompressible liquid subject to a periodically varying pressure, *Sov. Phys.-Acoustics, 10*, 28-32, 1964.

## Section 4.4

Bannister, R.W., Barker, P.H., Browning, D.G. and Denham, R.N., Ambient sea noise measurements near New Zealand, Paper P4 (Abstract), *J.A.S.A., 55*, 418, 1974.

Bardyshev, V.I., Velikanov, A.M. and Gershman, S.G., Experimental studies of underwater noise in the ocean, *Sov. Phys.-Acoustics, 16,* 512-513, 1970; also, *17*, 252-253, 1971.

Bom, N., Effect of rain on underwater noise level, *J.A.S.A., 45*, 150-156, 1969.

Fitzpatrick, H.M. and Strasberg, M., *op. cit.*

Franz, G.J., Splashes as sources of sound in liquids, *J.A.S.A., 31*, 1080-1096, 1959; also *D.T.M.B. Repts. C-595*, Jan. 1955 and *C-627*, July 1955.

Furduev, A.V., Undersurface cavitation as a source of noise in the ocean, *J. Atmospheric and Oceanic Physics, 2*, 523-533, 1966.

Heindsman, T.E., Smith, R.H. and Arneson, A.D., Effect of rain upon underwater noise levels, *J.A.S.A., 27*, 378-379, 1955.

Knudsen, V.O., Alford, R.S. and Emling, J.W., "Survey of Underwater Sound, Report No. 3, Ambient Noise," *Div. 6.1 Nat. Defense Res. Com. Rept. 1848*, 1944.

Knudsen, V.O., Alford, R.S. and Emling, J.W., Underwater ambient noise, *J. Marine Res., 7*, 410-429, 1948.

Perrone, A.J., Ambient noise spectrum level as a function of water depth, *J.A.S.A., 48*, 362-370, 1970.

Piggott, C.L., Ambient sea noise at low frequencies in shallow water of the Scotian Shelf, *J.A.S.A., 36*, 2152-2163, 1964.

Urick, R.J., *Principles of Underwater Sound for Engineers*, McGraw-Hill, New York, 1967 (Chapter 7).

Wenz, G.M., Acoustic ambient noise in the ocean: spectra and sources, *J.A.S.A., 34*, 1936-1956, 1962.

## Sections 4.5-4.8

Arndt, L.K., Responses of Arrays of Isotropic Elements in Detection and Tracking, *U.S. Navy Electronics Lab. Rept. 1456*, April 1967.

Bartberger, C.L., *Lecture Notes on Underwater Acoustics*, U.S. Naval Air Development Center, Johnsville, Pa., 1965 (AD 468869) (pp. 163-168, 199-203, 238-260, 272-283, 319-331).

Bobber, R.J., *Underwater Electroacoustic Measurements*, U.S. Govt. Printing Office, Washington, 1970 (Chapter 2).

Carter, A.H. and Williams, A.O., Jr., A new expansion for the velocity potential of a piston source, *J.A.S.A., 23*, 179-184, 1951.

Chetaev, D.N., The effect of subsonic flow velocity on the radiation impedance of a piston in an infinite baffle, *Sov. Phys.-Acoustics, 2*, 319-327, 1956.

Crane, P.H.G., Method for the calculation of the acoustic radiation impedance of unbaffled and partially baffled piston sources, *J. Sound and Vibr., 5*, 257-277, 1967.

Cremer, L., Heckl, M. and Ungar, E.E., *Structure-Borne Sound*, Springer-Verlag, Berlin, 1972 (Section 6.5).

Feit, D. and Duncan, M.E., Numerical evaluation of the radiation impedance for a piston in a nonrigid baffle, *J.A.S.A., 43*, 885-886, 1968.

Greenspon, J.R. and Sherman, C.H., Mutual radiation impedance and near-field pressures for pistons on a cylinder, *J.A.S.A., 36*, 149-153, 1964.

Herrey, E.M.J., Approximate formula for the radiation resistance of a piston set in an infinite wall, *J.A.S.A., 25*, 154-155, 1953.

Horton, C.W., Sr., *Signal Processing of Underwater Acoustic Waves*, U.S. Govt. Printing Office, Washington, 1969 (Chapters 9 and 14).

Hueter, T.F. and Bolt, R.H., *Sonics*, Wiley, New York, 1955 (Chapter 3).

Jones, R.C., Theory of directional patterns of continuous source distributions on a plane, *J.A.S.A., 16*, 147-171, 1945.

Junger, M.C., Surface pressures generated by pistons on large spherical and cylindrical baffles, *J.A.S.A., 41*, 1336-1346, 1967.

Junger, M.C. and Feit, D., *op cit.* (Chapters 3, 5 and 8).

Karnovskii, M.I., Calculations of the radiation resistance of several types of distributed radiator systems, *Sov. Phys.-Acoustics, 2*, 280-293, 1956.

Kinsler, L.E. and Frey, A.R., *op. cit.* (Chapter 7).

Laird, D.T. and Cohen, H., The directivity patterns for acoustic radiation from a source on a rigid cylinder, *J.A.S.A., 24*, 46-49, 1952.

Lindsay, R.B., *op. cit.* (Section 9.10).

Mangulis, V., Pressure on a vibrating circular piston in an infinite baffle, *J.A.S.A., 36*, 1734-1735, 1964.

Molloy, C.T., Calculation of the directivity index for various types of radiators, *J.A.S.A., 20*, 387-405, 1948.

Morse, P.M., *op cit.* (Sections 27 and 28).

Morse, P.M. and Ingard, K.U., *op. cit.* (Chapters 7 and 11).

Rschevkin, S.N., *op. cit.* (Chapter 11).

Schelkunoff, S.A., Mathematical theory of linear array, *Bell System Tech. J., 22*, 80-107, 1943.

Smaryshev, M.D., Radiation impedance and gain of extended periodic linear arrays, *Sov. Phys.-Acoustics, 14*, 499-503, 1968.

Smith, P.W., Jr., Directive Receiving Arrays, *Bolt Beranek and Newman Rept. 913*, March 1962.

Stenzel, H., *Handbook for the Calculation of Sound Propagation Phenomena* (in German), Julius Springer, Berlin, 1939; translated by A.R. Stickley, *NRL Trans. 130*.

Urick, R.J., *op. cit.* (Chapter 3).

Vinogradova, E.L. and Furduev, V.V., Directivity factor of a linear array of directional transmitters, *Sov. Phys.-Acoustics, 12*, 161-163, 1966.

Winder, A.A. and Loda, C.J., *Introduction to Acoustical Space-Time Information Processing*, O.N.R., ACR-63, Washington, Jan. 1963 (Sections E and H).

Young, R.W., Image interference in the presence of refraction, *J.A.S.A., 19*, 1-7, 1947.

## Section 4.9

Alfredson, R.J. and Davies, P.O.A.L., The radiation of sound from an engine exhaust, *J. Sound and Vibr., 13*, 389-408, 1970.

Dunham, W.H., "Flow-Induced Cavity Resonances in Viscous Compressible and Imcompressible Fluids," in *Proc. Fourth Symposium on Naval Hydrodynamics*, O.N.R., ACR-92, Washington, 1962 (pp. 1057-1081).

Ffowcs Williams, J.E., "Jet Noise at Very Low and Very High Speed," in *Aerodynamic Noise*, H.S. Ribner (Ed.), Univ. of Toronto Press, 1969 (pp. 131-146).

Harrington, M.C. and Dunham, W.H., Studies of the mechanism for flow-induced cavity resonance, Paper G8 (Abstract), *J.A.S.A., 32*, 921, 1960.

Ingard, K.U. and Dean, L.W., "Excitation of Acoustic Resonators by Flow," in *Proc. Second Symposium on Naval Hydrodynamics*, O.N.R., ACR-38, Washington, 1958 (pp. 137-148).

Krishnamurty, K., Acoustic Radiation from Two-Dimensional Rectangular Cutouts in Aerodynamic Surfaces, *N.A.C.A. Tech. Note 3487*, Aug. 1955.

Morfey, C.L., Acoustic properties of openings at low frequencies, *J. Sound and Vibr., 9*, 357-366, 1969.

Morse, P.M., *op cit.* (Section 23).

Plett, E.G. and Summerfield, M., Jet engine exhaust noise due to rough combustion and nonsteady aerodynamic sources, *J.A.S.A., 56*, 516-522, 1974; *57*, 755, 1975.

Sorokin, V.I., Investigation of water-air reconators, *Sov. Phys.-Acoustics, 4*, 188-195, 1958.

Westervelt, P.J. and McQuillin, R.J., Theory of pulse jet noise generation, Paper D7 (Abstract), *J.A.S.A., 29*, 1252, 1957.

## Sections 4.10 and 4.11

Baron, M.L., Bleich, H.H. and Mathews, A.T., Forced vibrations of an elastic circular cylindrical body of finite length submerged in a fluid, *Int. J. of Solids and Structures, 1*, 3-22, 1965.

Bleich, H.H. and Baron, M.L., Free and forced vibrations of an infinitely long cylindrical shell in an infinite acoustic medium, *J. Applied Mech., 21*, 167-184, 1954.

Chen, L.H. and Schweikert, D.G., Sound radiation from an arbitrary body, *J.A.S.A., 35*, 1626-1632, 1963.

Chertock, G., Sound radiation from prolate spheroids, *J.A.S.A., 33*, 871-876, 1961; also *D.T.M.B. Rept. 1516*, Nov. 1961.

Chertock, G., Sound radiation from vibrating surfaces, *J.A.S.A., 36*, 1305-1313, 1964.

Chertock, G., Solutions for sound-radiation problems by integral equations at the critical wave numbers, *J.A.S.A., 47*, 387-388, 1970.

Chertock, G., Integral Equation Methods in Sound Radiation and Scattering from Arbitrary Surfaces, *N.S.R.D.C. Rept. 3538*, June 1971.

Chertock, G., Sound radiated by low-frequency vibrations of slender bodies, *J.A.S.A., 57*, 1007-1016, 1975.

Copley, L.G., Integral equation method for radiation from vibrating bodies, *J.A.S.A., 41*, 807-816, 1967.

Copley, L.G., Fundamental results concerning integral representations in acoustic radiation, *J.A.S.A., 44*, 28-32, 1968.

Donaldson, J.M., Reduction of sound radiated from ship structures, *Applied Acoustics, 1*, 275-291, 1968.

Greenspon, J.E., Theoretical developments in the vibrations of hulls, *J. of Ship Res., 6*, (4)26-46, 1963.

Heckl, M., Vibrations of point-driven cylindrical shells, *J.A.S.A., 34*, 1553-1557, 1962.

Hess, J.L., Solution of the Helmholtz Equation for Steady Acoustic Waves, *Douglas Aircraft Div. Rept. 31655*, April 1964.

Junger, M.C., Vibrations of elastic shells in a fluid medium and the associated radiation of sound, *J. Applied Mech., 19*, 439-445, 1952.

Junger, M.C., Dynamic behavior of reinforced cylindrical shells in a vacuum and in a fluid, *J. Applied Mech., 21*, 35-41, 1954.

Junger, M.C., Radiation and scattering by submerged elastic structures, *J.A.S.A., 57*, 1318-1326, 1975.

Junger, M.C. and Feit, D., *op. cit.* (Chapters 4, 8 and 10).

Kellogg, O.D., *Foundations of Potential Theory*, Dover Publications, New York, 1953 (Chapter 6).

Lamb, Sir Horace, *Hydrodynamics*, 6th Edit., Dover, New York, 1945 (pp. 496-501).

MacNeal, R.H., *Electric Circuit Analogies for Elastic Structures*, Wiley, New York, 1962 (Chapter 8).

McCormick, J.M. and Baron, M.L., Sound radiation from submerged cylindrical shells of finite length, *J. Engin. for Industry, 87B*, 393-405, 1965.

Morse, P.M. and Feshbach, H., *Methods of Mathematical Physics*, Vol. II. McGraw-Hill, New York, 1953.

Murray, M.T., High and low-frequency approaches to the acoustic radiation problem, *J. Sound and Vibr., 34*, 327-356, 1974.

Pond, H.L., Low-frequency sound radiation from slender bodies of revolution, *J.A.S.A., 40*, 711-720, 1966.

Schenck, H.A., Improved integral formulation for acoustic radiation problems, *J.A.S.A., 44*, 41-58, 1968.

Strasberg, M., Radiation from unbaffled bodies of arbitrary shape at low frequencies, *J.A.S.A., 34*, 520-521, 1962.

Tsokos, C.P. and North, E.L., Sound Radiation from a Cylindrical Shell, *Electric Boat Div. Rept. U413-62-173* (and addendum), Dec. 1962 and April 1963 (AD 422496).

Warburton, G., Vibration of a cylindrical shell in an acoustic medium, *J. Mech. Engin. Science, 3*, 69-79, 1961.

# CHAPTER 5

# STRUCTURAL VIBRATIONS

## 5.1 Structure-Borne Sound

In the previous two chapters we dealt with a number of sources that radiate sound directly into the fluid medium. However, many noise sources in marine systems are not in direct contact with the fluid. Vibrations generated by such sources are transmitted by structures to radiating surfaces. The transmission of structural vibrations and radiation of sound by such vibrations constitute the subject of *structure-borne sound.* This field was originally developed in Germany in the 1940's where it was applied both to submarine noise reduction and to building acoustics. An early exposition by L. Cremer (1950) is still a classic. Rapid progress in understanding the role of structures in both architectural and marine acoustics was made in the 1950's and 1960's, and the field can now be considered to have matured. Several recent books devoted exclusively to this subject are included in the references at the end of this chapter.

Most structures can be classified as either beam-like or plate-like. Beams are structures having only one dimension long compared to a vibrational wavelength, while plates have two dimensions that are relatively large. While it is somewhat of an oversimplification, it is nevertheless generally true that the primary role of beam structures is transmission of vibrations; plates, on the other hand, are usually in contact with a fluid medium and so are principal radiators of structure-borne sound. The present chapter deals with structural vibrations of beams and beam-like structures, while Chapter 6 covers sound radiation from plate vibrations.

Structures can experience a number of types of vibrations, as discussed in Section 5.2. However, the dominant mode of transmission of vibrational energy is by flexural (bending) vibrations and these are also the most efficient radiators of sound. It was recognition of the central role of flexural vibrations that has made possible the tremendous progress in this field of the past 40 years. Chapters 5 and 6 deal almost exclusively with flexural vibrations and their radiation.

In addition to the role of flexural motions in transmitting vibrations from machines to the hull where they can radiate sound into the water, they are also a dominant low-frequency vibrational mode of ship structures. The final two sections of the present chapter deal with beams immersed in fluids and with the calculation of low-frequency bending vibrations of ship hulls, called *whipping* modes in Section 4.11.

## 5.2 Wave Motions in Solids

As an introduction to the treatment of structural vibrations, it is useful first to define the various types of sonic vibrations that can occur in solids. Some of these vibrations occur only within the body of the solid, while others involve its surfaces. Solids of various shapes can be classed according to the ratios of various dimensions to each other and to a wavelength. Thus, as mentioned in Section 5.1, *rods*, *bars* and *beams* are structures having only one dimension large compared to a wavelength, while *plates* have two large dimensions, and all of the dimensions of *bulk solids* are relatively large.

In Section 2.2, the wave equation was derived for acoustic disturbances in liquids. One of the assumptions made as a part of the derivation was: "the fluid cannot withstand static shear stresses, in the manner of a solid." Obviously, then, a most important distinction between solids and liquids is the ability of a solid to withstand static shear stresses. Because of this property, wave motions in solids are considerably more complex than those in fluids. Not only do solids transmit compressional waves similar to those in fluids, but also they sustain shear waves, flexural (bending) waves and various combinations of compressional, shear and flexural waves, as well as surface waves.

The solids of interest in structure-borne sound are for the most part homogeneous and isotropic. The vibrations are of small amplitude and so may be treated as linear, or Hookesian. Thus any deformations, or strains, are directly proportional to the stresses causing them.

### Longitudinal Waves in Bars

One form of wave motion in solids is that which arises if one strikes, or otherwise excites, one end of a thin rod or bar. A longitudinal compressional wave is set up in the bar which travels at a speed, $c_\ell$, given by

$$c_\ell = \sqrt{\frac{Y}{\rho}}, \tag{5.1}$$

where $Y$ is *Young's modulus*, defined as the stress required to produce unit strain, and $\rho$ is the density. Most metals commonly used in structures have longitudinal wave speeds between 4900 and 5200 m/sec.

### Shear Waves

Another form of wave motion that can exist in a solid is associated with twisting, or torsional, motions which occur in a plane perpendicular to the direction of propagation of the wave. Such waves depend on the ability of a solid to sustain shear. They propagate at a speed, $c_s$, which depends on the shear modulus of the solid,

$$c_s = \sqrt{\frac{G}{\rho}}. \tag{5.2}$$

The *shear modulus*, $G$, is invariably less than half Young's modulus, so shear waves travel more slowly than do longitudinal waves.

### Compressional Waves in Bulk Solids

When longitudinal motions take place in a thin rod, there are associated changes in the diameter and cross-sectional area which reduce the relative volume change. These lateral changes play an important role in the wave process, making it easier for waves to propagate. When all the dimensions of a solid body are large compared to a wavelength, the lateral motions cannot occur in the same way as in a rod, and the medium is effectively less compressible. Defining the *bulk modulus*, $B$, as the ratio of the hydrostatic pressure to the fractional change in volume or density, as in Eq. 2.53, irrotational compressional waves are found to travel in the volume of a large solid at a speed given by

$$c_B = \sqrt{\frac{B + 4/3\,G}{\rho}}\,, \tag{5.3}$$

which expression reduces to that for a liquid when the shear modulus, $G$, approaches zero.

**Poisson's Ratio**

The quantity that measures the lateral constrictions of a rod experiencing longitudinal vibrations is called *Poisson's ratio*. It is the ratio of the relative change in the diameter of the rod to the relative change in length:

$$\sigma \equiv -\frac{L}{D}\frac{dD}{dL}\,. \tag{5.4}$$

The relative change in area is $2\sigma$, while that of the volume is $1 - 2\sigma$. It follows that virtually incompressible solids, such as rubber, have values of Poisson's ratio close to 0.5. Values for most metals are between 0.27 and 0.35.

The three elastic moduli, $Y$, $G$ and $B$, are related to each other through Poisson's ratio by

$$\frac{G}{Y} = \frac{1}{2(1 + \sigma)} \tag{5.5}$$

and

$$\frac{B}{Y} = \frac{1}{3(1 - 2\sigma)}\,. \tag{5.6}$$

It follows that the wave speeds are related by

$$c_s = c_\ell \sqrt{\frac{1}{2(1 + \sigma)}} \tag{5.7}$$

and

$$c_B = c_\ell \sqrt{\frac{1 - \sigma}{(1 + \sigma)(1 - 2\sigma)}} \tag{5.8}$$

In the limit, for an incompressible solid, the shear wave speed equals about 3/5 of the longitudinal wave speed; bulk waves cannot be sustained at all, since $c_B$ approaches infinity. These relations for $c_s$ and $c_B$ relative to $c_\ell$ are plotted in Fig. 5.1.

**Longitudinal Waves in Plates**

Plates are solids that are large compared to a wavelength in two dimensions and smaller than a

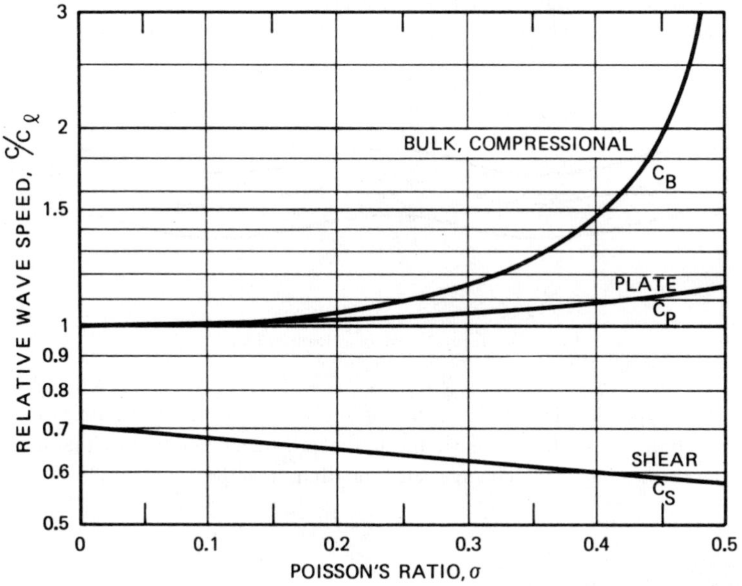


Fig. 5.1. Wave Speeds in Solids as Functions of Poisson's Ratio

wavelength in one dimension. Longitudinal waves travel in plates at a speed, $c_p$, which is slightly larger than the speed in bars and rods:

$$c_p = c_\ell \sqrt{\frac{1}{1 - \sigma^2}} = c_s \sqrt{\frac{2}{1 - \sigma}} \; . \tag{5.9}$$

As shown in Fig. 5.1, this ratio varies from about 1.05 for typical metals to 1.15 for rubber-like, almost incompressible solids.

### Surface Waves

Waves can propagate on the surface of a thick solid in much the same manner as surface waves do on the ocean. Such surface waves, which decay exponentially toward the interior, are called *Rayleigh waves* and are of considerable importance at very high frequencies, especially in ultrasonics applications. Smaller waves found on plates are termed *Lamb waves* and are also important in ultrasonics.

When a longitudinal wave propagates in a plate, the surfaces experience up and down motions associated with the Poisson effect. These surface waves can also radiate sound. However, most plate structural vibrations occur as bending motions, and radiation associated with longitudinal plate waves is usually less important.

**Flexural (Bending) Waves**

Beams and plates often experience wave motions in which one surface is experiencing stretching at the same time that the opposite surface is experiencing contraction. As shown in Fig. 5.2, the result of this combination is that the center of the beam or plate oscillates about the

Fig. 5.2. Flexural Wave in a Beam or Plate

rest plane. In this type of wave motion, the structure flexes, or bends. For small amplitude vibrations, the amount of stretching and contraction is a linear function of the distance from a plane, termed the *neutral plane*, which experiences neither, as shown in Fig. 5.3.

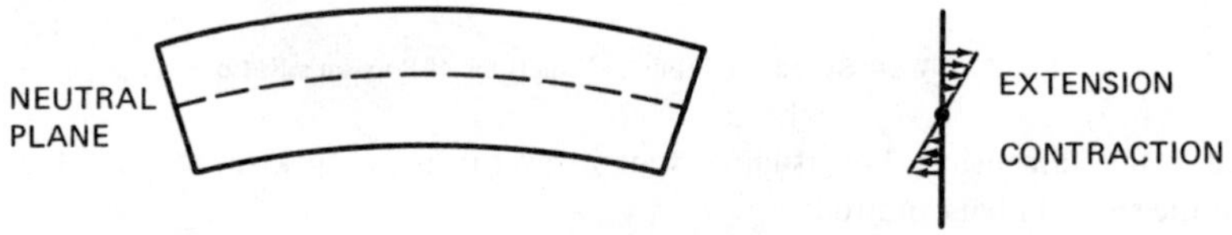


Fig. 5.3. Stretching and Contraction of a Section of a Bending Beam

Examples of flexural vibrations from everyday experience including tuning forks, tall buildings swaying in the wind, bending vibrations of aircraft wings, and the quiver of an arrow striking a target. They are important because they are readily excited. A given force will generally cause much larger flexural amplitudes than any other type of vibration.

Cremer made a significant contribution to architectural acoustics in recognizing the overriding importance of bending (flexural) vibrations for both the transmission of vibrations in structures and the radiation of sound. Since flexural waves also play the dominant role in vibration of and radiation of sound by ship hulls and other structures, the remainder of this chapter is devoted to a detailed exposition of their properties.

## 5.3 Beam Bending Equations

Differential equations relating to bending vibrations of beams can be derived by considering the forces and moments acting on a differential element together with the motions resulting from such action. Figure 5.4 shows such a beam element of length $dx$. The displacement of the neutral plane from an arbitrary reference is represented by $w$. The cross-sectional plane is shown rotated by an angle $\theta$ from the normal. The element experiences shear, hence the angle of rotation of the cross-sectional plane is greater than that of the neutral plane. A fiber element is shown at a distance $z$ from the neutral plane. The longitudinal strain, or extension, of this fiber is represented by $d\xi$. The width of the element is represented by $b(z)$.

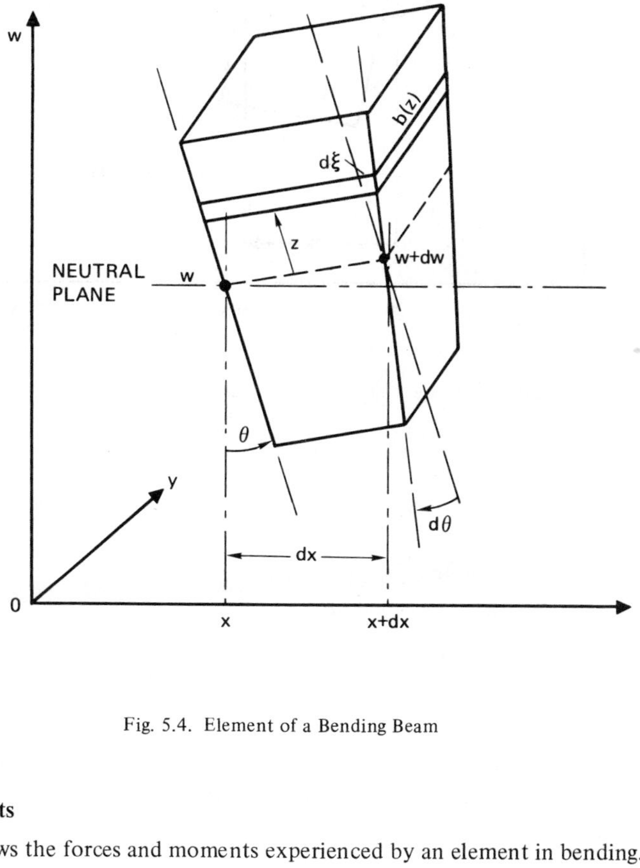


Fig. 5.4. Element of a Bending Beam

**Forces and Moments**

Figure 5.5 shows the forces and moments experienced by an element in bending. Although the net extensional force on the element, $F_x$, is zero, each fiber experiences a force proportional to its extension and given by

$$dF_x = - Yb\, d\xi = - Yb \frac{\partial \xi}{\partial x} dx , \tag{5.10}$$

where $Y$ is Young's modulus and $b$ is the width of the element, as previously defined. From Fig. 5.4 it is clear that the extension of each fiber is proportional to its distance from the neutral plane and is also a function of the curvature of the element. From geometric considerations, it

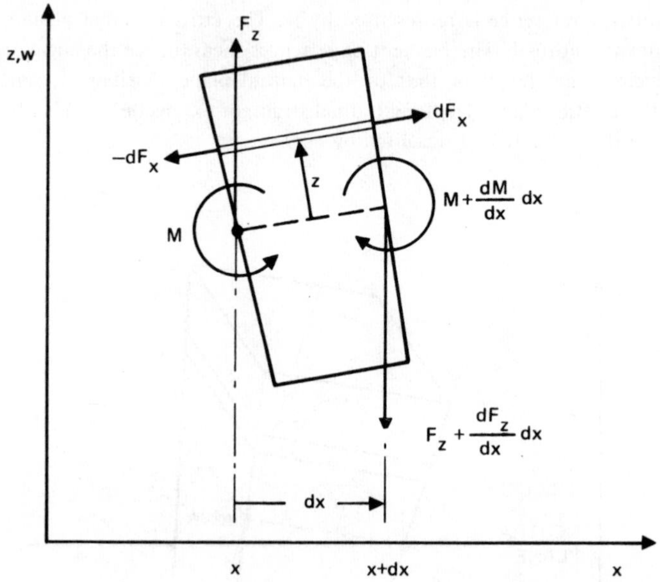


Fig. 5.5. Forces and Moments Associated with Flexure

follows that

$$d\xi = \frac{\partial \xi}{\partial x} dx = z \, d\theta = z \frac{\partial \theta}{\partial x} dx \ . \tag{5.11}$$

Substituting into Eq. 5.10, the extensional force is

$$dF_x = - Ybz \frac{\partial \theta}{\partial x} dx \ . \tag{5.12}$$

Although the net extensional force is zero, this force causes a rotational moment about an axis in the neutral plane perpendicular to the plane of the motion, given by

$$M = \int z \, dF_x = \int z \frac{\partial F_x}{\partial z} dz \ . \tag{5.13}$$

Using Eq. 5.12 for the extensional force,

$$M = - \int Ybz^2 \frac{\partial \theta}{\partial x} dz = - Y \frac{\partial \theta}{\partial x} \int bz^2 \, dz \ . \tag{5.14}$$

The integral in this expression is the *moment of inertia*, $I$, of the beam cross-sectional area relative to the neutral plane. It is usual to express it as the product of the *cross-sectional area*, $S$, and the square of the *radius of gyration*, $\kappa$. Thus,

$$M = -YI\frac{\partial\theta}{\partial x} = -YS\kappa^2\frac{\partial\theta}{\partial x} . \qquad (5.15)$$

The product of Young's modulus and the moment of inertia is called the *bending stiffness* or *rigidity*, $B$.

**Transverse Acceleration**

As shown in Fig. 5.5, the beam element experiences a net perpendicular force, $dF_z$, which force is related to the transverse acceleration of the element by Newton's second law. Thus,

$$\mu\frac{\partial^2 w}{\partial t^2}dx = -dF_z = -\frac{\partial F_z}{\partial x}dx , \qquad (5.16)$$

where $\mu$ is the total mass involved in the motion per unit length of the beam, including any entrained mass, $m_e$, of the fluid as well as the mass of the structure. Defining $\epsilon$ as the ratio of the entrained mass to that of the structure,

$$\mu = (1+\epsilon)\int_S \rho_s\, dS = (1+\epsilon)\bar{\rho}_s S \qquad (5.17)$$

and

$$\frac{\partial F_z}{\partial x} = -\mu\ddot{w} = -(1+\epsilon)\bar{\rho}_s S\ddot{w} , \qquad (5.18)$$

where each dot represents a differentiation with respect to time.

**Rotational Acceleration**

The perpendicular force, $F_z$, and the net moment on the element combine to create a rotational torque on the element about an axis through its center of gravity (c.g.) perpendicular to the plane of the motion. This torque causes rotational acceleration of the element. From the rotational form of Newton's second law,

$$I'\ddot{\theta}\,dx = -\left(F_z + \frac{\partial M}{\partial x}\right)dx , \qquad (5.19)$$

where $I'$ is the *mass-moment of rotatory inertia* about the c.g. and is given by

$$I' \equiv \int \rho_s b z'^2\, dz' = \bar{\rho}_s S\kappa'^2 . \qquad (5.20)$$

In this expression, $z'$ is measured from the c.g. If the section is symmetric and homogeneous, $I'$ will equal $\rho_s I$. We will find it useful to represent the ratio of $I'$ to the product $\bar{\rho}_s I$ as a non-dimensional *coefficient of relative rotatory inertia*, $\alpha'$, as

$$\alpha' \equiv \frac{I'}{\bar{\rho}_s I} . \tag{5.21}$$

Equation 5.19 can now be written

$$\alpha' \bar{\rho}_s I \ddot{\theta} = - F_z - \frac{\partial M}{\partial x} . \tag{5.22}$$

**Considerations of Shear**

Equations 5.15, 5.18 and 5.22 are three independent equations relating the transverse force, $F_z$, moment, $M$, section angle, $\theta$, and section displacement, $w$. A fourth equation is needed in order to solve for $w$ or $\theta$ alone. Early investigators, including Rayleigh, assumed that any shear distortion of the element would be negligible and that the slope of the neutral plane would equal the angle of rotation, $\theta$. Timoshenko (1921) was the first to include shear distortion. He noted that the transverse force causes the slope of the neutral plane to be less than $\theta$ by an amount given by the shear strain divided by the shear modulus, i.e.,

$$\frac{\partial w}{\partial x} = \theta - \frac{F_z}{KGS} , \tag{5.23}$$

where $K$ is a factor, always less than unity, that takes into account warping of the cross section and the lack of constancy of the shear force over the entire section. $K$ depends on both section shape and Poisson's ratio.

The product $KGS$ has the dimensions of a force. It is useful to follow Plass (1958) and define a non-dimensional *shear parameter*, $\Gamma$, by

$$\Gamma \equiv \frac{Y}{KG} = \frac{1}{K}\left(\frac{c_\ell}{c_s}\right)^2 = \frac{2(1 + \sigma)}{K} . \tag{5.24}$$

Since $K$ is always less than unity, this parameter always exceeds 2. Equation 5.23 relating the slope of the neutral plane to the transverse force can now be written

$$\frac{\partial w}{\partial x} = \theta - \frac{\Gamma}{YS} F_z . \tag{5.25}$$

**Differential Equation for Bending**

Equations 5.15, 5.18, 5.22 and 5.25 can be treated as a set of four coupled equations and their solution found by finite difference, or other computational methods. They can also be combined to form a single fourth-order differential equation for the displacement, $w$. In its most general form, the resultant equation is quite complicated and of little practical use. However, it can be shown that a number of the terms are invariably small compared to others and can be eliminated without materially affecting the result.

To derive the differential equation for bending, the second derivative with respect to $x$ of Eq. 5.15 and the first derivatives of Eqs. 5.22 and 5.25 are combined with Eq. 5.18, and certain third-order terms involving spatial derivatives of beam dimensions are eliminated. The result is an equation for flexural displacement of a beam that involves only even-order space and time derivatives,

$$\mu\ddot{w} + \frac{\partial^2}{\partial x^2}\left(YI\frac{\partial^2 w}{\partial x^2}\right) - \left(\Gamma(1+\epsilon) + \alpha'\right)\bar{\rho}_s I\frac{\partial^2 \ddot{w}}{\partial x^2} + \frac{\alpha'\Gamma\bar{\rho}_s\kappa^2\mu}{Y}\ddddot{w} = f(x,t)\ , \tag{5.26}$$

where $f(x,t)$ is any applied force per unit length. Assuming that the material is homogeneous, and using Eq. 5.1 for $c_\ell$, the resultant equation is

$$\ddot{w} + \frac{c_\ell^2\kappa^2}{1+\epsilon}\left(\frac{\partial^4 w}{\partial x^4} + \frac{2}{I}\frac{dI}{dx}\frac{\partial^3 w}{\partial x^3} + \frac{1}{I}\frac{d^2 I}{dx^2}\frac{\partial^2 w}{\partial x^2}\right) - \left(\Gamma(1+\epsilon) + \alpha'\right)\frac{\kappa^2}{1+\epsilon}\frac{\partial^2 \ddot{w}}{\partial x^2}$$
$$+ \frac{\alpha'\Gamma\kappa^2}{c_\ell^2}\ddddot{w} = \frac{f(x,t)}{\mu}\ . \tag{5.27}$$

This differential equation is more general than the equation originally derived by Timoshenko. It includes effects of non-uniformities and of entrained mass as well as rotatory inertia and shear distortion.

**Equation for Uniform Beams**

Timoshenko's equation applies to uniform beams and also to non-uniform beams for which spatial derivatives of the moment of inertia are negligible. Retaining entrained mass terms, Eq. 5.27 becomes

$$\ddot{w} + \frac{c_\ell^2\kappa^2}{1+\epsilon}\frac{\partial^4 w}{\partial x^4} - \left(\Gamma(1+\epsilon) + \alpha'\right)\frac{\kappa^2}{1+\epsilon}\frac{\partial^2 \ddot{w}}{\partial x^2} + \frac{\alpha'\Gamma\kappa^2}{c_\ell^2}\ddddot{w} = \frac{f(x,t)}{\mu}\ . \tag{5.28}$$

This final equation is the basis for analyses of structural vibrations covering a wide frequency range. Its validity has been corroborated by a number of investigators. Huang (1961) found it to give results in excellent agreement with those of exact elasticity theory. Further, Ripperger and Abramson (1957) confirmed Timoshenko's theory as applied to relatively high frequencies by experiments involving the response of beams to hammer blows. Equations 5.27 and 5.28 may therefore be used with confidence over the entire frequency range of interest in structure-borne sound.

**Euler-Bernoulli (E-B) Equation**

When dealing with relatively thin beams and/or low frequencies, the first two terms in Eq. 5.28 are dominant and the equation takes a simple form:

$$\ddot{w} + \frac{c_\ell^2 \kappa^2}{1 + \epsilon} \frac{\partial^4 w}{\partial x^4} = \frac{f(x,t)}{\mu} . \tag{5.29}$$

This equation was derived independently by Euler and Bernoulli in the 19th century. In their derivations, they ignored rotatory motion of the beam element and also shear distortion, which amounts to setting both $\alpha'$ and $\Gamma$ equal to zero. Their equation is often quite useful, and many texts use it exclusively when treating flexural vibrations. In what follows we will find that low-frequency limits of more complete expressions are solutions of the E-B equation.

## 5.4 Speed of Flexural Waves

### Harmonic Solutions of the Timoshenko Equation

The complete Timoshenko beam equation can be used to solve for the displacement, $w$, of the neutral plane for a given force distribution. Also of interest in acoustics is the effective phase speed for flexural motions as a function of frequency. Equation 5.28 is a fourth-order linear differential equation and not strictly a wave equation. However, only even-order derivatives are involved. As a result, when motion at a single frequency is assumed, an effective wave speed can be found.

We may express the complete solution of Eq. 5.28 as the sum of four terms, of the form

$$\underline{w} = \sum_{i=1}^{4} \underline{A}_i \, e^{i(\omega t - k_i x)} . \tag{5.30}$$

Substituting Eq. 5.30 and its derivatives into Eq. 5.28 yields

$$- \omega^2 \underline{A}_i + c_\ell^2 \frac{\kappa^2}{1 + \epsilon} k_i^4 \underline{A}_i - (\Gamma(1 + \epsilon) + \alpha') \frac{\kappa^2}{1 + \epsilon} \omega^2 k_i^2 \underline{A}_i$$

$$+ \frac{\alpha' \Gamma \kappa^2}{c_\ell^2} \omega^4 \underline{A}_i = \frac{f(x,\omega)}{\mu} . \tag{5.31}$$

This equation can be used to solve forced vibration problems, provided only that the effects of any non-uniformities of the beam are negligible. Expressions for wave phase speeds can be obtained by considering the homogeneous equation for free vibrations in the absence of any external forces. Setting the forcing function equal to zero results in a quartic algebraic equation for $k_i$ for which there are four solutions. Two of the solutions are real and two are imaginary. The two real solutions are equal in magnitude but opposite in sign and represent flexural waves traveling in opposite directions. We may represent these values of $k_i$ by $\pm k_f$, since $k_f$ has all the properties of a wave number for propagating sinusoidal components. The two imaginary solutions are represented by $\pm i\gamma$. These terms have exponential form and account for non-sinusoidal distortions that occur at discontinuities in the geometry of the structure, especially at the ends. Thus, the solution of the homogeneous form of Eq. 5.31 may be written

$$\underline{w} = \underline{A} e^{-ik_f x} + \underline{B} e^{ik_f x} + \underline{C} e^{-\gamma x} + \underline{D} e^{\gamma x} . \tag{5.32}$$

Alternatively, in terms of sinusoids and hyperbolic functions,

$$\underline{w} = \underline{a} \sin k_f x + \underline{b} \cos k_f x + \underline{c} \sinh \gamma x + \underline{d} \cosh \gamma x \ . \tag{5.33}$$

We will return to these equations when dealing with resonances of finite structures in the next section.

Since the two real solutions are wave solutions, Eq. 5.31 can be transformed into an equation for the flexural wave phase speed, $v_f$, which is related to the wave number by

$$v_f(\omega) = \frac{\omega}{k_f} \ . \tag{5.34}$$

The homogeneous form of Eq. 5.31 can be written

$$\left(1 - \alpha'\Gamma(1+\epsilon)\left(\frac{\omega}{\Omega}\right)^2\right)\left(\frac{v_f}{c_\ell}\right)^4 + \left(\Gamma(1+\epsilon) + \alpha'\right)\left(\frac{\omega}{\Omega}\right)^2\left(\frac{v_f}{c_\ell}\right)^2 - \left(\frac{\omega}{\Omega}\right)^2 = 0 \ . \tag{5.35}$$

where $\Omega$ is a reference angular frequency defined by

$$\Omega \equiv c_\ell^2 \sqrt{\frac{\mu}{YI}} = \frac{c_\ell}{\kappa}\sqrt{1+\epsilon} \ . \tag{5.36}$$

This is a non-dimensional form of the complete Timoshenko beam equation, expressed as a quartic for the relative flexural wave speed as a function of a relative frequency and three dimensionless parameters representing the effects of entrained mass, shear distortion and rotatory inertia.

Applying the quadratic theorem, the complete solution of Eq. 5.35 is

$$\left(\frac{v_f}{c_\ell}\right)^2 = \frac{\sqrt{\left(\Gamma(1+\epsilon) - \alpha'\right)^2\left(\frac{\omega}{\Omega}\right)^4 + 4\left(\frac{\omega}{\Omega}\right)^2} - \left(\Gamma(1+\epsilon) + \alpha'\right)\left(\frac{\omega}{\Omega}\right)^2}{2\left(1 - \alpha'\Gamma(1+\epsilon)\left(\frac{\omega}{\Omega}\right)^2\right)} \ . \tag{5.37}$$

This is a complex function of the parameters, which fortunately can be represented quite accurately in terms of approximate solutions applicable at low, intermediate and high frequencies.

### Low-Frequency Approximation

Examining Eqs. 5.35 and 5.37, it is apparent that the terms which involve the shear parameter and the relative rotatory inertia are proportional to the square of the relative frequency. These terms are negligible for relatively low frequencies, for which

$$\left(\frac{v_f}{c_\ell}\right)_\ell \doteq \sqrt{\frac{\omega}{\Omega}} = \sqrt{\frac{\omega\kappa}{c_\ell\sqrt{1+\epsilon}}} = \frac{1}{c_\ell}\sqrt[4]{\frac{\omega^2 YI}{\mu}} \qquad \left(\Gamma\left(\frac{\omega}{\Omega}\right)^2 << 1\right). \tag{5.38}$$

This same result could have been derived directly from the homogeneous form of the E-B equation, Eq. 5.29. We can now interpret $\Omega$ to be the value of $\omega$ for which the flexural wave speed would equal the longitudinal wave speed, if the E-B equation were valid at all frequencies.

Since the flexural wave speed depends on frequency, low-frequency flexural waves are dispersive. The speed $v_f$ is the phase speed for a monochromatic component. If a wideband pulse is transmitted, it will travel with a group velocity, $v_g$, equal to twice the phase speed at the median frequency, provided Eq. 5.38 is a valid approximation.

### High-Frequency Limit

At the very highest frequencies, flexural waves degenerate into shear waves. Although these waves have little practical importance in structure-borne sound, the expression for their phase speed is useful as a limit. In the high-frequency limit, the entrained mass approaches zero, and

$$\left(\frac{v_f}{c_\ell}\right)_h^2 \doteq \frac{1}{\Gamma} = K\left(\frac{c_s}{c_\ell}\right)^2 \qquad \left(\Gamma\left(\frac{\omega}{\Omega}\right) >> 1\right) . \tag{5.39}$$

Since the effective shear area is always less than the cross-sectional area, the limiting flexural wave speed is always somewhat lower than the shear wave speed. In terms of the low-frequency, E-B result, the high-frequency limit may be expressed by

$$\frac{v_{f_h}}{v_{f_\ell}} \doteq \frac{1}{\sqrt{\Gamma\left(\frac{\omega}{\Omega}\right)}} . \tag{5.40}$$

### Intermediate-Frequency Approximation

Between the lowest and highest frequencies, the wave speed curve, as given by its complete solution in Eq. 5.37, makes a smooth transition from the low-frequency values of Eq. 5.38 to its high-frequency limit given by Eq. 5.39. In this intermediate frequency range the entrained mass has a decreasing effect. In addition, Budiansky and Kruszewski (1953) and others have shown that the effects of shear distortion are always at least three times as great as those of rotatory inertia. These facts can be used in deriving approximate relations for the flexural wave speed for intermediate frequencies. Equation 5.37 can be written

$$\left(\frac{v_f}{c_\ell}\right)^2 = \left(\frac{v_f}{c_\ell}\right)_\ell^2 \left[\frac{\sqrt{1+(1-\bar{\alpha})^2\delta^2} - (1+\bar{\alpha})\delta}{1-4\bar{\alpha}\delta^2}\right], \tag{5.41}$$

where

$$\delta \equiv \frac{\Gamma(1+\epsilon)}{2}\left(\frac{\omega}{\Omega}\right) \tag{5.42}$$

and

$$\bar{\alpha} \equiv \frac{\alpha'}{\Gamma(1 + \epsilon)} . \tag{5.43}$$

The parameter $\bar{\alpha}$ expresses the magnitude of the rotatory inertia correction relative to that for shear. This factor never exceeds 1/3 and is often smaller. In the limit as $\bar{\alpha} \rightarrow 0$, Eq. 5.41 reduces to

$$\frac{v_f}{v_{f_\ell}} \doteq \sqrt{\sqrt{1 + \delta^2} - \delta} . \tag{5.44}$$

Since the effect of rotatory inertia is relatively small, Eq. 5.44 can be used to calculate corrections to the E-B solution for all frequencies. The correction is not significant for values of $\delta$ less than about 0.05. For values of $\delta > 3$, Eq. 5.44 gives values in very close agreement with those from the high-frequency expression, Eq. 5.40. Between these limits it may differ from that given by Eqs. 5.37 and 5.41 by as much as 3%, as shown in Fig. 5.6. Since values of other quantities such as entrained mass are often uncertain, Eqs. 5.38 and 5.44 are recommended for calculation of the flexural wave speed throughout the entire frequency range unless very precise values are required, when Eq. 5.41 should be used.

### Solid Rectangular Bars

The equations for bending vibrations derived thus far in this chapter are quite general in that they apply to any type of cross section and include entrained mass. Beam structures having solid,

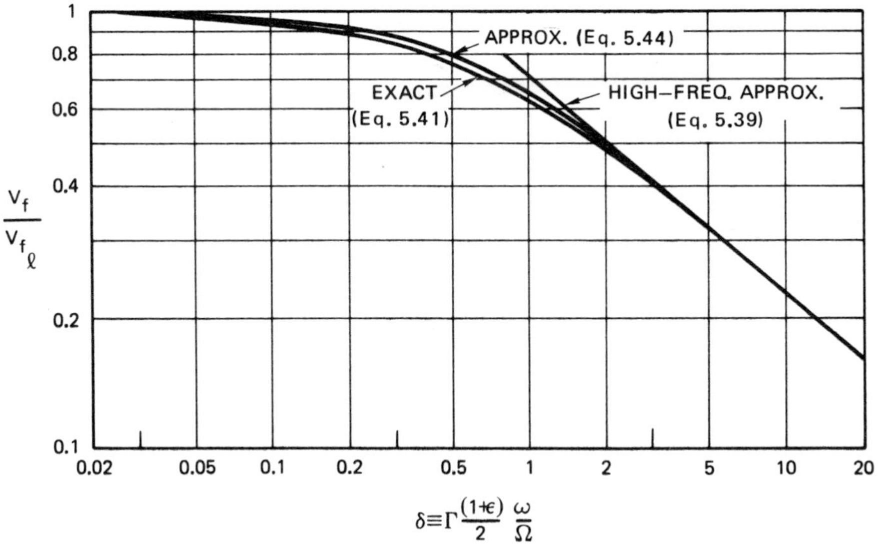


Fig. 5.6. Flexural Wave Speed Relative to Low-Frequency Approximation, for $\alpha = 1/3$

rectangular cross sections are frequently encountered in practice. It is instructive to consider the special case of such uniform rectangular beams vibrating *in air*. For solid bodies of rectangular cross section having width $b$ and thickness $h$,

$$\kappa = \frac{h}{\sqrt{12}} , \tag{5.45}$$

$$\alpha' = 1 , \tag{5.46}$$

$$K \doteq \frac{4 + \sigma}{5} , \tag{5.47}$$

and

$$\Gamma = \frac{2(1 + \sigma)}{K} \doteq 10 \left( \frac{1 + \sigma}{4 + \sigma} \right) \doteq \frac{5}{2} \left( 1 + \frac{3}{4} \sigma \right) . \tag{5.48}$$

The other parameters used in the analysis become

$$\Omega = \frac{c_\ell}{\kappa} = \frac{c_\ell}{h} \sqrt{12} \tag{5.49}$$

and

$$\delta = \frac{\Gamma}{2} \frac{\omega}{\Omega} \doteq \frac{5}{8\sqrt{3}} \left( 1 + \frac{3}{4} \sigma \right) \frac{\omega h}{c_\ell} . \tag{5.50}$$

The low-frequency approximation of Eq. 5.38 leads to

$$\left( \frac{v_f}{c_\ell} \right)^2_\ell \doteq \frac{\omega}{\Omega} = \frac{\omega h}{c_\ell \sqrt{12}} , \tag{5.51}$$

and the high-frequency limiting value is

$$\left( \frac{v_f}{c_\ell} \right)^2_h \doteq \frac{1}{\Gamma} \doteq \frac{4 + \sigma}{10(1 + \sigma)} \doteq \frac{0.4}{1 + \frac{3}{4} \sigma} . \tag{5.52}$$

The low-frequency solution can also be expressed in terms of the flexural wave number, $k_f$, by dividing both sides of Eq. 5.51 by $v_f$, giving

$$\frac{v_{f\ell}}{c_\ell} = \frac{\omega h}{v_{f\ell} \sqrt{12}} = \frac{k_f h}{\sqrt{12}} . \tag{5.53}$$

The intermediate-frequency correction given by Eq. 5.44 can be used for solid rectangular bars with $\delta$ given by Eq. 5.50. However, for metal bars the more exact solution of Eq. 5.41 has an especially simple form. For most metals, the shear parameter, Eq. 5.48, is close to 3. Taking $\Gamma = 3$ and $\alpha' = 1$, Eq. 5.37 reduces to

$$\left(\frac{v_f}{v_{f\ell}}\right)^2 \doteq \frac{\sqrt{1 + \left(\frac{\omega}{\Omega}\right)^2} - 2\,\frac{\omega}{\Omega}}{1 - 3\left(\frac{\omega}{\Omega}\right)^2} \; . \tag{5.54}$$

This result is plotted in Fig. 5.7. Also shown is the high-frequency limit and a simple approximate formula,

$$\frac{v_f}{v_{f\ell}} \doteq \frac{1}{\sqrt{1 + \frac{5}{2}\left(\frac{\omega}{\Omega}\right)}} \; . \tag{5.55}$$

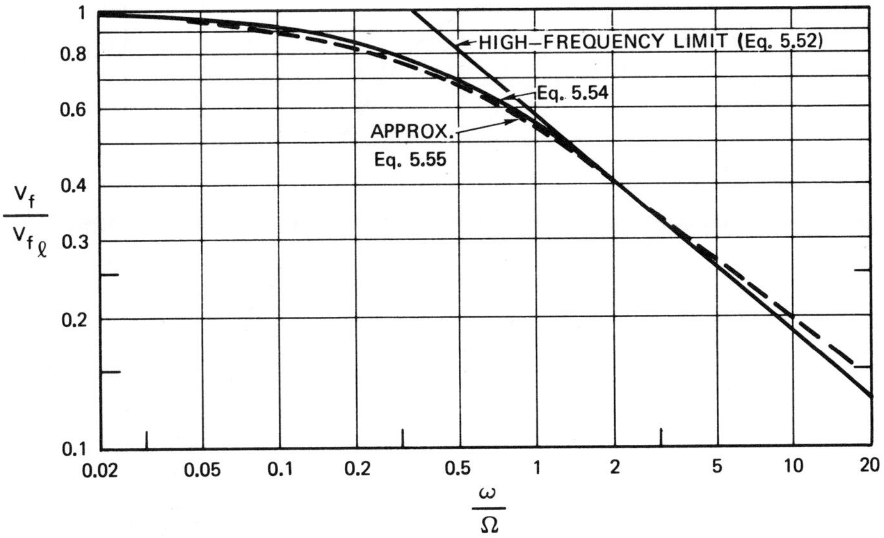


Fig. 5.7. Relative Flexural Wave Speed of Solid Metal Rectangular Bars

Nelson (1971) derived a universal dispersion curve for solid rectangular bars which he expressed in terms of the flexural wave number, $k_f$. His results for metal bars can be represented by the expression

$$\frac{v_f}{v_{f\ell}} \doteq \frac{2}{1 + \sqrt{1 + \frac{3}{4}(k_f h)^2}} \qquad (5.56)$$

up to $k_f h \doteq 8$, as shown in Fig. 5.8. Above $k_f h = 8$, Nelson's values are in good agreement with

$$\frac{v_{f_h}}{v_{f\ell}} \doteq \frac{2}{k_f h} \; . \qquad (5.57)$$

Most of the expressions for flexural wave speeds given in the present section on rectangular bars can be applied to solid rods having circular cross sections. Since the radius of gyration is

$$\kappa = \frac{D}{\sqrt{8}} \; , \qquad (5.58)$$

it is only necessary to replace $h$ by $\sqrt{(3/2)}D$ wherever it occurs.

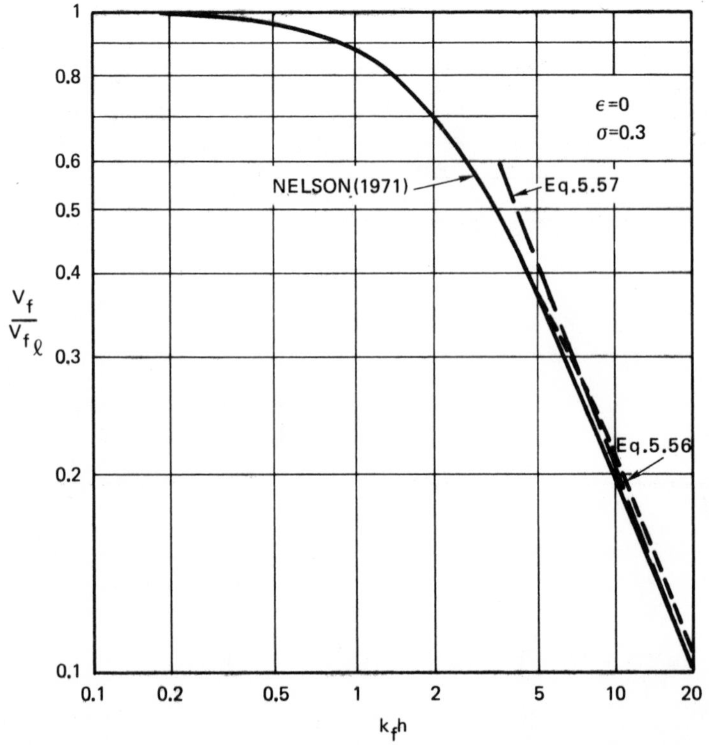


Fig. 5.8. Dispersion Curves for Rectangular Metal Beams

## 5.5 Flexural Resonances

Just as an organ pipe has resonant frequencies which are related to the ratio of its length to the acoustic wavelength, so finite length beams have resonant frequencies for flexural vibrations. Beam resonant frequencies depend upon method of support, much as pipe resonances depend on whether the pipe end is open or closed. Since flexural resonances of finite structures play an important role in structure-borne sound, considerable attention has been given to this subject in the literature.

### Uniform Thin Beams

There are two approaches that can be used to find resonances of uniform beams. The more common one starts from the assumption that the solution of the differential equation involves four terms, as given by Eqs. 5.32 and 5.33. Values of the four coefficients can be found by using either of these two equations, its first three derivatives, and mathematical expressions for the physical conditions at the ends. Resonance frequencies are then determined by assuming that the applied force is zero.

In the second approach, a wave is considered to travel from one end, to reflect from the other end, and to reflect again from the first. Resonance occurs when the wave that has completed a round trip is in phase with a wave that is just starting out. In this approach, the beam equation is used to find the flexural wave speed, from which the time of travel can be computed. The boundary conditions at the ends merely act to impose phase shifts. Both methods will be developed. The first is more usual and the second has the advantage that it can be readily applied to many non-uniform beams.

In the frequency regime for which the E-B equation, Eq. 5.29, is valid, the complete solution of the homogeneous equation is as given by Eqs. 5.32 and 5.33 except that $\gamma = k_f$. From Eq. 5.38,

$$k_f \doteq \frac{\omega}{v_{f\ell}} = \frac{1}{c_\ell}\sqrt{\omega\Omega} = \sqrt{\frac{\omega}{\kappa c_\ell}\sqrt{1+\epsilon}} = \sqrt[4]{\frac{\mu\omega^2}{YI}} \, . \tag{5.59}$$

For an infinite beam, all values of $k_f$ are valid solutions of the homogeneous equation. However, for a finite beam only certain values can occur and these are dependent on the end conditions.

The mathematical end conditions depend on the physical nature of the end attachments. There are three basic end conditions generally considered:

a) free,

b) clamped, and

c) simply supported.

For a *free end*, no requirement is imposed on $w$ or on its first derivative. However, both the moment and the force must be zero. From the derivation of the bending equation in Section 5.3, it can readily be shown that these conditions require that the second and third derivatives of $w$ be zero. For a *clamped end*, both $w$ and its first derivative must be zero. For a *simply-supported end*, both $w$ and the moment must be zero, from which the second derivative of $w$ must also be zero.

With these end conditions and simultaneous solution of the resultant equations, it can readily be shown that, for free and/or clamped end conditions, the condition for resonance of a beam of length $L$ is given by

$$\cos k_f L \cosh k_f L = \pm 1 , \qquad (5.60)$$

where the plus sign applies to bars that are free or clamped at both ends, and the minus sign applies to a beam that is free at one end and clamped at the other. If both ends are simply supported, the corresponding resonance condition is

$$\sin k_f L = 0 . \qquad (5.61)$$

The frequencies that satisfy Eqs. 5.60 or 5.61 are the resonance frequencies.

Except for the lowest frequency resonances, the beam length is large compared to a flexural wave length, i.e., $k_f L >> 1$. The hyperbolic cosine in Eq. 5.60 is therefore large compared to unity, and the resonance condition is simply that $\cos k_f L$ be zero. Thus, for free and clamped ends, the condition for resonance is

$$k_{f_m} L \doteq (2m - 1) \frac{\pi}{2} , \qquad (5.62)$$

where the index, $m$, indicates the number of nodes that occur along the length of the beam. Solving for the resonance frequency,

$$f_m = \frac{\omega_m}{2\pi} = k_{f_m}^2 L^2 \frac{\kappa c_\ell}{2\pi L^2 \sqrt{1 + \epsilon}} \doteq (2m - 1)^2 \frac{\pi}{8} \frac{\kappa c_\ell}{L^2 \sqrt{1 + \epsilon}} . \qquad (5.63)$$

It follows that, in the low-frequency regime, the frequency separation between resonances increases linearly with frequency.

For a beam free at one end but clamped at the other, $m$ can be any integer starting with 1. However, the case $m = 1$ has to be ruled out for a beam free at both ends (free-free) because it would imply a rigid-body translation or rotation of the beam. Since no external forces or moments are allowable in a resonance condition, this case is not admissible. The lowest natural frequency of a free-free beam is therefore the two-noded one, for which $m = 2$. Figure 5.9 illustrates some of

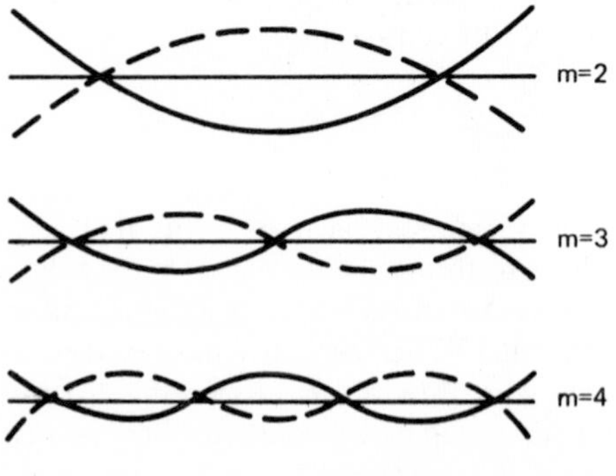


Fig. 5.9. Low-Order Resonances of a Free-Free Beam

the lower order resonances of a free-free beam. Since a clamped end is a node, the lowest order resonance of a clamped-clamped beam is also the two-noded one. The resonances of clamped-clamped beams are therefore also given by Eq. 5.63 with $m \geqslant 2$.

The resonance frequencies for free and clamped thin beams given by Eq. 5.63 are quite accurate for $m \geqslant 3$. However, the values for $m = 1$ and $m = 2$ are somewhat in error. The reason for this is that at the lowest resonances the hyperbolic cosine is not sufficiently large and the cosine, while small, can not be set equal to zero. Equation 5.63 can be made to give correct resonance frequencies if $m$ is adjusted slightly. The adjusted values for $m$ are given in Table 5.1.

Table 5.1.
Resonance Conditions for Thin Beams Using Equation 5.63

| No. of Nodes | Clamped-Free | Free-Free Clamped-Clamped |
|---|---|---|
| 1 | m = 1.0968 | ——— |
| 2 | m = 1.994 | m = 2.0056 |
| 3 | m = 3.000 | m = 3.000 |

The resonance condition for a simply-supported beam is satisfied by

$$k_{f_m} L = (m - 1)\pi \qquad (m \geqslant 2) \ , \tag{5.64}$$

from which the resonance frequencies are

$$f_m = \frac{\omega_m}{2\pi} \doteq (m - 1)^2 \frac{\pi}{2L^2} \frac{\kappa c_\ell}{\sqrt{1 + \epsilon}} \ , \tag{5.65}$$

and no corrections are required, even for the fundamental.

The upper frequency limit for applicability of thin-beam resonance conditions, $\delta < 0.03$, can be translated into a limitation on the order of the resonance. Thus, thin-beam approximations are valid provided

$$m < \frac{0.08L}{\kappa\sqrt{\Gamma}} \ . \tag{5.66}$$

Higher order resonances require use of the complete Timoshenko equation.

**Correction for Shear and Rotatory Inertia**

The thin-beam approximations for resonance frequencies are only valid as long as the flexural wave speed is given closely by the E-B equation. At higher frequencies, shear and rotatory inertia influence the result in two ways: first, the phase speed is reduced relative to the E-B value; second, the effects of the ends are increased, introducing a phase shift.

The effect of the flexural wave speed on the wave number is readily calculated from the results of the previous section. Thus, from Eq. 5.44,

$$k_f = \frac{\omega}{v_f} = k_{f_o}\frac{v_{f\ell}}{v_f} \doteq \frac{k_{f_o}}{\sqrt{\sqrt{1+\delta^2}-\delta}} = k_{f_o}\sqrt{\sqrt{1+\delta^2}+\delta}\ , \tag{5.67}$$

where $k_{f_o}$ is the low-frequency approximation, as given by Eq. 5.59. The parameter $\gamma$ which controls the space-rate-of-decay of the influence of the ends is given by

$$\gamma = k_{f_o}\frac{v_f}{v_{f\ell}} = k_{f_o}\sqrt{\sqrt{1+\delta^2}-\delta} = k_f\left(\sqrt{1+\delta^2}-\delta\right)\ . \tag{5.68}$$

It is to be noted that the low-frequency wave number, $k_{f_o}$, equals the geometric mean of $\gamma$ and $k_f$.

Leibowitz and Kennard (1964) have shown that when end conditions are applied to the full Timoshenko solution, Eq. 5.33, and its derivatives, the resonance condition for beams with free and/or clamped ends becomes

$$\pm 1 = \cos k_f L \cosh \gamma L + \left(\frac{k_f^2-\gamma^2}{2\gamma k_f}\right)\sin k_f L \sinh \gamma L\ . \tag{5.69}$$

Substituting for $\gamma$ from Eq. 5.68, one finds

$$\pm 1 = \cos k_f L \cosh \gamma L + \delta \sin k_f L \sinh \gamma L\ , \tag{5.70}$$

from which it can be shown that, for $m \geqslant 2$,

$$k_{f_m} L \doteq (2m-1)\frac{\pi}{2} + \tan^{-1}\delta\ . \tag{5.71}$$

Equation 5.71 is identical to Eq. 5.62 except for the phase shift. The effect of this phase shift is to raise the resonance frequency from its low-frequency value. However, the effects of shear and rotatory inertia on the wave number itself, as expressed by Eq. 5.67, are much greater. The net result is that the resonances in the intermediate-frequency region are lower in frequency than they would be if the thin-beam solution were applicable. Since $\delta$ is itself a function of the frequency, solutions for resonance frequencies require an iterative process. A formula which fits the results very well is

$$\frac{f_m}{f_{m\ell}} = \frac{\omega_m}{\omega_{m\ell}} \doteq \frac{2}{1+\sqrt{1+6\left(1-\dfrac{4}{(2m-1)\pi}\right)\delta_{m\ell}}}\ , \tag{5.72}$$

where $\delta_\ell$ is calculated in terms of the low-frequency estimate of resonance by

$$\delta_{m\ell} = \frac{\Gamma(1+\epsilon)}{2}\frac{\omega_{m\ell}}{\Omega} = \frac{\Gamma\sqrt{1+\epsilon}}{2}\frac{\omega_{m\ell}\kappa}{c_\ell} = \frac{\Gamma}{2}\left((2m-1)\frac{\pi}{2}\frac{\kappa}{L}\right)^2\ . \tag{5.73}$$

Substituting this expression into Eq. 5.72 leads to a formula for the correction factor in terms of the order of the resonance and geometric factors,

$$\frac{f_m}{f_{m\ell}} = \frac{\omega_m}{\omega_{m\ell}} \doteq \frac{2}{1 + \sqrt{1 + 3\Gamma(m - 1)^2\pi^2 \dfrac{\kappa^2}{L^2}}} . \tag{5.74}$$

This same expression also applies to resonances of simply-supported beams. It is graphed in Fig. 5.10.

In the limit at high frequencies,

$$\omega_{m_h} = k_{f_m} v_{f_h} \doteq \frac{(m - 1)\pi}{L} \frac{c_\ell}{\sqrt{\Gamma}} , \tag{5.75}$$

and

$$\frac{\omega_{m_h}}{\omega_{m\ell}} \doteq \frac{1}{\pi(m - 1)\dfrac{\kappa}{L}\sqrt{\Gamma}} = \frac{L}{(m - 1)\pi}\sqrt{\frac{KGS}{YI}} . \tag{5.76}$$

This relation is also plotted in Fig. 5.10. Equation 5.74 can be rewritten in terms of the ratio of the two limiting values of resonance frequency as

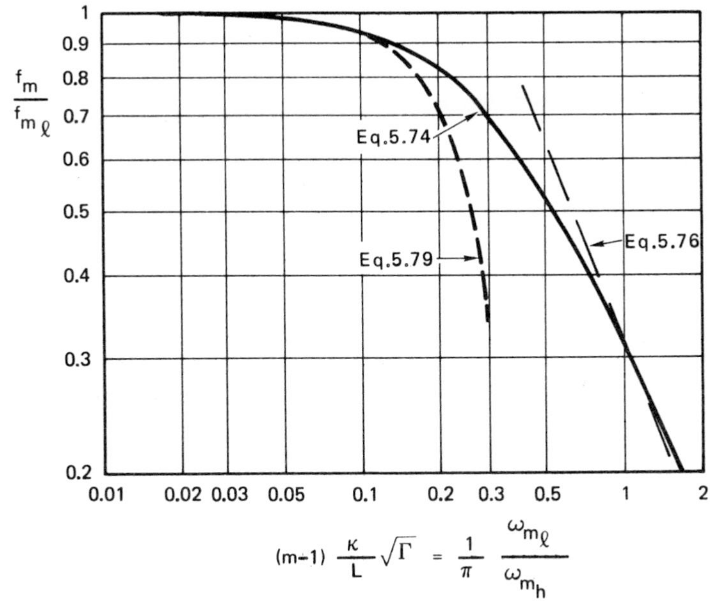


Fig. 5.10. Correction Factor for Beam Resonance Frequencies

$$\frac{f_m}{f_{m\ell}} = \frac{\omega_m}{\omega_{m\ell}} \doteq \frac{2}{1 + \sqrt{1 + 3\left(\omega_{m\ell}/\omega_{m_h}\right)^2}} \tag{5.77}$$

Thus, the procedure to be used in calculating flexural resonances is as follows: first, calculate the E-B value from Eq. 5.63 or 5.65; next, calculate the high-frequency limit for the same order from Eq. 5.75, or its ratio to the low-frequency value from Eq. 5.76; and, finally, correct the E-B value from Fig. 5.10 or Eq. 5.77.

For solid rectangular bars having $\sigma \doteq 0.3$, Eq. 5.74 reduces to

$$\frac{f_m}{f_{m\ell}} = \frac{\omega_m}{\omega_{m\ell}} \doteq \frac{2}{1 + \sqrt{1 + 3(m-1)^2\left(\frac{\pi}{2}\right)^2\left(\frac{h}{L}\right)^2}} \; . \tag{5.78}$$

This result differs significantly from the formula originally derived by Timoshenko (1921) and published in a number of texts. The Timoshenko formula,

$$\frac{f_m}{f_{m\ell}} = \frac{\omega_m}{\omega_{m\ell}} \doteq 1 - \frac{3}{4}m^2\left(\frac{\pi}{2}\right)^2\left(\frac{h}{L}\right)^2 \; , \tag{5.79}$$

agrees with Eq. 5.78 only up to a 10% correction. For higher frequencies it overestimates the correction by increasing amounts, as shown in Fig. 5.10.

**Wave Approach**

In the approach to resonances used thus far, boundary conditions at the ends were used to evaluate the four coefficients of the complete solution for uniform beams and thus to determine resonances. The wave approach to resonance calculation allows a single unified solution independent of the frequency regime, and it has the important advantage that it can readily be applied to non-uniform beams.

In the wave approach, emphasis is placed on the two wave terms of Eq. 5.32 and resonance is found in the same manner as for an organ pipe or for standing waves on a string. The boundary conditions at each end are assumed to act independently and to introduce phase shifts between incident and reflected waves. The condition for resonance is that a wave that has made a round trip and is starting out again be exactly in phase with a wave being generated. This is the well-known condition for standing waves in any kind of linear resonator. Stated differently, the condition for resonance is that the change in phase of the motion at one location in the time that the wave makes a complete round trip be equal to the phase shifts suffered by the traveling wave upon reflection from the two ends. The phase shift at a fixed point during the time of travel, $T$, is

$$\Phi_o = \omega T \; . \tag{5.80}$$

Resonance occurs when

$$\Phi_o - (\Delta\phi_1 + \Delta\phi_2) = 2\pi m \; . \tag{5.81}$$

The time of travel, $T$, is obtained by integrating the reciprocal of the velocity,

$$T = 2 \int_0^L \frac{1}{v_f} dx \;. \qquad (5.82)$$

Combining Eqs. 5.80, 5.81 and 5.82, the general resonance condition for any type of plane wave motion may be written

$$\frac{1}{2}\Phi_o = \omega_m \int_0^L \frac{1}{v_f} dx = \int_0^L k_{f_m} dx = m\pi + \overline{\Delta\phi} \;, \qquad (5.83)$$

where $\overline{\Delta\phi}$ is the average of the phase shifts at the two ends. The integer $m$ equals the number of nodes of the vibration along the structure.

The problem of calculating resonances using Eq. 5.83 reduces to the two separable tasks of determining the wave speed, or wave number, and finding the average phase shifts. The wave speed or wave number can be calculated using any of the previously developed approximations. Except at the very lowest resonances, $m = 1$ to $m = 3$, the two ends may be considered to act independently. The exponential term is zero for a simply-supported end, producing a $-180°$ phase shift at all frequencies.

The situation is not so simple for free and clamped end conditions. The reduction of $\gamma$ relative to $k_f$, which occurs for thick beams, implies a change in the influence of the exponential terms. Not only does the influence extend further from each end, but also the relative amplitude increases. As an example, consider a clamped end at $x = 0$. The expressions for the displacement and the slope are

$$\underline{w}(0) = \underline{A} + \underline{B} + \underline{C} \;, \qquad (5.84)$$

and

$$\frac{\partial \underline{w}}{\partial x}(0) = -\, ik_f L(\underline{A} - \underline{B}) - \gamma L\underline{C} \;. \qquad (5.85)$$

Setting both equal to zero,

$$\underline{A} = \underline{B}\,\frac{1 - i\left(\dfrac{\gamma}{k_f}\right)}{1 + i\left(\dfrac{\gamma}{k_f}\right)} = \underline{B}\,\frac{1 - \left(\dfrac{\gamma}{k_f}\right)^2 - 2i\left(\dfrac{\gamma}{k_f}\right)}{1 + \left(\dfrac{\gamma}{k_f}\right)^2} \;. \qquad (5.86)$$

The phase angle introduced by the reflection equals the angle whose tangent is the imaginary part of the ratio of $A$ to $B$ divided by its real part:

$$\Delta\phi = tan^{-1} \frac{-2\left(\dfrac{\gamma}{k_f}\right)}{1 - \left(\dfrac{\gamma}{k_f}\right)^2} = - tan^{-1}\left[\frac{2\left(\sqrt{1+\delta^2} - \delta\right)}{1 - \left(\sqrt{1+\delta^2} - \delta\right)^2}\right] = - tan^{-1}\frac{1}{\delta} \ . \tag{5.87}$$

Since $\delta$, defined by Eq. 5.42, is a function of frequency, the phase shift varies with frequency, from $-\pi/2$ at low frequencies to zero at the highest frequencies. The phase shift at a free end is also given by Eq. 5.87.

For uniform beams, application of Eq. 5.83 with the appropriate phase shifts leads to resonance conditions identical to those derived by the more common method, as expressed by Eq. 5.71 for free and/or clamped ends and by Eq. 5.64 for simply-supported ones.

## 5.6 Non-Uniform Beams

Turbine blades and ship hulls are examples of beam structures whose resonance frequencies are affected by non-uniformities of their cross sections. There are two ways in which these non-uniformities act to alter flexural wave speeds and hence resonance frequencies. Variations of the radius of gyration along the beam result in different values of the flexural wave speed at each section, as computed by the formulas of Section 5.4. In addition, changes of the moment of inertia, $I$, add terms to the basic differential equation. Thus, the correct differential equation for non-uniform beams, Eq. 5.27, includes two terms involving derivatives of $I$ that are not considered in Timoshenko's equation, Eq. 5.28.

A number of approaches have been used to find resonances of non-uniform beams. Some beams vary smoothly and solutions can be found by analytic methods. Other cases are better treated by dividing the structure into a number of finite elements and solving the resultant network matrix. The author's wave approach to finding resonances described in the previous section can also be applied to non-uniform beams. It is relatively simple to use and can often replace other methods.

### Finite-Element Methods

In the finite-element approach, the structure is divided into as few as 4 to as many as 400 discrete elements, and the basic bending relations are expressed as a set of four equations for each element. The resultant matrix of simultaneous equations is then solved by an analog or digital computer. Resonance frequencies are those frequencies for which the resultant solution agrees with the end conditions.

When dealing with a finite section of length $\Delta x$, Eqs. 5.15, 5.18, 5.22 and 5.25, which relate forces and moments to displacements and angles, may be written in the form

$$\Delta\theta = -\left(\frac{\Delta x}{YI}\right)M \ , \tag{5.88}$$

$$\Delta F_z = (\mu\Delta x)\omega^2 w \ , \tag{5.89}$$

$$(I'\Delta x)\omega^2\theta = F_z\Delta x + \Delta M \ , \qquad (5.90)$$

and

$$\Delta w = \theta\Delta x - \left(\frac{\Delta x}{KGS}\right)F_z \ . \qquad (5.91)$$

The computation is started by assuming a frequency and assigning arbitrary values to the non-zero quantities at one end and zero to the others. The four equations are then used to calculate the changes over length $\Delta x$. The procedure is followed until the other end is reached. It is then repeated for other values of frequency. Those values of frequency which give the proper values at the second end are resonance frequencies.

Prior to the development of high-speed digital computers, McCann and MacNeal (1950) and Trent (1950) independently developed electrical analogy methods for solving vibrating-beam problems. In these methods, the expressions in parentheses in Eqs. 5.88-5.91 are represented by electric circuit elements, usually inductances and capacitances. Two nets are used, coupled by transformers. One net deals with forces and involves mass and shear; the other has elements for bending rigidity and rotatory inertia related to Eqs. 5.88 and 5.90. Figure 5.11 shows such a coupled circuit for a beam element. With the electric analog, resonances are indicated by peaks of the voltages that occur as frequency is varied. Damping can be taken into account by adding resistances. The problem with this method is to pick a scaling factor such that the circuit elements will have reasonable values.

Other finite-element methods assume a deflection curve and use variational techniques to determine modal frequencies.

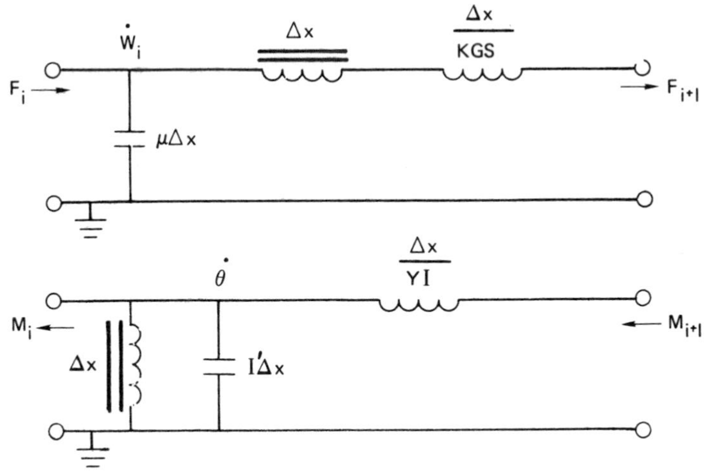


Fig. 5.11. Electric Circuit Analogy for Section of a Vibrating Beam

**Wave Method**

The wave approach described in the previous section can be extended to non-uniform beams provided that the terms in Eq. 5.27 that involve derivatives of the moment of inertia are small. Substituting Eq. 5.44 for $v_f$ and Eq. 5.38 for $v_{f\ell}$ into Eq. 5.83, the expression for resonance frequencies of a moderately non-uniform beam is

$$\int_0^L \sqrt{\frac{\sqrt{1+\epsilon}}{\kappa c_\ell}\left(\sqrt{1+\delta^2}+\delta\right)}\, dx$$

$$= \int_0^L \sqrt[4]{\frac{\mu}{YI}\left(\sqrt{1+\delta^2}+\delta\right)^2}\, dx = \frac{m\pi + \overline{\Delta\phi}}{\sqrt{\omega_m}} . \qquad (5.92)$$

Since the parameter $\delta$, defined by Eq. 5.42, is a function of frequency as well as of position, solution of Eq. 5.92 requires an iterative procedure.

There are several practical ways of solving Eq. 5.92. In one method, the integral is evaluated at a number of frequencies spanning the range of interest and the result plotted as a function of $\omega$. The right-hand side is also plotted as a function of $\omega$ for a number of mode numbers. Each intersection represents a resonance frequency. In a second method, the effect of non-uniformity is separated from that of shear. The low-frequency approximation for the resonance frequency is found from

$$\omega_{m\ell} = \left(\frac{m\pi + \overline{\Delta\phi_\ell}}{\int_0^L \sqrt{\frac{\sqrt{1+\epsilon}}{\kappa c_\ell}}\, dx}\right)^2 , \qquad (5.93)$$

and the high-frequency approximation from

$$\omega_{m_h} = \frac{c_\ell\left(m\pi + \overline{\Delta\phi_h}\right)}{\int_0^L \sqrt{\Gamma}\, dx} = \frac{c_s\left(m\pi + \overline{\Delta\phi_h}\right)}{\int_0^L \frac{1}{\sqrt{K}}\, dx} . \qquad (5.94)$$

Either Eq. 5.77 or Fig. 5.10 is then used to estimate the correction for shear in terms of the ratio of the two limiting values.

An advantage of the wave method relative to most finite-element methods is that, when carrying out the integrations, the beam can be divided into natural elements rather than into even parts. Another advantage is that the effects of non-uniformity and of shear are clearly distinguishable. The major disadvantage is that it is not valid when derivatives of the moment of inertia are important or when end conditions at one end affect the other. Both of these problems occur only at the lowest frequencies, i.e., for the lowest-order modes.

**Tapered Cantilever Beams**

The limitations of the wave approach can best be understood by examining the extreme case of a doubly-tapered cantilever beam. Such a beam, having rectangular cross section, is shown in Fig. 5.12. It is usual to express each resonance of a tapered beam in terms of that of a uniform

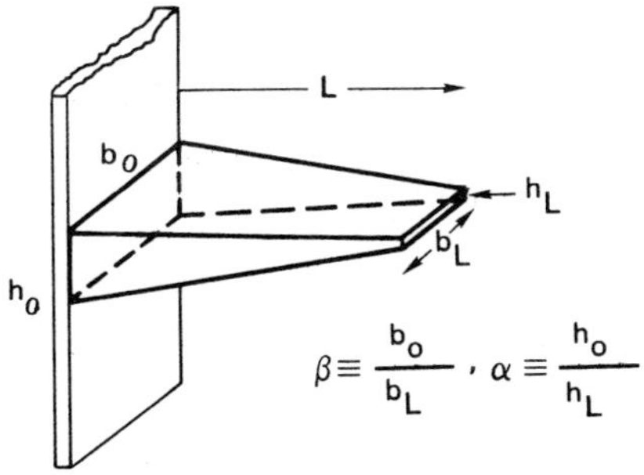


Fig. 5.12. Doubly-Tapered Cantilever Beam

beam having the same dimensions as its base. Using the wave approach and ignoring any effects of shear distortion, this ratio is

$$\left(\frac{\omega_m}{\omega_m(0)}\right)_\ell = \frac{L^2/\kappa_o}{\left(\frac{1}{L}\int_0^L \frac{dx}{\sqrt{\kappa}}\right)^2} = \frac{1}{\left(\int_0^L \sqrt{\frac{h_o}{h}}\, d\left(\frac{x}{L}\right)\right)^2} . \tag{5.95}$$

Expressing the thickness, $h$, by

$$\frac{h}{h_o} = \frac{1}{\alpha}\left(1 + (\alpha - 1)\left(1 - \frac{x}{L}\right)\right) , \tag{5.96}$$

it follows that

$$\left(\frac{\omega_m}{\omega_m(0)}\right)_\ell = \left(\frac{\alpha - 1}{2\alpha - 2\sqrt{\alpha}}\right)^2 . \tag{5.97}$$

This result is independent of both the resonance order and taper of the width. Also, it predicts that resonance frequencies of tapered beams should always be lower than those of a uniform beam having dimensions of the base throughout.

Martin (1956) measured the resonances of a number of tapered beams. He found that the fundamental increases with increasing taper, while all of the harmonics decrease. Mabie and Rogers (1964, 1972 and 1974) calculated the resonance frequencies of doubly-tapered cantilever beams, starting with the differential equation

$$\mu\ddot{w} + YI\left(\frac{\partial^4 w}{\partial x^4} + \frac{2}{I}\frac{dI}{dx}\frac{\partial^3 w}{\partial x^3} + \frac{1}{I}\frac{d^2 I}{dx^2}\frac{\partial^2 w}{\partial x^2}\right) = 0 \;, \tag{5.98}$$

which accounts for changes of the cross section but not for shear distortion. Their results are summarized in Fig. 5.13. It is clear from these results that derivatives of the moment of inertia are important for the first four or five resonances, and that the wave approach solution given by Eq. 5.97 is accurate for higher order resonances.

Since doubly-tapered cantilever beams represent an extreme, it appears that derivatives of the moment of inertia can be neglected when dealing with moderately non-uniform beams, especially when calculating resonances involving five or more nodes. This matter is discussed further in Section 5.11 on the flexural resonances of ship hulls.

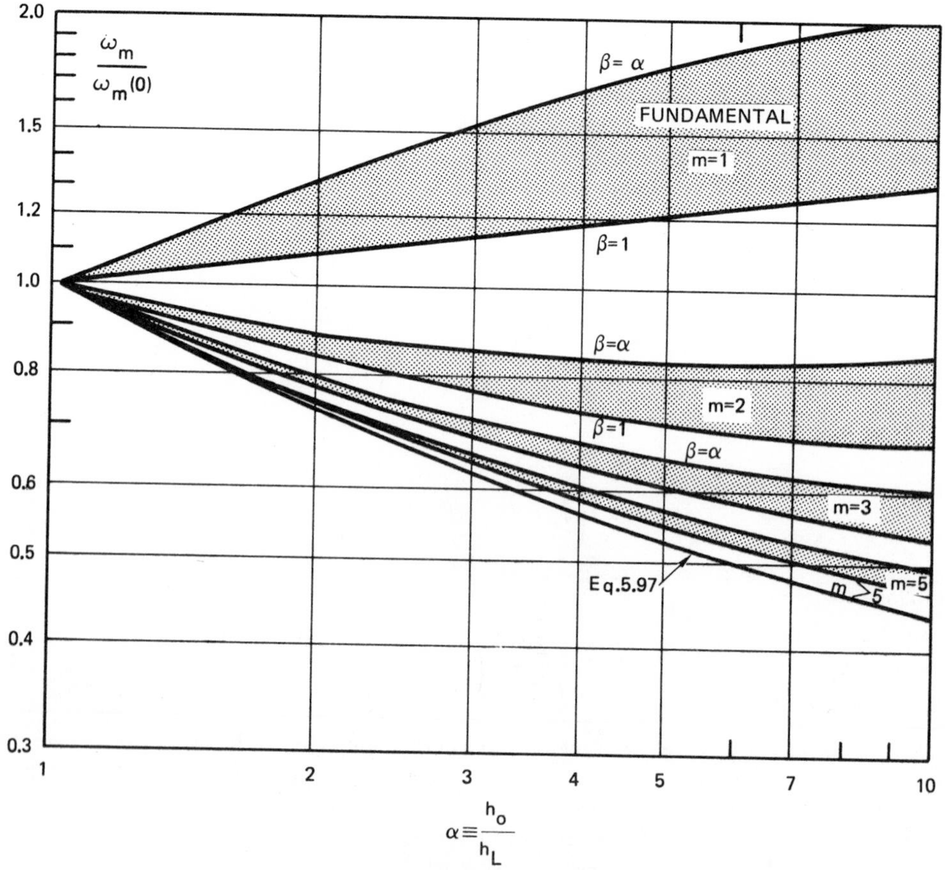


Fig. 5.13. Effect of Taper on Resonance Frequencies of Cantilever Beams, as computed by Mabie and Rogers (1972, 1974)

## 5.7 Forced Vibrations of Non-Resonant Structures

### Mechanical Impedances

As discussed in the introduction of this chapter, beam-like structures often act as transmitters of vibrations from sources to radiating surfaces. The response of beams to exciting forces and their properties as transmitters of vibrations are commonly described in terms of input and transfer impedances and/or admittances, or mobilities. Since the differential equations describing bending are linear, vibratory responses are proportional to exciting forces. *Mechanical impedances* are defined as ratios of exciting forces to resultant structural vibratory velocities. Thus,

$$\underline{Z}(\omega) \equiv \frac{\underline{F}(\omega)}{\underline{\dot{w}}(\omega)} \ . \tag{5.99}$$

If the velocity is measured at the point of application of the force, the resultant is called the *input impedance*. If the velocity is measured at a different location, then a *transfer impedance* is determined. Since force and velocity are generally not in phase, impedance is a complex quantity consisting of a real, or resistive, component and an imaginary, or reactive, term.

The resistive component of the impedance controls the flow of power in the system. If the source is a vibratory velocity, then the power transferred to the structure is given by

$$W = \underline{F}^* \cdot \underline{\dot{w}}_i = RP(\underline{Z})\overline{\dot{w}_i^2} = R\overline{\dot{w}_i^2} \ . \tag{5.100}$$

If the source is in the nature of a force, then the power transferred is

$$W = \underline{w}^* \cdot \underline{F}_i = RP\left(\frac{1}{\underline{Z}}\right)\overline{F_i^2} = \frac{R}{|Z|^2}\overline{F_i^2} \ . \tag{5.101}$$

The reciprocal of impedance is called either *admittance* or *mobility*. The power absorbed or transferred when the source is a force is therefore proportional to the real part of the admittance, called *conductance* in analogy to electric circuits.

While almost all structures have resonances, their impedances as non-resonant structures have special significance. Thus, when dealing with excitation of one end of a finite beam, the solution involves its impedance as a semi-infinite beam, and excitation far away from a beam end is related to that for an infinite beam. The two derivations are closely related. We will first consider semi-infinite beams.

### Semi-Infinite Beams

A *semi-infinite beam* is defined as a beam that is not only long relative to a flexural wave length but also sufficiently long that any wave reflected from the far end would be damped out and therefore negligible at the near end. Thus, in the vicinity of the near end, only two terms are required to describe the motion. Equation 5.32 can be written

$$\underline{w}(x) \doteq \underline{A}\, e^{-ik_f x} + \underline{C}\, e^{-\gamma x} \ . \tag{5.102}$$

Since the beam must be free to respond to a force at its end, the moment there must be zero. From Eqs. 5.15, 5.18 and 5.25, the moment is

$$\underline{M} = - YI \frac{\partial \theta}{\partial x} = - YI \left( \frac{\partial^2 \underline{w}}{\partial x^2} + \frac{\Gamma \mu \omega^2}{YS} \underline{w} \right) . \tag{5.103}$$

Using Eqs. 5.42, 5.59, 5.67 and 5.68, the coefficient of $\underline{w}$ can be expressed in terms of $\delta$, $k_f$ and $\gamma$ by

$$\frac{\Gamma \mu \omega^2}{YS} = 2\delta \frac{\omega \Omega}{c_\ell^2} = 2\delta k_f \gamma = k_f^2 - \gamma^2 . \tag{5.104}$$

Hence,

$$\underline{M} = - YI \left( \frac{\partial^2 \underline{w}}{\partial x^2} + (k_f^2 - \gamma^2) \underline{w} \right) . \tag{5.105}$$

The second spatial derivative of Eq. 5.102 is

$$\frac{\partial^2 \underline{w}}{\partial x^2} = - k_f^2 \underline{A}\, e^{-ik_f x} + \gamma^2 \underline{C} e^{-\gamma x} . \tag{5.106}$$

Substituting Eqs. 5.102 and 5.106 into Eq. 5.105 and setting the moment at $x = 0$ equal to 0 yields a relation between the two complex coefficients $\underline{A}$ and $\underline{C}$,

$$- k_f^2 \underline{A} + \gamma^2 \underline{C} + (k_f^2 - \gamma^2) (\underline{A} + \underline{C}) = 0 , \tag{5.107}$$

from which

$$\underline{A} = \frac{\gamma^2 + (k_f^2 - \gamma^2)}{k_f^2 - (k_f^2 - \gamma^2)} \underline{C} = \left( \frac{k_f}{\gamma} \right)^2 \underline{C} . \tag{5.108}$$

Since velocity at any point is related to displacement by the time derivative, it follows that

$$\dot{\underline{w}}(x) = i\omega \underline{w} = i\omega \underline{C} \left[ \left( \frac{k_f}{\gamma} \right)^2 e^{-ik_f x} + e^{-\gamma x} \right] . \tag{5.109}$$

The expression for the force corresponding to this velocity is somewhat more complicated. From Eqs. 5.22, 5.25 and 5.105,

$$\underline{F} = \underline{F}_z = YI \left( \frac{\partial^3 \underline{w}}{\partial x^3} + (k_f^2 - \gamma^2) \frac{\partial \underline{w}}{\partial x} \right) + \alpha' \rho_s I \omega^2 \left( \frac{\partial \underline{w}}{\partial x} + \frac{\Gamma}{YS} \underline{F}_z \right) . \tag{5.110}$$

After some manipulation, this becomes

$$\frac{\underline{F}}{YI} = \frac{\underline{w}''' + (1 + \bar{\alpha}) (k_f^2 - \gamma^2) \underline{w}'}{1 - 4\bar{\alpha}\delta^2} , \tag{5.111}$$

where each prime indicates a differentiation with respect to $x$. Carrying out the differentiations of Eq. 5.102 with $\underline{A}$ given by Eq. 5.108, an expression for a force at $x = 0$ is

$$\underline{F}(0) = YI\underline{C}k_f^2 \frac{ik_f\left(1 - 2\bar{\alpha}\delta\dfrac{k_f}{\gamma}\right) - \gamma\left(1 + 2\bar{\alpha}\delta\dfrac{\gamma}{k_f}\right)}{1 - 4\bar{\alpha}\delta^2} . \tag{5.112}$$

The required force appears to become very large as the denominator approaches zero. However, the magnitude of the numerator also becomes zero and the ratio remains finite. Just as was done when deriving the flexural wave speed in Section 5.4, a close approximation for the force can be derived by ignoring the terms involving rotatory inertia. Setting $\bar{\alpha} = 0$, Eq. 5.112 becomes

$$\underline{F}(0) = YI\underline{C}k_f^2\,(ik_f - \gamma) . \tag{5.113}$$

Dividing the force by the velocity at the end, $x = 0$, the input impedance is

$$\underline{Z}_i \equiv \frac{\underline{F}(0)}{\underline{\dot{w}}(0)} = \frac{YI\underline{C}k_f^2\,(ik_f - \gamma)}{i\omega\underline{C}\left(\left(\dfrac{k_f}{\gamma}\right)^2 + 1\right)} = \frac{YI}{\omega}k_f\gamma\frac{k_f + i\gamma}{\dfrac{k_f}{\gamma} + \dfrac{\gamma}{k_f}} = \mu v_f\frac{1 + i\left(\dfrac{\gamma}{k_f}\right)}{1 + \left(\dfrac{\gamma}{k_f}\right)^2} . \tag{5.114}$$

where the ratio of $\gamma$ to $k_f$ is given in Eq. 5.68 as a function of $\delta$.

At low frequencies, i.e., for $\delta < 0.05$, the input impedance reduces to

$$\underline{Z}_{i\ell} = \mu v_{f\ell}\frac{1 + i}{2} . \tag{5.115}$$

Thus, at low frequencies the resistive and reactive components of the input impedance are equal. As frequency increases and effects of shear distortion are felt, the resistive term becomes somewhat larger and the reactive term smaller. At very high frequencies, $\delta > 3$, the reactive term is negligible and $v_f$ in Eq. 5.114 can be replaced by $v_{f_h}$.

The power transferred to a semi-infinite beam by a velocity source is given by

$$W_i = R_i\overline{\dot{w}_o^2} = \frac{\mu v_f}{1 + \left(\dfrac{\gamma}{k_f}\right)^2}\overline{\dot{w}_o^2} , \tag{5.116}$$

while that transferred by a force source is

$$W_i = \frac{R_i}{|Z_i|^2}\overline{F^2} = \frac{1}{\mu v_f}\overline{F^2} . \tag{5.117}$$

This simple result is valid over the entire frequency range. Effects of shear at higher frequencies are incorporated in the expression for the flexural wave speed.

**Infinite Beams**

A beam may be considered infinite if the excitation occurs far enough from the ends that reflected energy is negligible. The derivation of the input impedance for this case is actually somewhat simpler than that for a semi-infinite beam. The force generates waves that progress away from the point of application, $x = 0$, in both directions. Thus, for $x \geqslant 0$,

$$\underline{w}(x \geqslant 0) = \underline{A}\, e^{-ik_f x} + \underline{C}\, e^{-\gamma x} . \tag{5.118}$$

At the point of application of the force, the beam moves straight up and down without rotation. The boundary condition is therefore $\theta(0) = 0$. From Eq. 5.25, it follows that $w'(0) = 0$. Taking the derivative of Eq. 5.118 and setting it equal to zero, one finds

$$\underline{A} = i \frac{\gamma}{k_f} \underline{C} , \tag{5.119}$$

from which it follows that the velocity is

$$\underline{\dot{w}}(x \geqslant 0) = i\omega \underline{C} \left( i \frac{\gamma}{k_f} e^{-ik_f x} + e^{-\gamma x} \right) . \tag{5.120}$$

Since the applied force creates waves progressing in both directions, it must be twice as large as that required to create only the positive-direction wave. Setting $\theta$ and $w'$ equal to zero, Eqs. 5.15, 5.18, 5.22 and 5.25 yield

$$\underline{F} = -2 \frac{\partial \underline{M}}{\partial x} = 2YI \frac{\partial^2 \underline{\theta}}{\partial x^2} = 2YI \frac{\partial^3 \underline{w}}{\partial x^3} . \tag{5.121}$$

Taking the third derivative of Eq. 5.118, with $\underline{A}$ given by Eq. 5.119, Eq. 5.121 becomes

$$\underline{F} = -2YI\underline{C}\gamma \left(k_f^2 + \gamma^2\right) = -4YI\underline{C}\gamma k_{f_o}^2 \sqrt{1 + \delta^2} , \tag{5.122}$$

from which the input impedance is

$$\underline{Z}_i = \frac{F}{\underline{\dot{w}}_o} = 2\mu v_f \left( 1 + i \frac{k_f}{\gamma} \right) . \tag{5.123}$$

At low frequencies, this is four times as large as that for a semi-infinite beam, Eq. 5.115. As the frequency increases, the reactive term increases more rapidly than the resistive term. The magnitude of the impedance therefore continues to increase with frequency rather than approaching a constant value, as does that of a semi-infinite beam.

The power transferred by a velocity source to an effectively infinite beam is

$$W_i = R_i \overline{w_o^2} = 2\mu v_f \overline{\dot{w}_o^2} , \tag{5.124}$$

while that received from a force is

$$W_i = \frac{R_i\overline{F^2}}{|Z_i|^2} \doteq \frac{1 - \dfrac{\delta}{\sqrt{1+\delta^2}}}{4\mu v_f}\overline{F^2} \,. \tag{5.125}$$

The latter expression shows that away from their ends beams become increasingly resistant to the absorption of power from applied forces as frequency increases. It was this fact that led to the statement in Section 5.4 that flexural waves are not usually dominant at the higher frequencies, i.e., for $\delta > 3$.

**Role of Damping**

The criterion for a finite beam to behave as an infinite beam is that reflected energy be negligible. This will occur if power is absorbed at an end or if the vibration is sufficiently damped in traveling from the source to the end. Every flexing beam experiences at least a little damping. The alternating extensional motions of its fibers involve storing and release of energy, which process invariably involves energy dissipation.

In dealing with linear systems at a fixed frequency, energy dissipation can be incorporated into the analysis by replacing certain real quantities with complex ones, the imaginary components of which are proportional to the dissipation. This was done in Section 2.4 in considering damped sound waves in slightly lossy fluids and in Section 4.3 relevant to pulsating bubbles. In treating beam flexural vibrations, the elastic moduli $Y$ and $G$ control energy storage and therefore account for dissipation. Since the two moduli are related through Poisson's ratio by Eq. 5.5 and that ratio is usually real, the same loss factor applies to both. The procedure used is to replace $Y$ by $Y(1 + i\eta)$ and $G$ by $G(1 + i\eta)$ wherever they occur. When this is done,

$$c_\ell \rightarrow c_\ell\sqrt{1 + i\eta} \doteq c_\ell\left(1 + i\frac{\eta}{2}\right) , \tag{5.126}$$

$$v_{f\ell} \rightarrow v_{f\ell}\sqrt[4]{1 + i\eta} \doteq v_{f\ell}\left(1 + i\frac{\eta}{4}\right) , \tag{5.127}$$

$$\delta \rightarrow \frac{\delta}{\sqrt{1 + i\eta}} \doteq \delta\left(1 - i\frac{\eta}{2}\right) , \tag{5.128}$$

and

$$k_{f_o} = \frac{\omega}{v_{f\ell}} \rightarrow k_{f_o}\left(1 - i\frac{\eta}{4}\right) . \tag{5.129}$$

The effect of damping on input impedances of non-resonant structures is usually quite small. In effect, the out-of-phase components are altered slightly. Thus, neglecting secondary effects, the input impedance of a semi-infinite beam becomes

$$\underline{Z}_i \doteq \mu v_f \frac{1 + i\left(\dfrac{\gamma}{k_f} + \dfrac{\eta}{4}\right)}{1 + \left(\dfrac{\gamma}{k_f}\right)^2} \quad . \tag{5.130}$$

Unless $\eta > 0.5$, the effect of damping is quite small.

A more important effect of damping is that it causes spatial decay of the vibrations. Without damping, the vibratory motion would be the same at all positions on a non-resonant beam remote from the source. The effect of damping is to introduce attenuation. Substituting Eq. 5.129 for $k_f$ in Eq. 5.109, the velocity at distance $x$ becomes

$$\underline{\dot{w}} = i\omega\underline{C}\left(\frac{k_f}{\gamma}\right)^2 e^{-(\eta/4)k_f x}\, e^{i(\omega t - k_f x)} \quad . \tag{5.131}$$

Thus, the space-rate-of-decay of the vibration is

$$-\frac{1}{\dot{w}}\frac{d\dot{w}}{dx} = \frac{1}{4}\eta k_f \doteq 13.65\eta \qquad dB/wavelength \quad . \tag{5.132}$$

A beam can be treated as effectively infinite if the source is located distance $1/2\eta$ flexural wavelengths from the nearest reflecting termination.

Damping also controls the rate at which a vibration will decay once the source is removed. Thus, it can readily be shown that, upon securing a source, a flexural vibration will decay at a rate given by

$$-\frac{1}{\dot{w}}\frac{d\dot{w}}{dt} = \frac{1}{2}\eta\omega = 27.3\eta f \qquad dB/sec \quad . \tag{5.133}$$

Damping is often measured by finding the time-rate-of-decay of vibration.

## 5.8 Forced Vibrations of Resonant Structures

### Role of Resonances

As discussed in Section 5.5, finite beams are multiply-resonant systems. When allowed to vibrate freely, finite beams vibrate at one or more of their resonance frequencies. These resonances also play an important role in the beam's response to an applied force, acting as *modes* or *eigen-frequencies*. Response of a beam to applied forces can be calculated as the sum of its responses at all of the eigen-frequencies. Skudrzyk (1958 and 1968) has based his extensive treatment of this subject on the fact that any lumped or homogeneous system can be represented by an infinite number of series-resonant circuits all connected in parallel, each of which represents one mode. Obviously, the closer the exciting frequency is to the resonant frequency of a mode, the greater its excitation, provided the force is not applied at a spatial node of that mode.

Usually one is interested in a structure over a range of frequencies. The approach taken is to plot its calculated or measured impedance or admittance as a function of frequency. Resonances and/or anti-resonances will then show clearly and the suitability of the system for its intended application should be clear. Skudrzyk (1968) and Snowdon (1968) have shown that input impedance and admittance functions are characterized by alternating resonances and anti-resonances, while transfer functions sometimes exhibit only resonances.

**Modal Responses**

The total impedance of a number of parallel circuits is the reciprocal of the sum of their admittances. In most cases, the location and nature of the source is such that the different modes experience different amounts of excitation. The total response of the structure is then the sum of the modal responses weighted by the excitation of each. For an infinite number of undamped modes,

$$\dot{w} \sim \frac{F}{\mu L} \sum_{m=1}^{\infty} \frac{\omega \phi_m}{\omega_m^2 - \omega^2} , \tag{5.134}$$

where $\phi_m$ is a weighting function giving the relative force for each mode. Without damping, the response is infinite at each resonance.

In resonant systems, material damping has the important role of limiting resonant and anti-resonant responses. From Eqs. 5.63 and 5.126,

$$\omega_m \rightarrow \omega_m \left( 1 + i \frac{\eta}{2} \right) , \tag{5.135}$$

and the mean-square velocity is

$$\overline{\dot{w}^2} \sim \frac{\overline{F^2}}{\mu^2 L^2} \sum_{m=1}^{\infty} \frac{\omega^2 \phi_m^2}{\left(\omega_m^2 - \omega^2\right)^2 + \eta^2 \omega_m^4} . \tag{5.136}$$

The half-power points on the resonance curve occur when the two terms in the denominator of Eq. 5.136 are equal, i.e., at

$$\left| \omega_m - \omega \right| \doteq \frac{\eta}{2} \omega_m . \tag{5.137}$$

It follows that the sharpness of the resonance, as given by its $Q$, is

$$Q \equiv \frac{f}{\Delta f} = \frac{\omega_m}{2 \left| \omega_m - \omega \right|} = \frac{1}{\eta} . \tag{5.138}$$

It can also be shown that at low frequencies the amplitude of the motion occurring at a resonance is $Q$ times that which would occur if the system were non-resonant. Also, at low-frequency anti-resonances the impedance is $Q$ times that for the non-resonant system. Thus, the input impedance of a structure treated as non-resonant equals the geometric mean of the values at resonances and anti-resonances.

**Broadband Excitation**

In many instances the exciting force covers a band of frequencies that is wide compared to the bandwidths of any resonances within the band. In this case, the response of each resonance is obtained by integrating over frequency across the resonance. Thus

$$\overline{\dot{w}_m^2} \sim \frac{\overline{F^2}\,\phi_m^2}{\mu^2 L^2(\omega_2 - \omega_1)} \int_{\omega_1}^{\omega_2} \frac{\omega^2 d\omega}{(\omega_m^2 - \omega^2)^2 + \eta^2\omega^4}$$

$$\doteq \frac{\overline{F_m^2}}{\mu^2 L^2(\omega_2 - \omega_1)} \; \frac{\pi}{2\eta\omega_m} , \qquad (5.139)$$

provided $(\omega_2 - \omega_1)$ is large compared to the width of the resonance. The power accepted by this resonance is given by Eq. 5.100 as

$$W_m = R\overline{\dot{w}_m^2} = \eta\omega\mu L \cdot \overline{\dot{w}_m^2} \doteq \frac{\pi}{2} \; \frac{\overline{F^2}\,\overline{\phi_m^2}}{\mu L(\omega_2 - \omega_1)} . \qquad (5.140)$$

If the density of resonances is $dN/d\omega$, then there will be

$$N = \frac{dN}{d\omega}(\omega_2 - \omega_1) \qquad (5.141)$$

resonances within the band, and the total power will be

$$W_i \doteq \frac{\pi}{2} \; \frac{\overline{F^2}}{\mu L} \; \frac{dN}{d\omega} , \qquad (5.142)$$

provided each resonance is excited equally.

The expression of power transferred to a resonant structure is seen to depend only on the modal density divided by the total effective mass. Following Nelson (1972), we may write

$$\frac{dN}{d\omega} = \frac{dN}{dk_f}\,\frac{dk_f}{d\omega} = \frac{1}{v_f}\,\frac{dN}{dk_f}\left(1 - k_f\frac{dv_f}{d\omega}\right) = \frac{L}{\pi v_f}\left(1 - k_f\frac{dv_f}{d\omega}\right) , \qquad (5.143)$$

and the input power becomes

$$W_i \doteq \frac{\overline{F^2}}{2\mu v_f}\left(1 - k_f\frac{dv_f}{d\omega}\right) . \qquad (5.144)$$

At low frequencies, the dispersion term is 1/2 and the power reduces to

$$W_{i\ell} = \frac{\overline{F^2}}{4\mu v_{f\ell}} , \qquad (5.145)$$

in complete agreement with that for an infinite beam, as given by Eq. 5.125. It follows that the response of a resonant structure to wideband excitation is the same as that of a non-resonant structure having the same parameters.

## 5.9 Attenuation of Structural Vibrations

In Section 1.1 it was noted that reducing the efficiency of vibration transmission from a source to a radiating surface is usually the easiest way of achieving noise reduction., There are a number of ways of attenuating such structural vibrations, several of which will be discussed briefly in this section. Readers desiring more information are referred to the extensive list of references on this subject at the end of this chapter.

### Isolation Mounts

The most common method of reducing structural vibrations is to interpose a relatively flexible vibration isolator between a source of vibrations and a structural member. The force generated by a machine, $F_i$, normally would act to cause both the machine and its foundation to vibrate. If the two are rigidly connected, they must share the same velocity and the input force must be divided between them in proportion to their impedances. The force transmitted to the foundation is therefore

$$\underline{F}_f = \frac{F_i \underline{Z}_f}{\underline{Z}_s + \underline{Z}_f} , \tag{5.146}$$

where $\underline{Z}_f$ is the foundation impedance and $\underline{Z}_s$ is the internal impedance of the source. If we now interpose an isolator with impedance $\underline{Z}_i$ between source and foundation, the isolator and foundation will share the same force but divide the velocity. In other words, they will act as parallel impedances. The force imparted to the foundation will then be given by

$$\underline{F}_f^i = \frac{F_i \dfrac{\underline{Z}_f \underline{Z}_i}{\underline{Z}_i + \underline{Z}_f}}{\underline{Z}_s + \dfrac{\underline{Z}_f \underline{Z}_i}{\underline{Z}_i + \underline{Z}_f}} = \frac{F_i \underline{Z}_i \underline{Z}_f}{\underline{Z}_i \underline{Z}_s + \underline{Z}_f \underline{Z}_s + \underline{Z}_f \underline{Z}_i} . \tag{5.147}$$

The effectiveness of the mount is defined as the ratio of non-isolated to isolated foundation forces and is given by

$$e \equiv \left| \frac{\underline{F}_f}{\underline{F}_f^i} \right| = \left| \frac{\underline{Z}_i \underline{Z}_s + \underline{Z}_f \underline{Z}_s + \underline{Z}_f \underline{Z}_i}{\underline{Z}_i (\underline{Z}_f + \underline{Z}_s)} \right| . \tag{5.148}$$

This expression is somewhat simpler if instead of the impedances of the elements one uses their mobilities, or admittances. Thus

$$e = \left| \frac{\underline{Y}_f + \underline{Y}_s + \underline{Y}_i}{\underline{Y}_f + \underline{Y}_s} \right| . \tag{5.149}$$

The logarithmic expression for mount effectiveness is called *insertion loss*. Insertion loss measures the value of an isolator as a noise reduction device. It is more meaningful than the often measured transmission loss, which is the ratio of the vibratory motion of the source to that of the foundation. This ratio is given by

$$t \equiv \left| \frac{\dot{\underline{w}}_s}{\dot{\underline{w}}_f} \right| = \left| \frac{\underline{Z}_i + \underline{Z}_f}{\underline{Z}_i} \right| = \left| \frac{\underline{Y}_i + \underline{Y}_f}{\underline{Y}_f} \right| , \qquad (5.150)$$

and is always larger than the insertion loss. It only measures whether an isolator is operational, i.e., whether $\underline{Z}_i << \underline{Z}_f$ as it must be for maximum effectiveness.

The expressions for mount effectiveness given by Eqs. 5.148 and 5.149 are general. We can better understand how mounts work by considering some special cases. The simplest system is one in which the machine is a mass, the isolator is a lossy spring and the foundation presents infinite impedance. In this ideal case,

$$e_i \doteq \left| 1 - \left( \frac{f}{f_o} \right)^2 (1 - i\eta) \right| , \qquad (5.151)$$

where $f_o$ is the resonance frequency of source mass and isolator spring constant, and $\eta$ is the loss factor of the system, assumed less than 0.1. As shown in Fig. 5.14, the mount is ineffective at low frequencies. In fact, at resonance, it serves to magnify the transmitted force by an amount that is only limited by damping. Well above resonance, the effectiveness of an ideal mount increases by 12 dB/octave.

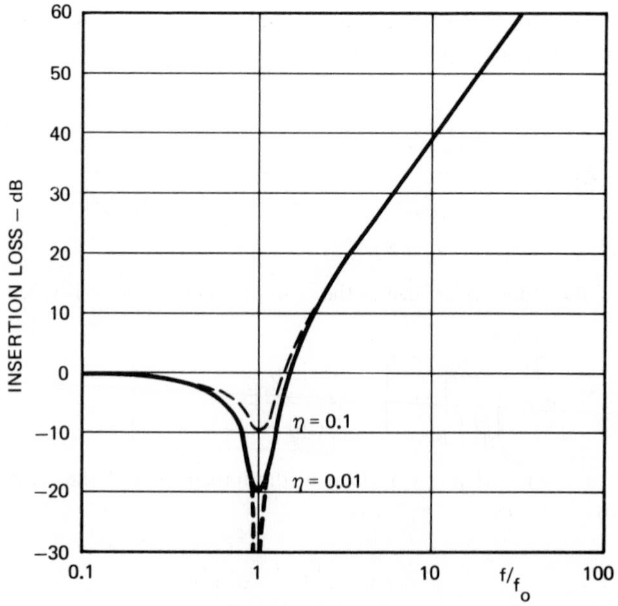


Fig. 5.14. Insertion Loss of an Ideal Isolation Mount

In the ideal case, insertion loss increases indefinitely with increasing frequency and the optimum mount is the one with the lowest resonant frequency. In practical shipboard systems, however, actual insertion losses seldom exceed 30 dB and 10 to 20 dB are typical. There are a number of reasons for this departure from the ideal. First, springs used as isolators are themselves distributed systems which may have resonances at high frequencies. At these resonances, their mobilities are very small and mount effectiveness, by Eq. 5.149, is close to unity. It is to avoid such wave effects that most modern isolators are composed extensively of rubber, used either in compression or in shear. A second reason for less than ideal performance of mounts on ships is the relative mobility of the foundation. Foundations are generally composed of beams which, being finite, resonate at a number of frequencies. At such resonances the foundation impedance can become very small relative to that of the source itself. In such a case,

$$e \doteq \left| 1 + \frac{\underline{Z}_f}{\underline{Z}_i} \right| , \qquad (5.152)$$

and the mount effectiveness is controlled by the ratio of foundation to isolation impedances. At resonances, as discussed in Section 5.8, the impedance is entirely controlled by the resistive component. It is for this reason that Sykes (1958, 1960), Klyukin (1961), Ungar (1962) and others have recognized the importance of building extra damping into foundation structures. The final reason for less than ideal mount performance is that the machine itself also has resonances. With increasing frequency, its mobility tends to become constant on the average, rather than to decrease as it would if it were a pure mass. Since springs composed of rubber have almost constant mobility at high frequencies, the insertion loss tends toward a constant, limiting value.

**Applied Damping**

The importance of damping in limiting system responses at resonances has been stressed in both Section 5.8 and the discussion of vibration isolation mounts. As will be indicated in Chapter 6, damping also controls plate resonant vibrations and thereby affects sound radiation. For instance, mastic undercoat is used on automobiles and railway cars to reduce their resonant responses and make them sound less *tinny*. In fact, development of damping for plates and structural members has been one of the more active areas of noise control development over the past 30 years.

One approach to damping has been the development of a number of structural materials having high internal damping. In his review of this subject, Adams (1972) noted several materials having favorable damping characteristics. However, these materials are quite expensive and most research in this area has focused instead on ways of damping ordinary metal structures. Many rubbers have high internal damping and much of the research has concentrated on the development of rubber-like (viscoelastic) materials that can be sprayed on or otherwise readily attached to metal. Oberst (1952, 1954, 1956) and his co-workers in Germany have developed chemical methods to produce such damping materials.

Oberst analyzed the damping of plates by *homogeneous layers* of damping material, attributing the damping to the extensional-compressional motion which these layers experience as the structure flexes. Consider the single-layer treatment sketched in Fig. 5.15. The solid rectangular base is characterized by Young's modulus $Y$ and thickness $H_1$. The viscoelastic layer has thickness $H_2$ and its Young's modulus, which includes damping, is $Y_2(1 + i\eta_2)$. The neutral plane of the combined

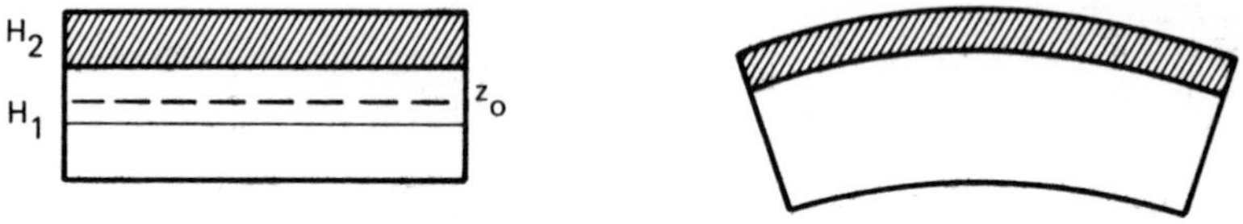


Fig. 5.15. Homogeneous Damping Treatment

plate is displaced $z_o$ from the centerline of the base section due to the additional layer. The bending rigidity per unit width of the combined structure is given by

$$\underline{B} = B(1 + i\eta) = \sum \underline{Y}_i I_i = Y_1 \frac{H_1^3}{12} + Y_1 H_1 z_o^2 + \underline{Y}_2 \frac{H_2^3}{12} + \underline{Y}_2 H_2 \left( \frac{H_1 + H_2}{2} - z_o \right)^2 . \tag{5.153}$$

The displacement of the neutral plane can be found from the requirement that the net extensional force be zero; thus,

$$Y_1 H_1 z_o = Y_2 \sqrt{1 + \eta^2} H_2 \left( \frac{H_1 + H_2}{2} - z_o \right) . \tag{5.154}$$

Assuming the extensional stiffness of the damping layer, $Y_2 H_2$, to be small compared to that of the base, $Y_1 H_1$,

$$z_o \doteq \frac{Y_2 H_2}{Y_1 H_1} \sqrt{1 + \eta^2} \left( \frac{H_1 + H_2}{2} \right) . \tag{5.155}$$

Substituting Eq. 5.155 into Eq. 5.153, the effective damping factor of the combination is

$$\eta \doteq \eta_2 \frac{Y_2 H_2}{Y_1 H_1} \frac{3H_1^2 + 6H_1 H_2 + 4H_2^2}{H_1^2 + \frac{Y_2 H_2}{Y_1 H_1} (3H_1^2 + 6H_1 H_2 + 4H_2^2)} . \tag{5.156}$$

For many cases, this reduces to

$$\eta \doteq 3\eta_2 \frac{Y_2 H_2}{Y_1 H_1} \left( 1 + \frac{H_2}{H_1} \right)^2 , \tag{5.157}$$

showing that the damping is proportional to the product of the loss coefficient of the material and the extensional thickness of the damping layer, magnified by a factor that represents the relative separation of the centers of the two layers.

Oberst's results are plotted in Fig. 5.16. For very thin layers, the dependence on relative thickness is linear, but the resultant loss factor is less than 0.01. If a damping treatment is to be really useful, it should produce a loss factor of at least 0.05, which for most materials requires a thickness of treatment of the same order as that of the base. Ross, Ungar and Kerwin (1959) showed that, using the best damping materials then available, a thickness ratio of 1.25 was required to achieve $\eta = 0.1$ on steel structures, and a ratio of 0.7 on aluminum ones. These thicknesses correspond to weight ratios of 16% for steel and 28% for aluminum.

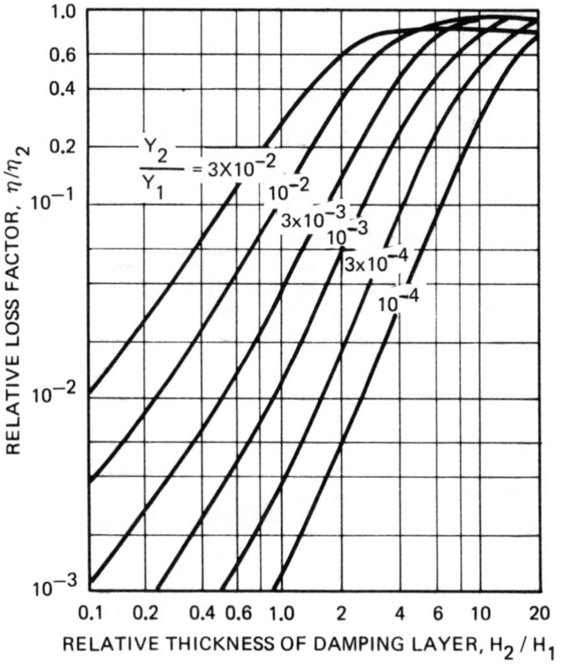


Fig. 5.16. Relative Damping as a Function of Layer Thickness, after Oberst (1952)

The problem with homogeneous damping treatments is that they are relatively heavy and bulky. They were developed for use on relatively light plates and are of little use on beams. Kerwin (1959) observed that the use of a thin metal cover on top of a damping layer causes the latter to experience shear and that such shearing action can be more efficient in producing damping. He derived an expression for the loss factor of *constrained-layer damping treatments* and verified the results experimentally. Ross, Ungar and Kerwin (1959) published formulas for optimized constrained-layer treatments, finding that the same weight of treatment produces from two to four times as much damping as that of a homogeneous layer. Significant damping can be achieved with treatments weighing less than 8% as much as the base. If very high damping is desired, a sandwich can be built in which two equal metal bars or plates are separated by a thin viscoelastic layer, as described by Kurtze (1959). In this case, the resultant loss factor is about 25% of that of the damping material.

As found by Kerwin, Ross and Ungar, shear damping treatments are more frequency and/or temperature dependent than are homogeneous, extensional types. Figure 5.17 shows the frequency dependence of a typical shear treatment at two temperatures. There are several ways of

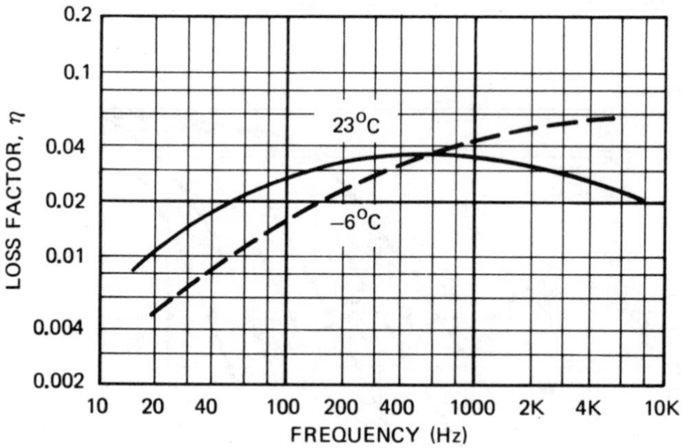


Fig. 5.17. Frequency and Temperature Dependencies of a Typical Shear Damping Treatment, from Ross, et al (1959)

overcoming this problem. Ungar and Ross (1959) analyzed multiple-layer treatments and found that increasing the number of layers broadens the peak region, as shown in Fig. 5.18. Grootenhuis (1970) has developed treatments in which two different viscoelastic materials are used under a single constraining layer, achieving significant broadening of the region of high damping.

A major advantage of shear damping is its applicability to beam structures. Ruzicka (1961) and Ungar (1962) have developed and evaluated a number of different ways of incorporating damping in beams, some of which are shown in Fig. 5.19.

**Impedance Mismatches**

Another approach to the attenuation of flexural waves is the introduction of changes of cross section and the attachment of mass elements, all of which create impedance mismatches which act to reflect a fraction of an incident flexural wave. Cremer (1953, 1956) analyzed cross-sectional changes, finding a transmission loss of 3 dB for a 5:1 ratio of section thicknesses, which increases about 4 to 5 dB for every doubling of this ratio. Rader and Mao (1971) have analyzed this case by analogy to Snell's law. When bending waves are made to turn a corner, a 3 dB reduction occurs. This can be increased by simultaneously changing the structural rigidity. Cremer also found that the attachment of a concentrated mass load to a beam may produce a change in moment of inertia

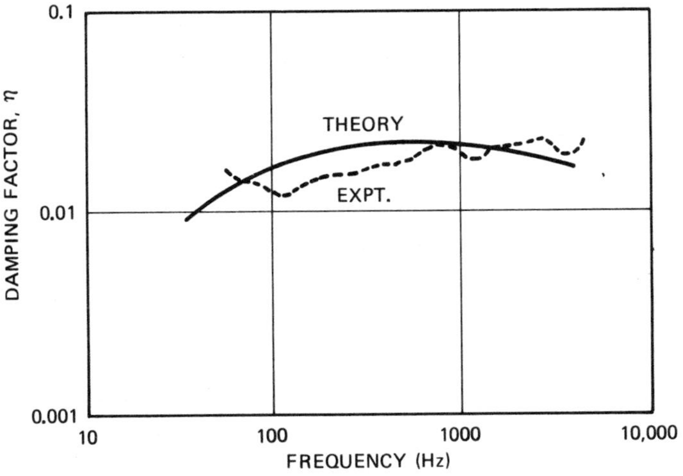


Fig. 5.18. Damping Curve for a Double-Layer Damping Treatment Having a Total Weight of 5% of the Base Plate, from Ungar and Ross (1959)

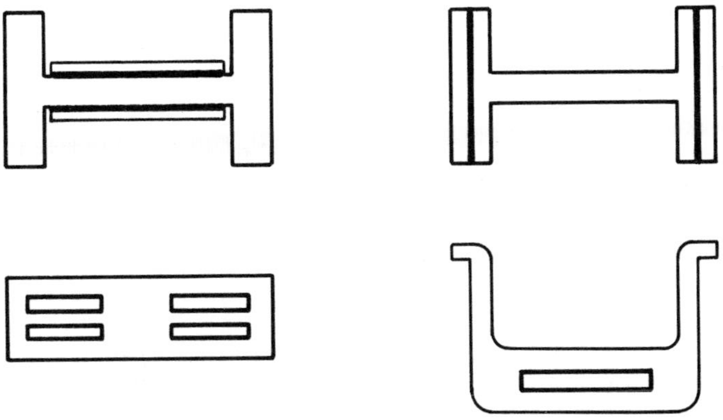

Fig. 5.19. Examples of Damped Beam Structures, after Ruzicka (1961) and Ungar (1962)

sufficient to cause as much as 20 to 30 dB of attenuation above a minimum frequency. Below this frequency, the mass acts as though distributed and the loss is negligible.

Periodically-spaced impedance discontinuities in the form of attached masses are not as effective as might be expected. The reason is that the structure itself develops resonances with nodes at the attachments. Waves at these frequencies are passed without attenuation. Mead (1970) and Sen

Gupta (1970) have analyzed periodic structures by methods similar to those developed by Brillouin (1953) to analyze energy propagation in crystal lattices. They defined a complex propagation constant which is sometimes real, corresponding to attenuation, and which is imaginary in certain frequency bands that pass energy virtually unattenuated. Obviously, multiple attachments are best used with irregular spacings, so that there will be significant attenuation at all frequencies above the low-frequency limit.

### Vibration Absorbers and Suppressors

Yet another way of attenuating flexural waves is by attaching devices to a vibrating structure that will either absorb the energy or feed back a cancelling signal that suppresses the vibration. Klyukin (1960), having noted that vibration-sensing instruments act to suppress the vibrations they are intended to measure, proposed a number of different passive vibration absorbers. These attachments, which are resonant, consist of masses on springs with dampers. Such systems having $Q$'s as low as 2 can provide as much as 40 dB of attenuation over an octave. Machinery on isolation mounts located inside ships undoubtedly contribute to the damping of hull flexural vibrations by just this mechanism.

Active electromechanical feedback vibration suppressors have been developed and tested by Knyazev and Tartakovskii (1965, 1966 and 1967). The dispersive nature of flexural waves makes such an approach more difficult than when the wave speed is constant, but this difficulty was overcome with a phase-compensating feedback system. Attenuations at resonances of the order of 15 dB were achieved. In a parallel development, Rockwell and Lawther (1964) demonstrated similar reductions for a uniform beam supported by rubber mounts, using a co-located sensor and feedback source. In principle, and with sufficient investment, active dampers would be very effective.

## 5.10 Fluid Loading

Immersion of a structure in a relatively dense fluid such as water can change its vibrational characteristics significantly. As compared to vibrations in air, the effective mass of the structure is increased by the mass of the entrained fluid, and both fluid viscosity and the radiation of sound add to the damping. Of these effects, the first two are more important for beams, while the last is a major consideration for plates (see Chapter 6).

### Entrained Mass

Entrained mass has been accounted for in the derivations given in Sections 5.3-5.8 by inclusion of the relative entrained mass, $\epsilon$, defined as the ratio of entrained mass to that of the structure. However, its significance was not evaluated, nor were methods for its calculation discussed. In many instances, such as heavy foundation structures, the relative entrained mass is very small. However, in the case of neutrally buoyant structures, such as ship hulls, the entrained mass may exceed the structural mass. From Eqs. 5.65 and 5.115 it is apparent that low-frequency resonance frequencies are inversely proportional to $\sqrt{1 + \epsilon}$ and that flexural impedances increase linearly with total mass. Accurate calculation of entrained mass therefore becomes increasingly important as its magnitude increases, and it is not surprising that naval architects have given extensive attention to this subject. At these frequencies, compressibility of the fluid is unimportant and classical incompressible hydrodynamics theory can be used.

As derived by Morse (1948) and others, the entrained mass of an infinitely long, rigid, cylindrical rod oscillating in a plane equals that of the displaced fluid. Thus, for a rigid cylinder,

$$\epsilon = \frac{\rho_o}{\rho_s} \ . \qquad (5.158)$$

However, actual structures are neither cylindrical, infinite nor rigid. Lewis (1929) assumed vibrational mode shapes to be the same as those in air and calculated the entrained mass for slender bodies of circular, rectangular and ship-like cross sections in incompressible fluids. His results are usually written in the form

$$m_e = \rho_o \frac{\pi b^2}{4} J_m(b/L)C(b/h, S/bh) \ , \qquad (5.159)$$

where $J_m$ accounts for finite flexural wavelengths and $C$ is a shape factor which equals unity for circular and elliptical cross sections. Chertock (1975) has obtained Lewis' results by a simpler formulation derived from the Helmholtz integral, Eq. 4.140. Townsin (1969) has matched other theoretical and measured values of $J$ for various order modes by

$$J_m \doteq 1.02 - 3\frac{b}{L}\left(1.2 - \frac{1}{m}\right) \ . \qquad (5.160)$$

Because of the complexity of ship structures and of their resultant vibrations, simple formulas for entrained mass are not likely to be accurate. On the other hand, values within ±10% are sufficiently accurate for most purposes.

## Hydrodynamic Damping

Damping due to fluid viscosity depends on section shape, amplitude of the motion, and the steady-state flow speed. Sharp edges increase this damping. Blake and Maga (1975) found values of the hydrodynamic loss factor to be from $10^{-2}$ to $10^{-1}$ for struts in water. Further discussion of this topic is beyond the scope of the present volume.

## Sound Radiation

As long as the cross-sectional circumference of a submerged beam is small, each section will radiate sound as an unbaffled piston. As discussed in Section 4.8, unbaffled structures radiate as dipoles at low frequencies, with radiation efficiencies proportional to $(ka_o)^3$. Since the various sections of a long beam vibrate out of phase, the radiation efficiency for beam vibrations should be even less than that for a free piston.

Yousri and Fahy (1973) and Kuhn and Morfey (1974) have calculated the sound radiated by a uniform beam, finding a strong dependence on both the aspect ratio of the beam and the ratio of the flexural wave speed to the speed of sound. Their results have been confirmed by experiments reported by Blake (1974). His data show $\eta_{rad} < 10^{-3}$ when $v_f < 0.5c_o$. In view of these results, one can conclude that radiation damping of structural vibrations is generally negligible for beam-like structures in comparison with hydrodynamic damping.

## 5.11 Flexural Resonances of Ship Hulls

Although the sound radiated is negligible, resonant flexural vibrations of ship hulls are of vital importance to naval architects both because of potential damage to the structure and because of adverse responses of humans exposed to such vibrations. The problem faced by a ship designer is to estimate both the driving and resonance frequencies and to take steps to prevent their coincidence.

The methods discussed in Section 5.6 pertaining to the calculation of resonance frequencies of non-uniform beams are all applicable to this problem. Using the terminology used earlier in this chapter, ship hulls are characterized by very large values of the shear parameter, $\Gamma$, and much smaller values of the relative rotatory inertia coefficient, $\alpha'$. Thus, examples of ship structures described by McGoldrick and Russo (1955) and Andersson and Norrand (1969) have values of $\Gamma$ greater than 200, while $\alpha'$ seldom exceeds 10. The reason for the high $\Gamma$ is that the effective shear-carrying area of a ship is a very small fraction of the total cross section.

There are two important practical consequences of the high values of $\Gamma$ found for ships. First, shear effects are experienced even at the lowest resonance, and calculations which ignore shear are seriously in error. Secondly, since $\alpha' << \Gamma$, it is quite safe to ignore rotatory inertia when calculating ship flexural motions. Thus, the approximations involved in Sections 5.4 and 5.7 in calculating flexural wave speeds and input impedances, in which $\alpha'$ was set equal to zero, are especially valid.

Methods used by naval architects to calculate flexural resonances of ships are described by Leibowitz and Kennard (1961) and by McGoldrick (1960). These include finite-element techniques involving both analog and digital computers. Generally, the ship is divided into 20 equal sections, each of which is assumed to form a Timoshenko beam element. Also, there are more than a dozen semi-empirical formulas which can be used to find the fundamental frequency. The higher order modes can then be assumed to be linearly related to the fundamental. One especially simple formula for the fundamental, based on measured natural frequencies of commercial ships, relates this frequency inversely to the length by

$$f_{fund} \doteq \frac{A}{L} \; (Hz) \; , \qquad (5.161)$$

where $A = 215$ if $L$ is in meters and $A = 700$ if $L$ is in feet.

The wave approach to resonance calculation described in Sections 5.5 and 5.6 would seem to be particularly well suited to this problem. The author has attempted to use this method to calculate the resonances of a specific ship with moderate success. The problem is to determine the phase shift caused by the ends. When the ends are each assumed to cause a 90° phase shift, as they would for a free-free uniform beam, frequencies calculated for the lowest order resonances are much too low. On the other hand, if it is assumed that the shear rigidity is zero at the ends and the phase shifts are zero, then these frequencies are somewhat too high. Based on this single attempt, it appears that the assumption of zero phase shift is more useful. However, more research needs to be done.

One advantage of the wave approach, as compared to finite-element methods, is that the ship can be divided into sections at natural boundaries. The flexural wave speed for each section can then be calculated and the total travel time found from

$$T = \sum_{i=1}^{N} \frac{\Delta L_i}{v_{f_i}} \quad . \tag{5.162}$$

Using the symbology of naval architecture, the reciprocal of the flexural wave speed, Eq. 5.44, can be calculated from

$$\frac{1}{v_f} \doteq \left[ \sqrt{\frac{\mu}{\omega^2 YI} + \left(\frac{\mu}{2KGS}\right)^2} + \frac{\mu}{2KGS} \right]^{1/2} \quad . \tag{5.163}$$

Since $v_f$ depends on frequency, the procedure used is to calculate $T$ for four or five frequencies covering the likely range of resonances and to plot $T$ vs $\omega$ or $f$. Since resonances occur when

$$T = \frac{m\pi + \overline{\Delta\phi}}{L\omega_m} \quad , \tag{5.164}$$

this expression for $T$ can also be plotted as a function of frequency for various values of $m$, and resonance frequencies are then those values for which the curves from Eq. 5.162 and 5.164 intersect.

It seems unlikely that more than five modes would occur with sufficient strength to be excited. For higher frequencies, attenuation due to both hydrodynamic damping and reflections at structural discontinuities would preclude the occurrence of flexural resonances that involve wave travel over the entire hull length. Instead, resonances involve vibrations of only part of the length of the ship. Such compartment resonances are usually dominant at frequencies above about 10 times that of the lowest flexural resonance.

## REFERENCES


Sections 5.1-5.5

Bishop, R.E.D. and Johnson, D.C., *The Mechanics of Vibration*, Cambridge University Press, Cambridge, 1960 (Chapters 6 and 7).

Budiansky, B. and Kruszewski, E.T., Transverse Vibrations of Hollow Thin-Walled Cylindrical Beams, *N.A.C.A. Tech. Rept. 1129*, 1953.

Cowper, G.R., The shear coefficient in Timoshenko's beam theory, *J. Appl. Mech., 33*, 335-350, 1966.

Cremer, L., The Propagation of Structure-Borne Sound, *Dept. of Scientific and Indust. Res. (London) Sponsored Res. Rept. Ser. B*, No. 1, 1950; also, *Acustica, 3*, 317-335, 1953.

Cremer, L., Heckl, M. and Ungar, E.E., *Structure-Borne Sound*, Springer-Verlag, New York, 1973 (Chapter 2).

Huang, T.C., The effect of rotatory inertia and of shear deformations on the frequency and normal mode equations of uniform beams with simple end conditions, *J. Appl. Mech., 28*, 579-584, 1961.

Junger, M.C., "Structure-Borne Noise," in *Structural Mechanics*, Pergamon Press, Oxford, 1960 (pp. 334-377).

Junger, M.C. and Feit, D., *Sound, Structures and Their Interaction*, M.I.T. Press, Cambridge, Mass., 1972 (Chapter 6).

Kinsler, L.E. and Frey, A.R., *Fundamentals of Acoustics*, 2nd Edit., Wiley, New York, 1962 (Chapter 3).

Leibowitz, R.C. and Kennard, E.H., Shear and Rotatory Inertia Effects on Beam Vibrations, *D.T.M.B. Rept. 1822*, July 1964.

Leonard, R.W. and Budiansky, B., On the Speed of Traveling Waves in Beams, *N.A.C.A. Tech. Note 2874*, Jan. 1953.

Lindsay, R.B., *Mechanical Radiation*, McGraw-Hill, New York, 1960 (Chapters 6 and 7).

Miklowitz, J., Flexural wave solutions of coupled equations representing the more exact theory of bending, *J. Appl. Mech., 20*, 511-514, 1953; *21*, 204-205, 1954.

Morse, P.M., *Vibration and Sound*, 2nd Edit., McGraw-Hill, New York, 1948 (Chapter 4).

Morse, P.M. and Ingard, K.U., *Theoretical Acoustics*, McGraw-Hill, New York, 1968 (Section 5.1).

Nelson, H.M., A universal dispersion curve for flexural wave propagation in plates and bars, *J. Sound and Vibr., 18*, 93-100, 1971.

Plass, H.J., Jr., Some solutions of the Timoshenko beam equation for short-pulse loading, *J. Appl. Mech., 25*, 379-385, 1958.

Rayleigh, Lord, *Theory of Sound*, Vol. I, 2nd Edit., London, 1894; Dover, New York, 1945 (Chapter 8).

Ripperger, E.A. and Abramson, H.N., A study of the propagation of flexural waves in elastic beams, *J. Appl. Mech., 24*, 431-434; *25*, 153-155, 1957.

Skudrzyk, E., *Simple and Complex Vibratory Systems*, The Pennsylvania State University Press, University Park, Pa., 1968 (Chapter 6).

Snowdon, J.A., *Vibration and Shock in Damped Mechanical Systems*, Wiley, New York, 1968 (Chapters 7-11).

Timoshenko, S., On the correction for shear of the differential equation for transverse vibrations of prismatic bars, *Phil. Mag., 41*, 744-746, 1921.

Timoshenko, S., *Vibration Problems in Engineering*, 3rd Edit., Van Nostrand, Princeton, 1955 (Chapter 6).

Timoshenko, S., Young, D.H. and Weaver, W., Jr., *Vibration Problems in Engineering*, 4th Edit., Wiley, New York, 1974 (Chapter 5).

Traill-Nash, R.W. and Collar, A.R., "The effects of shear flexibility and rotatory inertia on the bending vibrations of beams," *Quart, J. Mech. and Appl. Math, 6*, 186-222, 1953.

Wang, T.M., Natural frequencies of continuous Timoshenko beams, *J. Sound and Vibr., 13*, 409-414, 1970.

## Section 5.6

Benscoter, S.U. and MacNeal, R.H., Introduction to Electric-Circuit Analogies for Beam Analysis, *N.A.C.A. Tech. Note 2785*, 1952.

Cranch, E.T. and Adler, A.A., Bending vibrations of variable section beams, *J. Appl. Mech., 23*, 103-108, 1956.

Davis, R., Henshell, R.D. and Warburton, G.B., A Timoshenko beam element, *J. Sound and Vibr., 22*, 475-487, 1972.

Gaines, J.H. and Volterra, E., Transverse vibrations of cantilever bars of variable cross section, *J.A.S.A., 39*, 674-679, 1966.

Leibowitz, R.C. and Kennard, E.H., Theory of Freely Vibrating Non-Uniform Beams, *D.T.M.B. Rept. 1317*, May 1961.

Mabie, H.H. and Rogers, C.B., Transverse vibrations of tapered beams with end loads, *J.A.S.A., 36*, 463-469, 1964.

Mabie, H.H. and Rogers, C.B., Transverse vibrations of double-tapered cantilever beams, *J.A.S.A., 51*, 1771-1774, 1972; and *55*, 986-991, 1974.

MacNeal, R.H., *Electric Circuit Analogies for Elastic Structures*, Wiley, New York, 1962 (Chapter 8).

Martin, A.I., Some integrals relating to the vibration of a cantilever beam and approximation for the effect of taper on overtone frequencies, *Aero. Quarterly, 7*, 109-123, 1956.

McCann, G.D. and MacNeal, R.H., Beam vibration analysis with the electric-analog computer, *J. Appl. Mech., 17*, 13-26, 1950.

McGoldrick, R.T., Ship Vibration, *D.T.M.B. Rept. 1451*, Dec. 1960 (Chapters 3 and 4).

Russell, W.T. and MacNeal, R.H., An improved electrical analogy for the analysis of beams in bending, *J. Appl. Mech., 20*, 349-354, 1953.

Trent, H.M., An equivalent circuit for a vibrating beam which includes shear motions, *J.A.S.A., 22*, 355-357, 1950.

## Sections 5.7 and 5.8

Crandall, S.H. and Mark, W.D., *Random Vibration in Mechanical Systems*, Academic Press, New York, 1963.

Cremer, L., Heckl, M. and Ungar, E.E., *op. cit.* (Chapter 4).

Myklestad, N.O., The concept of complex damping, *J. Appl. Mech., 19*, 284-286, 1952.

Nelson, H.M., The modal density for flexural vibration of thick plates and bars, *J. Sound and Vibr., 25*, 225-261, 1972.

Skudrzyk, E., *op. cit.* (Chapters 1, 6, 7, 9 and 10).

Skudrzyk, E., Vibrations of a system with a finite or an infinite number of resonances, *J.A.S.A., 30*, 1140-1152, 1958.

Snowdon, J.C., *op. cit.* (Chapters 7-11).

Snowdon, J.C., Transverse vibration of free-free beams, *J.A.S.A., 35*, 47-52, 1963; *35*, 1997-2006, 1963; *37*, 240-249, 1965.

Timoshenko, S., Young, D.H. and Weaver, W., Jr., *op. cit.* (Section 5.13).

Ungar, E.E., Statistical energy analysis of vibrating systems, *J. Engin. for Industry*, 626-632, 1967.

Wright, D.V., "Impedance Analysis of Distributed Mechanical Systems," Chapter 3 in *Mechanical Impedance Methods for Mechanical Vibrations*, R. Plunkett (Ed.), A.S.M.E., 1958.

## Section 5.9

Adams, R.D., "The damping characteristics of certain steels, cast irons and other metals," *J. Sound and Vibr., 23*, 199-216, 1972.

Bobrovnitskii, Yu. I. and Maslov, V.P., Propagation of flexural waves along a beam with periodic point loading, *Sov. Phys.-Acoustics, 12*, 150-154, 1966.

Brillouin, L., *Wave Propagation in Periodic Structures*, Dover, New York, 1953.

Cremer, L., Heckl, M. and Ungar, E.E., *op. cit.* (Chapters 3 and 5).

Cremer, L., Calculation of sound propagation in structures, *Acustica, 3*, 317-335, 1953; *6*, Beihefte, 59, 1956 (in German).

DiTaranto, R.A., Theory of vibratory bending for elastic and viscoelastic layered finite-length beams, *J. Appl. Mech., 32*, 881-886, 1965.

DiTaranto, R.A. and Blasingame, W., Composite damping of vibrating sandwich beams, *J. Engin. for Industry, 89B*, 633-638, 1967.

Ferry, J.D., *Viscoelastic Properties of Polymers*, Wiley, New York, 1961.

Grootenhuis, P., The control of vibrations with viscoelastic materials, *J. Sound and Vibr., 11*, 421-433, 1970.

Hamme, R.N., "Vibration Damping," Chapter 14 of *Handbook of Noise Control*, C.M. Harris (Ed.), McGraw-Hill, New York, 1957.

Hamme, R.N., The Concept of Damping of Structureborne Sound and Vibration for Noise Control, *Geiger and Hamme Rept. USN-1*, April 1961.

Harris, C.M. and Crede, C.E. (Ed.), *Shock and Vibration Handbook*, McGraw-Hill, New York, 1961 (Chapters 3, 6, 10, 30, 32, 33, 35, 36 and 37).

Hixson, E.L., Application of mechanical equivalent circuits to vibration problems, *Noise Control, 7*, 24-35, 1961.

Junger, M., "Structure-Borne Noise," in *Structural Mechanics*, Pergamon Press, Oxford, 1960 (pp. 334-377).

Kerwin, E.M., Jr., Damping of flexural waves by a constrained visco-elastic layer, *J.A.S.A., 31*, 952-962, 1959.

Klyukin, I.I., Attenuation of flexural waves in rods and plates by means of resonance vibrating systems, *Sov. Phys.-Acoustics, 6*, 209-215, 1960; and *Sudostroyeniye, 12*, 4-8, 1961.

Klyukin, I.I., *Control of Noise and Sonic Vibration in Ships*, Sudpromgiz, Leningrad, 1961; translated U.S. Dept. of Commerce, Wash., 1963 (JPRS: 18,177; OTS-63-21340) (Chapters 12-14).

Knyazev, A.S. and Tartakovskii, B.D., Application of electromechanical feedback for damping of flexural vibrations in rods, *Sov. Phys.-Acoustics, 11*, 150-154, 1965; *12*, 36-41, 1966; *13*, 115-117, 1967.

Kurtze, G., Bending-wave propagation in multilayer plates, *J.A.S.A., 31*, 1183-1201, 1959.

Lazan, B.J., "Energy Dissipation Mechanisms in Structures, with Particular Reference to Material Damping," Section 1 of *Structural Damping*, J.E. Ruzicka (Ed.), A.S.M.E., 1959.

Lazan, B.J., *Damping of Materials and Members in Structural Mechanics*, Pergamon Press, Oxford, 1968.

Maslov, V.P. and Tartakovskii, B.D., Transmission of flexural waves through an arbitrary intermediate rod, *Sov. Phys.-Acoustics, 7*, 50-55, 1961.

Mead, D.J., "The Damping of Jet-Excited Structures," Chapter 18 in *Noise and Acoustic Fatigue in Aeronautics*, E.J. Richards and D.J. Mead (Ed.), Wiley, London, 1968.

Mead, D.J., Free wave propagation in periodically supported infinite beams, *J. Sound and Vibr., 11*, 181-197, 1970.

Mead, D.J., The damping properties of elastically supported sandwich plates, *J. Sound and Vibr., 24*, 275-295, 1972.

Muster, D. and Plunkett, R., "Isolation of Vibrations," Chapter 18 in *Noise Reduction*, L.L. Beranek (Ed.), McGraw-Hill, New York, 1960.

Nolle, A.W., Dynamic mechanical properties of rubberlike materials, *J. Polymer Sci., 5*, 1-54, 1950.

Oberst, H., Becker, G.W. and Frankenfeld, K., Über die Dämpfung der Biegeschwingungen dünner Bleche durch fest haftende Beläge, *Acustica, 2*, Beihefte *4*, 181-194, 1952; *4*, Beihefte *1*, 433-444, 1954.

Oberst, H., Werkstoffe mit extrem hoher innerer Dämpfung, *VDI-Berichte, 8*, 100-109, 1956; *Acustica, 6*, Beihefte *1*, 144-153, 1956.

Plunkett, R., Interaction between vibratory machine and its foundation, *Noise Control, 4*, 18-22, 1958.

Rader, D., and Mao, M., Flexural pulse propagation in nonuniform elastic bars by geometric acoustics, *Int. J. of Solids and Structures, 7*, 1505-1522, 1971.

Rockwell, R.H. and Lawther, J.M., Theoretical and experimental results on active vibration dampers, *J.A.S.A., 36*, 1507-1515, 1964.

Ross, D., Ungar, E.E., and Kerwin, E.M., Jr., "Damping of Plate Flexural Vibrations by Means of Viscoelastic Laminae," Section 3 of *Structural Damping*, J.E. Ruzicka (Ed.), A.S.M.E., 1959; Pergamon Press, New York, 1960 (pp. 50-87).

Ruzicka, J.E., Damping structural resonances using viscoelastic shear damping mechanisms, *J. Engin. for Industry, 83B*, 403-424, 1961.

Ruzicka, J.E. and Derby, T.F., *Influence of Damping in Vibration Isolation*, Shock and Vibration Monograph 7, U.S. Naval Res. Lab., Washington, 1971.

Sen Gupta, G., Flexural wave modes of periodically supported beams, *J. Sound and Vibr., 13*, 89-104, 1970.

Skudrzyk, E., *op. cit.* (Chapters 2, 3 and 13).

Snowdon, J.C., *op. cit.* (Chapters 1-5, 10 and 13).

Snowdon, J.C., Rubberlike materials, their internal damping and role in vibration isolation, *J. Sound and Vibr., 2*, 175-193, 1965.

Snowdon, J.C., Isolation and absorption of machinery vibration, *Acustica, 28*, 307-317, 1973.

Snowdon, J.C. and Ungar, E.E. (Ed.), *Isolation of Mechanical Vibration, Impact and Noise*, A.S.M.E., 1973.

Soliman, J.I. and Hallam, M.G., Vibration isolation between non-rigid machines and non-rigid foundations, *J. Sound and Vibr., 8*, 329-351, 1968.

Sykes, A.O., The effects of machine and foundation resilience and of wave propagation on the isolation provided by vibration mounts, *Trans. S.A.E., 66*, 533-548, 1958; also, *D.T.M.B. Repts. 1094* Oct. 1957 and *1276* Jan. 1959.

Sykes, A.O., Isolation of vibration, *Noise Control, 6*, 115-130, 1960.

Ungar, E.E. and Ross, D., Damping of Flexural Vibrations by Alternate Visco-elastic and Elastic Layers, *Proc. Fourth Annual Conf. on Solid Mechanics*, Univ. of Texas, 1959 (pp. 468-487); also, *WADC Tech. Rept. 59-509*, Nov. 1959.

Ungar, E.E., Loss factors of viscoelastically damped beam structures, *J.A.S.A., 34*, 1082-1089, 1962.

Ungar, E.E. and Dietrick, C.W., High-frequency vibration isolation, *J. Sound and Vibr., 4*, 224-241, 1966.

Ungar, E.E., "Damping of Panels," Chapter 14 in *Noise and Vibration Control*, L.L. Beranek (Ed.), McGraw-Hill, New York, 1971 (pp. 434-475).

## Sections 5.10 and 5.11

Andersson, G. and Norrand, K., A method for the calculation of vertical vibration with several nodes, and some other aspects of ship vibration, *Quart. Trans. Royal Inst. of Naval Arch., 111*, 367-383, 1969.

Blake, W.K., The radiation from free-free beams in air and water, *J. Sound and Vibr., 33*, 427-450, 1974.

Blake, W.K. and Maga, L.J., On the flow-excited vibrations of cantilever struts in water, *J.A.S.A., 57*, 610-625, 1975; also, *N.S.R.D.C. Rept. 4087*, Dec. 1973.

Chertock, G., Sound radiation by low-frequency vibrations of slender bodies, *J.A.S.A., 57*, 1007-1016, 1975.

Kuhn, G.F. and Morfey, C.L., Radiation efficiency of simply supported slender beams below coincidence, *J. Sound and Vibr., 33*, 241-245, 1974.

Landweber, L., Natural frequencies of cylinders and bodies of revolution vibrating transversely in a fluid, *J. Ship Research, 11*, 143-150, 1967; *15*, 97-114, 1971.

Leibowitz, R.C. and Kennard, E.H., Theory of Freely Vibrating Nonuniform Beams Including Methods of Solution and Applications to Ships, *D.T.M.B. Rept. 1317*, May 1961.

Lewis, F.M., The inertia of water surrounding a vibrating ship, *Trans. Soc. Naval Arch. and Mar. Eng., 37*, 1-20, 1929.

McGoldrick, R.T. and Russo, V.L., Hull investigation on SS Gopher Mariner, *Trans. Soc. Naval Arch. and Mar. Eng., 63*, 436-494, 1955; also *D.T.M.B. Rept. 1060*, July 1956.

McGoldrick, R.T., Ship Vibration, *D.T.M.B. Rept. 1451*, Dec. 1960 (Chapters 3-6, Appendix A).

Misra, P.N., Transverse vibrations of a ship hull in ideal fluid, determined through variational methods, *J. Ship Research, 18*, 185-202, 1974.

Morse, P.M., *op. cit.* (Section 26).

Townsin, R.L., Virtual mass reduction factors for ship vibration calculations, *Quart. Trans. Royal Inst. Naval Arch., 111*, 385-397, 1969.

Yousri, S.N. and Fahy, F.J., Sound radiation from transversely vibrating unbaffled beams, *J. Sound and Vibr., 26*, 437-439, 1973.

Yousri, S.N. and Fahy, F.J., An analysis of acoustic power radiated into a reverberation chamber by a transversely vibrating slender bar, *J. Sound and Vibr., 32*, 311-325, 1974.

# CHAPTER 6

# RADIATION BY PLATE FLEXURAL VIBRATIONS

Most underwater sound originating inside a marine vehicle is radiated by flexural vibrations of hull plates; this is especially true for frequencies above 100 Hz. The subject of plate radiation, along with the important topic of structural vibration, was first understood in Germany in the 1940's under the leadership of L. Cremer. Much of the material presented in this chapter is based on his work and that of a generation of investigators whom he influenced.

## 6.1 Plate Flexural Vibrations

In most recent analyses of plate flexural wave radiation the elastic equations for plate vibrations and the acoustic wave equation are treated as a system of coupled equations using solutions that are made to match at the plate surface. In this approach, the effect of the fluid is considered to be that of a load on the vibrating plate. Before considering the coupled problem, we will develop the applicable equations for plate flexural vibrations *in vacuo*.

### Bending Rigidity of Plates

When classical elasticity theory is applied to solid plates, it is found that longitudinal waves have a phase speed given by

$$c_p = \sqrt{\frac{Y}{\rho(1 - \sigma^2)}} = \frac{c_\ell}{\sqrt{1 - \sigma^2}} = c_s\sqrt{\frac{2}{1 - \sigma}} \,, \tag{6.1}$$

as was discussed in Section 5.2. The same classical theory leads to the result that the bending rigidity of a solid plate is

$$B_p = \frac{Y\kappa^2 S}{\sqrt{1 - \sigma^2}} = \frac{Yh^3}{12\sqrt{1 - \sigma^2}} = \frac{\rho_s c_p^2 h^3}{12} \tag{6.2}$$

per unit width. In deriving the equations for plate flexural motions from those developed for beams, these expressions replace $YI$ wherever it occurs.

### Thick Plate Bending Equations

The exact elasticity equations for bending of thick plates are very complex. A more tractable approximate equation analogous to that of Timoshenko for beams was derived by Mindlin (1951). Skudrzyk (1968) showed Mindlin's equation to be equivalent to the Timoshenko beam equation with $B$ as given by Eq. 6.2, $\alpha' = 1$ and $K$ related to $\sigma$ by

$$K_p \doteq 0.76 \left( 1 + \frac{2}{5} \sigma \right) . \tag{6.3}$$

The shear parameter for plates is given by

$$\Gamma_p = \frac{Y}{KG(1 - \sigma^2)} = \frac{2}{K_p(1 - \sigma)} \doteq 2.65 \left( 1 + \frac{3}{5} \sigma + \frac{3}{4} \sigma^2 \right) . \tag{6.4}$$

For a typical metal plate, $K_p \doteq 0.85$ and $\Gamma_p \doteq 3.3$.

With the above substitutions, the differential equation for plates corresponding to Eq. 5.26 can be written

$$\mu' \ddot{w} + \frac{\rho_s c_p^2}{12} \nabla^2 h^3 \nabla^2 w - 4.3 \rho_s \frac{h^3}{12} \nabla^2 \ddot{w} + \frac{3.3 \mu' h^2}{12 c_p^2} \ddddot{w} = p(x,y,t) , \tag{6.5}$$

where $\mu'$ is the mass per unit area, given by $\rho_s h$. The gradient operator, $\nabla$, replaces each derivative with respect to $x$, since motions propagate in two dimensions. It is assumed that changes of thickness occur relatively slowly, making spatial derivatives of thickness negligible. The bending equation corresponding to Eq. 5.28 can be written

$$\ddot{w} + \frac{c_p^2 h^2}{12} \nabla^4 w - \frac{4.3}{12} h^2 \nabla^2 \ddot{w} + \frac{3.3}{12} \frac{h^2}{c_p^2} \ddddot{w} = \frac{p}{\mu'} . \tag{6.6}$$

**Flexural Wave Speed**

Assuming an harmonic disturbance, the homogeneous equation for flexural motions in plates can be expressed as an equation for $k_i$, as done for beams by Eq. 5.31. The corresponding equation is

$$\omega^2 - c_p^2 \frac{h^2}{12} k_i^4 + (\Gamma_p + 1) \frac{h^2}{12} \omega^2 k_i^2 - \frac{\Gamma_p}{c_p^2} \frac{h^2}{12} \omega^4 = 0 . \tag{6.7}$$

As with the case for beams, the two real solutions for $k_i$ represent waves and the two imaginary solutions account for distortions at discontinuities. Assuming real values for $k_i$, Eq. 6.7 can be transformed into an equation for the flexural wave speed,

$$\left( 1 - \Gamma_p \left( \frac{\omega}{\Omega_p} \right)^2 \right) \left( \frac{v_f}{c_p} \right)^4 + (\Gamma_p + 1) \left( \frac{\omega}{\Omega_p} \right)^2 \left( \frac{v_f}{c_p} \right)^2 - \left( \frac{\omega}{\Omega_p} \right)^2 = 0 , \tag{6.8}$$

which corresponds to Eq. 5.35. The reference angular frequency, $\Omega_p$, is given by

$$\Omega_p \equiv \frac{c_p \sqrt{12}}{h} . \tag{6.9}$$

At low frequencies only the first two terms of Eq. 6.7 are important, and the expression for the flexural wave speed is then similar to that given by Eqs. 5.51 and 5.53 for bars,

$$v_{f\ell} \doteq c_p \sqrt{\frac{\omega}{\Omega_p}} = \sqrt{\frac{\omega h c_p}{\sqrt{12}}} = \frac{k_f h c_p}{\sqrt{12}} \; . \tag{6.10}$$

The high-frequency limit for $v_f$ is

$$v_{f_h} \doteq c_s \sqrt{K_p} \doteq 0.87 \left(1 + \frac{1}{5}\sigma\right) c_s \doteq 0.92 c_s \; , \tag{6.11}$$

which is about 57% of the longitudinal wave speed, $c_\ell$.

In the intermediate-frequency range, the flexural wave speed correction for plates is essentially the same as that for solid rectangular bars, as given by Eqs. 5.54, 5.55 and 5.56, and as plotted in Figs. 5.7 and 5.8.

**Plate Vibrations**

Plate vibrations are often more complex than those of beams since the motion is a function of two spatial variables. However, for relatively narrow strips the motion can be treated as straight-crested and the equations derived for beams can be used, with $c_\ell$ replaced by $c_p$. If the direction of propagation of the wave has direction cosines $n_x$ and $n_y$, then

$$k_f = \sqrt{k_{f_x}^2 + k_{f_y}^2} \; , \tag{6.12}$$

where $k_{f_x} = n_x k_f$ and $k_{f_y} = n_y k_f$. More often the plate extends in both directions and exciting forces produce motions that spread out uniformly in all directions.

Just as in Chapter 2 we treated acoustic waves from point sources in terms of symmetrical spherical waves, so we can analyze flexural waves spreading out from concentrated sources on plates as cylindrical waves in cylindrical (polar) coordinates with circular symmetry. The corresponding Laplacian in polar coordinates is

$$\nabla^2 = \frac{\partial^2}{\partial r^2} + \frac{1}{r}\frac{\partial}{\partial r} \; , \tag{6.13}$$

and the Helmholtz form of the wave equation, Eq. 2.12, becomes

$$\frac{\partial^2 \underline{\phi}}{\partial r^2} + \frac{1}{r}\frac{\partial \underline{\phi}}{\partial r} + k^2 \underline{\phi} = 0 \; . \tag{6.14}$$

This is a form of *Bessel's equation*, a solution of which is

$$\underline{\phi} = \underline{A} J_o(kr) \; , \tag{6.15}$$

where $J_o$ is a *Bessel function* of the first kind and zero order and has the shape of a damped cosine. For small values of $kr$,

$$J_o(kr) \doteq 1 - \left(\frac{kr}{2}\right)^2 \qquad (kr << 1) \ , \tag{6.16}$$

while for very large values of the argument,

$$J_o(kr) \doteq \sqrt{\frac{2}{\pi kr}} \cos\left(kr - \frac{\pi}{4}\right) \qquad (kr >> 1) \ . \tag{6.17}$$

It can be shown that the harmonic form of the plate equation is related to the Bessel equation of the form of Eq. 6.14. At low frequencies the plate equation reduces to

$$\mu' \omega^2 \underline{w} - \frac{c_p^2 \rho_s h^3}{12} \nabla^4 \underline{w} = - \underline{p} \ . \tag{6.18}$$

As in Eq. 5.59, the wave number may be expressed by

$$k_{f_o}^2 = \frac{\omega}{c_p \kappa} = \sqrt{12} \ \frac{\omega}{c_p h} \ . \tag{6.19}$$

Substituting for $\omega$, Eq. 6.18 can be written

$$\mu' c_p^2 \frac{h^2}{12} \left(\nabla^4 - k_{f_o}^4\right) \underline{w} = \underline{p} \ . \tag{6.20}$$

Setting $p = 0$, the homogeneous equation can then be expressed as two simultaneous equations:

$$\left(\nabla^2 + k_{f_o}^2\right) w_1 = 0 \tag{6.21}$$

and

$$\left(\nabla^2 - k_{f_o}^2\right) w_2 = 0 \ . \tag{6.22}$$

The first of these is a Bessel equation when expressed in cylindrical coordinates and has a solution of the form of Eq. 6.15. The second has as its solution Bessel functions of imaginary arguments. It follows that $w_1$ and $w_2$ are the wave and near-field components of the displacement, $w$.

Dyer (1960) and Skudrzyk (1968) have shown that the homogeneous form of the Mindlin-Timoshenko thick plate equation is equivalent to three simultaneous equations. These are

$$\left(\nabla^2 + k_f^2\right) w_1 = 0 \ , \tag{6.23}$$

$$\left(\nabla^2 - \gamma^2\right) w_2 = 0 \tag{6.24}$$

and

$$\left(\nabla^2 + k_s^2\right) H = 0 \ . \tag{6.25}$$

In these equations $k_f$ and $\gamma$ are related to $k_{f_o}$ by Eqs. 5.67 and 5.68, $H$ is a vector potential of the shear motion in the plane of the plate, and

$$k_s^2 = K_p k_{f_o}^2 \left[ 2\delta_p - \frac{\Gamma_p}{2\delta_p} \right] , \tag{6.26}$$

where $\delta_p$ is defined by

$$\delta_p \equiv \frac{\Gamma_p}{2} \left( \frac{\omega}{\Omega_p} \right) = \frac{\Gamma_p}{2} \left( \frac{k_{f_o} h}{\sqrt{12}} \right)^2 \doteq \frac{1}{2} \left( \frac{k_{f_o} h}{2} \right)^2 . \tag{6.27}$$

It can be seen from the above that $w_1$, $w_2$ and $H$ are all expressible by Bessel functions of either real or imaginary arguments.

**Input Impedance**

The derivation of the input impedance for a point force exciting a thin plate involves several types of Bessel functions and considerable manipulation. The approximate expression for the characteristic impedance is surprisingly simple, being

$$Z_i \doteq 8\sqrt{\mu' B_p} = \frac{4}{\sqrt{3}} \rho_s c_p h^2 = \frac{4}{\sqrt{3}} \mu' c_p h . \tag{6.28}$$

This expression, derived by Cremer (1950), is entirely real and is independent of frequency. Measurements reported by Skudrzyk et al (1961) and Snowdon (1974) of input impedances of resonant plates confirm that the characteristic impedance, as given by the geometric mean of resonant and anti-resonant minima and maxima, is in good agreement with that calculated from Eq. 6.28.

## 6.2 Fluid Loading

In writing the differential equations for plate flexural vibrations the forcing function was expressed as a pressure. This pressure, $p$, represents the sum of any applied external forcing function and the reaction on the plate of the fluid in contact with it. In this section we will consider the effect of fluid loading on a plate that experiences no other external forces.

**Boundary Conditions**

Fluid in contact with a plate shares the plate's motion at all points of contact. Boundary conditions are therefore the same as those considered in Section 2.5 dealing with sound transmission between two media. In this case the two media are the vibrating plate and a fluid on one side of it. The wave numbers corresponding to this vibration, $k_f$ in the plate and $k_o$ in the fluid, will usually be different because the speeds of waves in the two media are different. However, by Snell's law, the component of the wave number for the fluid that is parallel to the plate must match that of the flexural wave in the plate. From Eq. 2.14, the component of $k_o$ in the plane of the plate is

$$k_{x,y} \equiv \sqrt{k_x^2 + k_y^2} = \sqrt{k_o^2 - k_z^2}\ , \tag{6.29}$$

and this must equal $k_f$. It follows that

$$k_z = \sqrt{k_o^2 - k_f^2}\ . \tag{6.30}$$

Assuming straight-crested waves in the plate, any waves in the fluid will be plane waves, for which the acoustic velocity will be related to the acoustic pressure by Eq. 2.68, namely,

$$\mathrm{v}' = \left|\vec{\mathrm{v}}'\right| = \frac{p'}{\rho_o c_o}\ . \tag{6.31}$$

The normal component of the acoustic particle velocity must equal the velocity of the plate if the two are to remain in contact, hence

$$\dot{w} = \mathrm{v}_z' = \frac{\mathrm{v}_z'}{\mathrm{v}'}\,\frac{p'}{\rho_o c_o}\ . \tag{6.32}$$

The ratio of the normal component to the full acoustic particle speed equals the ratio of $k_z$ to $k_o$. It follows from Eqs. 6.30 and 6.32 that

$$\underline{p} = -\underline{p}' = -i\omega\rho_o c_o \frac{k_o}{\sqrt{k_o^2 - k_f^2}}\,\underline{w}\ , \tag{6.33}$$

which result has a number of important consequences that are dependent on the relative values of $k_o$ and $k_f$.

### Coincidence

When $k_o = k_f$, the fluid loading effect on flexural vibrations of an undamped plate approaches infinity. This corresponds to equality of the speeds of sound and flexural waves and was named the *coincidence effect* by Cremer (1942). As explained by Yaneske (1972), coincidence describes the maximum spatial coupling that can occur between waves in a plate and those in a fluid medium in contact with it. Actually, as noted by Kurtze and Bolt (1959), exact coincidence cannot occur since the implied infinite fluid loading would prevent the flexural wave speed from equalling that of the fluid. Nevertheless, the coincidence frequency is an important concept in dealing with plate radiation and fluid loading.

The *coincidence frequency*, $f_c$, is the frequency at which the flexural wave speed of a plate vibrating without fluid load would equal the sound speed in the fluid medium. For thin plates, using Eq. 6.10 for the flexural wave speed,

$$\omega_c = 2\pi f_c \doteq c_o^2\sqrt{\frac{\mu'}{B_p}} \doteq \frac{\sqrt{12}\,c_o^2}{hc_p}\ . \tag{6.34}$$

The corresponding wave number is

$$k_c \doteq \sqrt{12}\,\frac{c_o}{c_p h} . \tag{6.35}$$

For metal plates in air ($c_o \doteq 340$ m/sec and $c_p \doteq 5300$ m/sec),

$$f_c \doteq \frac{12}{h} \quad (air) , \tag{6.36}$$

where $h$ is the plate thickness in meters. For metal plates in water, the thick-plate intermediate-frequency correction, Eq. 5.54, must be used, and the result is

$$f_c \doteq \frac{275}{h} \quad (water) , \tag{6.37}$$

At frequencies other than coincidence, flexural wave speeds are either greater or less than the speed of sound in the fluid. It is sometimes useful to express the relative speed in terms of a *flexural wave Mach number*, given by

$$M_f \equiv \frac{v_f}{c_o} = \frac{k_o}{k_f} \doteq \frac{k_f}{k_c} \doteq \sqrt{\frac{\omega}{\omega_c}} , \tag{6.38}$$

where the last two relationships for coincidence wave number and frequency apply only when thin plate assumptions are valid.

**Entrained Mass**

Below coincidence $k_o < k_f$, and Eq. 6.33 for the pressure attributable to fluid loading becomes

$$\underline{p} = \frac{\rho_o \omega^2 \underline{w}}{\sqrt{k_f^2 - k_o^2}} . \tag{6.39}$$

This has the effect of adding a second mass term to Eq. 6.18, which equation now becomes

$$\left( \mu' + \frac{\rho_o}{\sqrt{k_f^2 - k_o^2}} \right) \omega^2 \underline{w} - \frac{\mu' c_p^2 h^2}{12} \nabla^4 \underline{w} = 0 . \tag{6.40}$$

Substituting for $c_p h$ from Eq. 6.19, this can be written

$$(1 + \epsilon)\underline{w} - \frac{1}{k_{f_o}^4} \nabla^4 \underline{w} = 0 , \tag{6.41}$$

where $\epsilon$ is the entrained mass and is given by

$$\epsilon = \frac{\rho_o}{\mu'\sqrt{k_f^2 - k_o^2}} = \frac{\rho_o}{\rho_s k_f h\sqrt{1 - (k_o/k_f)^2}} \doteq \frac{\rho_o c_p}{\sqrt{12}\rho_s c_o} \frac{1}{M_f\sqrt{1 - M_f^2}} . \tag{6.42}$$

The relative entrained mass is thus a function of the densities and sound speeds of the two media and of the relative Mach number. Table 6.1 lists values of the media constants for aluminum and

Table 6.1

$$\frac{\rho_o c_p}{\sqrt{12}\rho_s c_o}$$

| Metal | Fluid: Air $\rho_o = 1.21, c_o = 340$ | Fluid: Water $\rho_o = 1000, c_o = 1480$ |
|---|---|---|
| Alum. $\rho_s = 2700$, $c_p = 5400$ | 0.002055 | 0.390 |
| Steel $\rho_s = 7800$, $c_p = 5250$ | 0.000692 | 0.1313 |

steel plates in air and water, and Fig. 6.1 is a plot of the Mach number dependence. The entrained mass at first decreases with increasing frequency to a minimum at $M_f \doteq 0.7$ and then increases rapidly near coincidence.

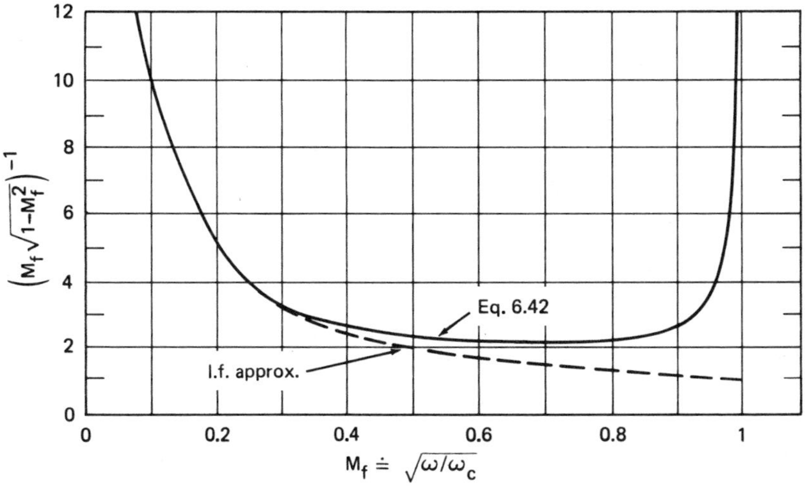


Fig. 6.1. Relative Entrained Mass Function

The entrained mass acts as a reactive load on the plate. From Eq. 4.10, the specific radiation reactance is

$$\sigma_x \equiv \frac{X_r'}{\rho_o c_o} = \frac{\mu' \epsilon \omega}{\rho_o c_o} = \frac{M_f}{\sqrt{1 - M_f^2}} , \tag{6.43}$$

which function is plotted in Fig. 6.2. Calculations of the flexural wave speed of a fluid-loaded plate should include the effects of entrained mass, as indicated in Section 5.4 for beams.

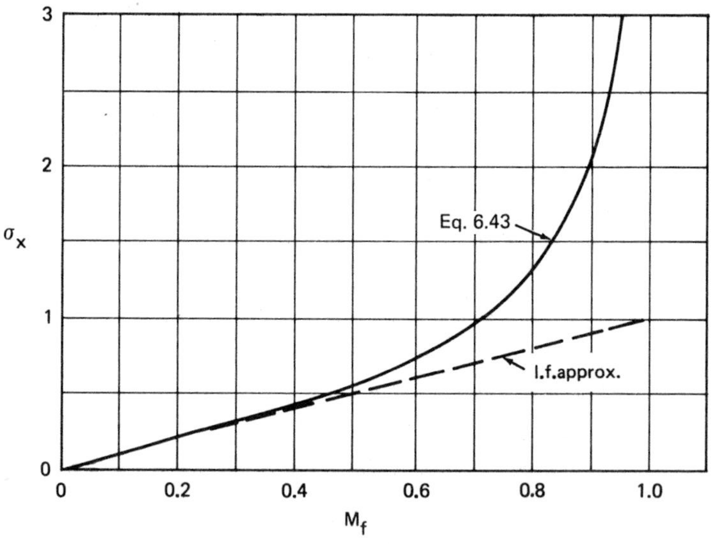


Fig. 6.2. Specific Radiation Reactance of Entrained Mass

**Radiation**

Above the coincidence frequency, the effect of fluid loading changes from that of an entrained mass to that of a radiation resistance and sound is radiated into the fluid. Thus, for $k_o > k_f$ the expression for the fluid pressure given by Eq. 6.33 is imaginary, representing radiation. It can be written as

$$\underline{p} = - i\omega^2 \mu' \beta \frac{M_f}{\sqrt{M_f^2 - 1}} \underline{w} , \tag{6.44}$$

where

$$\beta \equiv \frac{\rho_o c_o}{\omega \mu'} = \frac{\rho_o c_o}{\omega \rho_s h} = \left( \frac{\rho_o c_p}{\sqrt{12} \rho_s c_o} \right) \left( \frac{\omega_c'}{\omega} \right) \tag{6.45}$$

is the ratio of the specific radiation resistance of the fluid to the mass reactance of the plate per unit area. The frequency $\omega_c'$ is the low-frequency approximate value of the coincidence frequency as given by Eq. 6.34. The effect on the plate of fluid loading above coincidence is thus that of a radiation resistance. Equation 6.18 can be written

$$(1 - i\eta_r)\underline{w} - \frac{1}{k_{f_o}^4} \nabla^4 \underline{w} = 0 , \qquad (6.46)$$

where

$$\eta_r = \beta \frac{M_f}{\sqrt{M_f^2 - 1}} \qquad (6.47)$$

is the loss factor for sound radiation into the fluid. This function is plotted in Fig. 6.3. The motion of the plate above coincidence is damped by a loss factor, $\eta_T$, given by the sum of the radiation

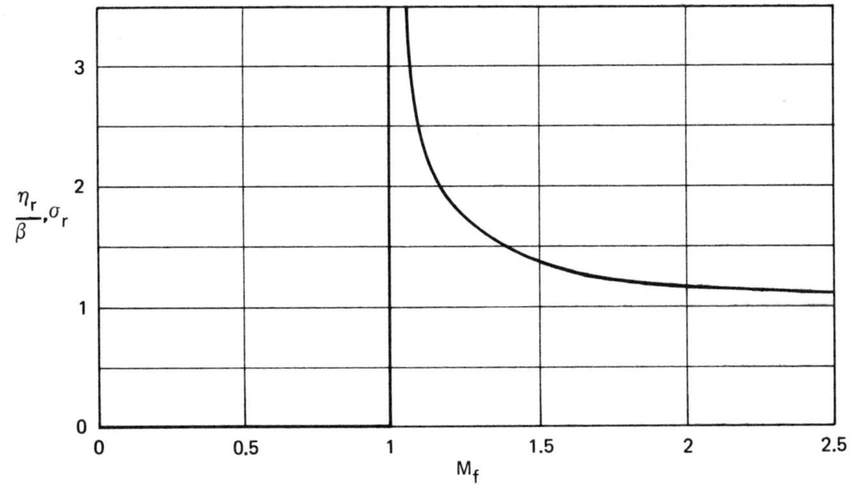


Fig. 6.3. Normalized Radiation Load Factor for Flat Plates

and structural damping loss factors. Since all power transmitted to the structure is eventually converted into sound and heat, the radiation efficiency is

$$\eta_{rad} = \frac{\eta_r}{\eta_T} = \frac{\eta_r}{\eta_r + \eta_s} . \qquad (6.48)$$

Radiation only occurs at relatively high frequencies for which it usually is necessary to include shear and rotatory inertia when calculating the flexural wave speed. It follows that the approximate relations for $M_f$, given by Eq. 6.38, are not valid. In fact, the highest possible value of $M_f$ is that given by using Eq. 6.11 for $v_f$:

$$M_{f_h} \doteq \frac{c_s \sqrt{K_p}}{c_o} \doteq 0.57 \frac{c_\ell}{c_o} . \tag{6.49}$$

The value is 8.5 for metal plates in air and only 2.0 for plates immersed in water.

As shown in Fig. 6.4, the requirement of trace matching of the acoustic and flexural waves establishes the direction of propagation of the acoustic wave. Thus,

$$\sin \theta_o = \frac{\lambda_o}{\lambda_f} = \frac{c_o}{v_f} = \frac{1}{M_f} . \tag{6.50}$$

Sound waves travel parallel to the plate when $M_f \doteq 1$ and approach the perpendicular as $M_f$ increases. The steepest angle is, of course, limited by the maximum value of $M_f$. Another approach to understanding Eq. 6.50 is to think of a plate with flexural waves as being composed of a line array of alternating-phase pistons spaced $\lambda_f/2$ apart. From the analysis of arrays in Section 4.7, the steered angle, $\theta_o$, for such an array is that given by Eq. 6.50.

The angle $\theta_o$ is real only if $M_f > 1$. When $M_f < 1$, it is imaginary, corresponding to the fact that below coincidence no sound is radiated from an infinite plate and the effect of fluid loading is entirely that of added mass, as discussed above.

Returning to Eq. 6.33, the intensity of the sound radiated into the fluid can be expressed as a function of the plate velocity and the flexural Mach number by

$$I = \frac{\overline{p'^2}}{\rho_o c_o} = \rho_o c_o \frac{k_o^2}{k_o^2 - k_f^2} \overline{\dot{w}^2} = \rho_o c_o \overline{\dot{w}^2} \frac{M_f^2}{M_f^2 - 1} . \tag{6.51}$$

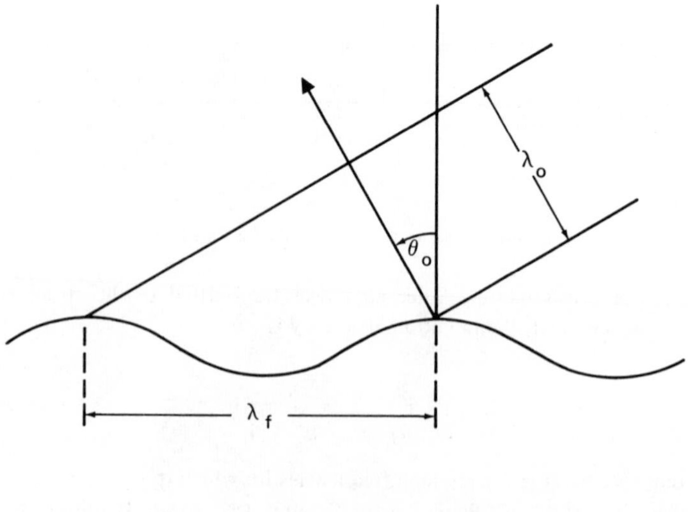


Fig. 6.4. Trace Matching of Acoustic and Flexural Waves

The power radiated per unit area of the plate is given by

$$W'_{ac} = I \cos \theta_o = \rho_o c_o \overline{\dot{w}^2} \frac{M_f}{\sqrt{M_f^2 - 1}} . \tag{6.52}$$

From Eq. 4.9, it follows that the specific radiation resistance is

$$\sigma_r = \frac{W'_{ac}}{\rho_o c_o \overline{\dot{w}^2}} = \frac{M_f}{\sqrt{M_f^2 - 1}} = \frac{1}{\cos \theta_o} , \tag{6.53}$$

and that the loss factor, $\eta_r$, equals the product of $\sigma_r$ and the impedance matching function, $\beta$, i.e.,

$$\eta_r = \beta \sigma_r = \frac{\beta}{\cos \theta_o} . \tag{6.54}$$

Figure 6.3, which is a plot of $\eta_r/\beta$, is thus also a plot of the specific radiation resistance, $\sigma_r$. These results were first derived by Gösele (1953) and Westphal (1954).

## 6.3 Point-Excited Infinite Plates

The conclusion that no sound is radiated below coincidence applies only to straight-crested waves on freely vibrating infinite plates. Sound will be radiated if a plate is excited by a concentrated force. As explained in Section 6.1, flexural waves spread out equally in all directions from a point source. The solution for the velocities is in terms of Bessel functions and includes exponential near-field terms as well as wave terms. The power radiated from point-excited thin plates has been derived by Heckl (1959, 1963) and Gutin (1964) and its directional properties by Maidanik and Kerwin (1966) and Feit (1966), as well as by Gutin.

**Radiation below Coincidence**

For low frequencies, for which $M_f << 1$, Heckl and Gutin used Fourier transform methods to derive the radiated power, finding

$$W_{ac} = \frac{\rho_o c_o k_o^2 \overline{F^2}}{2\pi\omega^2 \mu'^2} \left[ 1 - \beta \tan^{-1} \frac{1}{\beta} \right] , \tag{6.55}$$

where it is assumed that fluid loading occurs on one side only. The effect of fluid loading given by the term within the brackets is identical to that for piston radiation, Eq. 4.131, and is plotted in Fig. 6.5. For $\beta << 0.05$ it is essentially unity, while for $\beta > 2$ it is given by

$$1 - \beta \tan^{-1} \frac{1}{\beta} \doteq \frac{1}{3\beta^2} \quad (\beta > 2) . \tag{6.56}$$

The two limiting cases of light and heavy fluid loading lead to significantly different results.

*Light fluid loading* is experienced by metal plates in air, for which $\beta < 0.05$ over most of the frequency range of interest. For this case, it is instructive to express the radiated acoustic power in

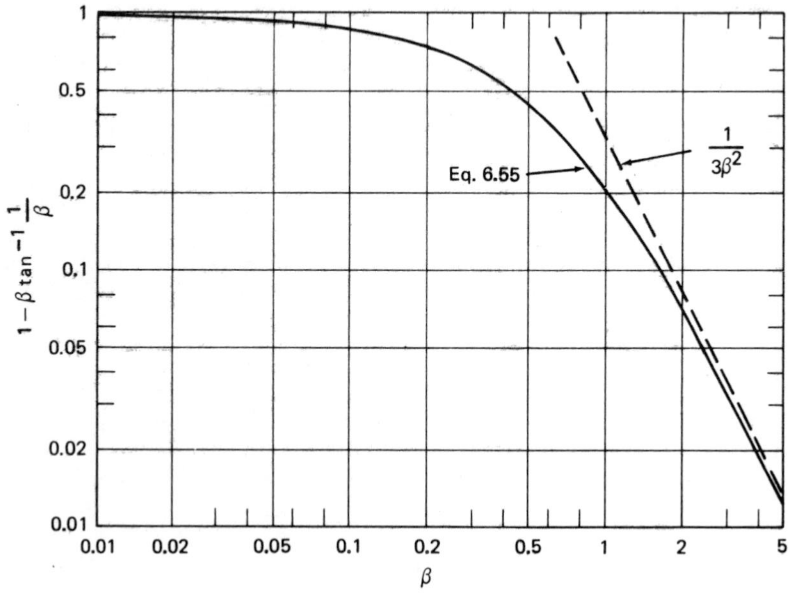


Fig. 6.5. Radiation Fluid Loading Factor, from Eq. 6.55

terms of the velocity $\dot{w}_o$ at the excitation point. Using Eq. 6.28 for the input impedance, Eq. 6.55 becomes

$$W_{ac} = \frac{32}{\pi} \rho_o c_o \frac{c_p^2 h^2}{12 c_o^2} \overline{\dot{w}_o^2} = \frac{32}{\pi} \frac{\rho_o c_o^3}{\omega_c'^2} \overline{\dot{w}_o^2} . \tag{6.57}$$

Comparing this result with that for a circular piston radiating in a baffle, as given by Eq. 4.123 supplemented by Eq. 4.9, one finds

$$\frac{32}{\pi} \frac{\rho_o c_o}{k_c'^2} \doteq \frac{32}{\pi} \rho_o c_o \frac{k_o^2}{k_f^4} = \frac{\pi}{2} \rho_o c_o k_o^2 a_o^4 , \tag{6.58}$$

from which it follows that the power radiated is the same as that for a circular piston of radius $a_o$ given by

$$a_o = \sqrt{\frac{8}{\pi}} \frac{1}{k_f} = \sqrt{\frac{2}{\pi^3}} \lambda_f \doteq \frac{1}{4} \lambda_f . \tag{6.59}$$

Practical sources extend over a finite area and may be treated as pistons in infinite baffles, with the piston radius being the sum of the radius of the applied force and a quarter of a flexural wavelength.

As found by Gutin (1964), Maidanik and Kerwin (1966) and Feit (1966), the radiation pattern under light loading conditions is virtually omnidirectional, the pressure at distance $r$ being given by

$$\underline{p}'(r,\theta) \doteq \frac{\rho_o F_o}{2\pi\mu' r} e^{i(\omega t - kr)} . \tag{6.60}$$

Under these conditions the radiation efficiency is given by

$$\eta_{rad} \doteq \frac{W_{ac}}{W_{vibr}} \doteq \frac{\frac{32}{\pi} \frac{\rho_o c_o}{\omega_c'^2} \overline{\dot{w}_o^2}}{Z_i \overline{\dot{w}_o^2}} = \frac{4}{\pi} \frac{\rho_o c_p}{\sqrt{12}\rho_s c_o} . \tag{6.61}$$

This is independent of both frequency and plate thickness, being about $9 \times 10^{-4}$ for steel plates in air and $2.6 \times 10^{-3}$ for aluminum plates.

For metal plates in water at low frequencies, $\beta > 1$ and therefore Eq. 6.56 for *heavy fluid loading* is applicable. Equation 6.55 for the radiated sound power reduces to

$$W_{ac} \doteq \frac{k_o^2 \overline{F^2}}{6\pi\rho_o c_o} = \frac{\omega^2 \overline{F^2}}{6\pi\rho_o c_o^3} , \tag{6.62}$$

which has a cubic dependence on Mach number typical of dipole radiation. Indeed, well below coincidence the directional pattern is a cosine one. Thus, when radiating into water, a point force acting on a thin plate radiates sound at low frequencies as though the plate were not there, very much in the same manner as an oscillating hydrodynamic force, as discussed in Sections 3.4 and 9.1.

## Directional Radiation at High Frequencies

Feit (1966) used the Mindlin-Timoshenko thick-plate equations in his analysis of radiation above the coincidence frequency, finding

$$\underline{p}' = \frac{ik_o F_o \cos\theta}{2\pi r} \times$$

$$\left[ 1 - i \frac{\cos\theta}{\beta} \frac{1 - \left(\frac{\omega}{\omega_c'}\right)^2 \left(\sin^2\theta - \left(\frac{c_o}{c_p}\right)^2\right) \left(\sin^2\theta - \Gamma_p \left(\frac{c_o}{c_p}\right)^2\right)}{1 + \left(\frac{\omega}{\omega_c'}\right)^2 \left(\frac{c_o}{c_p}\right)^2 \Gamma_p \left(\sin^2\theta - \left(\frac{c_o}{c_p}\right)^2\right)} \right]^{-1} , \tag{6.63}$$

where $\omega_c'$ is the coincidence frequency as calculated for a thin plate by Eq. 6.34. For heavy fluid loading, the second term inside the brackets is negligible and the pressure corresponds to the conditions for Eq. 6.62. On the other hand, if $\beta << 1$, as is usually true at high frequencies even in water, then Eq. 6.63 reduces to

$$p' = \frac{\rho_o F_o}{2\pi\mu' r}\left[\frac{1 + \left(\frac{\omega}{\omega_c'}\right)^2 \left(\frac{c_o}{c_p}\right)^2 \Gamma_p \left(\sin^2\theta - \left(\frac{c_o}{c_p}\right)^2\right)}{1 - \left(\frac{\omega}{\omega_c'}\right)^2 \left(\sin^2\theta - \left(\frac{c_o}{c_p}\right)^2\right)\left(\sin^2\theta - \Gamma_p\left(\frac{c_o}{c_p}\right)^2\right)}\right] . \quad (6.64)$$

The function in brackets is unity when $\theta = 0$. It follows that Eq. 6.60 applies in the direction perpendicular to the plate and that the expression in brackets is the directivity function, $D(\theta)$, as defined by Eq. 4.66. Above coincidence $D(\theta)$ has a peak at the angle, $\theta_m$, for which the denominator inside the brackets is zero, i.e., for which

$$\left(\frac{\omega_c'}{\omega}\right)^2 = \left(\sin^2\theta_m - \left(\frac{c_o}{c_p}\right)^2\right)\left(\sin^2\theta_m - \Gamma_p\left(\frac{c_o}{c_p}\right)^2\right) . \quad (6.65)$$

The lowest frequency for which the solution of this equation is real is the coincidence frequency itself, corresponding to $\theta_m = 90°$ and given by

$$\left(\frac{\omega_c'}{\omega_c}\right)^2 = \left(1 - \left(\frac{c_o}{c_p}\right)^2\right)\left(1 - \Gamma_p\left(\frac{c_o}{c_p}\right)^2\right) . \quad (6.66)$$

Putting in the constants appropriate to metal plates in water, $\omega_c$ is 21% higher than $\omega_c'$. This is in agreement with the value derived using Eq. 5.54 and expressed by Eq. 6.37. Solutions of Eq. 6.65 for $\theta_m$ at other frequencies are in good agreement with that expected for straight-crested waves, as given by Eq. 6.50 with $v_f$ calculated by the methods of Section 5.4. Figure 6.6 shows the angle of

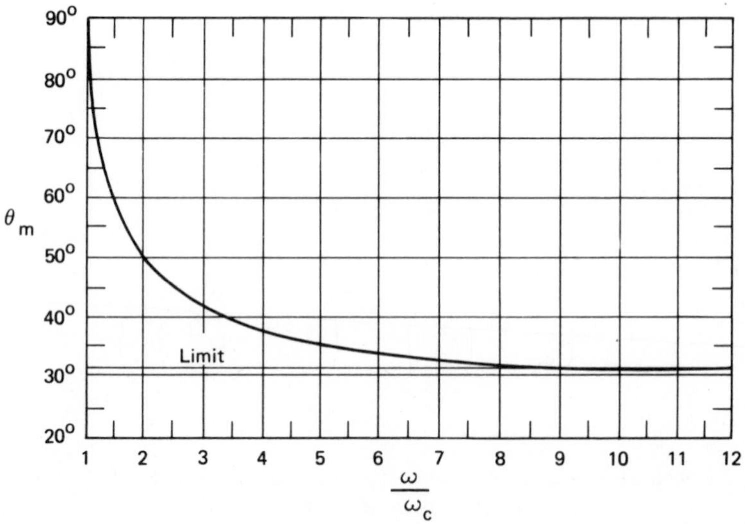


Fig. 6.6. Angle of Maximum Radiation for Metal Plates in Water, from Eq. 6.65

maximum radiation as a function of relative frequency for metal plates in water. Figure 6.7 shows a typical directional radiation pattern, as calculated by Feit. At very high frequencies, $\theta_m$ approaches the limit,

$$\sin \theta_{m_h} \doteq \frac{c_o}{v_{f_h}} = \frac{c_o}{c_p} \sqrt{\Gamma} \,, \tag{6.67}$$

which is about 31° for metal plates in water. In addition to the peak defined by Eq. 6.65, a second, smaller peak is sometimes observed at $\sin \theta_m = c_o/c_p$. This corresponds to radiation from the surface bulges associated with longitudinal plate waves. The angle for this secondary peak is about 3-2/3° in air and 16-1/2° in water.

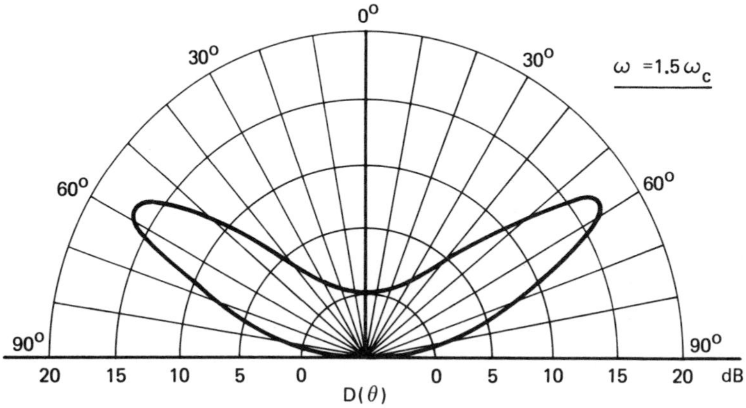


Fig. 6.7. Directional Radiation from Plate Flexural Vibrations at High Frequencies, after Feit (1966)

## 6.4 Radiation from Finite Plates

### Radiation Resistance

The acoustic power radiated by point excitation of a very large plate below coincidence is independent of the area of the plate. For such a plate, from Eq. 4.9 for $\sigma_r$ and Eq. 6.57 for $W_{ac}$, the specific radiation resistance for radiation into air at low frequencies is

$$\sigma_r = \frac{W_{ac}}{\rho_o c_o S \overline{\dot{w}_o^2}} = \frac{32}{\pi k_c'^2 S} \doteq 0.08 \frac{\pi \lambda_c'^2}{S} \,. \tag{6.68}$$

Since $\lambda'_c$ increases linearly with plate thickness, the radiation resistance for point-excited plates at low frequencies in air is proportional to the square of the plate thickness and inversely proportional to the area of the plate.

Gösele (1953, 1956) considered straight-crested standing flexural waves on baffled rectangular plates. He found

$$\overline{\sigma_r} \equiv \frac{W_{ac}}{\rho_o c_o S \overline{\overline{\dot{w}^2}}} \doteq \frac{\lambda'_c}{\pi L} \quad (M_f << 1) \; , \tag{6.69}$$

where $L$ is the plate length in the direction of the waves as illustrated by Fig. 6.8. Nikiforov (1964) and Smith (1964) each considered finite plates with various edge conditions. They reported that

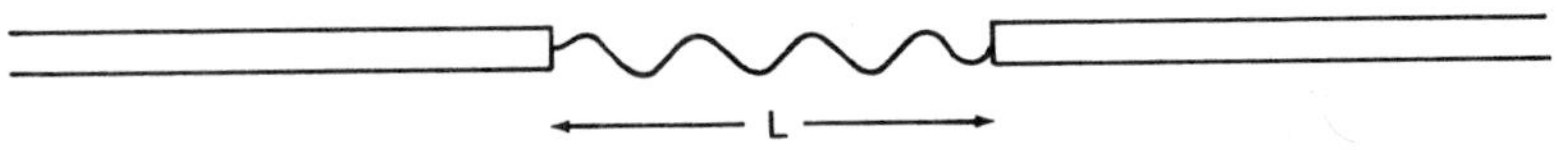


Fig. 6.8. Baffled Finite Plate with Straight-Crested Flexural Waves

clamped plates radiate most efficiently, that freely supported plates produce half as much sound and that plates with free edges radiate very little.

Gösele also considered traveling flexural waves for which the radiation efficiency is roughly half that of standing waves. His now classical plot of the radiation resistance for three relative plate lengths is reproduced in Fig. 6.9.

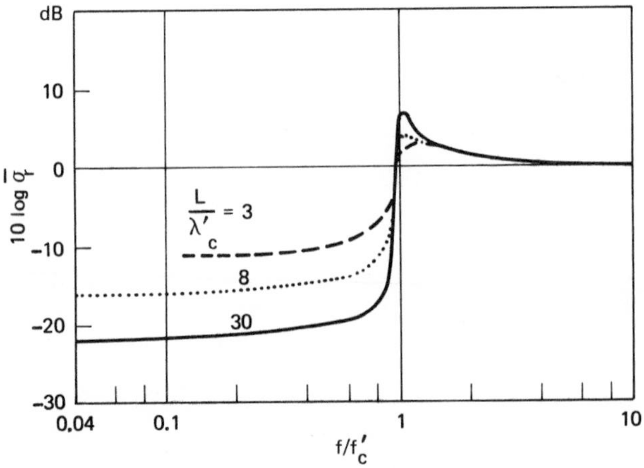


Fig. 6.9. Radiation Resistance of Traveling Waves on Finite Plates, after Gösele (1956)

**Modal Approach**

The general subject of radiation from plates and beam-plate systems can best be understood by following an approach to radiation problems developed by Maidanik (1962, 1974) which has received wide acceptance. As discussed in Section 5.8, finite systems have resonances which act as modes when the system is excited by an external force. All of the modes are excited to some degree. Maidanik considered all modes having flexural wavelengths shorter than that for sound waves in the fluid to be non-radiating, and those with longer wavelengths to radiate with unity efficiency. For frequencies above coincidence, most of the modes excited are radiating modes. Below coincidence, however, most of the vibratory energy is in non-radiating modes. To find the radiated power, one must calculate the fraction of the vibratory motion that is in radiating modes. Maidanik observed that below coincidence the reverberant flexural motions in the central area of a plate do not radiate and that radiation occurs only from strips at the edges that are about the width of a quarter of a flexural wavelength. Near-field pressure measurements by Blank (1968) confirm that the radiation is indeed from plate edges.

For plates that are large in both dimensions relative to a flexural wavelength but small compared to the wavelength in air, Maidanik found

$$\overline{\sigma_r} \doteq \frac{L_p \lambda'_c}{\pi^2 S} \sqrt{\frac{\omega}{\omega'_c}} = \frac{2L_p}{\pi k'_c S} \sqrt{\frac{\omega}{\omega'_c}} , \tag{6.70}$$

where $L_p$ is the plate perimeter. This relation shows a weak frequency dependence of 1.5 dB/octave, whereas that given by Eq. 6.68 for point excitation alone shows none. For a point-excited finite plate, the radiation is the sum of the forced-field component given by Eq. 6.68 and the reverberant, or edge, component given by Eq. 6.70. Before adding these two expressions, it is necessary to relate the mean-square reverberant plate velocity either to the force or to the plate velocity at the location of the force. The mean-square reverberant velocity of a flat plate can be calculated by equating the power dissipated to the vibratory power input. Thus,

$$\eta_T \omega \mu' S \overline{\overline{\dot{w}^2}} = \frac{\overline{F^2}}{Z_i} = Z_i \overline{\dot{w}_o^2} , \tag{6.71}$$

where $Z_i$, the input impedance, is a real quantity given by Eq. 6.28. It follows that

$$\frac{\overline{\overline{\dot{w}^2}}}{\overline{\dot{w}_o^2}} \doteq \frac{8}{\eta_T k_o k'_c S} = \frac{8}{\eta_T k_f^2 S} , \tag{6.72}$$

and that

$$\overline{\dot{w}^2} \doteq \frac{\overline{F^2}}{8 \eta_T \mu'^2 v_f^2 S} . \tag{6.73}$$

When the reverberant contribution is added to Eq. 6.68, the result is

$$\sigma_r = \frac{W_{ac}}{\rho_o c_o S\overline{w_o^2}} \doteq 0.08\,\frac{\pi \lambda_c'^2}{S}\left(1 + \frac{L_p \lambda_f}{4\pi \eta_T S}\right) . \qquad (6.74)$$

When the forced radiation is added to the reverberant contribution, Eq. 6.70 becomes

$$\overline{\sigma_r} = \frac{W_{ac}}{\rho_o c_o S\overline{\overline{\dot{w}^2}}} \doteq \frac{L_p \lambda_c'}{\pi^2 S}\sqrt{\frac{\omega}{\omega_c'}}\left(1 + \frac{2\eta_T k_f S}{L_p}\right) . \qquad (6.75)$$

**Effect of Damping**

In Section 5.9 it was indicated that damping is often an effective way of accomplishing noise reduction when it is used to attenuate structural vibrations and thereby reduce the excitation transmitted to a radiating surface. Originally, however, damping materials were developed for direct application to surfaces radiating into air. While several dB of radiation reduction were usually achieved, the resultant noise reduction was always found to be much less than the vibration reduction and consequently much less than what had been expected. Nikiforov (1963) explained this relative ineffectiveness of damping by noting that below coincidence most of the vibratory energy is in short wavelength modes which are relatively easy to dampen but which do not radiate, while the radiating long wavelength modes are only slightly affected by applied damping. Examination of Eq. 6.74 leads to the same conclusion. The most that damping can do is to reduce the second term. Since even without damping this term is often smaller than unity, it is apparent that damping will usually have relatively little effect on radiation by point-excited plates below coincidence.

**Orthotropic Plates**

Orthotropic plates, i.e., plates having directionally dependent flexural rigidity, are useful in analyzing many practical structures, at least over part of the frequency spectrum. Heckl (1960) was the first to recognize the importance of radiation from orthotropic plates. Maidanik (1966) expressed the bending rigidity as a vector quantity. As indicated by Eq. 6.34, the coincidence frequency varies inversely with the square root of the bending rigidity, $B_p$. It follows that the Mach number corresponding to a given frequency is highest in the direction of maximum flexural rigidity and lowest in the direction of least rigidity. In addition, it follows from Eqs. 6.68 and 6.70 that the specific radiation resistance is also highest for radiation associated with vibrations in the direction of highest bending rigidity. Stated another way, more of the modes are of the radiating type when the bending rigidity is increased.

Feit (1970) determined that radiation patterns for orthotropic plates have a range of frequencies for which directional radiation occurs in one direction but does not occur in the perpendicular plane. This phenomenon has been confirmed experimentally in connection with radiation from cylinders.

**Beam on a Plate**

Beam-plate systems are quite common. The presence of a single beam attached to a plate has three distinct effects: it changes any resonance frequencies; when a vibratory force excites one region of the plate, it acts to attenuate the vibratory velocities experienced at the other side; and it increases the sound radiated by the plate.

The effect of an infinite beam attached to a plate on the propagation of straight-crested flexural waves has been analyzed by Cremer (1948) and Ungar (1961). They found that transmission occurs only at those angles for which Snell's law is satisfied for flexural waves in the plate and flexural or torsional waves in the beam. Heckl (1961) considered finite systems and found that peak transmissions occur at frequencies close to beam resonance frequencies. For relatively high frequencies and long beams, Heckl found the broadband average transmission coefficient to be given by

$$\alpha_t^2 = \frac{\overline{\overline{v_2^2}}}{\overline{\overline{v_1^2}}} \doteq \frac{k_B \mu_p'}{k_p^2 \mu_B} \left( 1 + 64 \frac{\mu_p'}{k_p \mu_B} \right) , \qquad (6.76)$$

where subscript $p$ refers to plate and subscript $B$ to beam. The second term in Eq. 6.76 is negligible for heavy beams but important for relatively light ones. Heckl measured transmission through a 2.5 cm high steel beam on an 0.8 mm thick aluminum plate in air, finding transmission loss values of from 15 to 35 dB. Without including beam resonances in his analysis, Nikiforov (1969) showed that Eq. 6.76 can be derived by considering the transmission of diffuse fields by infinite beam-plate systems.

The attenuation of flexural waves by a beam or other obstacle may be reduced significantly if the plate is immersed in liquid. Lyapunov (1968) has shown that an appreciable fraction of the incident energy may be transferred past the obstacle by the near-field acoustic disturbance in the liquid.

As for sound radiation, Maidanik (1962), Lyon (1962) and Romanov (1971) have all shown that the presence of a beam can significantly increase plate radiation below coincidence. Maidanik established that beams have the effect of increasing the ratio of perimeter length to surface area, thereby increasing the contribution from the reverberant field, as implied by Eq. 6.70. Lyon evaluated the radiation resistance per unit length of beam for a number of assumed boundary conditions and found that

$$R_r' \doteq 0.6 \rho_o h_p c_\ell M_f \qquad (6.77)$$

at low frequencies, with only slight dependence on boundary assumptions. Romanov noted that the increase in radiation occurs if plate damping is small, but that heavy damping, $\eta > 0.1$, can negate the effect of the beam. It thus appears valuable to apply damping to plates for which attached beams would otherwise result in increased radiation.

**Periodic Structures**

Heckl (1961) examined plates with periodically-spaced beams both experimentally and theoretically. He found that the first of a series of beams has the greatest effect on vibration transmission. The first beam only passes waves which approach it at angles such that there is wave number matching between the incident waves and waves propagating in the beam. Since these angles are also the correct ones to pass the second beam, only scattering within the bays will result in additional attenuation by the second and subsequent beams. Heckl confirmed this understanding by showing experimentally that varying the spacing of identical beams has little effect but that varying the shape of one beam has significant effect. Thus, beams on plates can be considered to be filters which pass flexural waves having certain propagation directions and frequencies.

Putting identical filters in series adds little attenuation in their pass band. Variation of filter characteristics is much more effective in reducing transmission.

Maidanik (1962) and Plakhov (1967) found that periodically-spaced ribs increase the radiation from a plate by from 6 to 12 dB, the higher values being measured for plates radiating into air and lower ones being more typical of water loading. The theoretical expressions derived by both investigators are quite complex and imply considerable variability of the effect of multiple beams on sound radiation.

At very low frequencies, for which the spacing between beams becomes short compared to a flexural wavelength, the beams no longer act as periodic impedance elements. Instead they act to distribute stiffness in the parallel direction and add mass in the perpendicular direction. Thus, at very low frequencies periodic structures behave acoustically as orthotropic plates with the directional radiation characteristics previously discussed.

### Cylindrical Shells

The dominant effect of plate curvature is to add stiffness without adding mass. Thus, conclusions reached in our discussion of orthotropic plates apply to curved plates and are also indicative of properties of cylindrical shells. The parameter that expresses the relative importance of plate curvature is

$$\nu \equiv \frac{\omega a}{c_p}, \ or \ \frac{\omega a}{c_\ell}, \qquad (6.78)$$

where $a$ is the radius of curvature. If $\nu < 1$, curvature affects both vibrations and radiation significantly. On the other hand, for $\nu > 2$, curved surfaces behave as flat plates. Heckl (1962) calculated modal densities of cylindrical shells by using an approximate formula for resonance frequencies,

$$\nu_{m,n} \doteq \frac{(m\pi a/L)^2}{n^2 + (m\pi a/L)^2} + \frac{h}{\sqrt{12a}} \left(n^2 + (m\pi a/L)^2\right), \qquad (6.79)$$

where $m$ is the number of longitudinal modes, $n$ the number of circumferential ones, and $a$, $L$ and $h$ are the radius, length and thickness of the shell. Heckl found that for $\nu < 1$ there are approximately $\sqrt{\nu}$ as many resonances per frequency band as there would be for a flat plate. He also showed that low-order longitudinal modes of cylindrical shells have much higher flexural wave speeds than do those of flat plates. Manning and Maidanik (1964) measured the acoustic power radiated by a point-driven cylindrical shell in air. As shown in Fig. 6.10, they found that below coincidence the radiation resistance decreases at a rate of about 6 dB/octave until it reaches the value attributable to the force alone. Similar results were found by Szechenyi (1971).

As noted by Komarova (1969), applied damping is less effective in reducing radiation from cylinders than from plates. As she explained, most of the vibratory energy is in circumferential modes which, though readily damped, do not radiate efficiently. Radiation is dominated by the relatively stiff longitudinal modes which have higher flexural wave speeds and which are also harder to damp.

### Radiation from Hull Sections

Although curved plates and reinforcing ribs make hull structures quite complex, the discussion of orthotropic plates and cylindrical shells given thus far in this section indicates that general

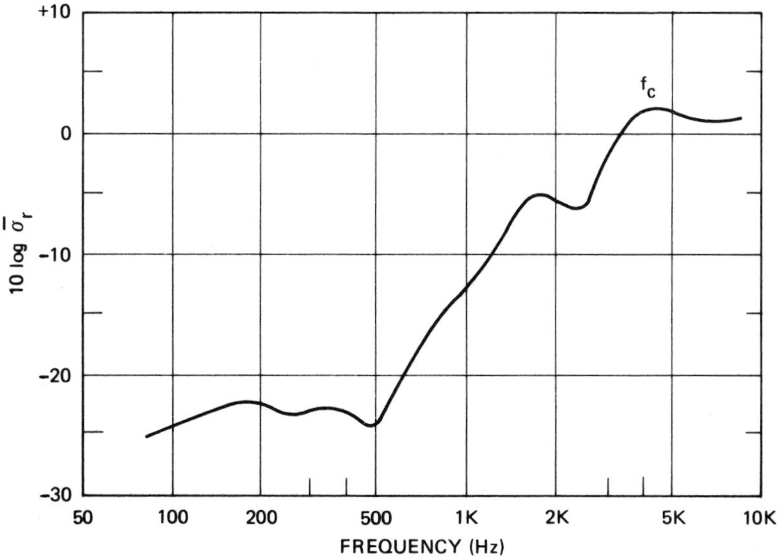


Fig. 6.10. Radiation from a Cylinder in Air, after Manning and Maidanik (1964)

characteristics of hull radiation can be predicted from rather elementary formulas. Thus, Eq. 6.62 can be used at low frequencies for which water loading is significant. This can be written:

$$W_{ac} \doteq \frac{\omega_c'^2 F^2}{\rho_o c_o^3} \frac{M_f^4}{6\pi} \qquad (M_f << 1) \ . \tag{6.80}$$

At high frequencies essentially all of the vibratory power accepted by the structure will be radiated. Thus,

$$W_{ac} \doteq \frac{\overline{F^2}}{Z_i} \doteq \frac{1}{8} \frac{\omega_c'^2 \overline{F^2}}{\rho_o c_o^3} \left( \frac{\rho_o c_p}{\sqrt{12} \rho_s c_o} \right) \qquad (M_f > 1) \ , \tag{6.81}$$

where the factor in parentheses is given in Table 6.1. The result of combining Eqs. 6.80 and 6.81 is shown in Fig. 6.11 for aluminum and steel plates in water. This ignores any reverberant contribution.

Donaldson (1968) measured the radiated power for several ship-like structures floating in a tank of water, finding good agreement with Fig. 6.11 for frequencies above about 400 Hz, corresponding in his case to $\omega/\omega_c' \doteq 0.02$. Below this frequency, the measured power exceeds the calculated power by an increasing amount. At the low frequencies, resonances are prominent and reverberant energy is apparently dominant. Donaldson's low-frequency results correspond to a radiation factor, as given by Fig. 6.11, of about − 45 dB. Thus his results are consistent with those of Fig. 6.11 provided a minimum floor of about − 45 dB is used for the lowest frequencies.

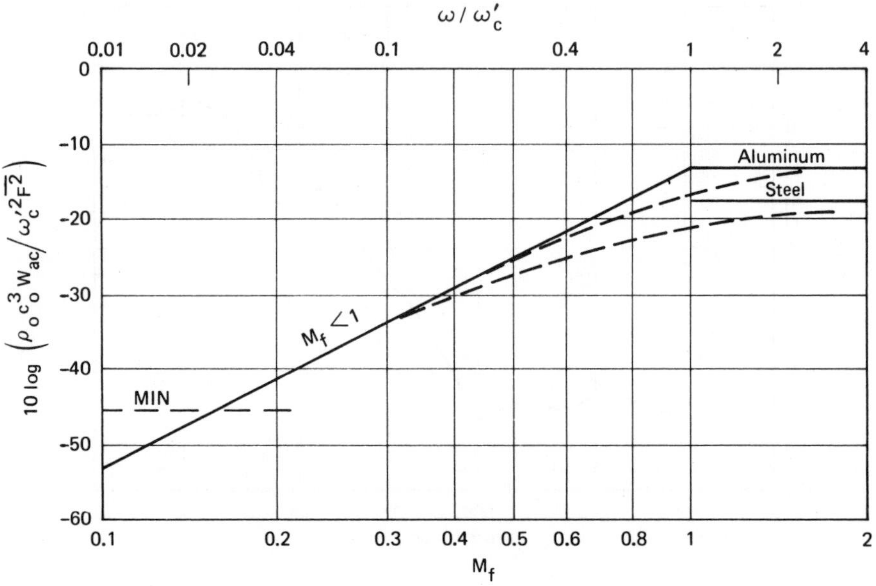


Fig. 6.11. Sound Radiation by Forces Applied to Flat Plates in Water

Equations 6.80 and 6.81 combined with Eq. 6.34 for $\omega_c'$ indicate that hull construction plays a relatively minor role in governing the acoustic power radiated by a given force. In the mid-frequency range for which Eq. 6.80 applies the power radiated is independent of hull parameters. At high frequencies, above the coincidence frequency, less sound is radiated the thicker the hull and the lower the value of $\omega_c'$. Steel radiates a few dB less than aluminum. No conclusions can be stated for the lowest frequencies since Donaldson's tests did not cover a wide range of plate thicknesses. The reverberant field is important at these frequencies and structural details may be expected to affect the amount of sound radiated at specific frequencies.

## 6.5 Transmission through Structures

A common situation in acoustics is that in which sound waves in one body of fluid are transmitted into a second fluid separated from it by a solid structure. In a sonar dome the aim is to minimize any effects of the structure. In other cases maximum transmission loss may be desired.

### Response of Structures to Sound Waves

The response of structures to incident sound waves is the inverse of the problem of radiation of sound by structures. Lyamshev (1959) noted that the *acoustic reciprocity principle*, whereby sources and receivers are interchangeable, applies equally well to structural radiation situations. Thus, the velocity of a plate structure that is excited by a uniformly distributed sound field is directly related to the sound field radiated by the same structure when excited by a point force.

The radiation resistance coefficients derived in the previous section are therefore indicative of the sound-absorbing properties of structures. Sound excites radiative long wavelength modes and does not excite non-radiative short modes. Thus, above coincidence flexural waves are readily excited by sound, but below coincidence their response is relatively weak.

**Low-Frequency Transmission through Walls**

Below the coincidence frequency, the dominant mechanism of sound transmission through plates and walls is that involving longitudinal waves. Consider the situation depicted in Fig. 6.12 in which fluid body 1 is separated from fluid body 2 by a solid wall of thickness $h$, which is thin

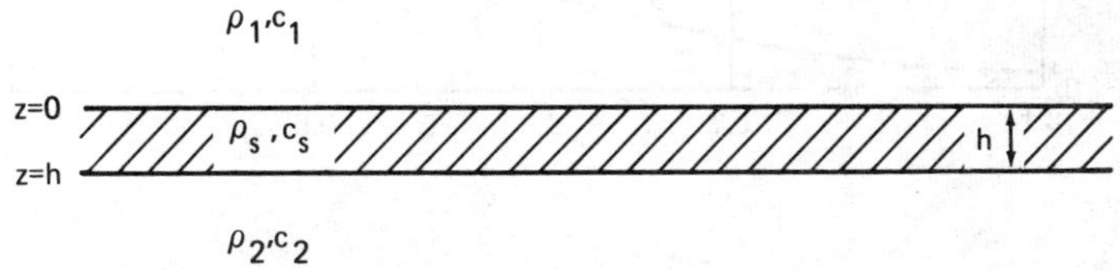


Fig. 6.12. Wall Separating Two Fluids

compared to a wavelength in the solid. The two fluids may be the same or different. It is assumed that both density and sound speed are higher in the structure than in the fluid. Application of Snell's law at both interfaces, taking into account phase shifts as well as amplitudes, results in

$$\alpha_t \equiv \frac{I_t}{I_i} = \frac{\overline{p_2^2}}{\rho_2 c_2} \bigg/ \frac{\overline{p_1^2}}{\rho_1 c_1} \doteq \frac{4\rho_2 c_2 \rho_1 c_1}{(\rho_2 c_2 + \rho_1 c_1)^2 + (\rho_s h\omega)^2} \tag{6.82}$$

for normal incidence. Taking the reciprocal, and noting that $\rho_s h$ equals the surface density $\mu'$, it follows that

$$\frac{1}{\alpha_t} = \frac{1}{4}\left(2 + \frac{\rho_1 c_1}{\rho_2 c_2} + \frac{\rho_2 c_2}{\rho_1 c_1} + \frac{\mu'\omega}{\rho_1 c_1} \cdot \frac{\mu'\omega}{\rho_2 c_2}\right), \tag{6.83}$$

and the *transmission loss, TL*, is 10 log $\alpha_t^{-1}$. There are several special cases of interest:

1. *Water to water.* The two fluids are identical and Eq. 6.83 reduces to

$$\frac{1}{\alpha_t} = 1 + \frac{1}{(2\beta)^2}, \tag{6.84}$$

where $\beta$ is the load factor defined by Eq. 6.45. The resultant $TL$ is plotted in Fig. 6.13, where it is seen that the loss is less than 3 dB provided $f < 1/4\, f_c$.

2. *Air to air.* Equation 6.84 applies and $\beta$ is very small. Hence,

$$TL \doteq 20 \log \frac{\mu'\omega}{2\rho_o c_o}. \tag{6.85}$$

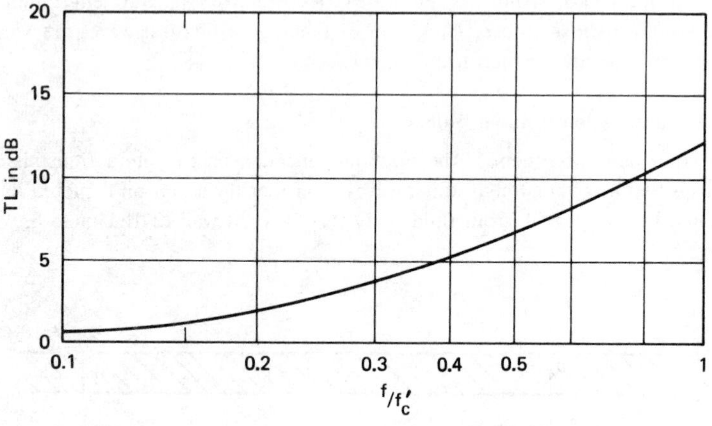


Fig. 6.13. Ideal Transmission Loss for Steel Plates in Water, from Eq. 6.84

The transmission loss increases with frequency and with structural density. This is the familiar *mass law* that governs transmission by walls at low frequencies up to about $1/2\, f_c$.

3. *Water to air.* In this case $\rho_1 c_1 >> \rho_2 c_2$, and Eq. 6.83 reduces to

$$\frac{1}{\alpha_t} \doteq \frac{\rho_1 c_1}{4\rho_2 c_2}\left(1 + \frac{1}{\beta_1^2}\right). \tag{6.86}$$

Since $\beta_1 > 1$ for water loading at low frequencies, this result differs very little from that derived in Section 2.5. Thus, well below coincidence the solid structure has no effect on the transmission loss. Only for $f > 1/5\, f_c$ does it reduce the power transmitted.

4. *Air to water.* In this case $\rho_1 c_1 << \rho_2 c_2$, and Eq. 6.83 reduces to

$$\frac{1}{\alpha_t} = \frac{\rho_2 c_2}{4\rho_1 c_1}\left(1 + \frac{1}{\beta_2^2}\right). \tag{6.87}$$

Since water is now the second medium, the result is identical to that for water to air, in conformity with the reciprocity theorem.

It is clear from these four examples that the structure plays a relatively minor role below coincidence if water loading occurs on one or both sides. Only in the air-to-air case can a large *TL* be achieved in the low-frequency regime.

### Use of Impedance Concepts

The equations for normal-incidence transmission loss at low frequencies can readily be extended to other angles of incidence and other types of wave motions in the structure by using relatively elementary network concepts. In this approach, each medium is characterized by one or more impedance elements in series or in parallel and these elements are placed in series with each other. The power transmission coefficient, $\alpha_t$, is the ratio of the power transmitted through the intervening structure to that which would have been transmitted if the structure were absent and medium 2 were identical to medium 1. Consider the circuit shown in Fig. 6.14. The power

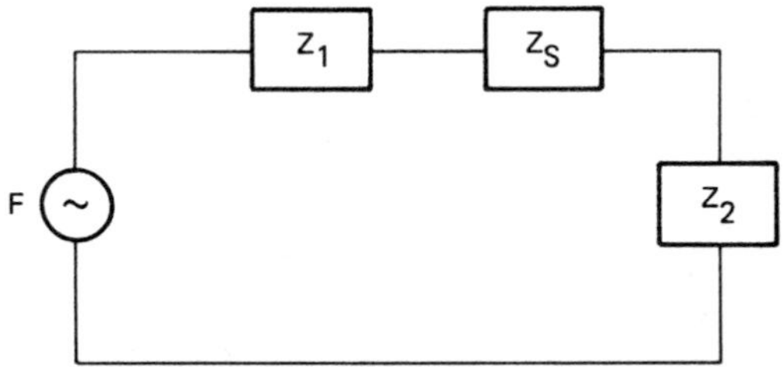


Fig. 6.14. Network Representing Transmission Loss

delivered to the load, $Z_2$, is

$$W_2 = \frac{R_2\overline{F^2}}{\left|\underline{Z}_1 + \underline{Z}_2 + \underline{Z}_s\right|^2} = \frac{R_2\overline{F^2}}{(R_1 + R_2 + R_s)^2 + (X_1 + X_2 + X_s)^2} . \quad (6.88)$$

If $Z_s = 0$ and $\underline{Z}_2 = \underline{Z}_1 = R_1$, then

$$W_2^0 = \frac{R_1\overline{F^2}}{(2R_1)^2} = \frac{\overline{F^2}}{4R_1} . \quad (6.89)$$

It follows that

$$\alpha_t \equiv \frac{W_2}{W_2^0} = \frac{4R_1R_2}{(R_1 + R_2 + R_s)^2 + (X_1 + X_2 + X_s)^2} \quad (6.90)$$

At a surface, the normal impedance for longitudinal waves in a fluid medium is given by

$$\underline{Z}_i = \frac{\rho_i c_i S}{\cos\theta_i} , \quad (6.91)$$

which is purely resistive. At frequencies sufficiently below coincidence, walls can be treated as masses for which $\underline{Z}_s = i\omega m = i\omega\mu' S$. Substituting these relations into Eq. 6.90 and assuming normal incidence, Eq. 6.83 can be derived for the transmission coefficient. For oblique incidence, each $\rho c$ product should be replaced by $\rho c/\cos\theta$, where $\theta$ is the angle relative to the normal.

**Role of Flexural Vibrations**

As discussed by Beranek (1959) and Schiller (1967), flexural waves become dominant in wall transmission for frequencies above about $1/2\, f_c'$. Those components of a diffuse sound field that match the reverberant wave field of the structure are transmitted virtually without loss. The remainder is reflected. The reverberant velocity of the structure is controlled by the damping factor as given by Eq. 6.73. Cremer, Heckl and Ungar (1973) used reciprocity to show that the radiation process is related to the absorption process by $k_o^2 S/4\pi$. They found that the effective wall impedance, $\underline{Z}_s$, for flexural waves above coincidence is a pure resistance given by

$$R_s^2 = \frac{k_o^2}{4\pi}\,\eta_T \omega\mu' Z_i S^2 = \frac{2}{\pi}\,k_o^2 \mu'^2 \eta_T v_f^2 S^2 \doteq \frac{2\eta_T}{\pi}\left(\frac{\omega}{\omega_c'}\right)(\omega\mu' S)^2 \; . \tag{6.92}$$

This resistance is relatively small when either fluid is a liquid, but is significant when both fluids are gases. Thus, for air-to-air transmission, substitution of Eq. 6.92 into Eq. 6.90 leads to

$$TL \doteq 10 \log \frac{R_s^2}{4R_1R_2} \doteq 20 \log \frac{\omega\mu'}{2\rho_o c_o} + 10 \log \frac{2\eta_T}{\pi} + 10 \log \frac{\omega}{\omega_c'} \; . \tag{6.93}$$

The first term is the mass law of Eq. 6.85, the second term is negative by an amount that depends on total damping and the third term is an additional dependence on frequency. It is apparent that, for frequencies controlled by flexural wave transmission, the amount of isolation that can be achieved by built-in damping is second only to that caused by the wall's mass.

**Sound Isolation by Walls**

When walls are being used to isolate one space from another acoustically, several things can be done to decrease the transmission. The most obvious is to raise the coincidence frequency above the frequency range for which high *TL* is desired. This poses a problem in that $f_c$ is inversely dependent on thickness and *TL* in the mass law regime is proportional to thickness. Kurtze (1959) and Kurtze and Watters (1959) proposed that the flexural wave speed be reduced without sacrificing mass by using multilayered plates in which a viscous liquid, a viscoelastic solid or a porous layer is placed between two thin elastic layers. A number of practical wall constructions have been developed using this principle.

It has been demonstrated that anything adding stiffness to a wall without adding much mass is detrimental to sound isolation. Venzke et al (1973) demonstrated that adding stiffeners to walls increases their sound radiation below coincidence and thereby decreases the *TL*. Shenderov (1963, 1969), Plakov (1968) and Warren (1974) demonstrated that periodically-spaced stiffeners on plates cause rejection bands for which the *TL* is high as well as pass bands for which it is low. Shenderov (1964) proved theoretically what a large number of investigators have found experimentally, namely, that the method of support of a panel affects its acoustic transmissivity.

It is clear that, at coincidence as well as above it, the *TL* of a wall is a direct function of its damping. Increasing the damping is probably the single most effective way of increasing *TL* in cases where it is impossible to use *limp* walls that have both high mass and low stiffness, i.e., low flexural wave speeds together with high surface mass densities.

## 6.6 Boundary-Layer Flow Noise

When fluid flows past a surface, a boundary layer is formed in which the flow velocity decreases from a value related to the free-stream velocity to zero at the surface. Often the boundary layer is characterized by turbulent flow conditions involving fluctuating velocities and pressures. The radiated and sonar self-noise associated with such turbulent pressure fluctuations is called *boundary-layer flow noise*. Although this topic has interested many investigators over the past 20 years, full understanding of all of the noise-generating mechanisms is still lacking. This section begins with a description of the significant characteristics of turbulent boundary-layer flows based primarily on papers published by the author.

**Turbulent Boundary Layers**

If a fluid were completely inviscid, it would theoretically be able to flow past a surface with finite relative speed. However, even a small amount of viscous friction is sufficient to cause zero local flow speed right at the surface. The transition region from the surface to the point where viscosity has no effect is termed the *boundary layer*. Close to the nose of a body, or in pipes at very low flow speeds, fluid viscosity dominates and the boundary layer is laminar. However, further downstream and/or at higher flow speeds the laminar shear layer becomes unstable and eddies form. These eddies become dominant and eddy momentum transfer becomes more important than viscous transfer as the boundary layer becomes turbulent. Since flow fluctuations associated with laminar flows are very small, laminar boundary-layer flow noise is negligible. It is the eddy motions of turbulent boundary layers that give rise to velocity and pressure fluctuations and thereby cause flow noise. Hence, all discussions of boundary-layer flow noise refer to the turbulent condition.

The physical quantities which characterize a *turbulent boundary layer* are the mean flow velocity distribution, $u(z)$, and the distributions of turbulent stresses, $\tau(z)$, eddy mixing lengths, $\ell(z)$, and turbulent velocity components, $u'$, $v'$ and $w'$. The thickness of the disturbed layer, $\delta$, is an indefinite quantity and it is common practice to describe the extent of the layer by the *displacement thickness*, $\delta^*$, defined by

$$\delta^* \equiv \int_0^\infty \left(1 - \frac{u}{u_1}\right) dz \,, \qquad (6.94)$$

and/or the *momentum thickness*, $\theta$, given by

$$\theta \equiv \int_0^\infty \left(1 - \frac{u}{u_1}\right) \frac{u}{u_1} \, dz \,, \qquad (6.95)$$

where $u_1$ is the flow velocity immediately outside the disturbed region. The displacement thickness measures the extent by which the ideal potential flow streamlines are displaced from the surface by the boundary layer, while the momentum thickness measures the momentum deficiency.

Figure 6.15 shows several typical turbulent boundary-layer velocity profiles. Each boundary layer consists of two basically different major regions, called inner and outer. The *inner region* is controlled by local wall conditions and the *outer region* is dominated by eddies that were created relatively far upstream. As shown in Fig. 6.16, a *blending region* connects the two. The inner region is further divided into three zones: a *laminar sublayer* in immediate contact with the wall in which the turbulence level is low and viscosity dominates, a *buffer zone* in which viscous and turbulent shear stresses are both active, and a *turbulent zone* in which the level of turbulence is governed by local wall conditions.

The velocity distribution in the *inner region* is related to the value of the shear stress at the

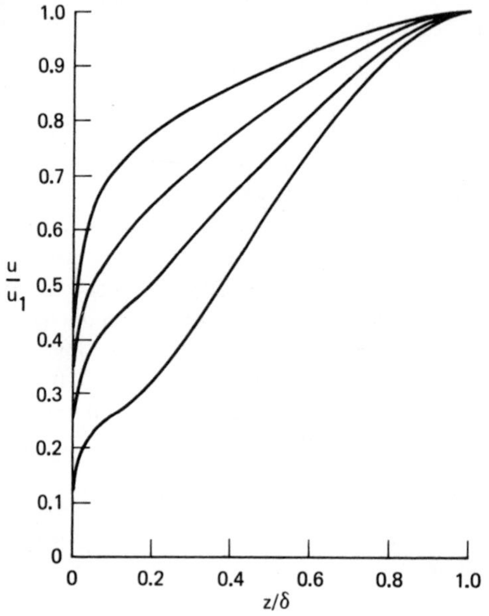


Fig. 6.15. Four Typical Turbulent Boundary-Layer Velocity Profiles, from Ross (1956)

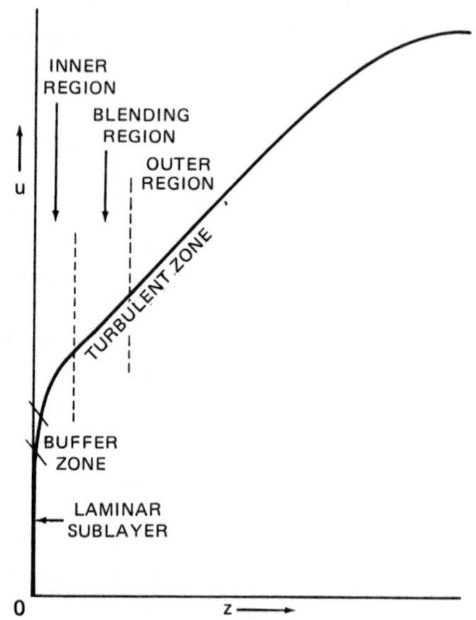


Fig. 6.16. Regions of a Turbulent Boundary-Layer Velocity Profile, from Ross (1956)

wall, $\tau_w$. This is usually expressed by a velocity, $u_\tau^*$, called the *friction velocity*, or wall-shear-stress velocity, defined by

$$u_\tau^* \equiv \sqrt{\frac{\tau_w}{\rho_o}} \ . \tag{6.96}$$

The inner velocity profile is a function of the *non-dimensional distance* from the wall,

$$z_\tau \equiv \frac{z u_\tau^*}{\nu} \ , \tag{6.97}$$

and the relative wall roughness. In the *laminar sublayer* adjacent to a smooth wall,

$$\frac{u}{u_\tau^*} = z_\tau \ . \tag{6.98}$$

As shown in Fig. 6.17, this linear region extends only as far as $z_\tau \doteq 5$. Beyond $z_\tau \doteq 20$ and extending outward for about 10% of the total boundary-layer thickness the velocity profile is

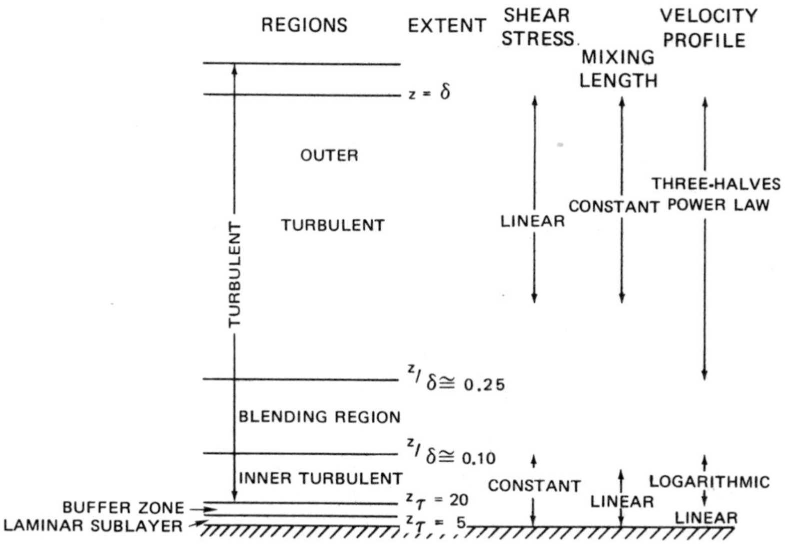


Fig. 6.17. Properties of the Regions of a Smooth-Wall Turbulent Boundary Layer, from Ross (1956)

logarithmic, of the form

$$\frac{u}{u_T^*} = A + B \log z_T \; . \qquad (6.99)$$

For smooth walls, both constants are approximately 5.6. That these coefficients are practically universal constants independent of pressure gradients, Reynolds number and upstream history was first proposed by Ludwieg (1949) and is known as the *law of the wall.* For smooth walls, the log-law relation of Eq. 6.99 intersects the linear relation of Eq. 6.98 at $u_T^* \doteq 11.5$.

As shown in Fig. 6.17, the *outer turbulent region* is characterized by having essentially constant eddy mixing length. Its velocity distribution is a defect relation in which the velocity is expressed relative to its undisturbed value by

$$\frac{u}{u_1} = 1 - f\left(\frac{z}{\delta}\right) \; . \qquad (6.100)$$

That the magnitude of the velocity defect should be a function of upstream rather than local conditions was proposed by Prandtl (1935) and by Schultz-Grunow (1938). Ross and Robertson (1950) demonstrated that this fact is central to an understanding of boundary-layer phenomena. They called the dependence of the outer profile on upstream conditions the *history effect*, and Coles (1956) later named it the *law of the wake*. The outer profile can be expressed as a power function of the distance inward from the outer edge of the layer, namely

$$\left(1 - \frac{u}{u_1}\right) \sim \left(1 - \frac{z}{\delta}\right)^n \; . \qquad (6.101)$$

Ross (1956) chose $n = 1.5$, writing

$$\frac{u}{u_1} = 1 - D\left(1 - \frac{z}{\delta}\right)^{3/2} \quad ; \tag{6.102}$$

other investigators have found better fits to their data using somewhat different values of the exponent. The critical point is that the outer region in all cases is a defect region in which the magnitude of the velocity deficiency and its shape are determined by upstream conditions.

The inner and outer profiles connect in the *blending region*. As shown in Fig. 6.15, this may involve an inflection point. In the blending region both local wall conditions and spatial history are important and no simple velocity profile has been proposed. Figure 6.18 shows how inner and

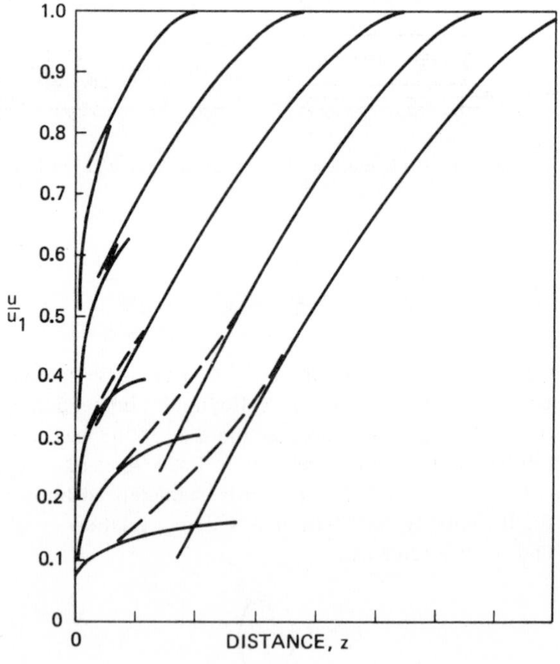


Fig. 6.18. Typical Boundary-Layer Profiles Illustrative of Blending Region, after Ross (1956)

outer regions blend for a number of typical velocity profiles. In some instances the functions for the two major turbulent regions seem to overlap and blending is unnecessary. However, for profiles that have large momentum deficiencies blending may occur through as much as 20% of the boundary layer.

Boundary layers on smooth plates in parallel flows having zero pressure gradients grow quite slowly and have outer turbulent regions which bear a constant relation to their inner regions. Clauser (1956) has called these *equilibrium boundary layers*. Unfortunately, most published boundary-layer analyses treat all boundary layers as though they were equilibrium layers. Not only does this lead to serious errors regarding the mean flow, but also, as will be discussed, it leads to erroneous results concerning turbulent boundary-layer noise. It is essential that the spatial history extending over an upstream distance of about 50 boundary-layer thicknesses be taken into account.

**Boundary-Layer Friction**

The drag which a body experiences due to its boundary layer can be expressed in terms of a dimensionless friction coefficient, $c_f$, defined by

$$c_f \equiv \frac{\tau_w}{\frac{1}{2}\rho_o u_1^2} = 2\left(\frac{u_\tau^*}{u_1}\right)^2 . \qquad (6.103)$$

As shown by Ross (1953, 1956), this friction coefficient is a function of a Reynolds number, $R_\theta$, defined in terms of the local momentum thickness,

$$R_\theta \equiv \frac{\theta u_1}{\nu} , \qquad (6.104)$$

and the effective velocity, $u_\theta$, at a distance out from the wall equal to the momentum thickness. Thus, the law of the wall can be written

$$\frac{u_\theta}{u_1} = \frac{u_\tau^*}{u_1}\left[5.6 + 5.6 \log\left(\frac{u_\tau^*}{u_1} R_\theta\right)\right] , \qquad (6.105)$$

the solution of which is approximately

$$\frac{u_\tau^*}{u_1} = \sqrt{\frac{c_f}{2}} \doteq \frac{u_\theta}{u_1}\left[0.7 + 5.0 \log\left(\frac{u_\theta}{u_1} R_\theta\right)\right]^{-1} . \qquad (6.106)$$

From his study of several hundred velocity profiles, Ross (1956) found

$$\frac{u_\theta}{u_1} \doteq 0.885 - \frac{3}{5} D . \qquad (6.107)$$

It follows that the friction coefficient for a smooth wall is a function of both the local momentum-thickness Reynolds number and previous history of the flow, as expressed by $D$ or an equivalent parameter.

The above relations apply only to walls that are hydraulically smooth, i.e., any roughnesses are smaller than the thickness of the laminar sublayer. Walls having larger roughnesses are called hydraulically rough. For such walls, the laminar sublayer is thicker than it would be for a smooth wall since turbulent motions cannot penetrate into the roughness region. As discussed by Hama (1954), the logarithmic and linear curves for a hydraulically rough wall intersect at a value of $z = \epsilon$ related to the roughness heights and type. It follows that

$$\frac{u}{u_\tau^*} = \frac{\epsilon u_\tau^*}{\nu} + 5.6 \log \frac{z}{\epsilon} \qquad (6.108)$$

in the inner turbulent region of rough boundary layers. It also follows that the skin friction coefficient is higher than for a smooth wall by an amount that depends on the ratio of $\epsilon u_\tau^*/\nu$ to 11.5.

**Boundary-Layer Turbulence**

The basic equations for viscous flows are the continuity equation and the Navier-Stokes form of the momentum equation. These were extended to turbulent conditions by Reynolds (1895), who assumed that instantaneous velocities could be expressed as the sum of time-independent mean values and fluctuating components in much the same manner as in Section 2.2 in deriving the acoustic wave equation. Reynolds found that the turbulent stress is given by

$$\tau_{ij} \doteq \left| \rho_o \overline{u_i' u_j'} \right| , \qquad (6.109)$$

which relation was used by Lighthill in deriving Eq. 3.16 for turbulence noise sources. The turbulent stresses in a boundary layer can also be related to the velocity gradient through a length scale, $\ell$, called the mixing length:

$$\tau = \left| \rho_o \ell^2 \left( \frac{\partial u}{\partial z} \right)^2 \right| . \qquad (6.110)$$

It follows that the level of turbulence is proportional to the product of the mixing length and the velocity gradient.

The 3/2-power velocity deficiency relation, Eq. 6.102, is consistent with the assumptions of constant mixing length and linear dependence of shear stress in the outer region, as indicated in Fig. 6.17. Thus, expressing $\tau$ by

$$\tau(z) = \tau_o \left( 1 - \frac{z}{\delta} \right) , \qquad (6.111)$$

it follows that

$$\frac{du}{dz} = \frac{\sqrt{\tau_o/\rho_o}}{\ell} \sqrt{1 - \frac{z}{\delta}} = \frac{u_{\tau_o}^*}{\ell} \sqrt{1 - \frac{z}{\delta}} \qquad (6.112)$$

and that

$$\frac{u}{u_1} = 1 - \frac{2}{3} \frac{\delta u_{\tau_o}^*}{\ell u_1} \left( 1 - \frac{z}{\delta} \right)^{3/2} . \qquad (6.113)$$

Comparing with Eq. 6.102, the magnitude of the deficiency, $D$, is related to the turbulence level by

$$D = \frac{2}{3} \frac{\delta}{\ell} \frac{u^*_{\tau_o}}{u_1} \approx \frac{\delta}{\ell} \sqrt{\frac{\overline{\overline{u'v'}}}{u_1^2}} . \qquad (6.114)$$

Both the turbulence level and the scale of the eddies in the outer region are dependent on upstream history. Since the mixing length is roughly proportional to the boundary-layer thickness and since this thickness is close to that of an equilibrium boundary layer, it follows that the velocity deficiency is primarily controlled by the level of turbulence generated upstream. Figure 6.19 shows a typical shear stress distribution in which the local wall shear stress, $\tau_w$, is significantly lower than the effective value, $\tau_o$, that describes the outer region.

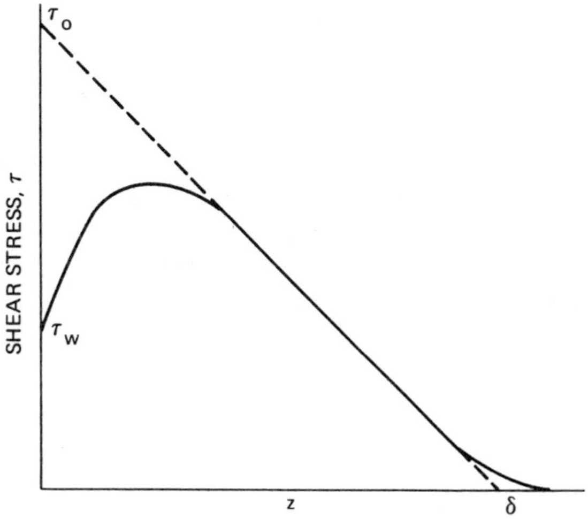


Fig. 6.19. Typical Shear Stress Distribution, from Ross (1956)

For boundary layers on flat plates with zero pressure gradients, $\tau_o$ is related to $\tau_w$ and a single universal velocity can be derived in terms of $u^*_\tau$. The boundary-layer turbulence level can in this case be related to the wall shear stress. However, such relationships between boundary-layer turbulence levels and local wall shear stress coefficients are applicable only when equilibrium conditions exist.

### Intermittency Effects

Equation 6.109 pertains to average turbulence levels in a turbulent flow. Actual turbulent shear flows are characterized by certain large scale phenomena that are called *intermittencies* to distinguish them from the smaller scale turbulent motions. These occur in both the outer and inner regions of a boundary layer. Corrsin and Kistler (1955) reported that the outer edge of a free turbulent shear flow is an irregular surface dividing non-turbulent from turbulent regions. The scale of the waviness is close to half the boundary-layer thickness. Thus, an instrument sensitive to turbulence placed in the outer part of a boundary layer will find itself in a turbulent field only part of the time, the percentage decreasing from 100% at $z \approx \delta/3$ to zero somewhat beyond the apparent boundary-layer thickness.

A second important intermittent effect was discovered by Kline et al (1967), who found evidence of semi-periodic eddy formation in the laminar buffer zone involving large-scale spanwise motions and explosive bursts of turbulence into the turbulent zone. Streaks of vorticity preceding the bursts were photographed and were found to move at speeds close to 13.8 $u_\tau^*$. The importance of this phenomenon was recognized by Black (1966) and by Landahl (1975). The latter concluded that these explosive bursts are a dominant source of high-frequency boundary-layer flow noise.

**Wall Pressure Fluctuations**

Many boundary-layer noise investigations of the past 20 years have concentrated on measuring various properties of wall pressure fluctuations associated with turbulent boundary layers on flat plates and in pipes. The results have been presented as fluctuation spectra and spatial correlations. As shown in Fig. 6.20, pressure fluctuation spectra sometimes peak at a non-dimensional fre-

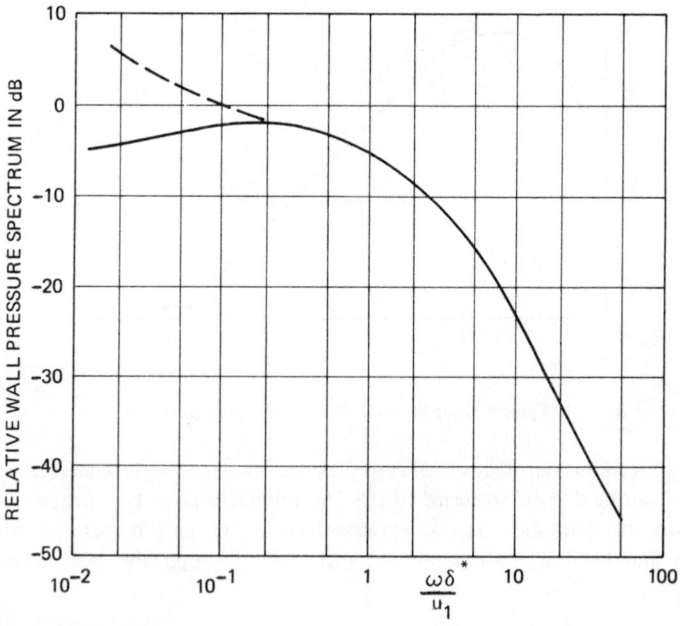


Fig. 6.20. Typical Wall Pressure Fluctuation Spectrum

quency ratio of about 0.2. They decrease markedly at higher frequencies by as much as 9 to 12 dB/octave. Moreover, as calculated by Corcos (1963, 1967) and confirmed by Gilchrist and Strawderman (1965), Lyamshev and Salosina (1966) and Geib (1967, 1969), measured high-frequency spectra are frequently affected by cancellation effects due to finite transducer size. Low-frequency spectra show a great deal of scatter, primarily due to extraneous noises but also due to actual differences of the test configurations.

The total wall pressure is dominated by low-frequency components and therefore is not much affected by transducer size. For equilibrium boundary layers with zero pressure gradient,

$$p_{rms} \approx 3c_f q_1 \approx 0.005 q_1 \, , \tag{6.115}$$

where

$$q_1 \equiv \frac{1}{2} \rho_o u_1^2 \, . \tag{6.116}$$

Different measurements have shown appreciable scatter for this quantity. Also, Mugridge (1971) found that wall pressures in the adverse pressure gradient region of a lifting airfoil are as much as 15 dB higher than those for a flat plate. Schloemer (1967) also found that the spectral distribution of pressure fluctuations is affected by favorable as well as adverse pressure gradients.

Longitudinal correlation measurements show that turbulence is convected by the mean flow. As would be expected, low-frequency components associated with larger eddies in the outer flow are convected at higher speeds than are higher-frequency, small-scale components. Typically, the convection velocity, $u_c$, for low-frequency components is about 80 to 85% of the free-stream flow speed while for the highest frequency components the ratio is only 60 to 65%.

Since turbulent pressure fluctuations are dependent on turbulence levels which in turn are related to hydrodynamic drag through the wall shear stress, it would be expected that anything that could be done to reduce drag would also reduce pressure fluctuations. Kadykov and Lyamshev (1970) confirmed that the addition of dilute polymer solutions reduces pressure fluctuations by from 1 to 8 dB. This reduction of pressure fluctuations is related to the drag reduction first reported by Toms (1948) and more recently confirmed by Fabula (1965), Van Driest (1970) and many others.

### Self-Noise of Flush-Mounted Hydrophones

One form of flow noise is that of flush-mounted hydrophones under a turbulent boundary layer. For such hydrophones, wall pressure fluctuations, sometimes referred to as *pseudo-sound*, are usually the dominant source of self-noise. The pseudo-sound component of the self-noise spectrum is given by the product of the pressure spectrum, as depicted in Fig. 6.20, and the hydrophone size cancellation spectrum; it therefore depends on the ratio of hydrophone size to boundary-layer thickness as well as on the dimensionless frequency.

At the lowest frequencies, hydrophone size effects are negligible and the pressure spectrum is approximately flat. As mentioned above, measurements in this frequency regime show considerable scatter depending on test configuration. However, as summarized by Haddle and Skudrzyk (1969) and by Blake (1970), the wall pressure spectrum can be estimated within a factor of two from

$$p'(\omega) \approx 0.003 \rho_o u_1^{3/2} \delta^{*1/2} \, . \tag{6.117}$$

Thus, low-frequency self-noise levels increase with boundary-layer thickness as well as with flow speed.

For somewhat higher frequencies, most measurements display a negative slope of about 9 dB/octave for about two decades of frequency. For this part of the spectrum, Lyamshev and

Salosina (1966) found

$$p'(\omega) \doteq 0.003 \rho_o u_c^{3/2} a^{1/2} \left( \frac{u_c}{\omega a} \right)^{3/2} \left( \frac{\delta *}{a} \right)^{3/4} . \qquad (6.118)$$

At a given frequency in this part of the spectrum, self-noise increases with the cube of flow speed.

At high frequencies the hydrophone size cancellation effect adds to the spectral slope of the turbulent fluctuations and produces a very rapid decrease of pseudo-sound flow noise. However, flow noise measurements by Skudrzyk and Haddle (1960) showed no such trend. In a later article, Haddle and Skudrzyk (1969) stressed the importance of directly radiated turbulence noise from the boundary layer itself and proposed that such acoustic noise dominates relative to pseudo-sound at the higher frequencies.

Hydrophone shape is important in the frequency region for which flow noise is dominated by pseudo-sound. The dimension which controls in Eq. 6.118 is that in the direction of motion of the flow. Thus, White (1967) has reported reductions of self-noise levels of up to 8 dB by using rectangular and elliptical transducers with their longest dimensions in the direction of flow. These lower flow noise levels in the pseudo-sound regime are associated with the fact that turbulent eddies are convected across the transducer face at a relatively slow speed. Defining a turbulent hydrodynamic wave number, $k_t$, as the ratio of the angular frequency to the convection wave speed, i.e.,

$$k_t \equiv \frac{\omega}{u_c} , \qquad (6.119)$$

one can interpret White's result as the reduction of response of a continuous line array having $kL > 1$, analogous to that for acoustic waves as derived in Section 4.7.

**Arrays of Flush-Mounted Hydrophones**

Just as an array of point transducers can be used in place of a continuous line as a spatial filter for acoustic waves, so an array of small transducers can be used to discriminate against turbulent pressure fluctuations. Jorgensen and Maidanik (1968) compared the filtering action of systems of two and three elements with that of a continuous line, finding equally good discrimination for the discrete systems provided $k_t d < 2$, where $d$ is the separation of the elements. Maidanik (1967) considered a larger number of elements and pointed out that the response could be altered by steering the array, i.e., by introducing phase shifts between the elements. More recently, Kennedy (1975) has shown that optimum beam-forming techniques can be used to design transducer arrays having maximum discrimination against turbulent pressure fluctuations while still having full sensitivity to sonic signals.

Maidanik and Jorgensen (1967) proposed the use of an even-number array of alternating polarity transducers as a system that would be insensitive to acoustic disturbances but would respond to turbulent fluctuations obeying certain relations between wave number and frequency. Such a system, which they termed a *wave-vector filter*, is analogous to a diffraction grating in optics. Its purpose is to study boundary-layer pressure fluctuations without interference from acoustic components of the flow noise. Blake and Chase (1971) applied wave-vector filters to a series of boundary-layer measurements, finding them useful in suppressing wind-tunnel background noise. Wave-vector filters are particularly valuable when making measurements of convection speed as a function of frequency.

**Radiated Flow Noise**

There are several basic physical mechanisms by which noise may be radiated from turbulent boundary layers. Controversy concerning their relative importance has pervaded the literature on this subject and the evidence does not solidly establish any one mechanism as dominant. Furthermore, the effectiveness of any of them is often dependent on secondary factors. It seems likely that in any given situation several physical mechanisms may contribute to the total noise field.

One source of radiated noise from any turbulent fluid motion is the direct quadrupole radiation from the turbulent stresses treated by Lighthill and discussed in Section 3.4. However, this radiation is strongly dependent on Mach number and is negligible at the low Mach numbers of liquid flows. Curle (1955) showed that in the presence of a rigid boundary fluctuating shear stresses can produce dipole radiation associated with the resultant wall pressure fluctuations. Powell (1960) noted that when the wall is planar, rigid and large compared to a wavelength these dipole components tend to cancel and in this case the only effect of the boundary is to augment the quadrupole radiation by a factor of four. More recently, Landahl (1975) reexamined this question in light of the discovery by Kline et al (1967) of turbulence bursts in the laminar buffer region. Landahl showed that the intensity of dipole radiation associated with these bursts is

$$I \sim \tau_w u_\tau^* \left( \frac{u_\tau^*}{c_o} \right)^3 S = \rho_o u_1^3 \left( \frac{c_f}{2} \right)^3 M^3 S \; . \tag{6.120}$$

Since $c_f$ varies with flow speed approximately as $u_1^{-1/5}$, this direct radiation can be expected to vary with flow speed to approximately the 5.4 power.

Haddle and Skudrzyk (1969) measured the noise radiated by metal shell and solid wood buoyant bodies of torpedo shape. Their measured levels were independent of body construction, from which they concluded that direct radiation from the turbulence was the dominant mechanism. However, other (unpublished) results indicate that noise radiated by buoyant bodies may come from the stabilizing fins rather than from the body itself. Since the same fins were used on both models, the Haddle and Skudrzyk results cannot be said to prove conclusively that rigid-wall turbulence radiation is dominant.

The mechanism that has received the most attention is that of excitation of flexural vibrations by wall pressure fluctuations and radiation by these vibrations. Evidence that this mechanism can be a dominant one was found by Ludwig (1962) and Maestrello (1965). Both investigators measured the noise radiated by rectangular panels in wind tunnels, finding roughly fifth-power dependencies on flow speed and inverse variation of radiated acoustic power with plate thickness.

While several theoretical analyses of flow noise involving wall flexural vibrations have been made, none can be said to be consistently in good agreement with experimental results. Most of the turbulent energy is convected at speeds that are low compared to the speeds of both plate flexural waves and sound in the acoustic medium. As a result, all but a very small fraction of the vibratory energy induced in the plate by the turbulence is in non-radiating modes. Radiation can only occur from that very small fraction of the turbulent energy that is in the very low wave number part of the spectrum and from any of the higher wave number vibratory components that are converted to low wave numbers through scattering by ribs, supports and other discontinuities.

The first attempt to calculate radiated flow noise involving plate flexural vibrations was made by Dyer (1958, 1959). He found that the mean-square plate vibration is independent of turbulence convection speed when that speed is small compared to the speed of flexural waves, as is true for liquids. Dyer also predicted that plate damping would be an effective method of reducing flow noise. A similar analysis by Aupperle and Lambert (1973) for thin plates gave results in good agreement with experimental data reported by Ludwig (1962). White (1966) and Davies (1971) applied modal analyses treating corner as well as edge modes to derive formulas for the radiated flow noise of thin panels in air. Their results also appear to be in good agreement with thin panel experimental measurements. Davies found that fluid loading effects can reduce radiated flow noise levels from thin panels by as much as 10 to 15 dB.

Turbulent pressure fluctuations seem clearly to excite structural vibrations in non-rigid walls. Strawderman and Brand (1969) and others have successfully calculated these vibrations using measured wall pressure spectra and Corcos' (1964) results for cross-power spectral densities. The degree to which these vibrations radiate and the ratio of their radiation to rigid-wall dipole radiation remain unknown. The author agrees with Vecchio and Wiley (1973), who concluded that flexural wave radiation is usually dominant at low frequencies while direct dipole radiation is often stronger at the higher frequencies.

**Domed Sonar Self-Noise**

In order to avoid the direct pseudo-sound noise of turbulent boundary-layer pressure fluctuations, most sonar receivers are located inside thin domes that isolate them from the turbulence while transmitting acoustic signals virtually undistorted. The turbulence is then on the other side of the structure from the receiver, and flexural vibrations and their radiation must be the dominant mechanism whereby flow noise is received. Analyses of this case have been published by Dyer (1958), Plakhov (1966), Maidanik (1968) and Dowell (1969, 1970). Dyer attempted a complete analysis of both vibration excitation and cavity radiation aspects of the problem but was forced for lack of sufficient information to make a number of simplifying assumptions. He noted that coincidence may occur within the frequency range of interest and that radiation should be treated differently in the two frequency regimes. Plakhov treated the problem in a manner similar to that of transmission through a wall placed between two fluids having respective wave speeds of $u_c$ and $c_o$. He concluded that those structural properties which increase the *TL* of a wall also tend to decrease turbulent flow noise. In agreement with this conclusion, Maidanik noted that ribs and other discontinuities that increase radiation of flexural waves from plates also increase the transmission of turbulence noise. Dowell included the effects of non-linear plate stiffness and cavity fluid motions, finding that flutter can occur in some cases when the panel is very thin.

In summary, while no single, simple formulation is available, it appears that domes do indeed reduce flow noise levels in most cases, and that dome design should follow the principles of good wall design by avoiding discontinuities that can act to transform vibrations from high wave number, non-radiating modes into low wave number, radiating modes.

## REFERENCES

Sections 6.1-6.4

Blake, W.K., The acoustic radiation from unbaffled strips with application to a class of radiating panels, *J. Sound and Vibr., 39*, 77-103, 1975.

Blank, F.G., Sound field near a vibrating elastic plate, *Sov. Phys.-Acoustics, 14*, 31-36, 1968.

Brekhovskikh, L.M., Propagation of flexural waves in plates, *J. Tech. Phys. (USSR), 14*, 9, 568-576, 1955 (in Russian).

Cremer, L., Theorie der Schalldämmung dunner Wände bei Schragen Einfall, *Akustische Zeit.,* 7, 81-104, 1942.

Cremer, L., The Propagation of Structure-Borne Sound, *Dept. of Scientific and Indust. Res. (London) Sponsored Res., Rept. Ser. B*, No. 1, 1950; also, *Acustica, 3*, 317-335, 1953.

Cremer, L., Heckl, M. and Ungar, E.E., *Structure-Borne Sound*, Springer-Verlag, New York, 1973 (Chapters 4 and 6).

Crighton, D.G., Force and momentum admittance of plates under arbitrary fluid loading, *J. Sound and Vibr., 20*, 209-218, 1972.

Donaldson, J.M., Reduction of noise radiated from ship structures, *Applied Acoustics, 1*, 275-291, 1968.

Dyer, I., Moment impedance of plates, *J.A.S.A., 32*, 1290-1297, 1960.

Feit, D., Pressure radiated by a point-excited elastic plate, *J.A.S.A., 40*, 1489-1494, 1966.

Feit, D., Sound radiation from orthotropic plates, *J.A.S.A., 47*, 388-389, 1970.

Franken, P.A., Input impedances of simple cylindrical structures, *J.A.S.A., 32*, 473-477, 1960.

Gösele, K., Radiation from plates excited into bending vibrations, *Acustica, 3*, 243-248, 1953; *6*, 94-98, 1956 (in German).

Gutin, L. Ya, Sound radiation from an infinite plate excited by a normal point force, *Sov. Phys.-Acoustics, 10*, 369-371, 1964.

Heckl, M., Radiation from point-excited plates, *Acustica, 9*, 371-380, 1959 (in German).

Heckl, M., Investigation of orthotropic plates, *Acustica, 10*, 109-115, 1960 (in German).

Heckl, M., Wave propagation of beam-plate systems, *J.A.S.A., 33*, 640-651, 1961.

Heckl, M., Vibrations of point-driven cylindrical shells, *J.A.S.A., 34*, 1553-1557, 1962.

Heckl, M., Radiation from a point-excited plate in water, *Acustica, 13*, 182, 1963 (in German).

Howe, M.S. and Heckl, M., Sound radiation from plates with density and stiffness discontinuities, *J. Sound and Vibr., 21*, 193-203, 1972.

Junger, M.C., "Structure-Borne Noise," in *Structural Mechanics*, Pergamon Press, Oxford, 1960.

Junger, M.C. and Feit, D., *Sound, Structures and Their Interaction*, M.I.T. Press, Cambridge, Mass., 1972 (Chapters 5 to 8 and 10).

Junger, M.C., Radiation and scattering by submerged elastic structures, *J.A.S.A., 57*, 1318-1326, 1975.

Kinsler, L.E. and Frey, A.R., *Fundamentals of Acoustics*, 2nd Edit., Wiley, New York, 1962 (Chapter 4).

Komarova, L.N., Radiation from shells, *Sov. Phys.-Acoustics, 15*, 332-335, 1969.

Kurtze, G. and Bolt, R.H., On the interaction between plate bending waves and their radiation load, *Acustica, 9*, Beihefte 1, 238-242, 1959.

Lyapunov, V.T., Flexural wave propagation in a liquid-loaded plate with an obstruction, *Sov. Phys.-Acoustics, 14*, 353-355, 479-482, 1968.

Lyon, R.H., Sound radiation from a beam attached to a plate, *J.A.S.A., 34*, 1265-1268, 1962.

Maidanik, G., Response of ribbed panels to reverberent acoustic fields, *J.A.S.A., 34*, 809-826, 1962.

Maidanik, G., The influence of fluid loading on the radiation from orthotropic plates, *J. Sound and Vibr., 3*, 288-299, 1966.

Maidanik, G. and Kerwin, E.M., Jr., Influence of fluid loading on the radiation from infinite plates below the critical frequency, *J.A.S.A., 40*, 1034-1038, 1966.

Maidanik, G., Vibrational and radiative classifications of modes of a baffled finite panel, *J. Sound and Vibr., 34*, 447-455, 1974.

Manning, J.E. and Maidanik, G., Radiation properties of cylindrical shells, *J.A.S.A., 36*, 1691-1699, 1964.

Mindlin, R.D., Influence of rotatory inertia and shear on flexural motions of isotropic elastic plates, *J. Appl. Mech., 18*, 31-38, 1951.

Morse, P.M. and Ingard, K.U., *Theoretical Acoustics*, McGraw-Hill, New York, 1968 (Chapter 10).

Nelson, H.M., A universal dispersion curve for flexural wave propagation in plates and bars, *J. Sound and Vibr., 18*, 93-100, 1971.

Nikiforov, A.S., Radiation from a plate of finite dimensions with arbitrary boundary conditions, *Sov. Phys.-Acoustics, 10*, 178-182, 1964.

Nikiforov, A.S., Vibration reduction of a single reinforcing beam, *Sov. Phys.-Acoustics, 15*, 541-542, 1969.

Plakhov, D.D., Sound field of a multispan plate, *Sov. Phys.-Acoustics, 13*, 506-510, 1967.

Rayleigh, Lord, *Theory of Sound*, Vol. I, Dover, New York, 1945 (Chapters 10 and 10A).

Romanov, V.N., Radiation of sound by an infinite plate with reinforcing beams, *Sov. Phys.-Acoustics, 17*, 92-96, 1971, and *18*, 490-493, 1972.

Rybak, S.A. and Tartakovskii, B.D., On the vibrations of thin plates, *Sov. Phys.-Acoustics, 9*, 51-55, 1963.

Skudrzyk, E.J., Kautz, B.R. and Greene, D.C., Vibration of, and bending-wave propagation in plates, *J.A.S.A., 33*, 36-45, 1961.

Skudrzyk, E., *Simple and Complex Vibratory Systems*, The Pennsylvania State University Press, University Park, Pa., 1968 (Chapters 8, 9, 12 and 14).

Smith, P.W., Jr., Coupling of sound and panel vibration below the critical frequency, *J.A.S.A., 36*, 1516-1520, 1964.

Snowdon, J.C., Forced vibration of internally damped rectangular and square plates, *J.A.S.A., 56*, 1177-1184, 1974.

Szechenyi, E., Modal densities and radiation efficiencies of unstiffened cylinders using statistical methods, *J. Sound and Vibr., 19*, 65-81, 83-94, 1971.

Ungar, E.E., Transmission of plate flexural waves through reinforcing beams, *J.A.S.A., 33*, 633-639, 1961.

Ver, I.L. and Holmer, C.I. "Interaction of Sound Waves with Solid Structures," Chapter 11 in *Noise and Vibration Control*, L.L. Beranek (Ed.), McGraw-Hill, New York, 1971 (pp. 270-357).

Westphal, W., Radiation of flexurally excited walls, *Acustica, 4*, 603-610, 1954 (in German).

Yaneske, P.P., A restatement of the principle of coincidence and resonance, *J. Sound and Vibr., 25*, 51-73, 1972.

## Section 6.5

Beranek, L.L., The transmission and radiation of acoustic waves by structures, *J. Inst. Mech. Engin., 6*, 162-169, 1959; also, Chapter 13 of *Noise Reduction*, L.L. Beranek (Ed.), McGraw-Hill, New York, 1960.

Cremer, L., Heckl, M. and Ungar, E.E., *op. cit.* (Chapter 6).

Crocker, M.J. and Price, A.J., Sound transmission using statistical energy analysis, *J. Sound and Vibr., 9*, 469-486, 1969.

Heckl, M., Several applications of the reciprocity principle in acoustics, *Frequenz, 18*, 299-304, 1964 (in German).

Kinsler, L.E. and Frey, A.R., *op. cit.* (Chapter 6).

Kurtze, G., Bending wave propagation in multilayer plates, *J.A.S.A., 31*, 1183-1201, 1959.

Kurtze, G. and Watters, B.G., New wall design for high transmission loss or high damping, *J.A.S.A., 31*, 739-748, 1959.

Kurtze, G., *Physik und Technik der Lärmbekämpfung*, G. Braun, Karlsruhe, 1964 (Chapters 4 and 5).

Lyamshev, L.M., A question in connection with the principle of reciprocity in acoustics, *Sov. Phys.-Doklady, 4*, 406-409, 1959.

Plakov, D.D., Transmission of a sound wave through a laminated plate reinforced with stiffness members, *Sov. Phys.-Acoustics, 14*, 67-70, 1968.

Richards, E.J. and Mead, D.J. (Ed.), *Noise and Acoustic Fatigue in Aeronautics*, John Wiley, London, 1968 (Chapters 3 and 23).

Schiller, K.K., Physical aspects of sound insulation through walls, *J. Sound and Vibr., 6*, 283-295, 1967.

Shenderov, E.L., Transmission of sound through a thin plate with interjacent supports, *Sov. Phys.-Acoustics, 9*, 289-294, 1963.

Shenderov, E.L., Sound transmission through a thin supported plate, *Sov. Phys.-Acoustics, 10*, 187-190, 1964.

Shenderov, E.L., Relationship of sound radiation by plates to their acoustic transmissivity, *Sov. Phys.-Acoustics, 12*, 336-338, 1966.

Smith, P.W., Jr., *op. cit.*, 1964.

Venzke, G., Dämmig, P. and Fischer, H.W., Influence of stiffeners on the sound radiation and transmission loss of metal walls, *Acustica, 29*, 29-40, 1973 (in German).

Ver, I.L. and Holmer, C.I., *op. cit.* (1971).

Warren, W.E., Low-frequency power radiation from a flat plate into an acoustic fluid, *J.A.S.A., 56*, 1764-1769, 1974.

White, P.H. and Powell, A., Transmission of random sound and vibration through a rectangular double wall, *J.A.S.A., 40*, 821-832, 1966.

Young, J.E., Transmission of sound through thin elastic plates, *J.A.S.A., 26*, 485-492, 1954.

## Section 6.6

Aupperle, F.A. and Lambert, R.F., Effects of roughness on measured wall-pressure fluctuations beneath a turbulent boundary layer, *J.A.S.A., 47*, 359-370, 1970.

Aupperle, F.A. and Lambert, R.F., Acoustic radiation from plates excited by flow noise, *J. Sound and Vibr., 26*, 223-245, 1973.

Black, T.J., "Some Practical Applications of a New Theory of Wall Turbulence," Paper 21 in *Proc. 1966 Heat Transfer and Fluid Mechanics Institute*, Stanford University Press, 1966 (pp. 366-386).

Blake, W.K., Turbulent boundary-layer wall pressure fluctuations on smooth and rough walls, *J. Fluid Mech., 44*, 637-660, 1970.

Blake, W.K. and Chase, D.M., Wave number-frequency spectra of turbulent-boundary-layer pressure measured by microphone arrays, *J.A.S.A., 49*, 862-877, 1971.

Bull, M.K., Wall-pressure fluctuations associated with subsonic turbulent-boundary-layer flow, *J. Fluid Mech., 28*, 719-754, 1967.

Clauser, F.H., "The Turbulent Boundary Layer," in *Advances in Applied Mechanics*, Vol IV, Academic Press, New York, 1956.

Coles, D., The law of the wake in the turbulent boundary layer, *J. Fluid Mech., 1*, 191-226, 1956.

Corcos, G.M., Resolution of pressure in turbulence, *J.A.S.A., 35*, 192-199, 1963.

Corcos, G.M., Structure of the turbulent pressure field in boundary-layer flows, *J. Fluid Mech., 18*, 353-378, 1964.

Corcos, G.M., The resolution of turbulent pressures at the wall of a boundary layer, *J. Sound and Vibr., 6*, 59-70, 1967.

Corrsin, S. and Kistler, A.L., Free-Stream Boundaries of Turbulent Flows, *N.A.C.A. Tech. Rept. 1244*, 1955.

Crighton, D.G. and Ffowcs Williams, J.E., Real space-time Green's functions applied to plate vibrations induced by turbulent flows, *J. Fluid Mech., 38*, 305-314, 1969.

Curle, N., The influence of solid boundaries upon aerodynamic sound, *Proc. Royal Soc. (London), A231*, 505-514, 1955.

Davies, H.G., Low-frequency random excitation of water-loaded rectangular plates, *J. Sound and Vibr., 15*, 107-126, 1971.

Davies, H.G., Sound from turbulent-boundary-layer-excited panels, *J.A.S.A., 49*, 878-889, 1971.

Dowell, E.H., Transmission of noise from a turbulent boundary layer through a flexible plate into a closed cavity, *J.A.S.A., 46*, 238-252, 1969.

Dowell, E.H., Noise or flutter or both, *J. Sound and Vibr., 11*, 159-180, 1970.

Dyer, I., "Sound Radiation into a Closed Space from Boundary Layer Turbulence," *Proc. Second Symposium on Naval Hydrodynamics*, O.N.R. ACR-38, Washington, 1958 (pp. 151-174).

Dyer, I., Response of plates to a decaying and convecting random pressure field, *J.A.S.A., 31*, 922-928, 1959.

Fabula, A.G., "The Toms Phenomenon in the Turbulent Flow of Very Dilute Polymer Solutions," in *Proc. Fourth Inter. Congr. on Rheology*, Interscience Publ., New York, 1965 (pp. 455-479).

Ffowcs Williams, J.E., The influence of simple supports on the radiation from turbulent flow near a plane compliant surface, *J. Fluid Mech., 26*, 641-649, 1966.

Ffowcs Williams, J.R. and Hall, L.H., Aerodynamic sound generation by turbulent flow near a half plane, *J. Fluid Mech., 40*, 657-670, 1970.

Gardner, S., On surface pressure fluctuations produced by boundary layer turbulence, *Acustica, 16*, 67-74, 1965.

Geib, F.E., Jr., Measurements on the effect of transducer size on the resolution of boundary-layer pressure fluctuations, *J.A.S.A., 46*, 253-261, 1969.

Gilchrist, R.B. and Strawderman, W.A., Experimental hydrophone-size connection factor for boundary-layer pressure fluctuations, *J.A.S.A., 38*, 298-302, 1965.

Haddle, G.P. and Skudrzyk, E.J., The physics of flow noise, *J.A.S.A., 46*, 130-157, 1969.

Hama, F.R., Boundary-layer characteristics for smooth and rough surfaces, *Trans. Soc. of Naval Arch. and Marine Eng., 62*, 333-358, 1954.

Hoyt, J.W. and Fabula, A.G., "The Effect of Additives on Fluid Friction," *Proc. Fifth Symposium on Naval Hydrodynamics*, O.N.R. ACR-112, Washington, 1964 (pp. 947-974).

Jorgensen, D.W. and Maidanik, G., Response of a system of point transducers to turbulent boundary-layer pressure field, *J.A.S.A., 43*, 1390-1394, 1968.

Kadykov, I.F. and Lyamshev, L.M., Influence of polymer additives on the pressure fluctuations in a boundary layer, *Sov. Phys.-Acoustics, 16*, 59-63, 1970.

Kennedy, R.M., Cancellation of turbulent boundary-layer pressure fluctuations, *J.A.S.A., 57*, 1062-1066, 1975.

Kline, S.J., Reynolds, W.C., Schraub, F.A. and Runstadler, P.W., The structure of turbulent boundary layers, *J. Fluid Mech., 30*, 741-773, 1967.

Landahl, M.T., Wave mechanics of boundary-layer turbulence and noise, *J.A.S.A., 57*, 824-831, 1975.

Leehey, P., "Trends in Boundary Layer Noise Research," in *Aerodynamic Noise*, H.S. Ribner (Ed.), University of Toronto Press, Toronto, 1969.

Lilley, G.M., Pressure Fluctuations in an Incompressible Turbulent Boundary Layer, *Cranfield College of Aero. Rept. 133*, June 1960.

Ludwieg, H., Instrument for measuring the wall shearing stress of turbulent boundary layers, *Ing.-Archiv, 17*, 207-218, 1949; translated in *N.A.C.A. Tech. Memo 1284*, 1950.

Ludwieg, H. and Tillmann, W., Investigation of the wall shearing stress in turbulent boundary layers, *Ing.-Archiv, 17*, 288-299, 1949; translated in *N.A.C.A. Tech. Memo 1285*, 1950.

Ludwig, G.R., An Experimental Investigation of the Sound Generated by Thin Steel Panels Excited by Turbulent Flow, *Univ. of Toronto, Inst. for Aero. Studies Rept. 87*, Nov. 1962.

Lyamshev, L.M., Analysis of acoustic radiation from a turbulent aerodynamic flow, *Sov. Phys.-Acoustics, 6*, 472-476, 1960.

Lyamshev, L.M. and Solosina, S.A., Influence of pickup dimensions on measurement of the spectrum of wall pressure fluctuations in a boundary layer, *Sov. Phys.-Acoustics, 12*, 228-229, 1966.

Maestrello, L., Measurement of noise radiated by boundary-layer excited panels, *J. Sound and Vibr., 2*, 100-115, 270-292, 1965.

Maestrello, L., Use of a turbulent model to calculate the vibration and radiation responses of a panel, *J. Sound and Vibr., 5*, 407-448, 1967.

Maidanik, G., Flush-mounted pressure transducer systems as spatial and spectral filters, *J.A.S.A., 42*, 1017-1024, 1967.

Maidanik, G. and Jorgensen, D.W., Boundary wave-vector filters for the study of the pressure field in a turbulent boundary layer, *J.A.S.A., 42*, 494-501, 1967.

Maidanik, G., Domed sonar system, *J.A.S.A., 44*, 113-124, 1968.

Mugridge, B.D., Turbulent boundary layers and surface pressure fluctuations on two-dimensional aerofoils, *J. Sound and Vibr., 18*, 475-486, 1971.

Plakhov, D.D., Sound field of an infinite plate acted upon by random pressure fluctuations, *Sov. Phys.-Acoustics, 12*, 415-418, 1966.

Powell, A., Aerodynamic noise and the plane boundary, *J.A.S.A., 32*, 982-990, 1960.

Prandtl, L., "The Mechanics of Viscous Fluids," in Vol. 3 of *Aerodynamic Theory*, W.F. Durand (Ed.), Julius Springer, Berlin, 1935.

Reynolds, O., On the dynamical theory of incompressible viscous fluids, *Phil. Trans. Royal Soc. (London), A186*, 123-164, 1895.

Richards, E.J. and Mead, D.J. (Ed.), *Noise and Acoustic Fatigue in Aeronautics*, John Wiley, London, 1968 (Chapters 8, 14 and 15).

Ross, D. and Robertson, J.M., Shear stress in a turbulent boundary layer, *J. Appl. Phys., 21*, 557-561, 1950.

Ross, D. and Robertson, J.M., A superposition analysis of the turbulent boundary layer in an adverse pressure gradient, *J. Appl. Mech., 18*, 95-100, 1951.

Ross, D., "A New Analysis of Nikuradse's Experiments on Turbulent Flow in Smooth Pipes," in *Proc. Third Midwestern Conf. on Fluid Mechanics*, Univ. of Minnesota, 1953; also *Ord. Res. Lab. Rept. 7958-246*, Sept. 1952.

Ross, D., A physical approach to turbulent-boundary-layer problems, *Trans. Am. Soc. Civil Engin., 121*, 1219-1254, 1956.

Schlichting, H., *Boundary-Layer Theory*, 6th Edit., McGraw-Hill, New York, 1968 (Chapters 3, 4, 18-22).

Schloemer, H.H., Effects of pressure gradients on turbulent-boundary-layer wall-pressure fluctuations, *J.A.S.A., 42*, 93-113, 1967.

Schubauer, G.B. and Tchen, C.M., *Turbulent Flow*, Princeton University Press, Princeton, 1959 (Chapter 4).

Schultz-Grunow, F., "Über das Nachwirken der Turbulenz bei örtlich und zeitlich verzögerter Grenzschichtströmung," *Proc. Fifth Inter. Cong. for Appl. Mech.*, Cambridge, Mass., 1938 (pp. 428-435).

Skudrzyk, E.J. and Haddle, G.P., Noise production in a turbulent boundary layer by smooth and rough surfaces, *J.A.S.A., 32*, 19-34, 1960; also *Proc. Second Symposium on Naval Hydrodynamics*, O.N.R. ACR-38, Washington, 1958 (pp. 75-105).

Strawderman, W.A. and Brand, R.S., Turbulent-flow-excited vibration of a simply supported rectangular flat plate, *J.A.S.A., 45*, 177-192, 1969.

Toms, B.A., "Some Observations on the Flow of Linear Polymer Solutions through Straight Tubes at Large Reynolds Numbers," in *Proc. Fifth Inter. Congr. on Rheology*, North Holland Publ. Co., Amsterdam, 1948 (pp. 135-141).

Townsend, A.A., Equilibrium layers and wall turbulence, *J. Fluid Mech., 11*, 97-120, 1961.

Van Driest, E.R., Turbulent drag reduction of polymeric solutions, *J. Hydronautics, 4*, 120-126, 1970.

Vecchio, E.A. and Wiley, C.A., Noise radiated from a turbulent boundary layer, *J.A.S.A., 53*, 596-601, 1973.

White, P.H., Transduction of boundary-layer noise by a rectangular panel, *J.A.S.A., 40*, 1354-1362, 1966.

White, P.H., Effect of transducer size, shape, and surface sensitivity on the measurement of boundary-layer pressures, *J.A.S.A., 41*, 1358-1363, 1967.

Willmarth, W.W. and Wooldridge, C.E., Measurements of the fluctuating pressure at the wall beneath a thick turbulent boundary layer, *J. Fluid Mech., 14*, 187-210, 1962; also *Univ. of Michigan Tech. Rept. 02920-2-T*, April 1962.

Willmarth, W.W. and Roos, F.W., Resolution and structure of the wall pressure field beneath a turbulent boundary layer, *J. Fluid Mech., 22*, 81-94, 1965.

Willmarth, W.W., Pressure fluctuations beneath turbulent boundary layers, *Ann. Rev. Fluid Mech., 7*, 13-38, 1975.

# CHAPTER 7

# CAVITATION

## 7.1 Introduction

The term *cavitation* was first used by R.E. Froude, S.W. Barnaby and Sir Charles Parsons in connection with propeller performance breakdown of early steamships. In 1895 Parsons built the first water tunnel to study cavitation, and some 20 years later he made the connection between cavitation and the erosion of marine propellers.

*Cavitation is the rupture of a liquid or of a liquid-solid interface caused by reduction of local static pressure.* A *rupture* is the formation of a macroscopic or visible bubble. Liquids contain many microscopic and submicroscopic voids which, as will be explained, act as *nuclei* for cavitation. However, cavitation is only said to occur when these voids grow to significant size. Cavitation is distinguished from boiling in being caused by a reduction of local static pressure rather than by an increase of temperature.

Cavitation occurs in many ways, can have both beneficial and deleterious effects, produces light as well as sound and is of interest to physicists, chemists, biologists and doctors as well as to many types of engineers. Controlled cavitation is used in the ultrasonics industry for cleaning, etching and cutting. It is also used to accelerate some chemical reactions, and it may be used in the practice of medicine for destruction of undesirable cells. However, most interest in cavitation is in avoiding its undesired effects. Not only does cavitation produce unwanted noise, but also it causes erosion damage to pipes, valves, pumps, turbines and propellers. It also causes damage in bearings, contributes to erosion of diesel-engine cylinder liners and limits the outputs of sonar transducers.

Cavitation is an especially important noise source in underwater acoustics. Since it involves volume changes, it is basically a monopole noise source. In marine vehicles, cavitation usually occurs most seriously on the propulsor. While submarines and torpedoes can often avoid cavitation by operating at deep depths, surface ships cannot avoid it. Propeller cavitation noise of surface ships is usually dominant over the entire spectrum from subaudible to ultrasonic frequencies; whenever submarines or torpedoes operate so as to experience cavitation, it is a dominant noise source for them as well.

Cavitation is described by the *cause* of the static pressure drop, the *location* of the rupture and the *contents* of the bubble. One cause of cavitation is the pressure drop occurring in the negative half cycle of a sound wave. A sound wave in a liquid having a sound pressure level (SPL) of 220 dB re 1 $\mu$Pa has a peak negative pressure of over 1 atm. Such *acoustic cavitation* can limit transducer outputs but also is used to produce beneficial effects in ultrasonics devices. A second cause of pressure drop is flow of liquids in hydraulic systems, called *hydraulic cavitation*. A third type is associated with the motion of bodies in a liquid, or the equivalent motion of liquids past stationary bodies. This is termed *body cavitation* for three-dimensional bodies and *hydrofoil cavitation* for flows past two-dimensional shapes. Since they experience the highest relative flow speeds, propeller blade tips are usually the first part of a vehicle to cavitate. *Propeller cavitation* is a most important source of underwater noise.

There are two locations where cavitation occurs: at a liquid-solid interface or within the volume of the liquid. While theory usually deals with *volume cavitation*, most cavitation actually occurs at or very close to solid surfaces, as *boundary* or *surface cavitation*.

All cavitation bubbles contain mixtures of vapor and gas, and cavitation is called vaporous or gaseous depending on which is dominant. *Vapor cavitation* causes most of the noise and erosion associated with cavitation, but *gaseous cavitation* can limit transducer outputs and cause serious effects in biological systems.

Robertson (1969) estimated that more than 10,000 papers have been published on cavitation, yet there are only a very few books devoted to this subject, most of which are the proceedings of symposia. Similarly, the subject is often mentioned in university courses but rarely treated in any detail. This lack of attention is hard to comprehend. The present chapter covers the physics of this phenomenon, with emphasis on those aspects important to an understanding of its noise production. The following chapter covers propeller cavitation and includes sections on surface ship noise and the contribution of such noise to the ocean's ambient background.

## 7.2 Tensile Strength of Liquids

A *fluid* is distinguished from a solid by the fact that it cannot permanently sustain a shear stress. Most persons would describe a *liquid* as an almost incompressible fluid that cannot sustain tension. Actually the latter attribute is not always true. Under certain conditions liquids can sustain very high tensions without rupturing. In fact, very pure liquids are capable of withstanding tensions of tens or even hundreds of atmospheres. It is impurities in a liquid that cause it to rupture at much lower pressures.

### Static Tensile Strength

The intermolecular forces resisting rupture of a pure, gas-free liquid are very strong. Calculations based on the kinetic theory of liquids predict static tensile strengths for water in excess of a thousand atmospheres. Other estimates, based on the van der Waals equation of state, predict maximum strengths of the order of 250 to 275 atm. Attempts at measurement within the volume of a liquid are often frustrated by ruptures at liquid-solid interfaces. However, several investigators have observed values in excess of 100 atm.

Extremely high tensions have only been measured with small samples of very pure liquid in very clean containers. However, tensions of up to an atmosphere or so can occur in the laboratory without such extreme measures. All that is required is that prior to the experiment the liquid be pressurized or other steps taken to eliminate undissolved air bubbles. It is this ability of water free of entrapped air to sustain tension that is responsible for boiler explosions. When water has been boiled for a long time, it may lose its air bubbles and be able to sustain several degrees of superheat. When this happens, each rupture releases a lot of energy. A crack may then occur, followed by an explosion.

### Cavitation Nuclei

It is now recognized that the seeds of cavitation and boiling are the many small impurities and/or microscopic bubbles that normally exist in a liquid. To understand how these nuclei control cavitation inception, consider a small, gas-filled, spherical void in a liquid. Because of the action of surface tension, the pressure inside the bubble is higher than that outside. Thus, the pressure outside the bubble can be reduced somewhat below zero, i.e., can become a tension, while the pressure inside the bubble remains positive. If the outside pressure is reduced below zero by an amount that exceeds the surface-tension pressure rise, then the pressure inside the bubble will be low enough that rapid vaporization can take place and rupture will occur.

The pressure drop across a stationary free surface due to surface tension is given by

$$\Delta p = p_i - p_o = \frac{2\sigma}{a}, \tag{7.1}$$

where $\sigma$ is the surface tension and $a$ is the radius of curvature of the surface. For water at room temperature, $\sigma \doteq 72$ dynes/cm. Figure 7.1 is a plot of the surface-tension pressure change as a function of radius, showing, for example, that a radius of $10^{-4}$ cm will sustain a pressure difference of 1.4 atm. Static tensions of over 100 atm. require that maximum bubble sizes be under $10^{-6}$ cm, i.e., so small as not to be visible under a powerful microscope.

While today there is no doubt that nuclei control cavitation inception, there is still considerable controversy in the literature concerning the exact nature of the nuclei and their causes. Akulichev (1965, 1966) has considered the roles of solid particles and of ions. He found that ions causing negative hydration reduce the tensile strength of water, while positive hydration ions have no effect. Apfel (1970) has explained experimental results of Strasberg (1959), Barger (1964),

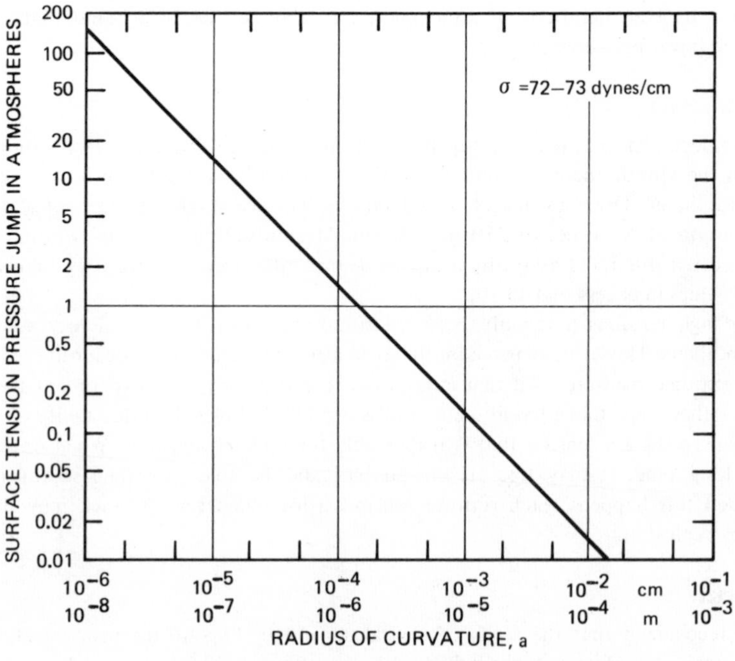


Fig. 7.1. Surface-Tension Pressure Difference Across a Water Surface as Function of Curvature

Galloway (1954) and others by assuming nuclei to be gas-filled crevices in tiny solid motes. Bernd (1966) considered the effects of surface films in stabilizing such nuclei. Sette and Wanderlingh (1962) showed that even cosmic rays can affect the nucleus population in a pure liquid. Sirotyuk (1965) has shown that tensile strength is clearly related to the distribution of nuclei, as has Lauterborn (1969) who found that repeated cavitation tends to use up the largest nuclei and that tensile strength therefore increases with time.

In summary, although the exact cause and nature of submicroscopic nuclei in liquids are uncertain, there is full agreement that somehow such gas nuclei do exist, and that the largest ones in a population determine the tensile strength of the liquid.

### Dynamic Tensile Strengths

Often, as in flowing liquids or in exposure to transient pulses, the liquid is under tension for only a short time. In such cases higher breaking strengths are found, either because the largest nuclei happen not to be in the peak negative-pressure region or because there is insufficient time for a microscopic bubble to grow into a macroscopic one. Many researchers have reported on cavitation inception experiments in a variety of liquids with a number of different types of setups. It is generally agreed that dynamic effects can be important when exposure times are shorter than about 1 msec.

Dynamic effects are especially important in ultrasonics, where exposure times per cycle are less than 0.03 msec. They are also important in many laboratory experiments, such as water tunnel tests, for which exposures of less than 1 msec are common. However, most full-scale marine occurrences involve exposure times in excess of 10 or even 100 msec, providing ample time for macroscopic cavities to form. Also, most liquids encountered in engineering situations are relatively dirty and contain numerous nuclei larger than $10^{-3}$ cm. Thus, it is only in model experiments and in ultrasonics that liquids sustain tension. Liquids in most practical situations break as soon as the local static pressure drops to vapor pressure, if not sooner.

## 7.3 Single Bubble Growth and Collapse

A cavitation nucleus subjected to sufficient tension to cause the inside pressure to drop to the vapor pressure will expand as a vapor bubble until it experiences a positive pressure, at which point it will cease growing, will reverse the procedure and collapse. A number of phenomena affect the rates of growth and collapse, different ones being important for different phases of the growth-collapse cycle. These include pressure and velocity fields of a moving boundary, surface tension, evaporation, heat conduction, viscosity and compressibility. A complete equation including all of these effects would not only be non-linear but would also be so complex that understanding of the physics would be lost. It would not show clearly how different effects are dominant during different phases of the process. Thus, heat conductivity is important in the initial stage of growth of bubbles in boiling but has little effect in cavitation except sometimes during the final stages of collapse. Compressibility can become important in the final stages of collapse if bubble wall speeds approach the speed of sound, but not otherwise. Viscosity plays a role in inception, and may do so again in final collapse.

However, except for the periods when cavity growth is initiated and when final collapse occurs, the two dominant effects are the interaction of the velocity and pressure fields of a moving surface. These are the basis of classical theory of cavitation dynamics which can therefore be very useful even though it ignores the other, less important effects.

**Classical Theory**

Classical theory of bubble dynamics treats a uniformly expanding spherical surface in an ideal incompressible medium. The velocity potential for such a surface, as derived by Lamb (1932), is given by

$$\Phi = \frac{a^2 \dot{a}}{r} , \tag{7.2}$$

where $a$ is its instantaneous radius. The equation of motion (Eq. 2.43 of Section 2.2) can be written in terms of the velocity potential. For an irrotational motion of an incompressible fluid, the result is

$$grad \left( \frac{p}{\rho_o} + \frac{1}{2} (\nabla \Phi)^2 - \frac{\partial \Phi}{\partial t} \right) = 0 . \tag{7.3}$$

Hence, for an expanding sphere,

$$\frac{p(r)}{\rho_o} + \frac{1}{2} \left( \frac{a^2 \dot{a}}{r^2} \right)^2 - \left( \frac{2a\dot{a}^2 + a^2 \ddot{a}}{r} \right) = \frac{p(\infty)}{\rho_o} , \tag{7.4}$$

which equation applies everywhere outside the surface of the sphere. On the surface, $r = a$ and Eq. 7.4 reduces to

$$a\ddot{a} + \frac{3}{2} \dot{a}^2 = \frac{1}{2a^2 \dot{a}} \frac{d}{dt} (a^3 \dot{a}^2) = \frac{p(a) - p(\infty)}{\rho_o} = \frac{P}{\rho_o} , \tag{7.5}$$

where $p(a)$ is the pressure in the liquid just outside the surface.

Rayleigh (1917) assumed that the pressure term is constant during bubble growth or collapse. Integrating Eq. 7.5 he found

$$a^3 \dot{a}^2 = \int_0^t 2 \frac{P}{\rho_o} a^2 \dot{a} \, dt = \frac{2}{3} \frac{P}{\rho_o} \int_0^t \frac{d}{dt} a^3 dt = \frac{2}{3} \frac{P}{\rho_o} \left( a^3(t) - a^3(0) \right) , \tag{7.6}$$

from which the velocity is

$$\dot{a} = \pm \sqrt{ \frac{2}{3} \frac{P}{\rho_o} \left| 1 - \left( \frac{a(0)}{a} \right)^3 \right| } \tag{7.7}$$

and the acceleration is

$$\ddot{a} = \pm \frac{a^3(0) P}{a^4 \rho_o} . \tag{7.8}$$

As previously indicated, these equations can be used to predict all but the initial and final stages of bubble growth and collapse.

Except when the bubble is very small, Eq. 7.7 predicts a constant rate of growth and Eq. 7.8 confirms that the acceleration becomes very small. From Eq. 7.7 the velocity during most of the growth stage is

$$\dot{a} \doteq \sqrt{\frac{2}{3}\frac{P}{\rho_o}} \; . \tag{7.9}$$

Under constant tension, the bubble will grow to a maximum size given approximately by

$$a_o \doteq \sqrt{\frac{2}{3}\frac{P}{\rho_o}}\, T_g \; , \tag{7.10}$$

where $T_g$ is the time spent in a negative pressure region. This result is only approximate, since it does not take into account either the acceleration and deceleration periods at the beginning and end of the expansion or the fact that the tension, $P$, is not always constant.

For the collapse phase, Lord Rayleigh found the total time of collapse, $T_c$, to be

$$T_c = \sqrt{\frac{3}{2}\frac{\rho_o}{P}} \int_0^{a_o} \frac{a^{3/2}\,da}{(a_o^3 - a^3)^{1/2}} = 0.915 a_o \sqrt{\frac{\rho_o}{P}} \; , \tag{7.11}$$

showing that the time of complete collapse is proportional to the *maximum bubble radius*, $a_o$, which, by Eq. 7.10, is itself proportional to the time of growth. Moreover, combining Eqs. 7.10 and 7.11, it is found that for the same static pressure difference the time a bubble takes to collapse is very close to three-quarters of the time it takes to grow.

In his original derivation of Eq. 7.7 for the bubble wall velocity during collapse, Rayleigh equated the sum of the kinetic and potential energies of the motion to the potential energy existing when the bubble is at its maximum radius. The potential energy at any instant is

$$E_{Pot} = PV(t) \doteq \frac{4}{3}\pi a^3 P \; , \tag{7.12}$$

while the kinetic energy for the entire velocity field given by Eq. 7.2 is

$$E_{Kin} = \frac{1}{2}\rho_o \int_a^{\infty} u^2 4\pi r^2\,dr = 2\pi\rho_o \int_a^{\infty} \dot{a}\left(\frac{a^4}{r^4}\right) r^2\,dr = 2\pi\rho_o \dot{a}^2 a^3 \; . \tag{7.13}$$

From this it follows that

$$\frac{4}{3}\pi a^3 P + 2\pi\rho_o \dot{a}^2 a^3 = \frac{4}{3}\pi a_o^3 P \; . \tag{7.14}$$

The velocity is given by

$$\dot{a}^2 = \frac{2}{3} \frac{P}{\rho_o} \left( \frac{a_o^3}{a^3} - 1 \right) , \tag{7.15}$$

in agreement with Eq. 7.7.

Figure 7.2 shows a typical bubble growth and collapse cycle as predicted by classical theory. Rayleigh himself recognized that compressibility must affect the final collapse stage, since

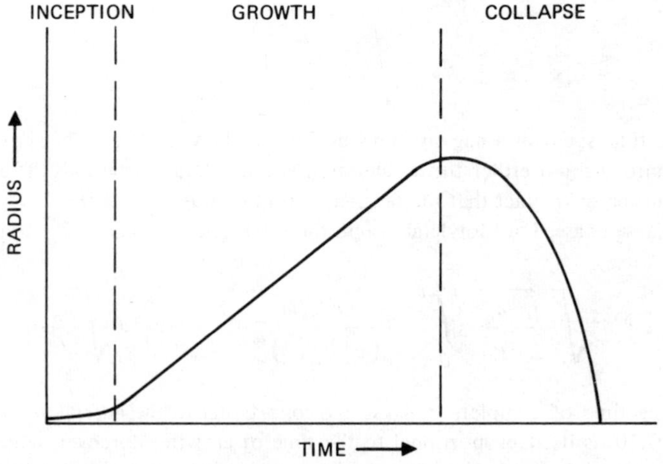


Fig. 7.2. Growth and Collapse of an Empty Bubble in an Ideal Incompressible Liquid according to Classical Theory

Eq. 7.15 predicts infinite velocity as the radius approaches zero. He also noted that, if the bubble contained any permanent gas, the kinetic energy would be consumed in compressing the gas and the motion would stop prior to complete collapse. Since his theory neglects all dissipative mechanisms, it implies that the bubble will oscillate indefinitely between its minimum and maximum radii. Such rebounding is actually observed but it dies rather quickly since energy is lost by sound radiation and heat conduction.

Photographic observations of bubble collapse reported by Knapp et al (1970) show good agreement with classical theory, except that the time of collapse is about 10% greater than that predicted.

### Pressure Inside a Bubble

Rayleigh's theory deals with the pressure just outside the bubble wall, which was taken to be equal to that inside the empty cavity, i.e., to be essentially zero. Actually, as indicated by Eq. 7.1, surface tension causes the pressure inside to be greater than that outside a static bubble. Also, the bubble is not empty; it contains vapor and some permanent gas. Thus, the pressure inside a static cavity is given by

$$p_i = p_v + p_g = p(a) + \frac{2\sigma}{a} , \tag{7.16}$$

where the surface tension is a function of temperature but is assumed to be independent of bubble radius. The gas pressure, $p_g$, will vary during any rapid changes of bubble volume. Since permanent gases go into and out of solution very slowly, the total amount of such gas is essentially constant, and the instantaneous gas pressure is related to an equilibrium value by

$$p_g(t) = p_{g_e}\left(\frac{a_e}{a}\right)^b , \tag{7.17}$$

where $b$ is 3 if the process is isothermal and $3\gamma$ if it is adiabatic.

In addition to the static pressure drop due to surface tension, a moving boundary also experiences a pressure difference attributable to the viscosity of the liquid. Viscosity appears in the Navier-Stokes equations in two terms, but Poritsky (1952) has pointed out that its dominant contribution to the problem under consideration here is at the boundary between the bubble and the fluid. If the bubble is expanding, viscosity adds a single term and Eq. 7.16 becomes

$$p_i = p_v + p_{g_e}\left(\frac{a_e}{a}\right)^b = p(a) + \frac{2\sigma}{a} + 4\mu\frac{\dot{a}}{a} . \tag{7.18}$$

Bahl and Ray (1972) have shown that the surface-tension term is only significant during collapse if $a_o$ is less than $15\sigma/p_o$. Poritsky noted that in a highly viscous liquid the viscosity term could prevent bubble collapse. However, it plays only a minor role in water.

### Effects of Compressibility

As already noted, classical theory predicts infinite collapse speed as the bubble radius approaches zero. However, one would expect compressibility effects to reduce the velocity when the speed approaches a Mach number of one. Gilmore (1952) and Hunter (1960) adapted equations originally derived to treat explosion bubbles and found that compressibility effects begin to become important when the Mach number exceeds 0.3, at a relative radius of about 5%. At a relative radius of 1%, the collapse speed is calculated to be only about 40% of that predicted by classical theory.

Gilmore's analysis ignored the contents of the bubble. Actually, as will be discussed in the following paragraphs, permanent gases also tend to cushion the collapse and to limit the maximum bubble collapse speed. Compressibility only becomes important if the partial pressure of the permanent gas is less than 1% of the ambient pressure, a condition which is quite rare.

While the hydrodynamic effects of compressibility are less important than was thought during the 1950's, it is this property of the liquid that makes possible the radiation of a significant fraction of the bubble energy as sound. The radiation of sound associated with bubble collapse will be discussed in Section 7.4.

### Effects of Permanent Gases

In Section 7.2 it was pointed out that permanent, dissolved gases can play a major role in determining the tensile strength of a liquid because they control the cavitation inception process. Another major effect is that of cushioning the final collapse process and storing some of the kinetic energy of a rapidly collapsing bubble as potential energy. As a result of this stored energy, bubbles do not collapse to zero radius but instead stop collapsing with a minimum radius that may be from 2 to 10% of their maximum radius. They then rebound, form new cavities and collapse again, often repeating the process four or five times. Instead of the ideal single collapse shown in Fig. 7.2, the history is more often as shown in Fig. 7.3.

As mentioned earlier, Rayleigh (1917) recognized the importance of permanent gas in arresting the collapse motion. He assumed isothermal conditions, for which the work of compression is given by the product of the initial pressure and volume and the logarithm of the initial volume divided by the instantaneous volume. Subtracting this energy from the kinetic energy, he found

$$\dot{a}^2 = \frac{2}{3}\frac{P}{\rho_o}\left(\frac{a_o^3}{a^3} - 1\right) - \frac{2}{3}\frac{Q}{\rho_o}\left(\frac{a_o}{a}\right)^3 ln\left(\frac{a_o}{a}\right)^3 , \tag{7.19}$$

where $Q$ is the pressure of the permanent gas when the bubble is at its maximum radius and $P$ is the collapse pressure.

From Eq. 7.19, Rayleigh estimated the minimum radius by setting $\dot{a}$ equal to zero, finding

$$a_m \doteq a_o\, e^{-P/3Q} . \tag{7.20}$$

He found the maximum pressure to be

$$p_{max} = Q\left(\frac{a_o}{a_m}\right)^3 = P\left(\frac{Q}{P}\right) e^{P/Q} , \tag{7.21}$$

from which, theoretically, the peak gas pressure becomes quite astronomical if the partial gas pressure, $Q$, is less than 2% of the collapse pressure, $P$.

It is closer to physical reality to assume that the compression of the gas is adiabatic. Noltingk and Neppiras (1950) derived an equation for a partially gas-filled bubble in an ideal, inviscid, incompressible liquid. Essentially, they modified Eq. 7.5 by a permanent gas term,

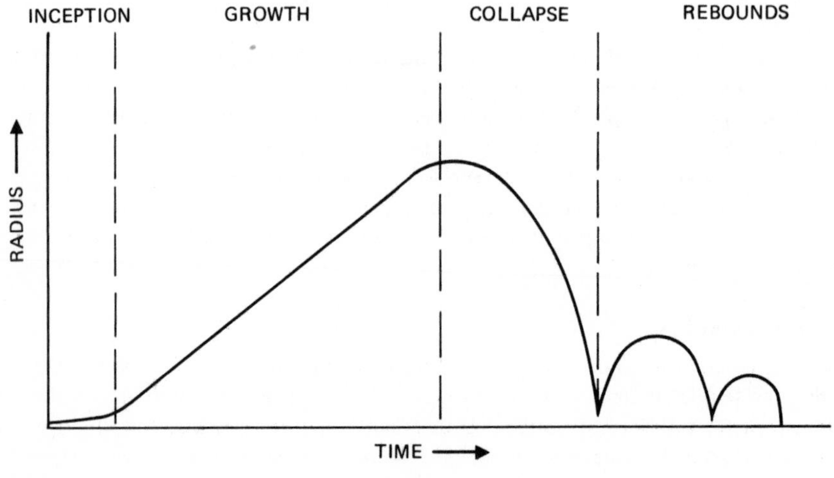


Fig. 7.3. Growth and Collapse of a Cavitation Bubble Having Finite Gas Content

$$a\ddot{a} + \frac{3}{2}\dot{a}^2 = \frac{1}{2a^2\dot{a}}\frac{d}{dt}(a^3\dot{a}^2) = \frac{P}{\rho_o}\left(1 + \frac{Q}{P}\left(\frac{a_o}{a}\right)^{3\gamma}\right), \tag{7.22}$$

from which they found the velocity to be

$$\dot{a} = \frac{2}{3}\frac{P}{\rho_o}\left(\frac{a_o}{a}\right)^3\left[1 - \left(\frac{a}{a_o}\right)^3 + \frac{Q}{P(\gamma - 1)}\left(1 - \frac{1}{\gamma - 1}\left(\frac{a_o}{a}\right)^{3(\gamma - 1)}\right)\right], \tag{7.23}$$

and the acceleration to be

$$\ddot{a} = -\frac{P}{\rho_o}\frac{a_o^3}{a^4}\left[1 + \frac{Q}{P(\gamma - 1)} - \frac{Q\gamma}{P(\gamma - 1)}\left(\frac{a_o}{a}\right)^{3(\gamma - 1)}\right]. \tag{7.24}$$

Setting the velocity equal to zero, they found the minimum radius to be given by

$$a_m \doteq a_o\left(\frac{Q}{P(\gamma - 1)}\right)^{1/3(\gamma - 1)}\left(1 + \frac{Q}{P(\gamma - 1)}\right)^{-1/3(\gamma - 1)}, \tag{7.25}$$

provided $a_m < 1/3\, a_o$. Figure 7.4 is a plot of this equation for two values of $\gamma$. The gas pressure inside the bubble corresponding to the minimum radius is

$$p_{max} \doteq Q\left(\frac{P(\gamma - 1)}{Q}\right)^{\gamma/(\gamma - 1)}\left(1 + \frac{Q}{P(\gamma - 1)}\right)^{\gamma/(\gamma - 1)}. \tag{7.26}$$

Setting $\ddot{a} = 0$, Eq. 7.24 predicts that the bubble wall will have its maximum collapse speed when

$$a_c = a_o\left(\frac{Q\gamma}{P(\gamma - 1)}\right)^{1/3(\gamma - 1)}\left(1 + \frac{Q}{P(\gamma - 1)}\right)^{-1/3(\gamma - 1)} = a_m\gamma\frac{1}{3(\gamma - 1)}, \tag{7.27}$$

and that this maximum speed will be

$$\dot{a}^2_{max} \doteq \frac{2P(\gamma - 1)}{3\rho_o\gamma}\left(\frac{P(\gamma - 1)}{Q\gamma}\right)^{1/(\gamma - 1)}\left(1 + \frac{Q\gamma}{P(\gamma - 1)}\right)^{\gamma/(\gamma - 1)}. \tag{7.28}$$

Since the compression is assumed to be adiabatic, this theory also yields

$$\theta_{max} = \theta_o\frac{p_{max}}{Q}\left(\frac{a_m}{a_o}\right)^3 = \theta_o\left(\frac{P(\gamma - 1)}{Q}\right)\left(1 + \frac{Q}{P(\gamma - 1)}\right) \tag{7.29}$$

as maximum temperature, where both $\theta$'s are measured in degrees Kelvin. Thus, incompressible theory predicts maximum temperatures in excess of a thousand degrees provided $Q < 0.1P$.

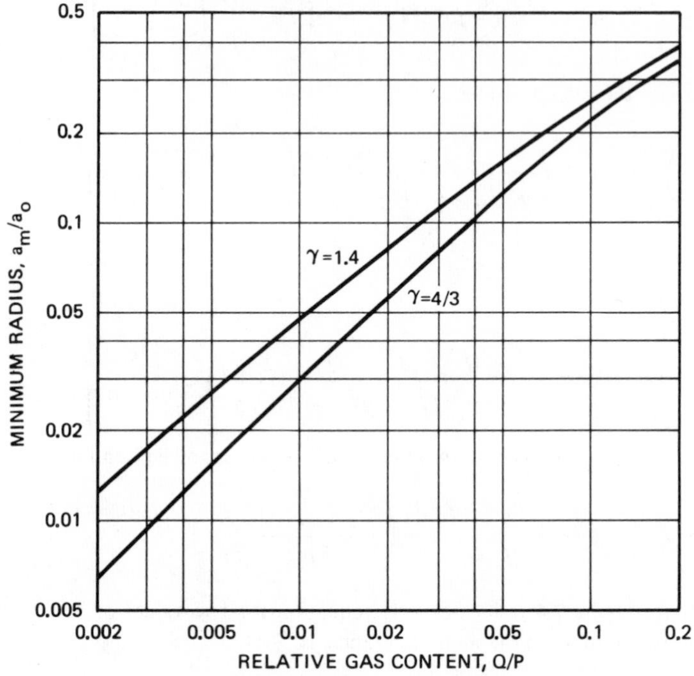


Fig. 7.4. Minimum Bubble Radius as Function of Relative Gas Content, for Two Specific Heats (Eq. 7.25)

The Noltingk-Neppiras incompressible equation can be expected to overestimate collapse speeds when it predicts Mach numbers in excess of 0.3. From Eq. 7.28, the maximum Mach number for bubble collapse is given by

$$M_{max} \doteq \sqrt{\frac{2P}{3\rho_o c_o^2}\left(\frac{\gamma - 1}{\gamma}\right)\left(\frac{P(\gamma - 1)}{Q\gamma}\right)^{1/2(\gamma - 1)}\left(1 + \frac{Q\gamma}{P(\gamma - 1)}\right)^{\gamma/2(\gamma - 1)}} \quad . \tag{7.30}$$

This can also be expressed in terms of the ratio of $a_m$ to $a_o$ by using Eq. 7.25 and neglecting several small terms. When this is done, the maximum Mach number is found to be virtually independent of $\gamma$ for $a_m/a_o$ up to about 0.25, corresponding to a relative gas pressure of about 10%. Over this range the maximum Mach number can be approximated by

$$M_{max} \doteq \left(0.015 \frac{a_o}{a_m}\right)^{3/2} \sqrt{P_A} \quad , \tag{7.31}$$

where $P_A$ is static pressure in atmospheres.

The maximum Mach number computed by the incompressible theory is plotted as a function of $P/Q$ in Fig. 7.5. It is clear that the validity of the incompressible assumption is a function of the collapse pressure as well as the relative gas content. Thus, incompressible theory is seen to be valid for values of $Q/P$ as low as 1% when the collapse pressure is 1 atm., but only for $Q/P > 4\%$ for a collapse pressure of 10 atm. For most practical cavitation problems, it seems reasonable to assume that the incompressible theory is valid unless the gas content is very low.

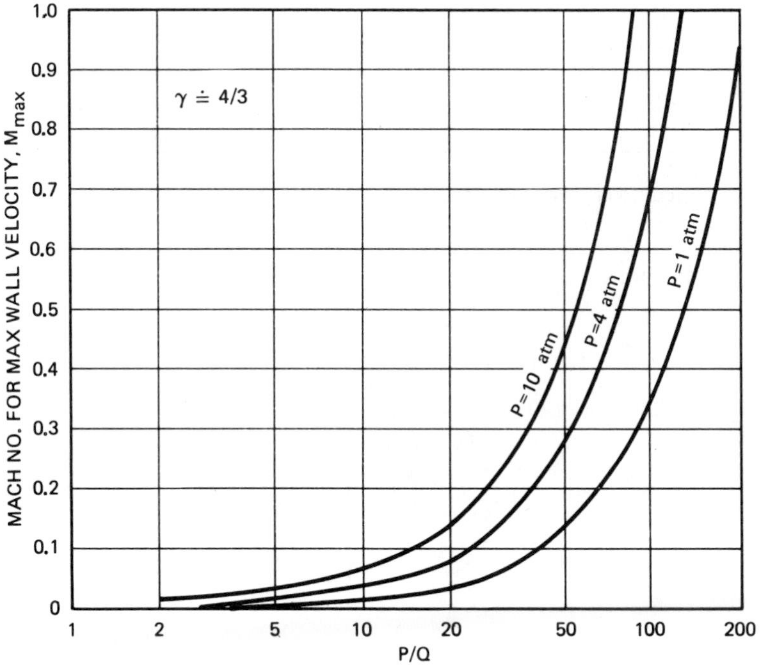


Fig. 7.5. Maximum Collapse Mach Number as a Function of Gas Content Using Incompressible Theory (Eq. 7.30)

Trilling (1952) included compressibility in his calculation of the collapse of a bubble containing gas. He assumed the speed of propagation of all disturbances to be equal to the speed of sound. Hickling and Plesset (1964) used Gilmore's (1952) results to solve for bubble motion when gas cushions the collapse. They found the minimum radius for a given gas to depend primarily on the ratio of the equilibrium gas pressure, $Q$, to the collapse pressure, $P$, and secondarily on the actual value of $P$. Their results for collapse pressures of 1 and 10 atm. are compared to the Noltingk-Neppiras incompressible theory in Table 7.1. Compressibility effects are seen to increase the minimum radius and thereby decrease maximum pressures and temperatures appreciably. The incompressible theory gives reasonable results if the permanent gas pressure exceeds 1% of the collapse pressure.

Within the range of validity of the Noltingk-Neppiras theory, Eq. 7.31 leads to simplification of some of the equations for bubble velocity and acceleration. Thus, Eq. 7.28 for the maximum

Table 7.1.
Comparison of Compresible and Incompressible
Theories for Collapse of Gas-Filled Cavities ($\gamma = 1.4$)

| $Q/P$ | Incompressible Theory Eq. 7.25 | Compressible Theory* P = 1 bar | Compressible Theory* P = 10 bars |
|---|---|---|---|
| | Relative Minimum Radius | | |
| 0.10 | 0.262 | 0.28 | |
| 0.010 | 0.047 | 0.060 | 0.074 |
| 0.0010 | 0.0069 | 0.018 | 0.025 |
| $10^{-4}$ | 0.0010 | 0.006 | 0.009 |
| $10^{-5}$ | | | 0.0035 |

*After Hickling and Plesset (1964).

velocity can be replaced by

$$\dot{a}^2_{max} \doteq \frac{1}{12}\frac{P}{\rho_o}\left(\frac{a_o}{a_m}\right)^3 \quad \left(\frac{Q}{P} < 0.1\right) , \tag{7.32}$$

and to a close approximation the wall velocity is

$$\dot{a}^2 \doteq 8\dot{a}^2_{max}\left(\frac{a_m}{a}\right)^3\left[1 - \left(\frac{a_m}{a}\right)^{3(\gamma - 1)} - \left(\frac{a}{a_o}\right)^3\right] , \tag{7.33}$$

and the acceleration is

$$a\ddot{a} \doteq -12\dot{a}^2_{max}\left(\frac{a_m}{a}\right)^3\left(1 - \gamma\left(\frac{a_m}{a}\right)^{3(\gamma - 1)}\right)\left(1 + \left(\frac{a_m}{a_o}\right)^{3(\gamma - 1)}\right) . \tag{7.34}$$

These equations are used in the analysis of noise radiation in the following section.

The Noltingk-Neppiras equation has been used for bubble collapse analyses by Khoroshev (1963). He presented his results as a correction to classical theory, the correction factor being given as a function of the relative gas content at maximum radius, $Q/P$. For example, Khoroshev calculated the time of collapse from

$$T_c = \int_{a_o}^{a_m} \frac{1}{\dot{a}}\, da , \tag{7.35}$$

finding for $Q/P$ less than about 20% that

$$T_c \doteq 0.915 a_o \sqrt{\frac{\rho_o}{P}}\left(1 + \frac{Q}{P}\right) . \tag{7.36}$$

He assumed $\gamma = 4/3$ since that value leads to tractable integrals.

Boguslavskii (1967) calculated the rate at which gas diffuses into a bubble, finding that it increases as the 5/2 power of the growth time. Since the volume grows as the cube of this time, the relative gas content diminishes somewhat as a bubble continues to grow. Gas diffusion also plays a role in the inception of acoustic cavitation and this subject has been treated in more detail by Hsieh and Plesset (1961) and by Eller (1969, 1975).

### Asymmetrical Bubble Collapse

The Noltingk-Neppiras theory, like the classical theory of Rayleigh, assumes spherical growth and collapse. Early photographic studies of cavitation bubbles by Knapp et al (1948,1970) confirmed symmetrical collapse and revealed the rebound phenomenon. More recently, Ellis (1966), Ivany et al (1966), Kozyrev (1966, 1969) and Mitchell and Hammitt (1973) have all found that bubbles collapsing close to solid boundaries collapse asymmetrically. The bubbles distort into prolate spheroidal cavities and the more remote surface collapses, forming a jet which passes through the closer wall and strikes the solid boundary. It is now believed that this mechanism explains cavitation erosion, as will be discussed in Section 7.6.

Theoretical studies by Chapman and Plesset (1972), Hsieh (1972) and Plesset and Chapman (1971) confirm that a solid boundary should indeed cause toroidal collapse with the formation of a jet. However, the seriousness of this effect relative to the conclusions of the Noltingk-Neppiras theory has not been evaluated.

### Summary and Conclusions

The phenomenon of bubble growth and collapse in cavitation is extremely complicated, involving motions of the liquid, compressibility, viscosity, surface tension, heat conduction, gaseous diffusion and thermodynamic effects. In addition, many bubbles collapse near a solid surface, making the assumption of spherical symmetry untenable. Despite all these complexities the dominant characteristics are correctly given by Rayleigh's classical theory for a bubble in an ideal liquid, as modified by the Noltingk-Neppiras correction to account for residual gases.

## 7.4 Single Bubble Cavitation Noise

### Expression for Radiated Energy

The volume changes that are inherent in the cavitation phenomenon radiate sound as monopoles. Expressions were derived in Section 4.1 for the power radiated by a volume source in terms of the acoustic pressure and for acoustic pressure in terms of volume acceleration. These equations can be combined to obtain an expression for the total energy radiated in terms of the volume acceleration:

$$E_{ac} = \int_0^\infty W_{ac}\,dt = 4\pi r^2 \int_0^\infty \frac{p^2(t)}{\rho_o c_o}\,dt = \frac{\rho_o}{4\pi c_o}\int_0^t \ddot{V}^2(t)\,dt$$

$$= \frac{\rho_o}{4\pi c_o}\int_{a(0)}^{a(t)} \frac{\ddot{V}^2}{\dot{a}}\,da \ . \qquad (7.37)$$

The volume is, of course, a function of the radius, and it can readily be shown that

$$\ddot{V} = 4\pi(2a\dot{a}^2 + a^2\ddot{a}) \ , \tag{7.38}$$

from which it follows that

$$E_{ac} = \frac{4\pi\rho_o}{c_o} \int_{a(0)}^{a(t)} \frac{(2a\dot{a}^2 + a^2\ddot{a})^2}{\dot{a}} \, da \ . \tag{7.39}$$

In evaluating this integral, it is expedient to deal separately with the growth and collapse phases.

**Growth Phase**

For most of the growth phase, the classical result of constant wall velocity is a good approximation to actual motion. The approximate result for total radiated energy is

$$E_{ac} \doteq \frac{16\pi\rho_o}{c_o} \int_0^{a_o} a^2\dot{a}^3 \, da = \frac{16\pi}{3}\left(\frac{2}{3}\right)^{3/2} \sqrt{\frac{P}{\rho_o c_o^2}} \, Pa_o^3 \ , \tag{7.40}$$

whence the ratio of radiated energy to potential energy of the bubble when fully expanded is

$$\frac{E_{ac}}{PV_o} \doteq \frac{8}{3}\sqrt{\frac{2P}{3\rho_o c_o^2}} \ , \tag{7.41}$$

which for almost all practical cases is less than 1%.

**Collapse Phase**

Most of the sound radiated by cavitation bubbles occurs during the collapse phase. One approach to calculating the sound radiated by a collapsing vapor-gas bubble is to use Rayleigh's classical theory to calculate volume acceleration and wall velocity and to use the Noltingk-Neppiras result for minimum radius. Using Eq. 7.15 for $\dot{a}^2$, the volume acceleration is

$$\ddot{V} = 4\pi\left[\frac{4}{3}\frac{P}{\rho_o} a\left(\frac{a_o^3}{a^3} - 1\right) - \frac{P}{\rho_o}\frac{a_o^3}{a^2}\right] = \frac{P}{\rho_o}\frac{V_o}{a^2}\left(1 - 4\left(\frac{a}{a_o}\right)^3\right) \ , \tag{7.42}$$

from which $\ddot{V}$ can also be expressed by

$$\ddot{V} = -2\pi\sqrt{\frac{2P}{3\rho_o}}\left(\frac{a_o}{a}\right)^{3/2} \frac{\left(1 - 4\left(\frac{a}{a_o}\right)^3\right)}{\left(1 - \left(\frac{a}{a_o}\right)^3\right)^{1/2}} \, a\dot{a} \ . \tag{7.43}$$

Using Eqs. 7.42 and 7.43 with Eq. 7.37, we find

$$\frac{E_{ac}}{PV_o} = \frac{-1}{2}\sqrt{\frac{2P}{3\rho_o c_o^2}} \int_1^{a_m/a_o} \left(\frac{a_o}{a}\right)^{5/2} \frac{\left(1 - 4\left(\frac{a}{a_o}\right)^3\right)^2}{\sqrt{1 - \left(\frac{a}{a_o}\right)^3}}\, d\left(\frac{a}{a_o}\right)$$

$$= \frac{-1}{6}\sqrt{\frac{2P}{3\rho_o c_o^2}} \int_1^{x_m} \frac{1 - 8x + 16x^2}{x\sqrt{x - x^2}}\, dx\ , \qquad (7.44)$$

where $x = (a/a_o)^3$.

These equations are derived under the assumption that the cavity is empty, but that somehow it suddenly stops collapsing at its minimum radius. When the more exact Noltingk-Neppiras equation is used, the results are modified slightly. As shown in Fig. 7.6, inclusion of gas causes the velocity term to decrease and the acceleration term to increase. Analysis shows Eq. 7.42 to be a good approximation for volume acceleration for the entire period. We are therefore justified in estimating sound radiation from classical theory using the Noltingk-Neppiras results only to calculate the minimum radius.

For values of $a_m$ corresponding to relative gas contents of under 10%, integration of Eq. 7.44 yields

$$\frac{E_{ac}}{E_{pot}} = \frac{E_{ac}}{PV_o} \doteq \frac{1}{3}\sqrt{\frac{2P}{3\rho_o c_o^2}} \left(\frac{a_o}{a_m}\right)^{3/2} \doteq M_{max} \qquad (7.45)$$

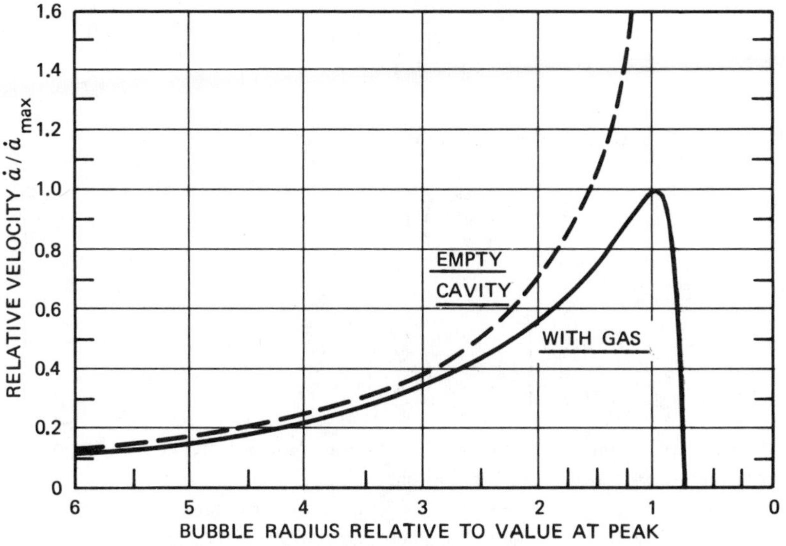


Fig. 7.6. Effect of Gas on Collapse Curve of a Bubble by Incompressible Theory (Eq. 7.33)

This simple result enables one to use previously derived expressions for the maximum Mach number to estimate the fraction of bubble energy radiated as sound. Since the Mach number is greater for lower gas concentrations and for higher collapse pressures, it follows that the fraction of potential energy radiated under these conditions is also greater.

In calculating the total energy radiated by collapse of a partially gas-filled vapor bubble, the energy for initial collapse and subsequent rebounds should be summed. Figure 7.7 shows pressure pulses corresponding to a rebound situation similar to that shown in Fig. 7.3. The total energy radiated may be assumed to be about twice that radiated during the initial collapse. It is physically impossible for a bubble to emit more sound energy than the potential energy which it had at its maximum radius; a reasonable estimate of the sound energy radiated may therefore be made by assuming that two thirds of the energy is radiated when $Q << P$ and, further, that if there is sufficient gas in the bubble to cushion the collapse and reduce the radiated sound, then double the value given by Eq. 7.45 will be applicable. Figure 7.8 uses these assumptions. It shows the fraction of potential energy estimated to be radiated as sound as a function of collapse pressure and relative gas content. When relative gas content is less than about 1/2%, it is clear that the energy radiated as sound depends entirely on the potential energy of the bubble. Relative gas contents greater than 1% should act to cushion the collapse and reduce the sound. Reductions of noise due to excess gas content were reported by Ross and McCormick (1948) and by Osborne (1947), and may also be inferred from measurements reported by others.

### Acoustic Pressures

Instantaneous radiated acoustic pressure is related to volume acceleration by Eq. 3.28. From Eq. 7.42, it can be written

$$p'(t) = \frac{\rho_o \ddot{V}\left(t - \frac{r}{c}\right)}{4\pi r} = \frac{P}{3\left(\frac{r}{a_o}\right)} \left(\frac{a_o}{a}\right)^2 \left(1 - 4\left(\frac{a}{a_o}\right)^3\right) , \qquad (7.46)$$

from which the peak positive acoustic pressure is

$$p^+_{max} = \frac{P}{3}\frac{a_o}{r}\left(\frac{a_o}{a_m}\right)^2 \left(1 - 4\left(\frac{a_m}{a_o}\right)^3\right) . \qquad (7.47)$$

Assuming $\gamma \doteq 4/3$, this yields

$$p^+_{max} \doteq \frac{P}{27}\frac{a_o}{r}\left(\frac{P}{Q}\right)^2 \left[1 + 6\left(\frac{Q}{P}\right) + 9\left(\frac{Q}{P}\right)^2 - 100\left(\frac{Q}{P}\right)^3\right] , \qquad (7.48)$$

showing that, for a fixed relative gas pressure, maximum radiated pressure is proportional to the product of collapse pressure and maximum bubble radius.

As shown in Fig. 7.7, the pressure is negative during the last stage of bubble growth and the first stage of collapse. By the time the radius decreases to 60% of its maximum value, the pressure becomes positive. The negative peak, which occurs when $a = a_o$, is given by

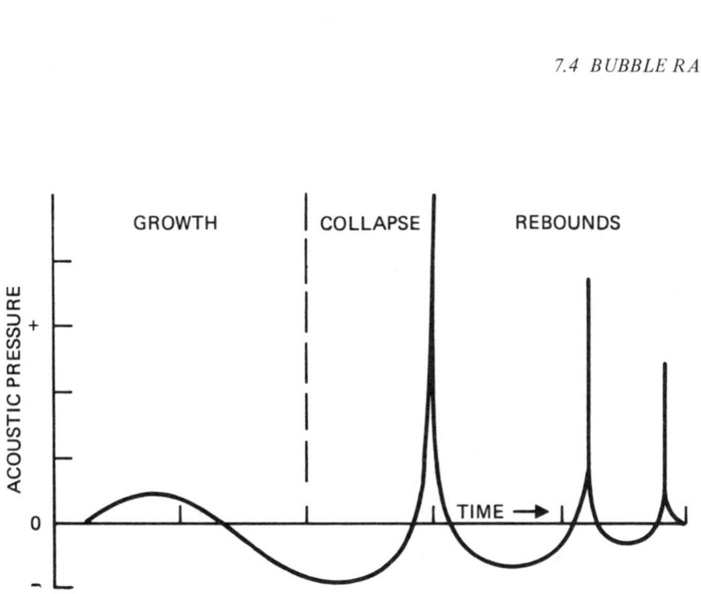


Fig. 7.7. Pressure Pulses from Collapsing Cavity

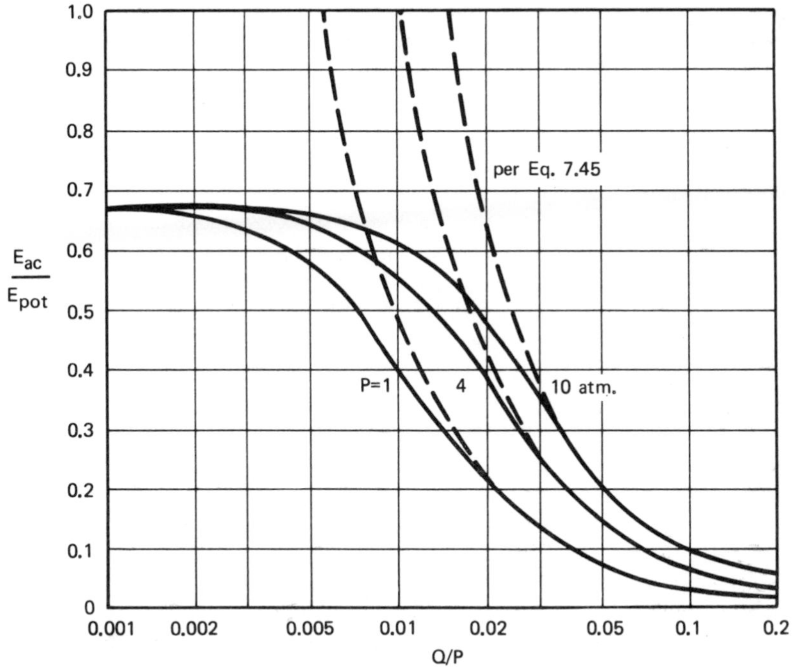


Fig. 7.8. Fraction of Energy Radiated as Sound as Function of Partial Gas Pressure

$$p^-_{max} = P \frac{a_o}{r} . \qquad (7.49)$$

The positive peak will not exceed the magnitude of the negative peak unless $Q < 0.2P$. When the partial gas pressure is less than 2% of $P$, the positive acoustic peak will exceed the negative one by a factor of several hundred.

### Spectrum

The radiation from a collapsing bubble consists of a relatively low-frequency, negative bubble-oscillation component and a very sharp positive peak, as may be inferred from the pressure pattern shown in Fig. 7.7. The low-frequency component dominates when the gas content is high, i.e., especially for gaseous cavitation, and the positive pulse is most important for vaporous cavitation. The radiated spectrum is related to the Fourier transform of the pulse and is flat up to a high frequency equal to the reciprocal of the pulse width. Above this frequency it decreases at a rate of 6 dB/octave.

The pressure pulses emitted by collapsing bubbles having low gas content are often of sufficient amplitude to produce non-linear effects in the medium leading to shock waves. However, this does not change the conclusions drawn as to the fraction of bubble energy radiated, nor is there an important effect on observed radiated spectra.

### Experimental Results

While there have been only a few experimental studies of sound radiated by collapsing cavities, the results have been similar. All of the investigators reported sharp pulses that increase in amplitude with increasing bubble size. Harrison (1952) studied single bubbles produced in the mouth of a Venturi nozzle. He found the peak pressure 10 cm from the point of collapse to be proportional to the initial collapse radius over a range from 0.2 to 1 cm. He also found that between 30 and 50% of the bubble potential energy was radiated as sound. These results are consistent with relative gas contents of about 2 to 3%. Harrison studied a spark bubble as well, getting very similar results. Mellen (1956) also studied spark-generated bubbles, finding the increase in peak pressure with bubble radius to vary as the 3/2 power to 1 cm and then linearly. His results are consistent with gas contents between 1-1/2 and 2%. The importance of gas content in controlling the radiated pulse was also confirmed by Osborne (1947).

These experiments are also in good agreement with most of the results of an analysis published by Khoroshev (1963). He also started from the Noltingk-Neppiras equation and derived expressions for acoustic pressures similar to Eq. 7.48. The analysis presented in this section has the advantage of being less complex and, in addition, it takes compressibility into account by using the fact that energy radiated as sound cannot exceed the initial potential energy of the bubble.

## 7.5 Broadband Cavitation Noise

Il'ichev and Lesunovskii (1963), Akulichev and Olshevskii (1968), Morozov (1968), Lyamshev (1969) and Boguslavskii et al (1970) have all treated cavitation as a random process and have used statistical methods to derive its spectral properties. Because of the pulse nature of the individual collapses and the random sequence of occurrence, the resultant spectrum covers a wide frequency range. As shown in Fig. 7.9, the spectrum rises sharply to a peak and then decreases at a rate of 6 dB/octave over a wide frequency band.

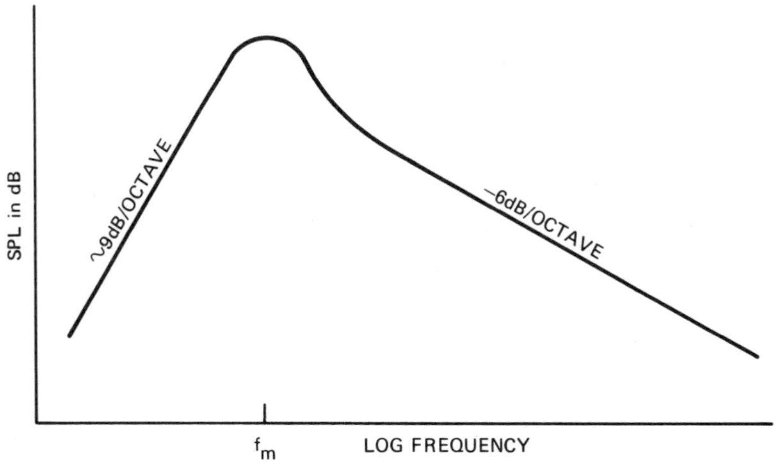


Fig. 7.9. Idealized Cavitation Spectrum

The acoustic power radiated by cavitation is the product of the average energy radiated per bubble and the number of bubbles collapsing per second. Since the energy radiated per collapse is proportional to the product of the collapse pressure and the maximum bubble volume, it follows that the radiated power is proportional to the total volume of cavitation produced per unit time,

$$W_{ac} \approx P \frac{\Delta V}{\Delta t} , \tag{7.50}$$

and that the proportionality constant is a function of the relative gas content, $Q/P$, as given by Fig. 7.8.

Measured cavitation spectra show peaks at frequencies related to the collapse time of the largest bubbles:

$$f_m \doteq \frac{1}{2a_o} \sqrt{\frac{P}{\rho_o}} . \tag{7.51}$$

The peak frequency is thus lower for larger bubbles. It increases, however, with collapse pressure. Below the peak, the spectrum increases at a rate of 6 to 12 dB/octave. At high frequencies, an octave or more above the peak, it decreases at a rate close to 6 dB/octave.

Several observers have noted that the intensity of high-frequency radiation decreases somewhat as cavitation becomes more developed. This may be due to increased gas content in the bubbles acting to cushion collapse and thus reduce the sound, or it may be caused by a change of acoustic properties of the medium itself due to the presence of many bubbles. Van Wijngaarden (1966) and others have noted that the sound speed is drastically reduced in a liquid containing bubbles.

Compressibility effects therefore become important at lower collapse velocities, tending to reduce maximum wall collapse speeds, Also, outer bubbles may effectively screen inner ones by absorbing energy that would otherwise radiate as sound. Akulichev and Il'ichev (1963, 1964) have pointed out that the presence of many bubbles in fully-developed cavitation may lead to additional non-linear effects, such as the production of sum and difference frequencies and the development of broad tonals at any modulation frequencies.

## 7.6 Other Effects of Cavitation

Only a small fraction of the vast literature on cavitation is devoted to noise aspects. Much of it is concerned with ultrasonics applications or with avoiding cavitation to prevent erosion damage. The following paragraphs give brief descriptions of some of these other phenomena associated with cavitation. Interested readers are referred to the books and articles listed at the end of the chapter.

### Sonoluminescence

It has been known for over 40 years that faint light is often emitted by cavitation. Termed *sonoluminescence*, this light serves no useful purpose but must be explained by any complete theory of cavitation. There are apparently two ways in which cavitation may generate light. If the gas content of a bubble is relatively low, then compression of the small amount of permanent gas may raise its temperature above 5000°K. Thus, Eq. 7.29 predicts peak temperatures in excess of this amount if the relative gas content is less than 2%. Heat conduction, compressibility and acoustic radiation would all act to reduce the actual temperature below that calculated. Nevertheless, there is considerable experimental evidence to indicate that one source of sonoluminescence is black-body radiation of hot gas at peak compression. Thus, Kuttruff (1962) and West and Howlett (1969) have observed the timing of sonoluminescence flashes and find them to occur just ahead of or at minimum bubble volume, prior to any rebound. Jarman and Taylor (1970) confirmed this result. Spectral measurements are indicative of black-body radiation at 8,000 to 12,000°K.

On the other hand, Jarman (1959) and others have found cases of light emission when the bubble is close to its maximum radius, which they attribute to electric discharges within the bubble. Degrois and Badilian (1962, 1966, 1969) have found that sonoluminescence intensities are higher for gaseous than for varporous cavitation. They also found that hydrogen peroxide is produced by gaseous cavitation, which is consistent with electric discharges occurring inside the bubbles. It thus appears that there is a second mechanism, namely electric discharges, operative when the gas content is high, and that thermal radiation causes the sonoluminescence when the gas content is low.

### Chemical Reactions

Cavitation is sometimes used to accelerate or to produce chemical reactions. Microstreaming of cavitation bubbles generates currents in liquids, a phenomenon equivalent to stirring, which thereby hastens chemical reactions. Other chemical reactions are directly caused by the high pressures and temperatures associated with cavitation or by its electric discharges. Hydrogen peroxide production and chlorine liberation from carbon tetrachloride are two examples. Depolymerization of large molecules is another example of a chemical change directly attributable to cavitation.

### Erosion Damage

The longest known effect of cavitation, discovered by Parsons and others in the early days of propeller-driven steamships, is erosion damage to metals. Research in this field has taken three directions. Cavitation inception has been investigated from the point of view of developing body shapes that avoid damage by avoiding cavitation. This will be covered in sections on body and hydraulic cavitation in the present chapter. Secondly, many investigators have studied the mechanisms by which erosion takes place. The third area has been the development of materials with a high degree of resistance to cavitation erosion.

Up until about 1965, there were two competing theories of cavitation erosion: mechanical and chemical. The mechanical theory asserted that the damage was done to the eroding surface by the impingement of shock waves generated by imploding bubbles. The chemical theory postulated erosion caused by electric discharges. It is now pretty much agreed that the cause of the damage is mechanical. What occurs is fatigue failure of the metal from repeated hammer-like blows associated with cavitation bubble collapse. However, present mechanical theory differs from the older one in that it is now believed that the hammer blows are provided by impact of high-velocity liquid jets generated by asymmetrical collapse of bubbles near a solid surface. As discussed in Section 7.3, liquid jets have been observed photographically, and recent calculations indicate that they have sufficient momentum to cause the observed pitting.

Cavitation damage depends significantly on properties of the liquid, especially on its gas content. To the extent that permanent gas cushions the collapse and reduces the noise output, it also reduces mechanical forces exerted on nearby surfaces and thus reduces erosion. High temperatures of the liquid reduce damage by increasing the vapor pressure, thereby reducing collapse pressures and speeds of bubble collapse.

The literature on cavitation erosion is extensive. Some of the readily available articles are listed at the end of this chapter.

## 7.7 Hydrodynamically-Produced Cavitation

The two major ways that cavitation occurs in engineering systems is through the use of acoustic fields, as in ultrasonics and transducer cavitation, and by dynamic effects of liquid flows. To the student of underwater noise mechanisms the latter is of greater interest, since cavitation noise of surface ships and underwater vehicles is invariably attributable to one or more hydrodynamic cavitation sources.

The term *hydrodynamic cavitation* covers all of the ways that cavitation may occur in liquids due either to fluid flow or to movement of a body through the liquid. It is convenient to discuss hydrodynamically-produced cavitation in terms of six types distinguished from each other by the location of the cavitation. These are:

*hydraulic cavitation*, inside pipe systems, including Venturis, nozzles, pipe bends and valves;

*body cavitation*, on the surfaces of three-dimensional bodies either immersed in flows or moving through liquids;

*hydrofoil cavitation*, on the surfaces of two-dimensional lifting foils due to motion relative to a liquid;

*vortex cavitation*, in the core of a line vortex;

*wake-turbulence cavitation*, in the turbulent eddies of a wake, usually of a three-dimensional body; and

*jet cavitation*, in turbulent eddies of a jet.

These various types are discussed in this and subsequent sections of the present chapter. Their occurrence in connection with propulsors is covered in Chapter 8.

### Cavitation Parameter

In treating the various types of hydrodynamic cavitation it is useful to define a dimensionless scaling parameter, $K$, that measures the condition of a flow relevant to cavitation. Such a *cavitation flow parameter* can be developed from consideration of the relation between static pressure, $p$, and flow speed, $U$. It follows from *Bernoulli's equation*,

$$p + \rho_o gz + \frac{1}{2}\rho_o U^2 = constant \quad , \tag{7.52}$$

that any pressure drop due to flow will be proportional to the product of density and the square of flow speed. Dividing the available static pressure, $p_o - p_v$, by the dynamic pressure of the flow leads to a dimensionless parameter, $K$,

$$K \equiv \frac{p_o - p_v}{\frac{1}{2}\rho_o U^2} \quad , \tag{7.53}$$

that measures the state of the flow relative to cavitation.

The cavitation parameter is reversed from most common parameters in that it actually measures the resistance of the flow to cavitation. The higher the cavitation parameter, the less likely cavitation is to occur; the lower it is, the more likely. If cavitation is occurring, lowering the flow parameter either by decreasing static pressure or by increasing flow speed will increase the extent of the cavitation; raising it may eliminate cavitation entirely.

The value of the cavitation parameter that marks the border between cavitation and no cavitation is called the *critical cavitation index*, or the *inception cavitation index*, $K_i$. For a given geometry it may have two values, depending on whether one starts at a point free of cavitation and measures inception, or whether one begins with existing cavitation and finds the condition for its disappearance. The former is the *incipient cavitation index* and the latter the *desinent cavitation index*. Any difference between them is referred to as *cavitation hysteresis*. These distinctions are generally not important in large engineering systems but are significant when working with models in water tunnels.

There are therefore two distinct types of cavitation parameters: a flow cavitation number, $K$, defined by Eq. 7.53, and, for each geometry, a critical, or inception, cavitation index, $K_i$. The amount of cavitation depends on the relation between these two. If the flow parameter is higher than the critical value, cavitation does not occur. Cavitation occurs only when the flow parameter is smaller than the critical value; the lower it is, the greater the extent of the cavitation zone.

### Body Cavitation

The analysis of cavitation of three-dimensional bodies is an example of use of the two cavitation parameters. As shown in Fig. 7.10, whenever fluid flows past a body, the fluid must speed up near the nose. By Bernoulli's principle, there is a reduction of static pressure below the ambient value, the magnitude of the drop being proportional to the dynamic pressure of the flow velocity and dependent on the shape of the body. If the pressure drop is greater than the available static pressure, cavitation may occur. The pressure distribution corresponding to the flow pattern of Fig. 7.10 is shown in Fig. 7.11. The flow is stopped at the nose of the body, which point is called the stagnation point. The static pressure there equals the sum of the ambient static pressure, $p_o$, and the dynamic pressure of the free-stream flow speed, $U_o$. The flow parts and speeds up and the streamlines on each side are bunched. It is in this region that body surface pressure drops below ambient, reaching a minimum value and then rising gradually. Since all pressure changes are proportional to the dynamic pressure, it is common practice to plot the pressure distribution in terms of a dimensionless pressure coefficient,

$$C_p \equiv \frac{p - p_o}{\frac{1}{2} \rho_o U_o^2} , \tag{7.54}$$

as in Fig. 7.11.

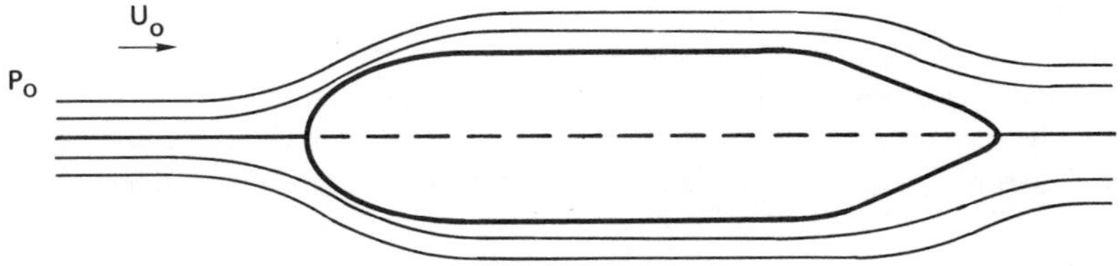


Fig. 7.10. Fluid Flow Past a Three-Dimensional Body

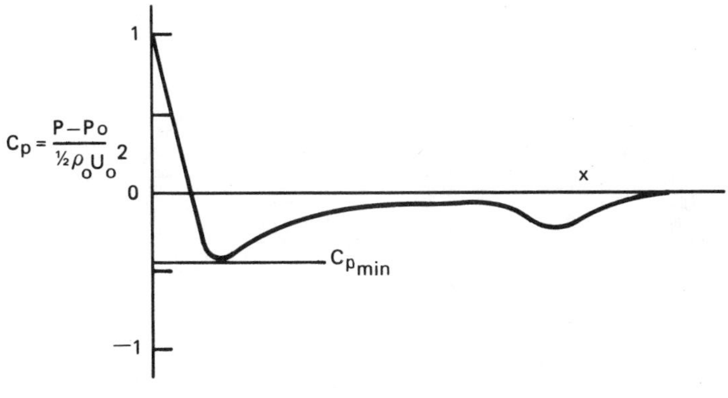


Fig. 7.11. Surface Pressure Distribution for Body in Fig. 7.10

Vapor cavitation may be expected to occur when the flow cavitation parameter is reduced to the absolute value of the minimum pressure coefficient. Thus, to a first approximation,

$$K_i \doteq \left| C_{p_{min}} \right| . \tag{7.55}$$

As discussed below, cavitation inception does not always occur at the value predicted by Eq. 7.55 because of secondary, scale effects. However, for most engineering purposes, the minimum pressure coefficient is a reliable indicator of the critical cavitation index. The smaller its absolute value, the less likely cavitation is to occur.

During World War II, exhaustive studies of a variety of body shapes were carried out in several water tunnels as part of a torpedo development program. As reported by Knapp (1945), Rouse and McNown (1948) and Knapp et al (1970), critical cavitation inception indices of from 0.25 to 1.2 were found for a series of ogive noses on parallel bodies. The value for a straight body with a hemispherical nose is 0.74. Blunt semi-ellipsoidal noses have critical indices as high as 2. In general, one can expect three-dimensional bodies to have critical indices in the range 0.25 to 2. If the operational cavitation parameter is above 3, cavitation is unlikely, while cavitation is almost certain if the parameter is below 0.25.

For underwater vehicles such as submarines and torpedoes operating 10 to 15 m below the surface, body cavitation will probably not occur for speeds lower than about 10 m/sec and will be almost certain above 40 m/sec. Corresponding values for other depths are shown in Fig. 7.12, which is a plot of the cavitation parameter as a function of flow speed and depth.

While body cavitation *per se* does not appear to be a problem for most underwater vehicles, this in itself does not mean that they are free of cavitation at normal operating speeds. As will be

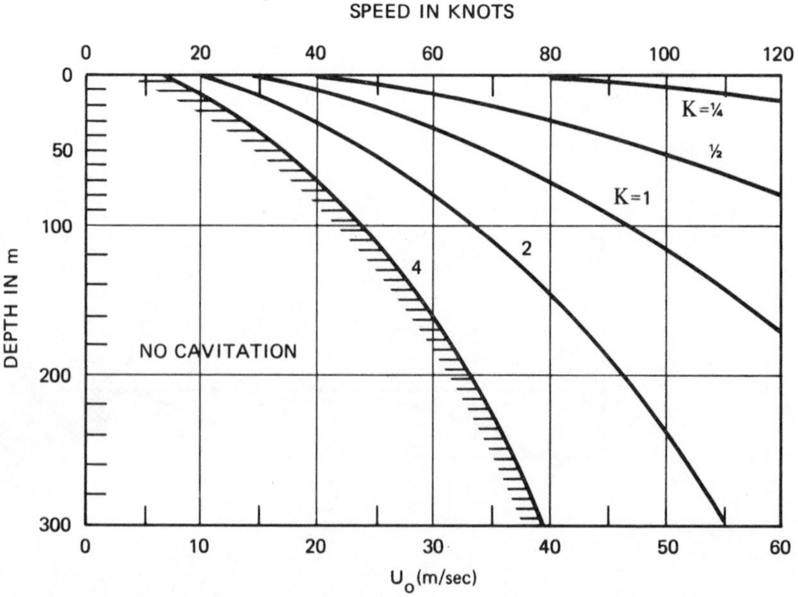


Fig. 7.12. Cavitation Parameter as Function of Depth and Speed of Advance

discussed in the next chapter, propeller cavitation occurs at much slower speeds than body cavitation. Also, any struts or fins are likely to cavitate at lower speeds than will the three-dimensional body itself.

### Scale Effects

As mentioned above, the minimum pressure coefficient is often only a rough indicator of the cavitation parameter for inception. Bodies of the same shape but of different size are often found in water tunnel tests to have different values of their critical indices. In fact, even the materials used to make the test models are found to affect cavitation inception. These phenomena are all treated as scale effects.

Parkin and Holl (1953) and Kermeen et al (1955) have reported on an extensive systematic test of scale effects in cavitation inception. Tests of seven sizes of parallel bodies with hemispherical noses and of four models with ogive noses were run in two water tunnels over a speed range of 6 to 30 m/sec. Results are summarized in Fig. 7.13. In general, it was found that inception occurred for indices lower than the theoretical value, $-C_{P_{min}}$. The measured inception values were closer to theoretical for larger diameter models and at the higher speeds for a given model. The data correlated with *Reynolds number*

$$R_N \equiv \frac{U_o D}{\nu} , \tag{7.56}$$

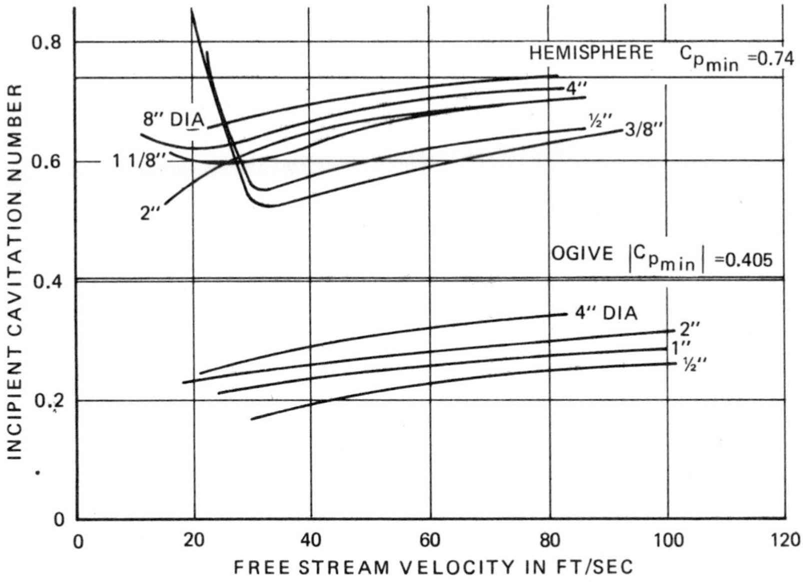


Fig. 7.13. Summary of Body Nose Cavitation Scaling Tests, as reported by Parkin and Holl (1953)

where $\nu$ is the kinematic viscosity, and with *Weber number*

$$W_N \equiv \frac{U_o \sqrt{D}}{\sqrt{\sigma/\rho_o}} \quad . \tag{7.57}$$

It was not possible to distinguish between them with any certainty.

Explanations of cavitation inception scaling in terms of nuclei dynamics have been attempted by Johnson and Hsieh (1966), Oshima (1961) and van der Walle (1962) with varying degrees of success. That scale effects are associated with nuclei growth is shown by the fact that both the nature of the model surface and the sharpness of the pressure distribution peak affect the results. Apparently nuclei can either be supplied by the model surface or by circulating microbubbles. Which of these will dominate depends on model material and on relative gas content of the tunnel water. For slow tunnel speeds and high gas contents, gaseous cavitation is often found to occur at critical indices above the theoretical value. As speed is increased and/or gas content lowered, this type disappears and vaporous cavitation occurs, at indices somewhat below theoretical. Experiments with Teflon models reported by van der Meulen (1972) seem to suggest that surface nuclei are more important than flow nuclei when inception occurs on the model surface. It would also be expected that Weber number, involving surface tension, would be more important than Reynolds number in these cases. On the other hand, Reynolds number should be more important for inception in a wake, as for sharp-edged disks, or in separated boundary layers. As reported by Holl and Wislicenus (1961), these trends have been confirmed by water tunnel tests.

Cavitation inception scaling is significant in most model testing programs and in some full-scale situations. However, it is generally not as important in practice as are the effects of roughness and of other deviations from ideal that are more commonly found in engineering systems.

**Effects of Surface Roughness**

Two types of deviation from smooth surface conditions have been studied in cavitation experiments. One is distributed surface roughness, produced either by applying sandpaper-like surface materials or by making grooves on the surface itself. The second is isolated, single roughness elements or protuberances. Arndt and Ippen (1968) and Arndt and Daily (1969) have treated the first case by correlating cavitation inception with the wall friction coefficient of the boundary layer. It is common practice to express the wall friction in terms of a dimensionless skin-friction coefficient, $c_f$, defined by

$$c_f \equiv \frac{\tau_w}{\frac{1}{2}\rho_o U^2} \quad , \tag{7.58}$$

where $\tau_w$ is the wall shear stress. Arndt and Ippen found that the smooth-wall cavitation index, $K_{i_s}$, is increased by a factor proportional to the skin-friction coefficient,

$$\Delta K_i \doteq 16 c_f \left(1 + K_{i_s}\right) \quad , \tag{7.59}$$

which formula is especially useful when dealing with hydraulic cavitation in rough conduits.

Isolated surface roughnesses are not so readily treated. Their effects depend upon shape, size relative to boundary-layer thickness, and location on the parent body. Holl (1960, 1965) has correlated his results using the relation

$$\Delta K_i = K_{i_o} (1 - C_p) , \tag{7.60}$$

where $K_{i_o}$ is the incipient cavitation number for the roughness element as measured on a flat plate, and $C_p$ is the local pressure coefficient at the location of the roughness. The flat-plate coefficient is a function of roughness shape, height relative to boundary-layer thickness, boundary-layer velocity distribution and Reynolds number. To a first approximation it is the boundary-layer velocity, $u_h$, at the height of the protuberance that controls the pressure drop and thereby the cavitation index. Some investigators write

$$K_{i_o} = K_h \left(\frac{u_h}{U}\right)^2 , \tag{7.61}$$

where $K_h$ depends on shape and on the Reynolds number defined in terms of $u_h$,

$$R_h = \frac{u_h h}{\nu} . \tag{7.62}$$

Thus, Borden (1966) has found that Holl's data on isolated roughnesses correlate well with an expression of the form

$$\log K_h = - A + B \log R_h , \tag{7.63}$$

where $A$ varies from 0.14 to 0.26 for two-dimensional roughness elements and from 0.7 to 1.7 for three-dimensional ones. $B$ is as low as 0.014 for a two-dimensional circular-arc bump, 0.10 for hemispheres and triangles and 0.37 for cylinders protruding normal to the surface.

**Vortex Cavitation**

Vortices associated with both lift and drag occur frequently in practical fluid flows. A *vortex* is a rotating flow; the bathtub vortex is a familiar example. Because of its rotation and the action of centrifugal force, the center of a vortex is a region of reduced static pressure where cavitation will occur if the vortex motion is strong enough. Since vortices are so common, they are often dominant sources of cavitation noise.

Although not an exact representation, most real vortices can be treated as ideal rectilinear vortices for which a central core rotates as a solid body and for which the flow outside the core obeys the laws of irrotational flow. The velocity field outside the core is often called the induced velocity field. Figure 7.14 shows an ideal vortex and the associated velocity and pressure fields. The core of radius $a$ has an angular speed $\omega$. Inside the vortex, the linear speed at any radius is $u = \omega r$. The strength of the vortex is measured by the maximum value of the circulation:

$$\Gamma \equiv 2\pi a u(a) = 2\pi a^2 \omega . \tag{7.64}$$

The induced velocity field satisfies the relation that curl $\vec{u} = 0$, which means that the product of the linear velocity and the radial distance is constant:

$$u(r) = \frac{a}{r}\, u(a) = \frac{\Gamma}{2\pi r} \, . \qquad (7.65)$$

As derived by Dean (1944), the pressure at the vortex surface, $r = a$, relative to the pressure at infinity is given by

$$p_\infty - p_a = \frac{1}{2}\, \rho_o u^2(a) = \frac{\rho_o \Gamma^2}{8\pi^2 a^2} \, . \qquad (7.66)$$

Inside the vortex, the centripetal force relation is

$$\frac{dp}{dr} = \rho_o r \omega^2 = \rho_o r \frac{\Gamma^2}{4\pi a^4} \, . \qquad (7.67)$$

Integrating from the outer radius into the center,

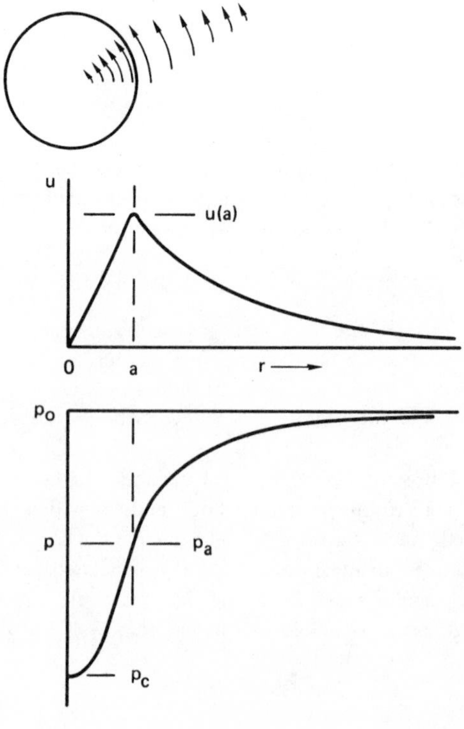


Fig. 7.14. Ideal Rectilinear Vortex

$$p_a - p_c = -\int_a^0 \frac{\rho_o \Gamma^2}{4\pi a^4} r dr = \frac{\rho_o \Gamma^2}{8\pi^2 a^2} . \qquad (7.68)$$

The pressure drop inside the vortex therefore equals that outside the vortex and the total pressure drop is

$$p_\infty - p_c = \frac{\rho_o \Gamma^2}{4\pi^2 a^2} . \qquad (7.69)$$

The smaller the core radius, the greater is the pressure drop associated with a given strength of vortex. If the vortex is occurring in a flow of speed $U$, then the incipient cavitation index of the vortex can be estimated from the pressure drop as

$$K_i \doteq \frac{p_\infty - p_c}{\frac{1}{2}\rho_o U^2} = \frac{1}{2}\left(\frac{\Gamma}{\pi a U}\right)^2 = 2\left(\frac{u(a)}{U}\right)^2 , \qquad (7.70)$$

again showing the critical dependence on the core radius or, alternatively, on the maximum velocity, $u(a)$.

Vortex cavitation is quite common on propellers, as will be discussed in Chapter 8. Vortices also occur at wing tips. When airplanes fly very high, vapor may condense in wing-tip vortices which then become visible as *contrails*. In water, similar vortices cavitate. A discussion of wing-tip vortex cavitation follows that of hydrofoils at the end of Section 7.8.

### Wakes and Jets

When relatively sharp-edged bodies are immersed in fluid flow, flow separation may occur at the edges and highly turbulent wakes may be produced. In such cases, as in underwater jets, cavitation first occurs at pressure minima associated with strong turbulent eddies. As for vortex cavitation, the amount of the pressure drop, and hence the value of the inception index, depends very much on Reynolds number. In fact, in a study of jet cavitation Jorgensen (1961) found a change of inception index of a factor of 3 for a Reynolds number change of about 8. Jorgensen also measured the sound radiated when the jet was thoroughly cavitating, finding the acoustic conversion efficiency to be between 0.5 and $3 \times 10^{-3} M$, where $M$ is the jet Mach number. The measured spectra rose at the rate of 12 dB/octave to a peak and then dropped at about 6 dB/octave. Shalnev (1951) observed that cavitation in wakes exhibits a periodicity that corresponds to the shedding frequency of the strongest vortices or eddies.

## 7.8 Hydrofoil Cavitation

Hydrofoil, or strut, cavitation is similar to body cavitation. However, two-dimensional hydrofoils are generally more susceptible to cavitation than are three-dimensional bodies of similar thickness and cross-sectional shape. Not only does the two-dimensionality produce larger pressure changes, but also the effects of operating at angles other than head-on may be very large. Figure 7.15 shows a hydrofoil at an angle of attack to the flow together with its pressure distribution. The negative pressure region is sharper than that for the same hydrofoil at a smaller angle of

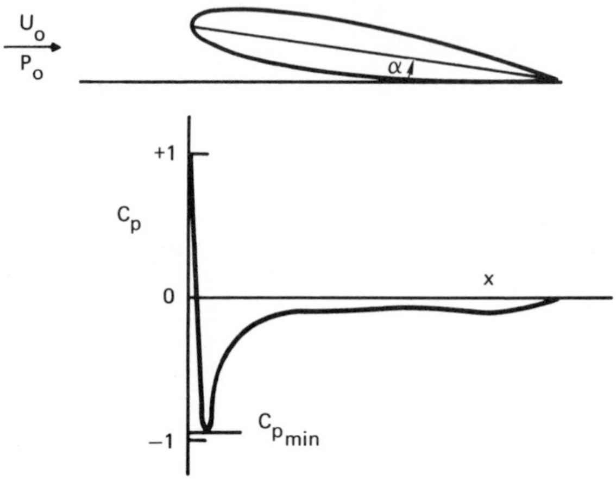


Fig. 7.15. Hydrofoil at Angle of Attack and Corresponding Pressure Distribution

attack. Critical cavitation indices of hydrofoils can be estimated from airfoil pressure distributions given in standard works on airfoils such as that of Abbott and von Doenhoff (1959). They present data on critical Mach numbers for airfoils from which minimum pressure coefficients can be obtained.

**Symmetric Struts**

The critical inception indices of symmetric struts at zero angle of attack are dependent primarily on thickness and secondarily on details of the profile. Figure 7.16 is a plot of the minimum pressure coefficient, assumed to equal the critical cavitation index, as a function of thickness-chord ratio for a number of symmetric hydrofoil families. To a first approximation, with a spread of ±25%,

$$K_i \doteq \left| C_{p_{min}} \right| \doteq 3 \frac{b}{s} . \qquad (7.71)$$

Based on this result, one would expect that the optimum strut form would be as thin as possible with a flat pressure distribution. Actually this is not always the case. If the gas content is high, flat pressure distributions having long growth times for nuclei are susceptible to gaseous cavitation. Also, as will be discussed shortly, such sections are likely to be quite sensitive to relatively small changes of the angle of attack. The optimum strut section is thus one whose design minimum pressure coefficient is only slightly lower than the minimum flow cavitation parameter for the particular application. Values of $K_i$ of less than 0.3 are extremely difficult to achieve in most practical circumstances, and values around 0.5 are more typical.

**Lifting Hydrofoils**

Hydrofoils are often used to produce lift as sections of wings and of propeller blades. Lift is usually achieved by both curvature of the section, called *camber*, and by operation at a positive angle of attack. Figure 7.17 shows the contour of a typical section designed to be used as a lift-producing hydrofoil. A cambered section is generally best used at an angle of attack such that the flow is close to parallel to the camber line at the nose of the section. The angle for which this occurs is called the *design angle of attack.*

The total force experienced by a lifting foil can be resolved into two components, one perpendicular to the flow, *lift*, and one parallel to the flow, *drag*. Since both of these forces are proportional to the size of the section and to the dynamic pressure of the relative flow, it is usual to express them by dimensionless coefficients,

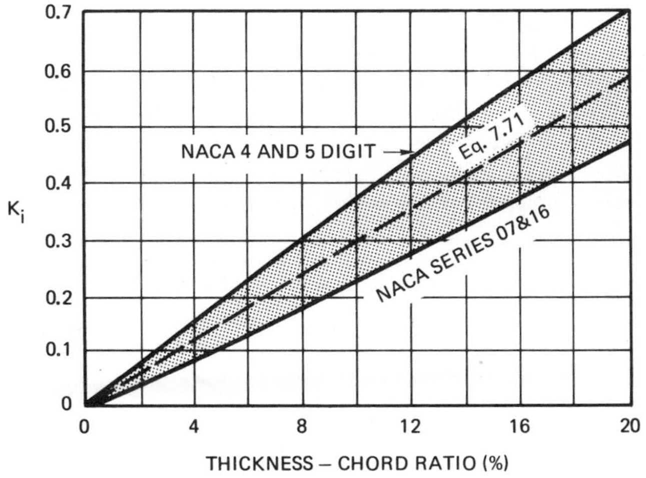


Fig. 7.16. Critical Cavitation Indices for Symmetric Hydrofoils at Zero Angle of Attack Based on Minimum Pressure Coefficients

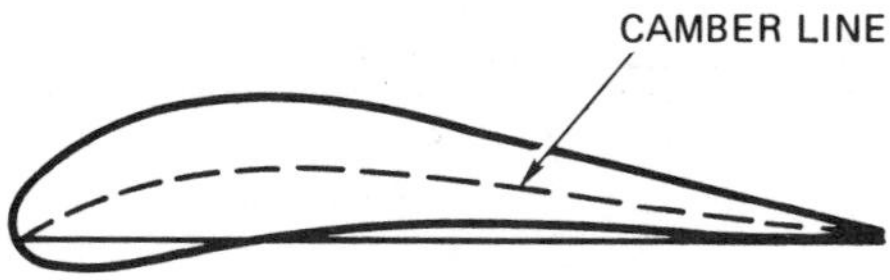


Fig. 7.17. A Typical Lifting Hydrofoil Section

$$C_L \equiv \frac{F'_L}{\frac{1}{2}\rho_o U^2 s} \tag{7.72}$$

and

$$C_D \equiv \frac{F'_D}{\frac{1}{2}\rho_o U^2 s} , \tag{7.73}$$

where $F'_L$ is the lift per unit width, $F'_D$ is the drag, and $s$ is the chord length of the section. This lift is approximately a linear function of the angle of attack over the useful range of attack angles,

$$C_L \doteq \bar{a}(\alpha - \alpha_o) , \tag{7.74}$$

where $\alpha_o$ is the angle producing zero lift and $\bar{a}$ is approximately 0.1/deg, or $1.8\pi$/radian. The drag coefficient has a minimum value near the design angle of attack and increases slowly at first and then very rapidly as the angle deviates from optimum. The lift and drag coefficients for a typical airfoil, the NACA 4412 section, are shown in Fig. 7.18 as a function of angle of attack. The break in the lift curve and rapid increase in drag at an angle of 14° are caused by flow separation. Since strong wake cavitation is also associated with separation, it is a condition to be avoided. The lift coefficient at separation is termed the *maximum lift coefficient,* $C_{L_{max}}$

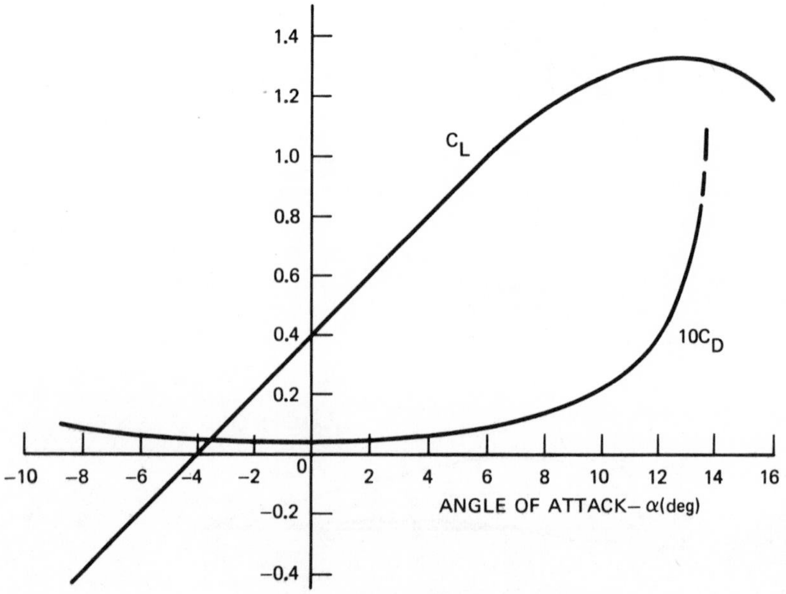


Fig. 7.18. Lift and Drag Coefficients of NACA 4412 Airfoils

Daily (1949) and Kermeen (1956) have measured the critical cavitation index of NACA 4412 hydrofoils and find good agreement with the minimum pressure coefficient as derived from data given by Abbott and von Doenhoff (1945, 1959). As shown in Fig. 7.19, the minimum pressure coefficient is smallest at or near the design angle of attack, and increases approximately parabolically as a function of angle to either side. Cavitation occurs on the suction surface at positive angles of attack and on the pressure face when the angle of attack is negative.

Airfoil sections have been developed by the N.A.C.A. (now N.A.S.A.) and other organizations in families in which a given basic shape is combined with camber functions to develop dozens of related shapes. By using different combinations of thickness, camber and angle of attack, one can produce the same lift with any member of a family. However, the minimum pressure coefficient, and consequently the critical cavitation index, will differ greatly. Ross (1947) studied several NACA airfoil families and concluded that for most families the minimum achievable cavitation index is given by

$$K_{i_{min}} \doteq K_{i_{sym}}(\alpha = 0) + 0.6C_L \, . \tag{7.75}$$

To achieve this minimum, the lift must be obtained primarily by camber and the section operated at close to its design angle of attack.

The choice of proper combinations of camber and angle of attack is very important. Thus, critical cavitation indices of hydrofoils producing a lift coefficient of 0.4 may vary from a minimum of about 0.6 to a maximum of 2.5, the highest values being found for relatively thin sections operated at angles of attack that are not optimum for the particular sections. This point is illustrated in Fig. 7.20, which shows critical cavitation indices for four symmetric sections in the same family. It is clear from this figure that relatively thin sections have lower critical cavitation

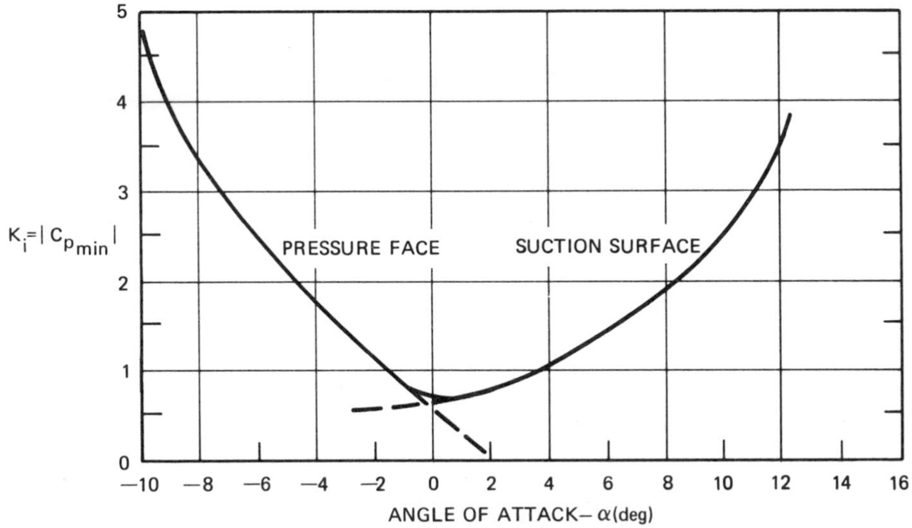


Fig. 7.19. Critical Cavitation Inception Index for NACA 4412 Hydrofoil, after Daily (1949) and Kermeen (1956)

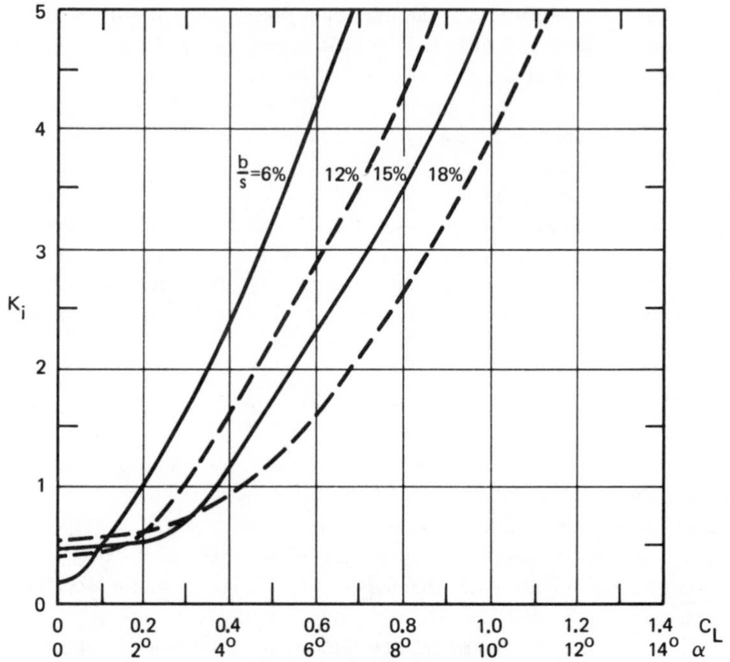


Fig. 7.20. Critical Cavitation Inception Indices Estimated for Four Symmetric NACA Series 65 Hydrofoils

indices when operated at design conditions, in accordance with Eq. 7.71, but that away from design angle thick sections are usually better.

The curves of Fig. 7.20 have important implications relevant to the choice of optimum sections in practical applications. Almost all flow situations experience fluctuations of angle of attack as well as of flow speed. Thin sections have much less tolerance for changes in attack angle than do thicker ones. As a result, a thicker section may be the better choice. In Fig. 7.20 the 6% thick section has the lowest index at zero lift, but the highest at angles greater than 1-1/2° from optimum. The 18% thick section, on the other hand, is the poorest near zero angle and is best for angles in excess of 3°.

The choice of hydrofoil sections for optimum cavitation performance is as much governed by the variability of inflow conditions as by mean values. The camber function should be chosen on the basis of mean inflow and mean lift to be produced, but the optimum thickness-chord ratio is more dependent on expected variations of inflow angle.

### Effects of Cavitation on Section Performance

When a hydrofoil experiences cavitation, the pressure distribution on the cavitating surface is altered. Flow streamlines are changed in such a way that static pressure in the cavitating region is close to vapor pressure. Thus, the minimum surface pressure coefficient of a cavitating hydrofoil equals the operating cavitation parameter rather than having a larger negative value. The loss of suction pressure reduces the lift developed. Figure 7.21 shows how the lift coefficient of a typical hydrofoil is limited by cavitation when the operating cavitation number alters the pressure distribution, and Fig. 7.22 shows how suction-surface pressure distributions are affected by cavitation.

Cavitation also affects section drag. A small amount of cavitation increases the drag but operation at a very low cavitation parameter reduces it. An alternate presentation showing the effects of cavitation is to plot $C_L$ and $C_D$ as functions of the operating cavitation parameter for constant angles of attack. Figure 7.23 shows lift and drag curves for the NACA 4412 section for two typical angles of attack. The peak drag is seen to occur at an operating parameter of about 40% of the critical inception value.

### Scale Effects

Many hydrofoils when operated near their design angles of attack have relatively flat pressure distributions. Holl (1960) reports that they are subject to gaseous cavitation if the gas content is sufficiently high and the flow speed not too great. Otherwise, hydrofoils tend to cavitate first in the turbulent eddies of their boundary layers, the inception of cavitation depending on both flow speed and section size.

Roughness also affects hydrofoil cavitation, pretty much in the same way as for three-dimensional bodies. In fact, many of the roughness results presented in Section 7.7 are based on experiments performed on two-dimensional models and/or calculations made for two-dimensional flows.

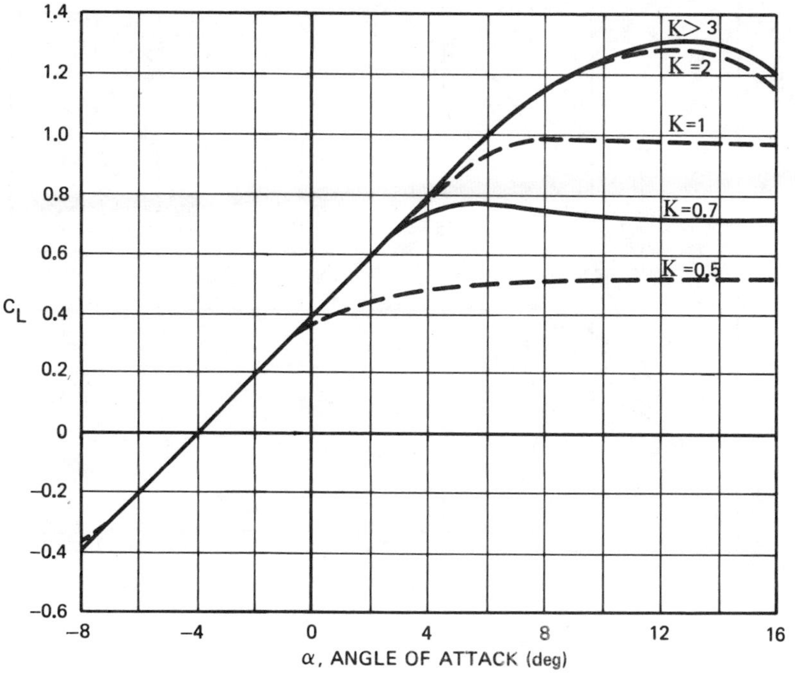


Fig. 7.21. Lift Curve for NACA 4412 Hydrofoil as a Function of Operating Cavitation Parameter, after Kermeen (1956)

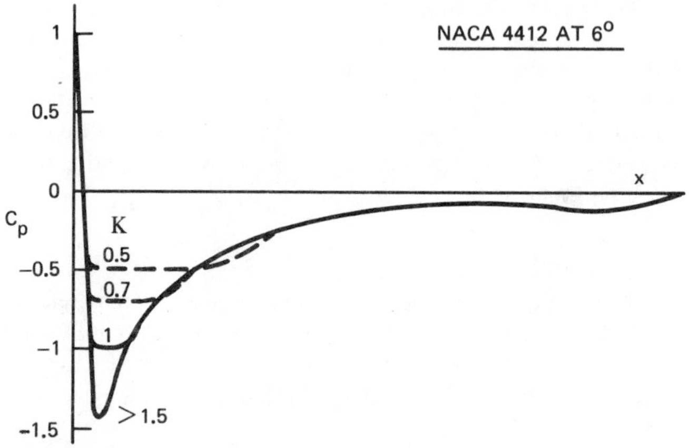


Fig. 7.22. Suction-Surface Pressure Distribution as a Function of Operating Cavitation Parameter

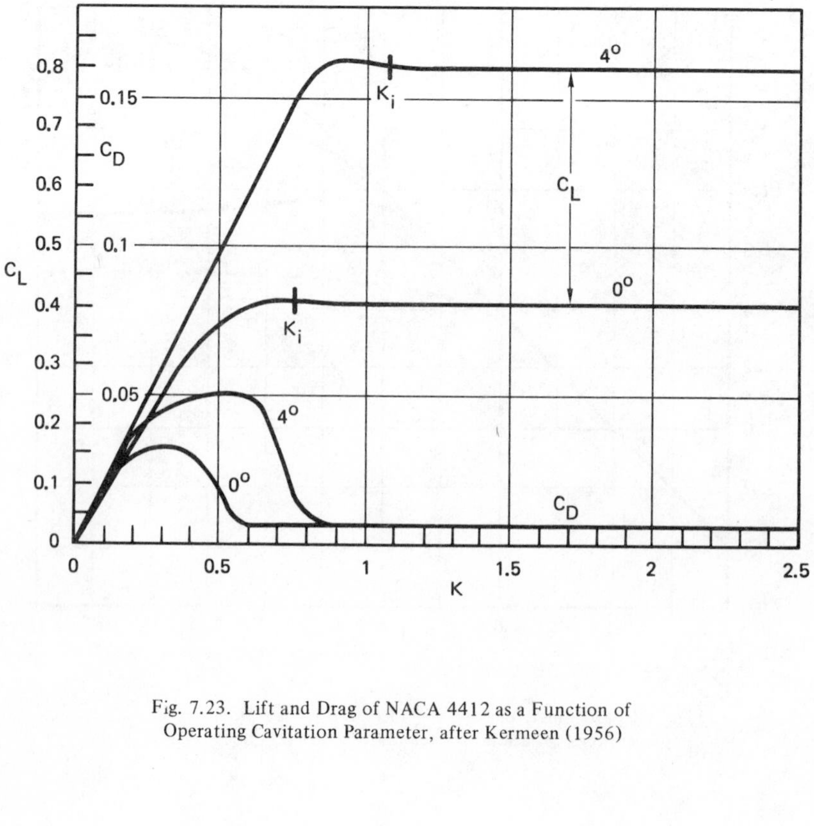


Fig. 7.23. Lift and Drag of NACA 4412 as a Function of Operating Cavitation Parameter, after Kermeen (1956)

**Wing-Tip Vortex Cavitation**

Hydrofoils are usually found as sections of finite wings or propeller blades. Their cavitation behavior in finite structures is modified somewhat by three-dimensional aspects of the flow. However, the most important difference is the formation of wing-tip vortices, which often cavitate at higher values of $K$ than the sections themselves.

To understand why these vortices occur, one may either examine the flow over a wing tip in detail or consider the vortex theory of lifting surfaces. According to the vortex theory, any lifting surface may be replaced by an equivalent system of vortices having total strength equal to the circulation around the section. The lift per unit span is related to the circulation by

$$F'_L = \rho_o \Gamma U_o \ , \tag{7.76}$$

and the circulation is related to the lift coefficient by

$$\Gamma = \frac{1}{2} s C_L U_o \ . \tag{7.77}$$

Vorticity is continuous. Any spanwise change of wing section circulation results in discharge of vorticity into a vortex sheet that trails behind the wing. Since the greatest changes of circulation occur near the wing tips, the shed vorticity is strongest there. The vorticity shed at the wing tip forms a tip vortex, which will cavitate if the pressure drop is greater than ambient pressure.

Vortex cavitation has been studied by Ackeret (1930) and by McCormick (1962). Figure 7.24 shows wing-tip vortices observed by McCormick. He measured the incipient cavitation index as a function of angle of attack and attempted to correlate his results with classical wing theory.

In basic wing theory, the wing is treated as a single horseshoe vortex, and the circulation of the tip vortex equals that of the wing. Combining Eqs. 7.70 and 7.77, the cavitation index of such a horseshoe vortex would be

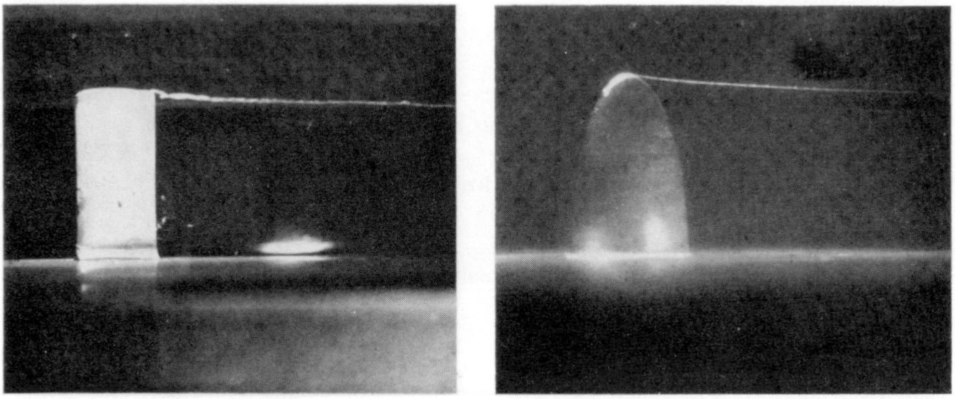

Fig. 7.24. Two Examples of Wing Tip-Vortex Cavitation, from McCormick (1962)

$$K_i \doteq \frac{1}{2}\left(\frac{\frac{1}{2}\,sC_L U}{\pi a U}\right)^2 = \frac{C_L^2}{8\pi^2\left(\frac{a}{s}\right)^2}\,, \qquad (7.78)$$

showing dependence on the square of the lift coefficient and therefore of the angle of attack as well as inverse dependence on the square of the core radius relative to the section chord. McCormick confirmed that critical cavitation indices of a number of wings varied approximately as the square of the angle of attack. The problem was to calculate the core radius theoretically. Ackeret had equated the so-called induced drag associated with the tip vortices to their energy per unit length, finding $a = 0.086b$, where $b$ is the wing span. However, McCormick found this relation to be at variance with his experimental results. One problem is that this theory leads to an expected dependence on aspect ratio, and McCormick found none. Another is that it predicts cavitation indices independent of Reynolds number, and he found a strong dependence on this factor.

In his own theoretical development McCormick related the core thickness to the thickness of the boundary layer developed on the lower surface. He concluded that the shape of the tip would be important and also that roughness of the pressure surface would affect cavitation inception. His experimental results are consistent with these theories. He predicted a strong Reynolds number effect, which was confirmed by tests over a 10:1 range, for which the inception index more than doubled. McCormick developed a rather complex equation to correlate his experimental data. However, conformity to his data within a reasonable scatter is given by

$$K_i \doteq 0.3 + 3C_L^2\,, \qquad (7.79)$$

where $C_L$ is measured about one chord length from the wing tip, and the Reynolds number is about $10^6$.

**Supercavitating Hydrofoils**

Cavitation is unavoidable for very fast surface craft. Rather than using conventional section shapes, it is preferable in such cases to use special hydrofoils which resemble wedges and which operate with fixed large cavities on the suction surface. The lift is then obtained from positive pressures on the lifting surface. Such hydrofoils designed to operate at cavitation numbers below 0.2 are called supercavitating hydrofoils. Since the cavity usually extends beyond the section, such foils are somewhat less noisy than standard hydrofoils for which individual bubbles collapse on the sections themselves.

## 7.9 Hydraulic Cavitation

Hydraulic cavitation generally refers to cavitation in enclosed systems such as pipes and conduits. Local pressure drops occur in such systems wherever there are constrictions or bends or where there are isolated roughnesses or other contour discontinuities. The criteria for cavitation inception are essentially the same as for hydrodynamic cavitation. A flow cavitation parameter can readily be defined for the undisturbed flow, and the critical inception index is usually about equal to the absolute value of the minimum pressure coefficient.

**Pipe Constrictions**

Pipe constrictions are either smooth and gradual as in a Venturi meter, or abrupt as for an orifice plate. Figure 7.25 shows the pressure drop associated with a well-designed, gradual Venturi

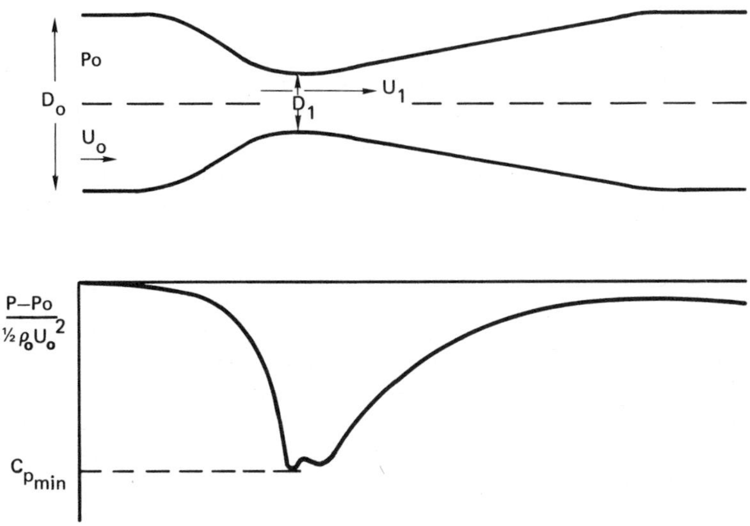


Fig. 7.25. Pressure Distribution for Flow through a Venturi Nozzle

nozzle. To a first approximation, the minimum pressure coefficient can be calculated simply by writing the Bernoulli equation for the average flow speeds,

$$p_o + \frac{1}{2}\rho_o U_o^2 \doteq p_1 + \frac{1}{2}\rho_o U_1^2 \ , \tag{7.80}$$

and the equation of continuity,

$$U_o D_o^2 = U_1 D_1^2 \ , \tag{7.81}$$

from which

$$\left| C_{p_{min}} \right| \doteq \frac{p_o - p_1}{\frac{1}{2}\rho_o U_o^2} \doteq \left(\frac{U_1}{U_o}\right)^2 - 1 = \left(\frac{D_o}{D_1}\right)^4 - 1 \ . \tag{7.82}$$

Actually the critical index may be somewhat larger, because the wall pressure is lower than the pressure at the center of the nozzle due to effects of streamline curvature; however, for a well-designed nozzle these effects are small.

If a sharp-edged orifice is used, cavitation will usually occur first downstream in violent eddies. The critical index will likely be significantly higher than that calculated using Eq. 7.82.

### Valves

Valve cavitation depends not only on the construction of the valve but also on its degree of openness. Ball (1957) found that the inception index for gate valves is 0.5 when open, increasing to 1.5 when half closed and rising even higher as they are closed further. He found globe valves to be less prone to cavitation than gate valves. Clearly it is best to avoid using valves in a slightly open position. When valves are required to cause significant pressure drops, the same effect can be achieved by the use of a large number of small-diameter parallel tubes each of which is either fully open or fully shut. Multiple orifice valves have been developed for use in systems where avoidance of cavitation is considered essential, as described by Müller (1958).

### Pipe Bends

At pipe bends the pressure builds up on the far wall and decreases on the inside wall. In fact, some flow meters use this pressure difference to determine the rate of flow. Critical cavitation indices of pipe bends depend upon the sharpness of the bend and vary from about 0.7 for gradual bends to about 2 for sharp ones. Kamiyama (1966) found values of 0.9 to 1.2 for 90° bends. He noted that, other things being equal, cavitation is less likely if the low-pressure region is shorter, thereby allowing less time for nuclei to grow into bubbles.

### Hydraulic Machinery

Just as the propulsor is the most likely place for cavitation to occur first for propelled vehicles, so cavitation of pumps or turbines is generally the most critical in hydraulic systems. Much research has been done on this subject, primarily motivated by the need to avoid cavitation erosion and energy losses. Bashta (1961), Khoroshev (1960), Shalnev (1951) and Wislicenus (1947) have studied pump cavitation from these points of view. A detailed discussion of cavitation in hydraulic machinery is beyond the scope of the present volume. The interested reader is directed to these references and also to the next chapter on propeller cavitation, since there are many similarities between pump and propeller cavitation.

## 7.10 Underwater Explosions

Detonation of an explosive charge creates a small pocket of gaseous reaction products at exceedingly high temperature and pressure. This expands at transonic speed, creating a strong shock wave which propagates outward at close to the speed of sound. The initial rapid expansion caused by the detonation continues past the point of static equilibrium, the gas pressure falling well below the ambient static pressure. The unstable bubble thus created then collapses in the same manner as a large cavitation bubble, overshooting and recompressing the permanent gas. The expansion and collapse processes are then repeated until the bubble has migrated upward to the surface or has broken up into a number of smaller bubbles. Extensive research on underwater explosions carried on during World War II has been summarized in a book by Cole (1948).

Underwater explosives and explosion-like impulsive sources are being used increasingly as sources for acoustic propagation measurements and for seismic profiling in connection with offshore oil prospecting. As their use has increased in recent years, these pulse sources have become important contributors to low-frequency ambient noise in the oceans. The significance of explosives as noise sources can be appreciated from a simple energy analysis. Detonation of a pound of TNT releases approximately $10^7$ Joules of energy. Dependent on the depth of the explosion, from 10 to 40% of this energy is radiated as sound. Thus, one 1-lb explosion every 15 minutes would release an average of about 1000 J/sec, i.e., 1 kW of continuous broadband noise. This is equivalent to an average total source pressure level of about 200 dB re 1 μPa at 1 m. Modern sources used in seismic profiling are equivalent to several ounces of TNT and are fired at intervals of 6 to 10 seconds. They therefore have average source levels of from 205 to 215 dBμPa. Comparing this with the total acoustic output of about 180 to 185 dBμPa for an average surface ship, as given in Chapter 8, it is apparent that seismic profiling by one vessel puts as much noise into the water as is emitted by from 200 to 1000 ordinary ships.

Two distinct types of sound are produced by explosions, as shown in Fig. 7.26. One is a shock wave pulse which is of very short duration and therefore produces much high-frequency energy. The other is dominantly tonal radiation by the bubble pulsations.

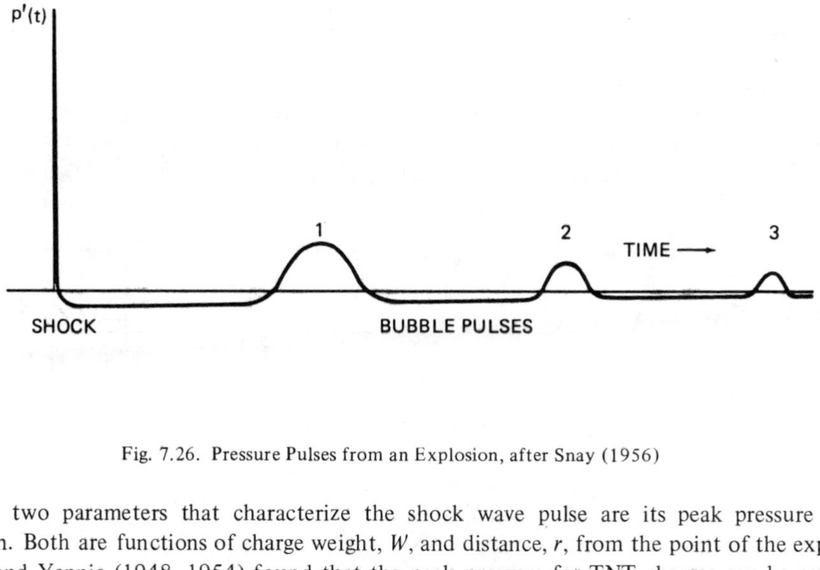


Fig. 7.26. Pressure Pulses from an Explosion, after Snay (1956)

The two parameters that characterize the shock wave pulse are its peak pressure and its duration. Both are functions of charge weight, $W$, and distance, $r$, from the point of the explosion. Arons and Yennie (1948, 1954) found that the peak pressure for TNT charges can be estimated from

$$P'_p \doteq 4 \times 10^7 \frac{W^{0.375}}{r^{1.13}} \text{ Pascals} , \tag{7.83}$$

where $W$ is in lbs of TNT and $r$ is distance in meters. Thus, the peak pressure is about $2.2 \times 10^5$ Pa at 100 m from a 1-lb charge. The duration of the shock-wave pulse is given by

$$\tau \doteq 0.075 W^{0.26} r^{0.22} \text{ msec} . \tag{7.84}$$

Since this time constant is often under a millisecond, the spectrum from the shock pulse is flat to over 1 kHz, decreasing 6 dB/octave at frequencies greater than $\tau^{-1}$. Blaik and Christian (1965) have confirmed that these values are virtually unaffected by depth of the explosion.

The fundamental bubble pulse frequency is the reciprocal of the time between the shock pulse and the first bubble pulse, which time is depth dependent and is given by

$$T_o \doteq \frac{1.6W^{1/3}}{(h + 10)^{5/6}} \; sec \; , \qquad (7.85)$$

where $h$ is the depth in meters. This relation is plotted in Fig. 7.27.

Although the peak pressure produced by the bubble pulse is independent of depth of the explosion, being given by

$$P'_B \doteq \frac{8.5 \times 10^6 W^{1/3}}{r} \; Pascals \; , \qquad (7.86)$$

the duration of the pulse is shorter at greater depths and the total bubble pulse energy therefore decreases. The bubble pulse component is suppressed if the explosion globe breaks the surface before reaching its maximum diameter or if the products can be kept within a container as is done with small charges.

In using explosions as sources, it is useful to know their spectral distributions of energy. Figure 7.28 is a plot of source spectrum levels for shallow detonations, expressed in terms of energy flux in J/m² in a 1 Hz band at 1 m. Figure 7.29 shows relative levels for 1-lb charges exploded at four deep submergences, as measured at a range of about 100 km by Kibblewhite and Denham (1970). They can be converted to source spectrum levels by adding about 50 dB to the values given.

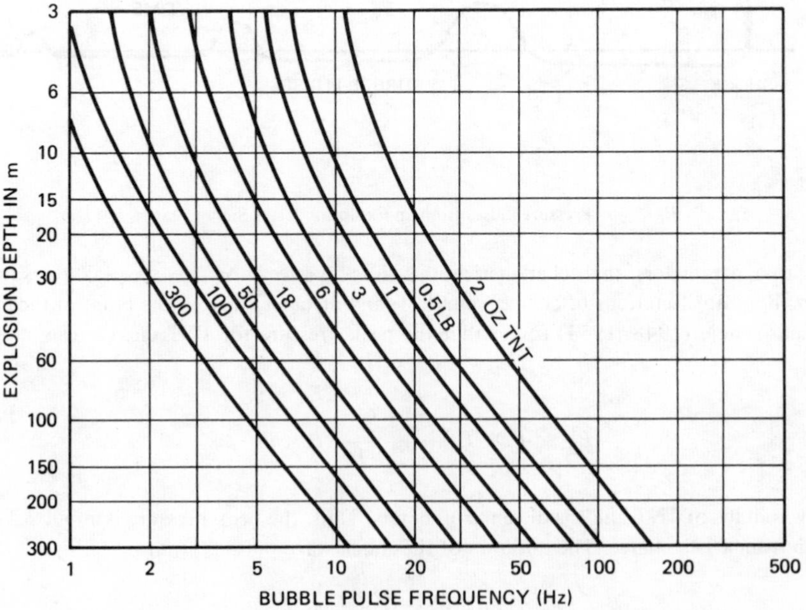


Fig. 7.27. Bubble Pulse Frequency as a Function of Depth

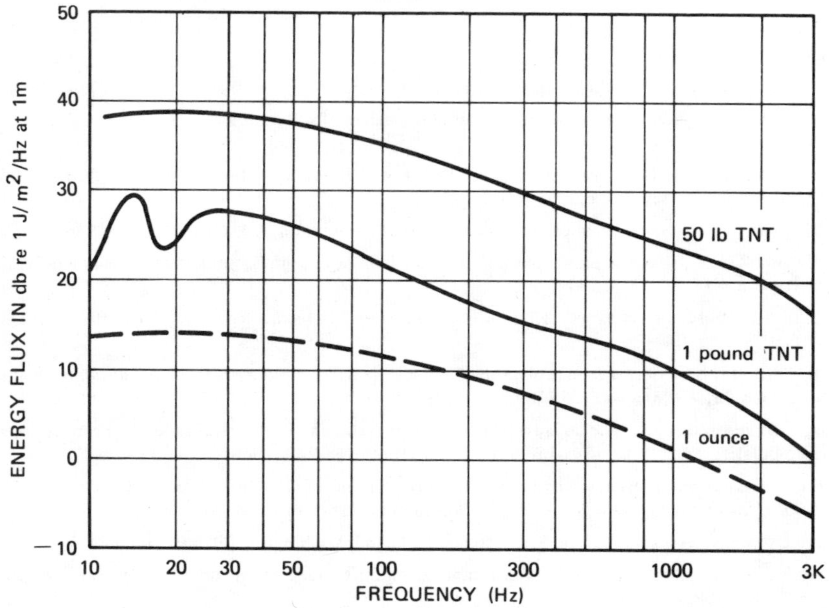


Fig. 7.28. Measured Spectra of Shallow Explosions, after Weston (1960)

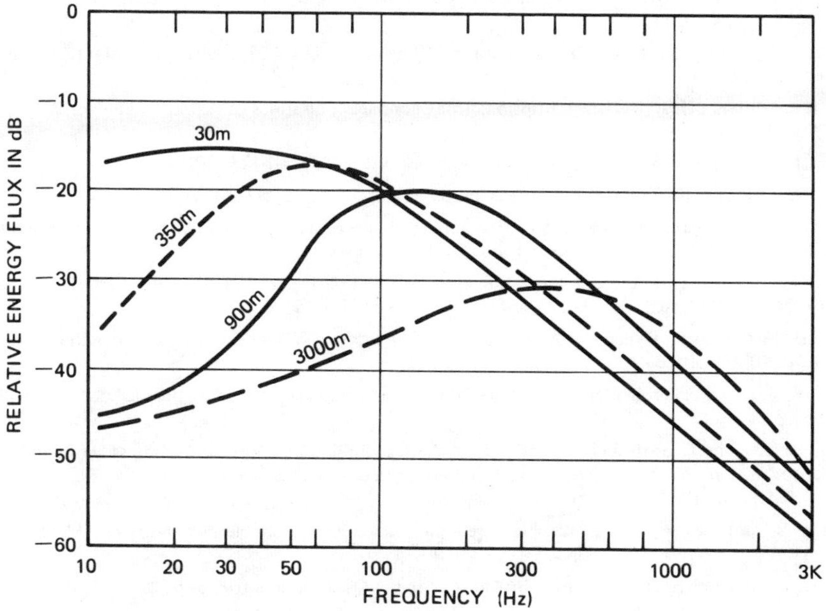


Fig. 7.29. Effect of Detonation Depth on Spectra of 1-lb Charges, after Kibblewhite and Denham (1970)

## REFERENCES

### Sections 7.1-7.3

Akulichev, V.A., Calculation of the cavitation strength of real liquids, *Sov. Phys.-Acoustics, 11*, 15-18, 1965.

Akulichev, V.A., Hydration of ions and the cavitation resistance of water, *Sov. Phys.-Acoustics, 12*, 144-149, 1966.

Akulichev, V.A., "Pulsations of Cavitation Voids," Part 4 of *High-Intensity Ultrasonic Fields*, L.D.Rozenberg (Ed.), Plenum Press, New York, 1971 (pp. 205-237).

Apfel, R.E., The role of impurities in cavitation threshold determination, *J.A.S.A., 48*, 1179-1186, 1970.

Bahl, S.K. and Ray, J., Collapse and expansion of a gas bubble in a liquid subject to surface tension, *Sov. Phys-Acoustics, 18*, 391-393, 1972.

Barger, J.E., Thresholds of acoustic cavitation, *Harvard Univ. Acoustics Res. Lab. Tech. Memo. 57*, April 1964.

Benjamin, T.B., "Pressure Waves from Collapsing Cavities," in *Second Symposium on Naval Hydrodynamics*, O.N.R., ACR-38, Washington, 1958 (pp. 207-229).

Benjamin, T.B. and Ellis, A.T., The collapse of cavitation bubbles and the pressures thereby produced against solid boundaries, *Phil. Trans. Royal Soc.* (London), *A260*, 221-240, 1960.

Bernd, L.H., "Cavitation, Tensile Strength, and the Surface Films of Gas Nuclei," in *Proc. Sixth Symposium on Naval Hydrodynamics*, O.N.R., ACR-136, Washington, 1966 (pp. 77-114).

Beyer, R.T., *Nonlinear Acoustics*, Naval Sea Systems Command, Washington, 1974 (Chapter 8).

Boguslavskii, Yu. Ya. and Korets, V.L., Cavitation threshold frequency dependence, *Sov. Phys.-Acoustics, 12*, 364-368, 1966.

Boguslavskii, Yu. Ya., Diffusion of a gas into a cavitation void, *Sov. Phys.-Acoustics, 13*, 18-21, 1967.

Bornhurst, W.J. and Hatsopoulos, G.N., Bubble-growth calculation without neglect of interfacial discontinuities, *J. Appl. Mech., 34*, 847-853, 1967.

Chapman, R.B. and Plesset, M.S., Nonlinear effects in the collapse of a nearly spherical cavity in a liquid, *J. Basic Engin., 94D*, 142-146, 1972.

Eisenberg, P., On the Mechanism and Prevention of Cavitation, *D.T.M.B. Repts. 712 and 842A*, July 1950 and June 1953.

Eller, A. and Flynn, H.G., Rectified diffusion during nonlinear pulsations of cavitation bubbles, *J.A.S.A., 37*, 493-503, 1965.

Eller, A.I., Growth of bubbles by rectified diffusion, *J.A.S.A., 46*, 1246-1250, 1969.

Eller, A.I., Effects of diffusion on gaseous cavitation bubbles, *J.A.S.A., 57*, 1374-1378, 1975.

Ellis, A.T., "On Jets and Shockwaves from Cavitation," in *Proc. Sixth Symposium on Naval Hydrodynamics*, O.N.R., ACR-136, Washington, Oct. 1966 (pp. 137-161).

Flynn, H.G., "Physics of Acoustic Cavitation in Liquids," Vol. I, Part B, Chapter 9 of *Physical Acoustics*, W.P. Mason (Ed.), Academic Press, New York, 1964 (pp. 57-172).

Flynn, H.G., Cavitation Dynamics: A Mathematical Formulation, *Harvard Univ. Acoustics Res. Lab. Tech. Memo. 50*, Jan. 1966.

Galloway, W.J., An experimental study of acoustically induced cavitation in liquids, *J.A.S.A., 26*, 849-857, 1954.

Gilmore, F.R., The Growth and Collapse of a Spherical Bubble in a Viscous Compressible Liquid, *C.I.T., Hydrodyn. Lab. Rept. 26-4*, April 1952. (Published in part in *Proc. Heat Transfer and Fluid Mech. Inst.*, U.C.L.A., June 1952).

Hickling, R. and Plesset, M.S., Collapse and rebound of a spherical bubble in water, *Phys. Fluids, 7*, 7-14, 1964.

Hickling, R., Some physical effects of cavity collapse in liquids, *J. Basic Engin, 88D*, 229-235, 1966.

Holl, J.W., Nuclei and cavitation, *J. Basic Engin., 92D*, 681-688, 1970.

Hsieh, D.-Y. and Plesset, M.S., Theory of rectified diffusion of mass into gas bubbles, *J.A.S.A., 33*, 206-215, 1961.

Hsieh, D.-Y., Some analytical aspects of bubble dynamics, *J. Basic Engin., 87D*, 991-1005, 1965; also, *C.I.T. Hydromech. Lab. Rept. 85-30*, April 1965.

Hsieh, D.-Y., On the dynamics of nonspherical bubbles, *J. Basic Engin., 94D*, 655-665, 1972.

Hunter, C., On the collapse of an empty cavity in water, *J. Fluid Mech., 8*, 241-263, 1960.

Iernetti, G., Cavitation threshold dependence on volume, *Acustica, 24*, 191-196, 1971.

Ivany, R.D., Hammitt, F.G. and Mitchell, T.M., Cavitation bubble collapse observations in a Venturi, *J. Basic Engin., 88D*, 649-657, 1966.

Khoroshev, G.A., Collapse of vapor-air cavitation bubbles, *Sov. Phys.-Acoustics, 9*, 275-279, 1963.

Kling, C.L. and Hammitt, F.G., A photographic study of spark-induced cavitation bubble collapse, *J. Basic Engin., 94D*, 825-833, 1972.

Knapp, R.T. and Hollander, A., Laboratory investigations of the mechanism of cavitation, *Trans. A.S.M.E., 70*, 419-435, 1948.

Knapp, R.T., Daily, J.W. and Hammitt, F.G., *Cavitation*, McGraw-Hill, New York, 1970 (Chapters 3 and 4).

Kobayashi, R., Growth and collapse of a cavity close to a solid boundary, *Repts. Inst. of High-Speed Mech.* (Japan), *18*, (173), 43-66, 1966.

Kozyrev, S.P., Cumulative collapse of vapor cavitation voids, *Sov. Phys.-Doklady, 11*, 766-768, 1966.

Kozyrev, S.P., On cumulative collapse of cavitation cavities, *J. Basic Engin., 90D*, 116-124, 1968, and *91D*, 857-858, 1969.

Lamb, Sir Horace, *Hydrodynamics*, 6th Edit., Cambridge University Press, 1932; Dover, New York, 1945 (Chapter 5).

Lauterborn, W., Photographic study of tensile strength of water using a centrifuge, *Acustica, 22*, 35-47, 1969 (in German).

Messino, D., Sette, D., and Wanderlingh, F., Statistical approach to ultrasonic cavitation, *J.A.S.A., 35*, 1575-1583, 1963.

Mitchell, T.M. and Hammitt, F.G., Asymmetrical cavitation bubble collapse, *J. Fluids Engin., 95*, 29-37, 1973.

Noltingk, B.E. and Neppiras, E.A., Cavitation produced by ultrasonics, *Proc. Phys. Soc. London, 63B*, 674-685, 1950.

Olson, H.G. and Hammitt, F.G., High-speed photographic studies of ultrasonically induced cavitation, *J.A.S.A., 46*, 1272-1283, 1969.

Plesset, M.S., The dynamics of cavitation bubbles, *J. Appl. Mech., 16*, 277-282, 1949.

Plesset, M.S., "Physical Effects in Cavitation and Boiling," Chapter 12 in *First Symposium on Naval Hydrodynamics*, Publ. 515, Nat. Acad. of Sci., Nat. Res. Coun., Washington, 1957 (pp. 297-323).

Plesset, M.S., "Bubble Dynamics," in *Cavitation in Real Liquids*, R. Davies (Ed.), Elsevier, Amsterdam, 1964 (pp. 1-18).

Plesset, M.S., Cavitating Flows, *C.I.T. Rept. 85-46*, April 1969.

Plesset, M.S., "The Tensile Strength of Liquids," in *Cavitation State of Knowledge*, J.M. Robertson and G.F. Wislicenus (Ed.), A.S.M.E., 1969 (pp. 15-25).

Plesset, M.S. and Chapman, R.B., Collapse of an initially spherical vapour cavity in the neighborhood of a solid boundary, *J. Fluid Mech., 47*, 283-290, 1971; also *C.I.T. Rept. 85-49*, June 1970.

Poritsky, H., The collapse and growth of a spherical bubble or cavity in a viscous fluid, *Proc. First U.S. Nat. Congr. on Appl. Mech.*, 1952 (pp. 813-821).

Rayleigh, Lord, On the pressure developed in a liquid during the collapse of a spherical cavity, *Phil. Mag., 34*, 94-98, 1917; also, *Scientific Papers of Lord Rayleigh*, Vol. VI, Dover, New York (pp. 504-507).

Robertson, J.M., "Cavitation Today – An Introduction," in *Cavitation State of Knowledge*, A.S.M.E., 1969 (pp. 1-9).

Safar, M.H., An acoustic method of determining the distribution of air nuclei which are responsible for cavitation in water, *J. Sound and Vibr., 9*, 308-312, 1969.

Sette, D. and Wanderlingh, F., Nucleation by cosmic rays in ultrasonic cavitation, *Phys. Rev., 125*, 409-417, 1962.

Sirotyuk, M.G., Cavitation strength of water and its distribution of cavitation nuclei, *Sov. Phys.-Acoustics, 11*, 318-322, 1965.

Sirotyuk, M.G., "Experimental Investigations of Ultrasonic Cavitation," Part 5 of *High-Intensity Ultrasonic Fields*, L.D. Rozenberg (Ed.), Plenum Press, New York, 1971 (Chapters 1 and 2).

Strasberg, M., The onset of ultrasonic cavitation in tap water, *J.A.S.A., 31*, 163-176, 1959; also, *D.T.M.B. Rept. 1078*, May 1957 (Revised Edition).

Trilling, L., The collapse and rebound of a gas bubble, *J. Appl. Phys., 23*, 14-17, 1952.

## Sections 7.4 and 7.5

Akulichev, V.A. and Il'ichev, V.I., Spectral indication of the origin of ultrasonic cavitation in water, *Sov. Phys.-Acoustics, 9*, 128-130, 1963.

Akulichev, V.A. and Il'ichev, V.I., Interaction of ultrasonics waves in cavitation, *Sov. Phys.-Acoustics, 10*, 10-12, 1964.

Akulichev, V.A., et al, Radiation of finite-amplitude spherical waves, *Sov. Phys.-Acoustics, 13*, 281-285, 1963.

Akulichev, V.A. and Ol'shevskii, V.V., Statistical characteristics of cavitation phenomena, *Sov. Phys.-Acoustics, 14*, 22-26, 135-139, 1968.

Akulichev, V.A., "Pulsations of Cavitation Voids," Part 4 of *High-Intensity Ultrasonic Fields, op. cit* (pp. 239-259).

Benjamin, T.B., "Pressure Waves from Collapsing Cavities," in *Proc. Second Symposium on Naval Hydrodynamics*, O.N.R., ACR-38, Washington, 1958 (pp. 207-233).

Boguslavskii, Yu. Ya., Ioffe, A.I. and Naugol'nykh, K.A., Sound radiation by a cavitation zone, *Sov. Phys.-Acoustics, 16*, 17-20, 1970.

Fitzpatrick, H.M. and Strasberg, M., "Hydrodynamic Sources of Sound," Chapter 10 of *First Symposium on Naval Hydrodynamics*, Publ. 515, Nat. Acad. of Sci., Nat. Res. Coun., 1957 (pp. 241-280); also, *D.T.M.B. Rept. 1269*, Jan. 1959.

Harrison, M., An experimental study of single bubble cavitation noise, *J.A.S.A., 24*, 776-782, 1952; also, *D.T.M.B. Rept. 815*, Nov. 1952 (revised).

Il'ichev, V.I. and Lesunovskii, V.P., On the noise spectra associated with hydrodynamic cavitation," *Sov. Phys.-Acoustics, 9*, 25-28, 1963.

Khoroshev, G.A., Collapse of vapor-air cavitation bubbles, *Sov. Phys.-Acoustics, 9*, 275-279, 1963.

Levkovskii, Yu. L., Modeling of cavitation noise, *Sov. Phys.-Acoustics, 13*, 337-339, 1967.

Levkovskii, Yu. L., Effect of diffusion on the sound radiation from a cavitation void, *Sov. Phys.-Acoustics, 14*, 470-473, 1968.

Lyamshev, L.M., On the theory of hydrodynamic cavitation noise, *Sov. Phys.-Acoustics, 15*, 494-498, 1969.

Mellen, R.H., Ultrasonic spectrum of cavitation noise in water, *J.A.S.A., 26*, 356-362, 1954.

Mellen, R.H., An experimental study of the collapse of a spherical cavity in water, *J.A.S.A., 28*, 447-454, 1956; also, *U.S. Navy Underwater Sound Lab. Repts. 279 and 326*, 1956.

Morozov, V.P., Cavitation noise as a train of sound pulses generated at random times, *Sov. Phys.-Acoustics, 14*, 361-365, 1968.

Osborne, M.F.M., The shock produced by a collapsing cavity in water, *Trans. A.S.M.E., 69*, 253-266, 1947.

Ross, D. and McCormick, B.W., Jr., Effect of Air Content on Cavitation Noise, Report to *Eighth Amer. Towing Tank Conf.*, Oct. 1948; also, *Ord. Res. Lab. Rept. 7958-115*, Oct. 1948.

Rozenberg, L.D., "The Cavitation Zone," Part 6 of *High-Intensity Ultrasonic Fields*, L.D. Rozenberg (Ed.), Plenum Press, New York, 1971 (pp. 377-387).

Sirotyuk, M.C., "Experimental Investigations of Ultrasonic Cavitation," Part 5 of *High-Intensity Ultrasonic Fields, op. cit.* (pp. 285-339).

van Wijngaarden, L., "Linear and Nonlinear Dispersion of Pressure Pulses in Liquid-Bubble Mixtures," *Proc. Sixth Symposium on Naval Hydrodynamics*, O.N.R., ACR-136, Washington, Sept. 1966 (pp. 115-135).

## Section 7.6

Bebchuk, A.S. and Rozenberg, L.D., On the problem of cavitation erosion, *Sov. Phys.-Acoustics, 3*, 95-96, 395-398, 1957; *4*, 372-373, 1958 and *6*, 496-497, 1960.

Degrois, M. and Badilian, B., Cavitation in liquids subjected to ultrasonic waves, and phenomenon of relaxation produced by ultrasound, *Comptes Rendus Acad. of Sci., 254*, 231-233, 837-839, 1213-1215, 1943-1945, 1962; also, *Acustica, 21*, 222-228, 1969; and *Ultrasonics, 4*, 38-39, 1966.

Eisenberg, P., Preiser, H.S. and Thiruvengadam, A., On the mechanisms of cavitation damage and methods of protection, *Trans. Soc. Naval Arch. and Mar. Engin., 73*, 241-286, 1965.

Elpiner, I.E., On the chemical action of ultrasonic waves, *Sov. Phys.-Acoustics, 5*, 135-146, 1959.

Elpiner, I.E., *Ultrasound: Physical, Chemical and Biological Effects*, Consultants Bureau, 1964 (Chapters 4 to 6).

Finch, R.D., Sonoluminescence, *Ultrasonics, 1*, 87-98, 1963.

Garcia, R. and Hammitt, F.G., Cavitation damage and correlations with material and fluid properties, *J. Basic Engin., 89D*, 753-763, 1967.

Golubnichii, P.I., Goncharov, V.D. and Protopopov, K.V., Sonoluminescence in various liquids, *Sov. Phys.-Acoustics, 16*, 115-117, 323-326, 1970.

Hammitt, F.G., Damage due to cavitation and sub-cooled boiling bubble collapse, *Proc. Inst. of Mech. Engin., 183*, 31-50, 1968.

Hickling, R., Effects of thermal conduction in sonoluminescence, *J.A.S.A., 35*, 967-974, 1963; also, *C.I.T. Rept. 85-21*, 1962.

Hickling, R., Some physical effects of cavity collapse in liquids, *J. Basic Engin., 88D*, 229-235, 1966.

Jarman, P., Measurements of sonoluminescence from pure liquids and some aqueous solutions, *Proc. Phys. Soc. London, 73*, 628-640, 1959.

Jarman, P.D. and Taylor, K.J., The timing of the main and secondary flashes of sonoluminescence from acoustically cavitated water, *Acustica, 23*, 243-251, 1970.

Kallas, D.H. and Lichtman, J.Z., "Cavitation Erosion," in *Environmental Effects of Polymeric Materials*, Vol. I, Interscience Publishers, 1968 (Chapter 2).

Knapp, R.T., Daily, J.W. and Hammitt, F.G., *op. cit.* (Chapters 4, 8 and 9).

Kornfeld, M. and Suvorov, L., On the destructive action of cavitation, *J. Appl. Phys., 15*, 495-506, 1944.

Kuttruff, H., Relation between sonoluminescence and acoustic cavitation in liquids, *Acustica, 12*, 230-254, 1962 (in German).

Naudé, C.F. and Ellis, A.T., On the mechanism of cavitation damage by nonhemispherical cavities collapsing in contact with a solid body, *J. Basic Engin., 83D*, 648-656, 1961.

Noltingk, B.E., "The Effects of Intense Ultrasonics in Liquids," in *Handbuch der Physik*, Vol. XI/2, 1962 (pp. 258-287).

Plesset, M.S. and Ellis, A.T., On the mechanism of cavitation damage, *Trans. A.S.M.E., 77*, 1055-1064, 1955.

Plesset, M.S., Temperature effects in cavitation damage, *J. Basic Engin., 94D*, 559-566, 1972.

Plesset, M.S., Cavitation and Cavitation Damage, *C.I.T. Rept. 85-58*, March 1973.

Shalnev, K.K., Varga, I.I. and Sebestyen, D., Investigations of the scale effects of cavitation erosion, *Phil Trans Royal Soc.* (London), *A260*, 256-266, 1966.

Sirotyuk, M.G., Effect of temperature and gas content of the liquid on cavitation processes, *Sov. Phys.-Acoustics, 12*, 67-71, 199-204, 1966.

*Symposium on Erosion and Cavitation*, Amer. Soc. of Testing Materials, Publ. 307, Phila., Pa. 1962.

Thiruvengadam, A., A unified theory of cavitation damage, *J. Basic Engin., 85D*, 365-376, 1963.

Thiruvengadam, A., On modeling cavitation damage, *J. Ship Res., 13*, 220-234, 1969.

Thiruvengadam, A., Cavitation erosion, *Appl. Mech. Rev., 24*, 245-253, 1971.

Thiruvengadam, A., Handbook of Cavitation Erosion, *Hydronautics Inc. Rept. 7301-1*, Jan. 1974.

West, C. and Howlett, R., Experimental measurements on cavitation bubble dynamics, *Acustica, 21*, 112-117, 1969.

## Sections 7.7-7.9


Abbott, I.H. and von Doenhoff, A.E., *Theory of Wing Sections*, Dover, New York, 1959; also, *N.A.C.A. Tech. Rept. 824*, 1945.

Ackeret, J., Experimental and theoretical investigations on cavitation in water, *Appl. Mech. and Thermodyn., 1*, 1-22, 1930 (in German); trans. *N.A.C.A. Tech. Memo. 1078*, 1945, and *D.T.M.B. Trans. 20*, 1936.

Arndt, R.E.A. and Ippen, A.T., Rough surface effects on cavitation inception, *J. Basic Engin., 90D*, 249-261, 1968.

Arndt, R.E.A. and Daily, J.W., "Cavitation in Turbulent Boundary Layers," in *Cavitation State of Knowledge*, A.S.M.E., 1969 (pp. 64-86).

Ball, J.W., Cavitation characteristics of gate valves and globe valves, *Trans. A.S.M.E., 79*, 1275-1283, 1957.

Bashta, T.M., Fluid cavitation in hydraulic systems, *Russian Engin. J., 41*, (9) 5-10, 1961.

Bernd, L.H., "Cavitation, Tensile Strength and the Surface Effects of Gas Nuclei," *Proc. Sixth Symposium on Naval Hydrodynamics*, O.N.R., ACR-136, Washington, Sept. 1966 (pp. 77-114).

Borden, A., "Prediction of Cavitation Inception Speeds on Rough Hydrodynamic Bodies," *Proc. Sixth Symposium on Naval Hydrodynamics*, O.N.R., ACR-136, Washington, 1966 (pp. 183-199).

Daily, J.W., Cavitation characteristics and infinite aspect-ratio characteristics of a hydrofoil section, *Trans. A.S.M.E., 71*, 269-284, 1949.

Dean, R.B., The formation of bubbles, *J. Appl. Phys., 15*, 446-451, 1944.

Glauert, H., *The Elements of Aerofoil and Airscrew Theory*, Cambridge University Press, Cambridge, 1948.

Goldstein, S. (Ed)., *Modern Developments in Fluid Dynamics*, Clarendon Press, Oxford, 1938; Dover, New York, 1965 (Chapters 9 and 10).

Holl, J.W., The inception of cavitation on isolated surface irregularities, *J. Basic Engin, 82D*, 169-183, 1960.

Holl, J.W., An effect of air content on the occurrence of cavitation, *J. Basic Engin., 82D*, 941-945, 1960.

Holl, J.W. and Wislicenus, G.F., Scale effects on cavitation, *J. Basic Engin., 83D*, 385-398, 1961.

Holl, J.W., "The Estimation of the Effect of Surface Irregularities on the Inception of Cavitation," in *Symposium on Cavitation in Fluid Machinery*, A.S.M.E., Nov. 1965 (pp. 3-15).

Holl, J.W. and Treaster, A.L., Cavitation hysteresis, *J. Basic Engin., 88D*, 199-212, 1966.

Holl, J.W., "Limited Cavitation," in *Cavitation State of Knowledge*, J.M. Robertson and G.F. Wislicenus (Ed.), A.S.M.E., 1969.

Johnson, V.E. and Hsieh, T., "The Influence of the Trajectories of Gas Nuclei on Cavitation Inception," *Proc. Sixth Symposium on Naval Hydrodynamics*, O.N.R., ACR-136, Washington, Oct. 1966 (pp. 163-182).

Johnsson, C.A., Correlation of predictions and full-scale observations of propeller cavitation, *Int. Shipbuilding Progress, 20*, 194-210, 1973.

Jorgensen, D.W., Noise from cavitating submerged water jets, *J.A.S.A., 33*, 1334-1338, 1961; also, *D.T.M.B. Rept. 1126*, Nov. 1958.

Kamiyama, S., Cavitation tests in pipe bends, *J. Basic Engin., 88D*, 252-260, 1966.

Karelin, V.Y., *Cavitation Phenomena in Centrifugal and Axial-Flow Pumps*, Sudpromgiz, 1963 (in Russian), translated by Nat. Engin. Lab., Scotland.

Kermeen, R.W., McGraw, J.T. and Parkin, B.R., Mechanism of cavitation inception and the related scale-effects problem, *Trans. A.S.M.E., 77*, 533-541, 1955; also, *C.I.T. Rept. 21-8*, July 1952.

Kermeen, R.W., Water Tunnel Tests of NACA 4412, Walchner Profile 7 and NACA 66, -012 Hydrofoils in Noncavitating and Cavitating Flows, *C.I.T. Hydrodyn. Lab. Repts. 47-5 and 47-7*, 1956.

Khoroshev, G.A., Pump vibration caused by cavitation, *Power Machinery*, No. 4, 26-30, April 1960 (in Russian); translated by Foreign Technology Div., U.S.A.F.

Knapp, R.T., "Fluid Dynamics," Vol. 20 of *N.D.R.C. Div. 6 Summary Technical Reports*, 1945.

Knapp, R.T., Daily, J.W. and Hammitt, F.G., *op. cit.* (Chapters 1, 5, 6, 7 and 11).

Landweber, L., The Axially-Symmetric Potential Flow about Elongated Bodies of Revolution, *D.T.M.B. Rept. 761*, Aug. 1951.

Lehman, A.F. and Young, J.O., Experimental investigations of incipient and desinent cavitation, *J. Basic Engin., 86D*, 275-284, 1964.

McCormick, B.W., Jr., On cavitation produced by a vortex trailing from a lifting surface, *J. Basic Engin., 84D*, 369-379, 1962.

Mises, R. von, *Theory of Flight*, McGraw-Hill, New York, 1945 (Chapters 6, 7, 8).

Müller, E.-A., "Some Experimental and Theoretical Results Relating to the Production of Noise by Turbulence," in *Proc. Second Symposium on Naval Hydrodynamics*, O.N.R., ACR-38, Washington, 1958 (pp. 45-51).

Numachi, F., Oba, R. and Chida, I., "Effect of Surface Roughness on Cavitation Performance of Hydrofoils," in *Symposium on Cavitation in Fluid Machinery*, A.S.M.E., Nov. 1965 (pp. 16-31).

Oossanen, P. van, Profile characteristics in cavitating and non-cavitating flows, *Int. Shipbuilding Progress, 18*, 115-130, 1971.

Parkin, B.R. and Holl, J.W., Incipient-Cavitation Scaling Experiments on Hemispherical and Ogive-Nosed Bodies, *Joint C.I.T. and Ord. Res. Lab. Rept. 7958-264*, May 1953.

Pearsall, I.S., "Acoustic Detection of Cavitation (in Pumps)," Paper 14 in *Vibrations in Hydraulic Pumps and Turbines, Proc. Inst. Mech. Engin., 181, 3A*, 1-8, 1966.

Pearsall, I.S., *Cavitation*, Mills and Boon, London, 1972.

Pokrovskii, B.V. and Yudin, E.Ya., Principal noise and vibration characteristics of centrifugal pumps, *Sov. Phys.-Acoustics, 12*, 303-309, 1966.

Ross, D., Airfoil Information for Propeller Design, *Ord. Res. Lab. Rept. 7958-71*, Nov. 1947.

Rouse, H. and McNown, J.S., Cavitation and Pressure Distribution of Head Forms at Zero Angle of Yaw, *State Univ. of Iowa, Studies in Engin. Bull. 32*, 1948.

Sarpkaya, T., Torque and cavitation characteristics of butterfly valves, *J. Appl. Mech, 28*, 511-518, 1961.

Shalnev, K.K., Cavitation of surface roughnesses, *J. Tech. Phys. USSR, 21*, 206-220, 1951; trans. *D.T.M.B. Trans. 259*, Dec. 1955.

Simpson, H.C., Macaskill, R. and Clark, T.A., "Generation of Hydraulic Noise in Centrifugal Pumps," Paper 12 in *Vibrations in Hydraulic Pumps and Turbines, Proc. Inst. Mech. Engin., 181, 3A*, 84-108, 1966.

Tachmindji, A.J. and Morgan, W.B., "The Design and Estimated Performance of a Series of Supercavitating Propellers," *Proc. Second Symposium on Naval Hydrodynamics*, O.N.R., ACR-38, Washington, 1958 (pp. 489-532).

Tulin, M.P., "Supercavitating Flow Past Foils and Struts," Paper 16 in *Proc. Symposium on Cavitation in Hydrodynamics*, Nat. Phys. Lab., London, Sept. 1955.

Tulin, M.P., "Supercavitating Propellers," *Proc. Fourth Symposium on Naval Hydrodynamics*, O.N.R., ACR-92, Washington, 1962 (pp. 239-286).

Tulin, M.P., "Supercavitating Flows," in *Cavitation in Real Liquids*, R. Davies (Ed.), Elsevier, Amsterdam, 1964.

van der Meulen, J.H.J., Cavitation on hemispherical nosed bodies, *Int. Shipbuilding Progress, 19*, 21-32, 333-341, 1972.

van der Walle, F., "On the Growth of Nuclei and the Related Scaling Factors in Cavitation Inception," in *Proc. Fourth Symposium on Naval Hydrodynamics*, O.N.R., ACR-92, 1962 (pp. 357-404); also, *Int. Shipbuilding Progress, 10*, 195-204, 1963.

Widnall, S.E., The structure and dynamics of vortex filaments, *Ann. Rev. Fluid Mech., 7*, 141-165, 1975.

Wislicenus, G.F., *Fluid Mechanics of Turbomachinery*, McGraw-Hill, New York, 1947; Dover, New York, 1965 (Chapters 4 and 13).

Young, J.O. and Holl, J.W., Effects of cavitation on periodic wakes behind symmetric wedges, *J. Basic Eng., 88D*, 163-176, 1966.

## Section 7.10

Akulichev, V.A., Boguslavskii, Yu. Ya., Ioffe, A.I. and Naugol'nykh, K.A., Radiation of finite-amplitude spherical waves, *Sov. Phys.-Acoustics, 13*, 281-285, 1967.

Arons, A.B. and Yennie, D.R., Energy partition in underwater explosion phenomena, *Rev. Modern Phys., 20*, 519-536, 1948.

Arons, A.B., Underwater explosion shock wave parameters at large distances from the charge, *J.A.S.A., 26*, 343-346, 1954.

Beyer, R.T., *Nonlinear Acoustics*, Naval Sea Systems Command, 1974 (Chapter 4).

Blaik, M. and Christian, E.A., Near-surface measurements of deep explosions I, Pressure pulses from small charges, *J.A.S.A., 38*, 50-56, 1965.

Christian, E.A. and Blaik, M., Near-surface measurements of deep explosions II, Energy spectra of small charges, *J.A.S.A., 38*, 57-62, 1965.

Cole, R.H., *Underwater Explosions*, Princeton University Press, Princeton, 1948; Dover, New York, 1965.

Esipov, I.B. and Naugol'nykh, K.A., Expansion of a spherical cavity in a liquid, *Sov. Phys.-Acoustics, 18*, 194-197, 1972.

Friedman, B., Theory of Underwater Explosion Bubbles, *Inst. for Math. and Mech., New York Univ.*, Sept. 1947; also in *Underwater Explosion Research*, Vol. II, O.N.R., 1950.

Herring, C., Theory of the Pulsations of the Gas Bubble Produced by an Underwater Explosion, *Nat. Def. Res. Com.*, Columbia Univ., Oct. 1941; also in *Underwater Explosion Research*, Vol. II, O.N.R., 1950.

Ioffe, A.I., Kozhelupova, N.G., Naugol'nykh, K.A. and Roi, N.A., Sound radiation from a long spark in water, *Sov. Phys.-Acoustics, 13*, 180-183, 1967.

Kibblewhite, A.C. and Denham, R.N., Measurements of acoustic energy from underwater explosions, *J.A.S.A., 48*, 346-351, 1970.

Kirkwood, J.G. and Bethe, H.A., The Pressure Wave Produced by an Underwater Explosion, *O.S.R.D. Rept. 588*, May 1942 (PB 32,182); also in *Shock and Detonation Waves*, W.W. Wood (Ed.), Gordon and Breach, New York, 1967 (pp. 1-34).

LeMéhaute, B., "Theory of Explosion-Generated Water Waves," in *Advances in Hydroscience*, Vol. 7, Academic Press, New York, 1971 (pp. 1-79).

Snay, H.G., "Hydrodynamics of Underwater Explosions," Paper 13 in *Symposium on Naval Hydrodynamics*, Nat. Acad. of Sci., Nat. Res. Coun. Publ. 515, Washington, 1956 (pp. 325-352).

Urick, R.J., *Principles of Underwater Sound for Engineers*, McGraw-Hill, New York, 1967 (Section 4.3).

Weston, D.E., Underwater explosions as acoustic sources, *Proc. Phys. Soc. London, 76*(2), 233-249, 1960.

# CHAPTER 8

# PROPELLER CAVITATION NOISE

Cavitation of marine propellers is the most prevalent source of underwater sound in the oceans. Furthermore, when it occurs, propeller cavitation is usually the dominant noise source for any single marine vehicle. Submarines and torpedoes often operate deep enough to avoid cavitation. Surface ships, on the other hand, generally have well-developed propeller cavitation, with the result that their entire radiated spectra from as low as 5 Hz to as high as 100 kHz are controlled by this source. The basic phenomena of cavitation and cavitation noise were considered in the previous chapter. Now these concepts are combined with propeller hydrodynamics relations to explain the fundamental characteristics of propeller cavitation noise. Data on surface ship radiated noise and an analysis of the contribution of this source to low-frequency ambient ocean noise are presented in the final two sections.

## 8.1 Types of Propeller Cavitation

Propeller blades are rotating twisted wings that produce hydrodynamic forces. Depending on operating conditions, they experience cavitation in a number of different places, as illustrated by three typical examples shown in Fig. 8.1. Prominent in these photographs are two types of vortex cavitation: tip-vortex and hub-vortex. Propeller tip-vortex cavitation, shown most clearly in Fig. 8.1(a), is similar to wing-tip cavitation, which was discussed in Section 7.8. Hub vortices such as that shown in Fig. 8.1(c) are formed when the lift is heavy on inboard sections. Vortex cavitation produces noise, but not as much as blade-surface cavitation, which is most clearly visible in Fig. 8.1(b). In this case, the cavitation is occurring on the suction, or back, surface of the blade. When the thrust produced is small or negative, blade-surface cavitation may occur on the driving face of the blade. In addition to two types of vortex cavitation, there are two types of blade-surface cavitation: back and face. Of these, blade-surface cavitation on the suction surface is the most noisy, and hub-vortex cavitation the least.

## 8.2 Blade-Surface Cavitation Noise

Of the various types of cavitation, blade-surface cavitation on the suction surface produces the highest noise levels. This is because the voids collapse rapidly when they reach a region of positive collapse pressure. Both types of vortex cavitation voids, on the other hand, remain in negative pressure regions for relatively long times, tend to fill with gas as well as vapor and so collapse with less energy release.

### Rotating Blade Experiments

Blade-surface cavitation can be made to occur on the surfaces of non-lifting as well as lifting

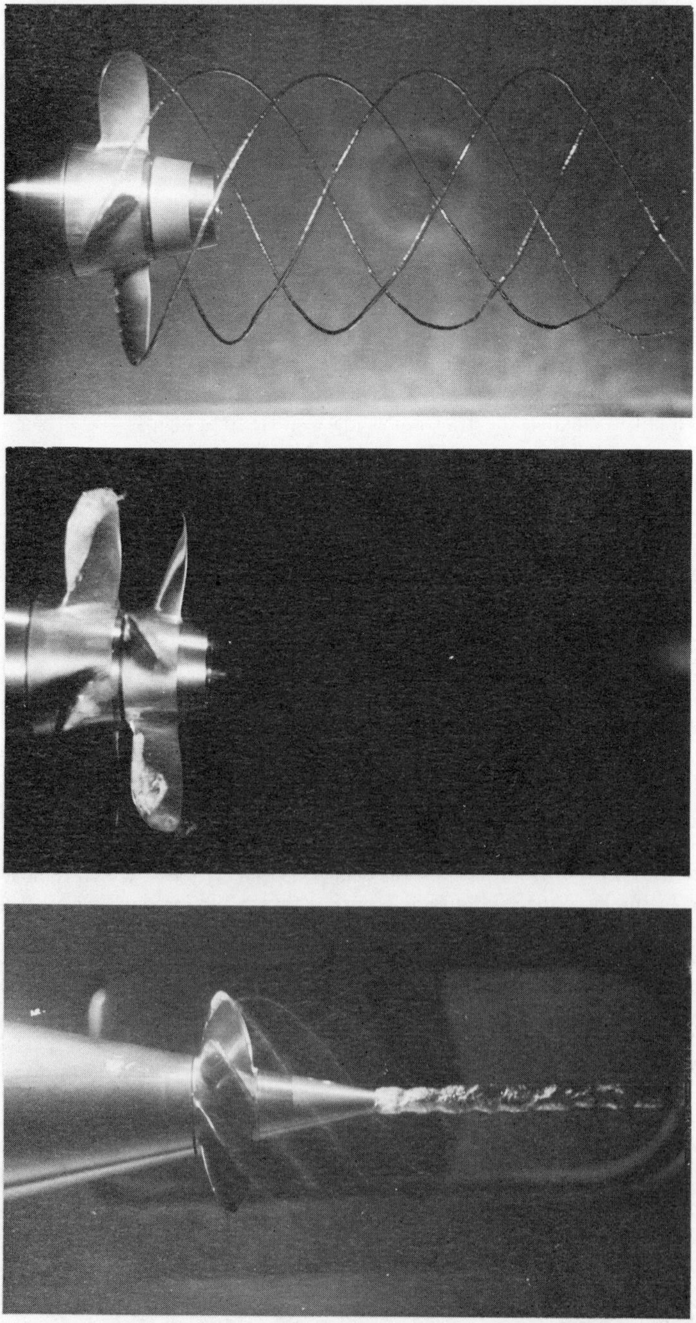

(a)

(b)

(c)

Fig. 8.1. Examples of Propeller Cavitation (Photographs taken in Garfield Thomas Water Tunnel, at The Pennsylvania State University)

blades. It can therefore be studied with an *eggbeater*-type rotating-blade apparatus in still water. Experiments of this type have been reported by Ross and McCormick (1948), Mellen (1954) and Lesunovskii and Khokha (1968). The results and analyses reported here are based on these three investigations.

Ross and McCormick reported on measurements made with an eggbeater apparatus in a lake. They measured radiated noise over the band from 17 to 60 kHz using a 1 kHz filter, finding the spectrum in this band to be continuous with a -6 dB/octave slope. As shown in Fig. 8.2, noise levels increase sharply with cavitation inception and then more gradually, even leveling off for some speed increments before resuming an upward trend. The "theoretical curves" shown in Fig. 8.2 are of the form

$$SPL = C + 10 \log \frac{N}{N_i} \left( \frac{N}{N_i} - 1 \right)^2 , \qquad (8.1)$$

which formula will be explained later in this section.

The noise measurements reported by Ross and McCormick were at frequencies above the peak of the cavitation spectrum. Measurements of a wide band including the peak were made by Mellen (1954) using a rotating rod 10 cm in diameter. As shown in Fig. 8.3, a complex triple peak was observed at about 2 kHz.

The most thorough study of blade-surface cavitation noise is that of Lesunovskii and Khokha. They studied zero-pitch airfoil-section blades having thickness-chord ratios of about 26% and diameters of 0.5 m. The critical tip index was found to be close to 1.9. Their measured spectra summarized in Figs. 8.4 and 8.5 reveal three distinctively different regimes of cavitation. The first regime, from inception to a relative speed of 1.27, is characterized by implosions of individual

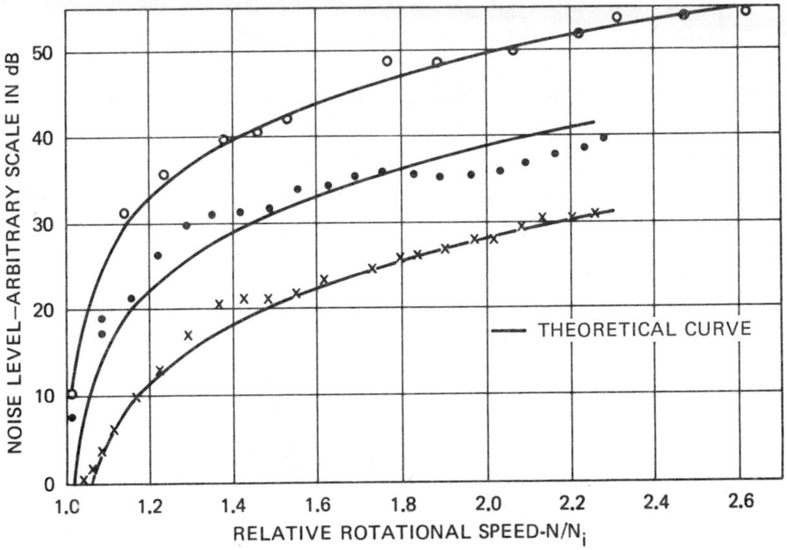


Fig. 8.2. Shape of Noise Curves for Typical Propeller Blades, after Ross and McCormick (1948)

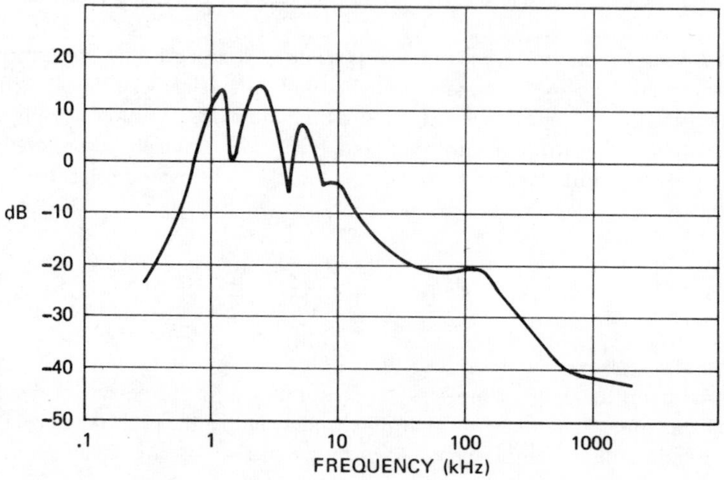


Fig. 8.3. Measured Spectrum of Cavitation Noise Using Rotating Rod, after Mellen (1954)

bubbles, called *transient cavitation*. The intensification of noise in this regime is due to increasing numbers of bubbles collapsing per second as well as increase of their size. The spectrum in this regime, corresponding to the lowest three curves in Fig. 8.4, exhibits a rounded peak. The second regime, from 1.28 to about 1.55, is characterized by a sharp spectral peak and by a peak in overall level. The sound is like a siren, the pitch of which becomes lower as the flow speed becomes greater. With a further increase in speed, the noise loses its tonality, becomes broadband and acquires a hissing character. The overall noise level rises about 15 dB in the third regime. As at lower speeds, the increase in level at low frequencies is more rapid than that at high frequencies.

**Scaling Relationships**

Ross and McCormick (1948) recognized that the representative local flow velocity for cavitation of a rotating blade is the tip velocity,

$$U_t = \pi n D \quad , \tag{8.2}$$

and that the appropriate flow cavitation parameter is the tip cavitation index,

$$K_t \equiv \frac{p_o - p_v}{\frac{1}{2}\rho_o U_t^2} = \frac{p_o - p_v}{\frac{1}{2}\rho_o(\pi n D)^2} . \tag{8.3}$$

The blades which they used had square edges and tips and critical values of the tip index of about 2.0. A slightly lower value was measured in the Russian experiments. Values as low as 1.0 have been observed with rounded tips.

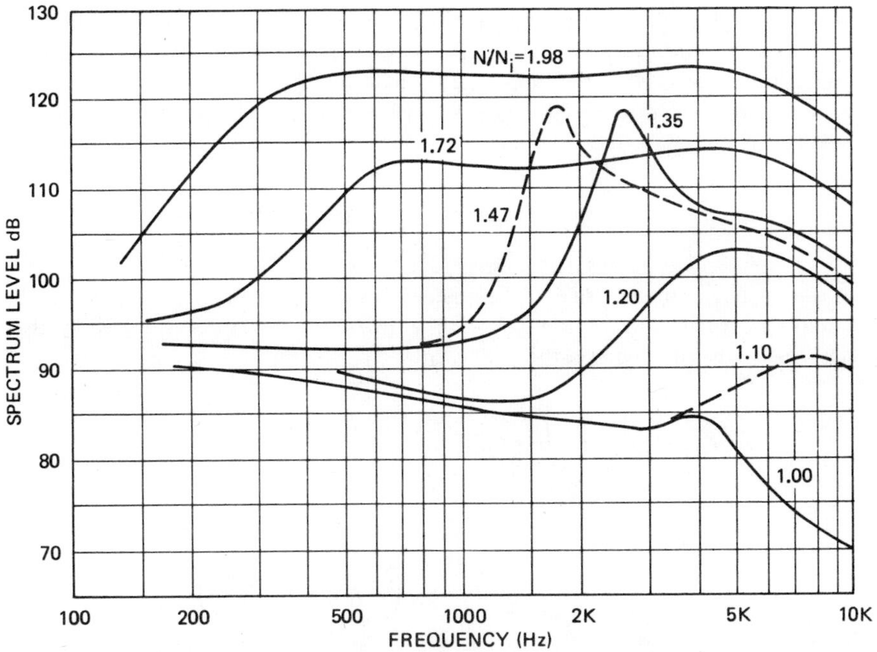


Fig. 8.4. Spectra Measured from Rotating Blades, after Lesunovskii and Khokha (1968)

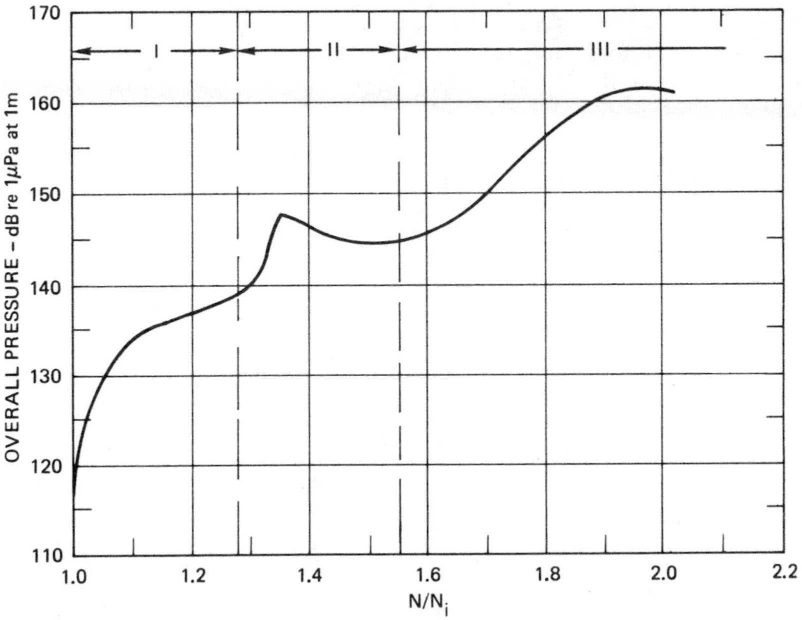


Fig. 8.5. Overall Noise Level as Function of Relative Rotational Speed, after Lesunovskii and Khokha (1968)

Ross and McCormick also developed an approximate theory for blade-surface cavitation noise scaling by means of dimensional analysis, basic physical reasoning and simplified assumptions concerning hydrofoil pressure distributions. They combined dimensional analysis with the result, described in Section 7.5, that acoustic power is proportional to the product of the collapse pressure and the volume of cavitation produced per unit time. From this synthesis they found

$$I \sim \frac{BsDPU_t}{r^2} f\left(K_t, K_{t_i}\right) , \tag{8.4}$$

where $I$ is the total acoustic intensity, $B$ the number of blades cavitating, $s$ the blade chord and $r$ the distance of the hydrophone from the source. The cavitating volume was estimated by assuming a triangular pressure distribution over the foil, whence

$$f\left(K_t, K_{t_i}\right) = \left(\sqrt{\frac{K_{t_i}}{K_t}} - 1\right)^2 = \left(\frac{U_t}{U_{t_i}} - 1\right)^2 . \tag{8.5}$$

Equation 8.4 then takes the form

$$I \sim \frac{\rho_o BsDK_{t_i}U_{t_i}^3}{r^2} \left[\left(\frac{U_t}{U_{t_i}}\right)\left(\frac{U_t}{U_{t_i}} - 1\right)^2\right] , \tag{8.6}$$

where the expression in brackets has the same speed dependence as that indicated by Eq. 8.1. When plotted on a log-log plot, Eq. 8.6 yields an average dependence on speed for well developed cavitation of about the fifth power. As we will see in Section 8.6 on merchant ship noise, this is in reasonably good agreement with trends found with full-scale ship propellers.

Equation 8.6 applies to the overall spectrum. Spectrum levels at frequencies above the spectrum peak can be estimated using a simple spectrum shape of the form

$$I_f = I_m \left(\frac{f_m}{f}\right)^2 \qquad (f \geq f_m) , \tag{8.7}$$

from which it follows that

$$I_f = \frac{If_m}{f^2} . \tag{8.8}$$

Peak frequency varies as the square root of pressure and inversely as the blade chord in accordance with Eq. 7.51. The frequency of the peak is also a function of the cavitation index, increasing as the index increases. From the results of Lesunovskii and Khokha, and also from some unpublished measurements on full-scale propellers, it appears that

$$f_m \sim \frac{1}{s}\sqrt{\frac{P}{\rho_o}}\, K_t^{3/2} . \tag{8.9}$$

From this it follows that the level at a given frequency varies as

$$I_f \sim \frac{BDK_{t_i} P^2}{\rho_o r^2 f^2} \left(1 - \frac{U_{t_i}}{U_t}\right)^2 , \tag{8.10}$$

which yields a slower dependence on speed than that for the overall level, and even predicts that at high speeds high-frequency spectrum levels will remain virtually constant.

**Dependence of Noise on Depth**

Equation 8.10 for the high-frequency noise spectrum can be written in terms of the ratio of the operating static pressure to that for which cavitation would be suppressed at the same tip speed,

$$I_f \sim \frac{\rho_o BDK_{t_i}^{5/2} U_t^4}{r^2 f^2} p_r^2 \left(1 - \sqrt{p_r}\right)^2 , \tag{8.11}$$

where $p_r$ is the ratio of the actual pressure relative to that for cavitation inception. As depicted in Fig. 8.6, Eq. 8.11 predicts a maximum for high-frequency noise levels for static pressures of 30 to 60% of the inception value. For lower pressures, the noise level increases with increasing static pressure. This effect was originally observed during World War II, when it was found that high-frequency noise from submarines sometimes increased with increasing depth, rather than decreasing as was expected. The effect was named the *anomalous depth effect*. The explanation is that increased pressure causes the bubbles to collapse more rapidly and with more energy, resulting in a marked increase in peak frequency and in energy radiated at frequencies above the peak. The

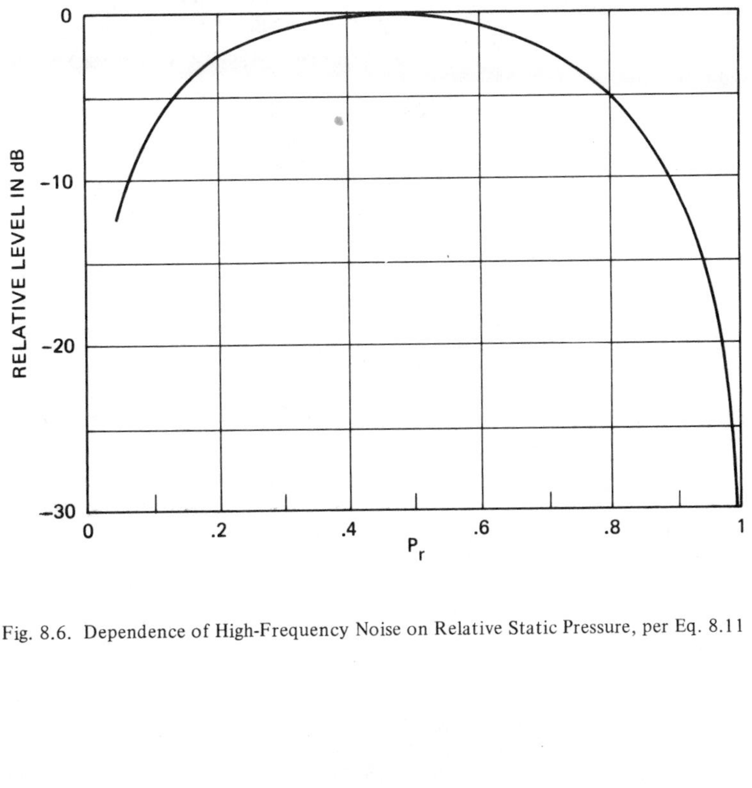


Fig. 8.6. Dependence of High-Frequency Noise on Relative Static Pressure, per Eq. 8.11

above analysis of cavitation noise provides a reasonable, though somewhat oversimplified, theoretical understanding of the anomalous depth effect and of other experimental data concerning cavitation noise.

### Effect of Gas Content

The eggbeater experiment described by Ross and McCormick (1948) was carried out at a small lake over a period of more than a year. It was observed that the same amount of cavitation produced more high-frequency noise in winter months than in summer. The maximum difference was close to 10 dB. The effect was explained in terms of gas content of the water. The bottom of the lake at which the tests were run was covered with decaying vegetation, and apparently gas was released in the summer when the water was warm. The cushioning effect of the gas reduced the high-frequency noise, in accordance with the analysis presented in Section 7.4.

## 8.3 Propellers in Uniform Inflows

Although marine propellers operate in non-uniform turbulent wakes of vehicles, model propellers are often tested in water tunnels under uniform flow conditions. The present section on propeller operation in uniform inflows precedes discussion in the next section of the effects of flow non-uniformities.

### Blade-Element Analysis

A propeller blade is essentially a twisted wing attached to a hub and can be understood in terms of aerodynamics theory. In aerodynamics, wings of finite span are usually analyzed by treating each section as a two-dimensional airfoil, the inflow velocity of which is composed of the vector sum of the flow velocity and the velocity induced by the trailing vortex system. Taking the same approach to propellers, *blade-element theory* was originally developed by Betz and Prandtl in Germany immediately after the first World War, and was further expanded by Goldstein (1929) and Theodorsen (1948).

The geometric essence of propeller blade-element analysis is illustrated by Fig. 8.7. Each differential element is formed by the intersection of a cylinder with the blade. The resultant airfoil experiences lift and drag forces due to its interaction with the inflow velocity, which is the vector sum of three components: the rotational component, $2\pi nr$; the forward speed, $U_a$, often called the velocity of advance; and the induced velocity, $w_i$, associated with the trailing vortex system. The lift and drag components of force contribute to both the thrust developed by the propeller and the torque required to keep it rotating. *Thrust* is the axial component of the resultant force,

$$dT = \cos\phi \, dF_L - \sin\phi \, dF_D \; ; \tag{8.12}$$

*torque* is associated with the force components in the propeller plane,

$$dQ = r(\sin\phi \, dF_L + \cos\phi \, dF_D) \; , \tag{8.13}$$

where angle $\phi$ is made by the resultant velocity vector with the propeller plane, as shown in Fig. 8.7. Both lift and drag are functions of the square of the inflow velocity and the angle of

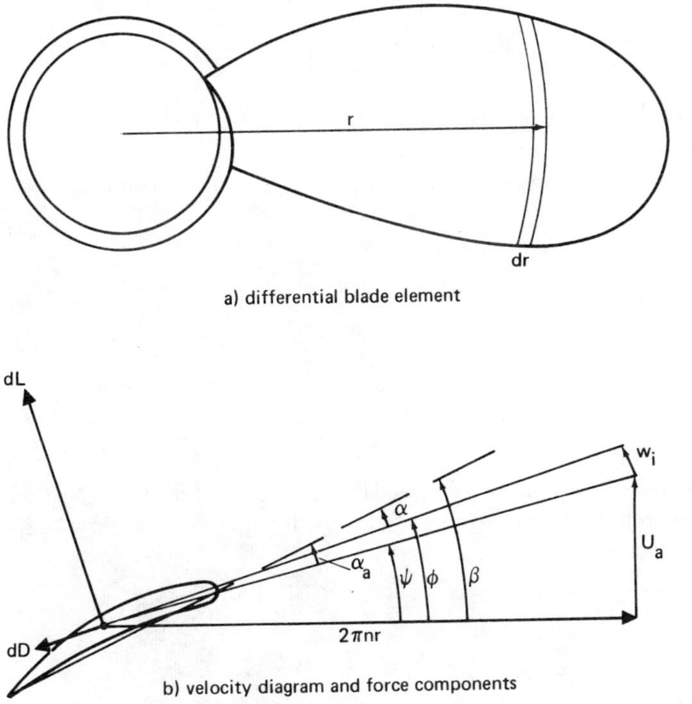


Fig. 8.7. Blade-Element Representation of a Marine Propeller

attack, $\alpha$, given by

$$\alpha = \beta - \phi \ . \tag{8.14}$$

The angle $\beta$ is the pitch angle of the blade-element chord. Since the induced velocity component is perpendicular to the resultant velocity, the magnitude of the inflow velocity can be estimated from the vector sum of the rotational and forward speeds,

$$U \doteq \sqrt{U_a^2 + (2\pi nr)^2} \ , \tag{8.15}$$

without actually calculating the induced velocity, $w_i$.

The elemental thrust and torque can be expressed in terms of the two-dimensional lift and drag coefficients of the airfoil section, given by Eqs. 7.72 and 7.73, and the magnitude of the resultant velocity, given by Eq. 8.15. The thrust is

$$dT = \frac{1}{2} \rho_o s \left( U_a^2 + (2\pi nr)^2 \right) \left( C_L \cos \phi - C_D \sin \phi \right) dr \tag{8.16}$$

and the torque is

$$dQ = \frac{1}{2} \rho_o s \left(U_a^2 + (2\pi nr)^2\right) \left(C_L \sin\phi + C_D \cos\phi\right) rdr . \tag{8.17}$$

The total thrust and torque are then obtained by integrating Eqs. 8.16 and 8.17 over the entire blade and multiplying by the number of blades.

The total thrust is often expressed in terms of a dimensionless *thrust coefficient*, defined by

$$C_T \equiv \frac{T}{\rho_o n^2 D^4} , \tag{8.18}$$

and the torque by the *torque coefficient*

$$C_Q \equiv \frac{Q}{\rho_o n^2 D^5} . \tag{8.19}$$

The power required to turn the propeller equals the product of the torque and the angular speed, while the useful propulsive power is the product of the thrust and the forward speed. Hence, the *propulsive efficiency* is given by

$$\eta_p = \frac{U_a}{2\pi n} \frac{T}{Q} = \frac{U_a}{2\pi nD} \frac{C_T}{C_Q} . \tag{8.20}$$

The ratio of the speed of advance to the rotational frequency, $n$, is a distance equal to that between the helical sheets that are traced out by the propeller motion. The ratio of this distance to the diameter is known as the *advance ratio*,

$$J \equiv \frac{U_a/n}{D} = \frac{U_a}{nD} , \tag{8.21}$$

and the *propeller efficiency* can be expressed by

$$\eta_p = \frac{J}{2\pi} \frac{C_T}{C_Q} . \tag{8.22}$$

Experimental measurements of propeller thrust and torque made in a water or wind tunnel are presented as plots of $C_T$, $C_Q$ and $\eta_p$ as functions of the advance ratio $J$. Figure 8.8 is typical. The efficiency peaks at an advance ratio usually about 75% of that for zero thrust.

### Momentum Theory Analysis

Blade-element theory is most useful when designing a specific propeller once the diameter and advance ratio have been chosen, but it is not readily applicable to the general problem of optimum performance propellers. Momentum theory, on the other hand, can be applied to find outside limits for propeller efficiency and general relationships between efficiency and size. This theory treats a propeller as an ideal actuator disk which produces a pressure jump without frictional

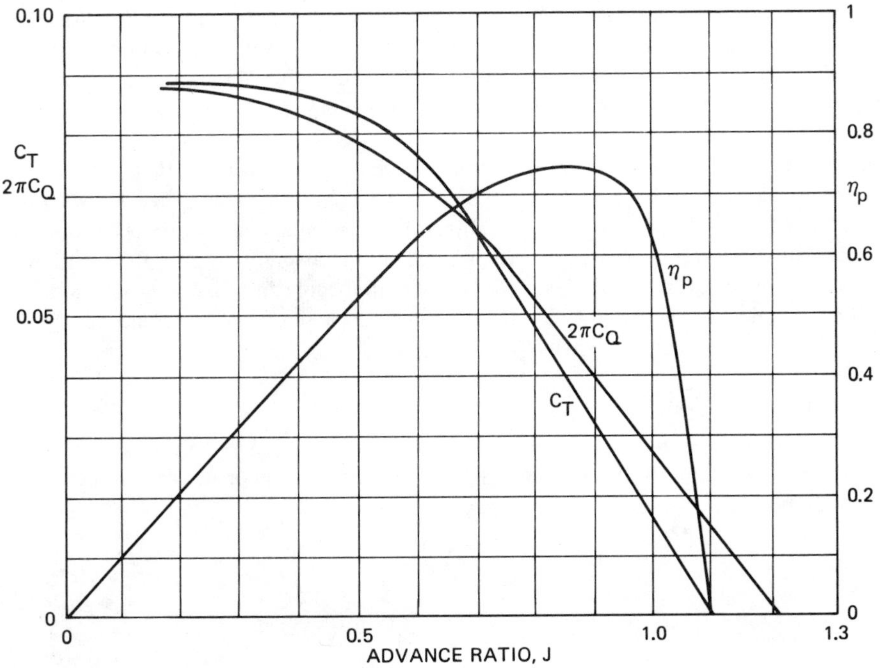


Fig. 8.8. Propeller Characteristic Curves from Open-Water Propeller Tunnel Measurements

losses. The product of the pressure jump and the propeller area equals the thrust. Associated with the pressure jump is acceleration of the flow. The rate of increase of flow energy measures the power required to drive the propeller. The smaller the pressure drop, the lower the energy; hence momentum theory predicts higher efficiencies for lightly loaded propellers. The result of application of momentum theory to this problem is a formula for the ideal, frictionless efficiency of a propeller, which may be written

$$\eta_i = \frac{2}{1 + \sqrt{1 + \tau}} , \tag{8.23}$$

where $\tau$ is the *thrust loading factor*,

$$\tau \equiv \frac{T}{\frac{1}{2} \rho_o U_a^2 S} = \frac{8}{\pi} \frac{C_T}{J^2} . \tag{8.24}$$

Equation 8.23 thus yields an expression for the ideal, frictionless efficiency as a function of thrust coefficient and advance ratio.

Momentum theory also specifies that the ideal radial distribution of thrust along the blade is that which imparts the least kinetic energy to the fluid for a given required momentum change. Under uniform inflow conditions this is achieved by uniform loading of an actuator disk. However, finite-bladed propellers impart angular momentum and energy as well as linear motion to the fluid. When this angular motion is taken into account, the optimum propeller is found to have a peak of its loading function at about 85% of the radius, with loading decreasing to zero at the tip and to near zero at the hub.

Since loading is reduced by increasing propeller diameter, momentum theory predicts higher propeller efficiencies for larger propellers. This conclusion, which has been known for many decades, has led many propeller designers to choose the maximum diameter propeller that will fit a given installation. However, it is a conclusion based on the assumption of uniform inflow conditions and, as will be seen in the next section, does not apply in radially varying wakes. Some propellers on ships are actually larger than optimum, and performance could be significantly improved by replacing them with smaller ones.

### Cavitation in Uniform Inflows

The ship operator is interested in knowing propeller cavitation performance in terms of forward speed of the vessel. He therefore tends to use a cavitation parameter defined in terms of the speed of advance,

$$K_a \equiv \frac{p_o - p_v}{\frac{1}{2}\rho_o U_a^2} . \tag{8.25}$$

However, as noted above, blade-surface cavitation of rotating blades is controlled by flow speed relative to the blade tip, and a cavitation parameter defined in terms of tip speed is more meaningful. Such a *tip cavitation parameter* is defined by

$$K_t \equiv \frac{p_o - p_v}{\frac{1}{2}\rho_o U_t^2} = \frac{p_o - p_v}{\frac{1}{2}\rho_o\left(U_a^2 + (\pi n D)^2\right)} = \frac{p_o - p_v}{\frac{1}{2}\rho_o(\pi n D)^2\left(1 + \left(\frac{J}{\pi}\right)^2\right)} , \tag{8.26}$$

which, for most practical values of $J$, is virtually the same as that for a rotating rod, as given by Eq. 8.3. Since the speed of advance is much smaller than the rotational component, the forward speed parameter, $K_a$, is always much larger than $K_t$. They are related by

$$K_a = \left[\left(\frac{\pi}{J}\right)^2 + 1\right] K_t . \tag{8.27}$$

It follows that for a given critical tip index the forward speed critical index can be lowered by operating at higher advance ratios, i.e., by choosing smaller diameter propellers. Thus, even for uniform inflows, cavitation considerations tend to contradict the conclusion of momentum theory by calling for smaller rather than larger diameter propellers.

Propeller cavitation inception tests are often carried out in uniform inflows in water tunnels, the critical index being determined as a function of the advance ratio. Figure 8.9 shows typical cavitation inception characteristics plotted in terms of the tip index defined by Eq. 8.26. At high

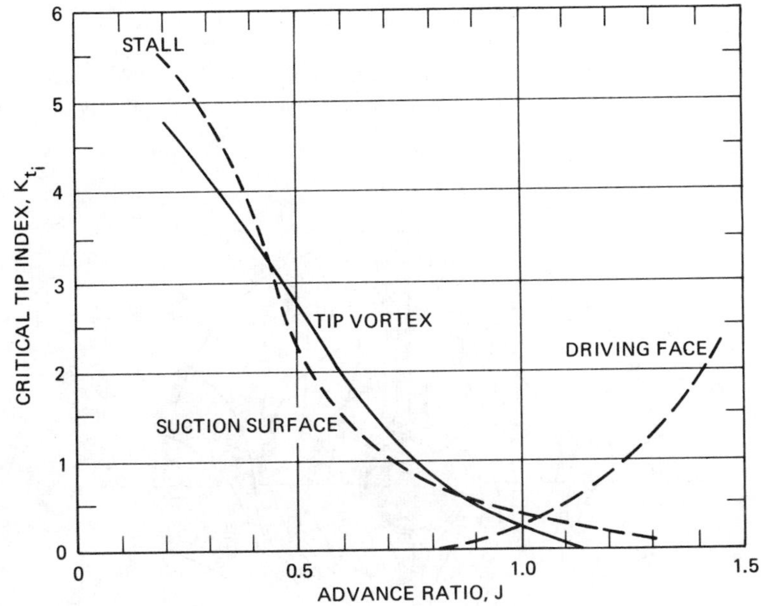


Fig. 8.9. Propeller Cavitation Inception Indices as Function of Advance Ratio in Uniform Inflow

values of the advance ratio, corresponding to small or negative values of the thrust coefficient, blade-section angles of attack are small, or negative, and driving face cavitation occurs first. As the advance ratio is decreased, and section angles of attack increased, face cavitation disappears and both suction-surface and tip-vortex cavitation become important. Finally, for very low advance ratios, angles of attack may become large enough to produce stalling, resulting in inception indices as high as 5 to 6. The optimum advance ratio for minimum inception index occurs generally at a point close to that for which efficiency is at a maximum.

Just as for hydrofoils (see Section 7.8), propellers with relatively thin blade sections achieve the lowest inception indices but are the least tolerant of operation at advance ratios differing from their design values. Thus, if a propeller is to be used in a uniform inflow environment at one specific advance ratio, thin sections are recommended, but for the more usual wake operation thicker sections are more satisfactory. In this respect, comparative tests of a number of different propellers run under uniform inflow conditions can be quite misleading when it comes to selecting the best propeller for non-uniform wake conditions.

## 8.4 Wake-Operating Propellers

Propeller-driven aircraft have tractor propellers operating under relatively uniform inflow conditions. By contrast, marine vehicles almost universally use pusher propellers operating in turbulent, non-uniform wakes. There are a number of reasons for the stern placement of marine propellers, including higher propulsion efficiencies, increased dynamic stability and shorter propeller shaft lengths. The only disadvantage is operation in a non-uniform flow field and this does not outweigh the advantages.

**Wake Diagrams**

Inflow conditions in the plane of the propeller are illustrated by wake diagrams in which equi-velocity contours are plotted. Figure 8.10 shows such a diagram for a typical single-screw

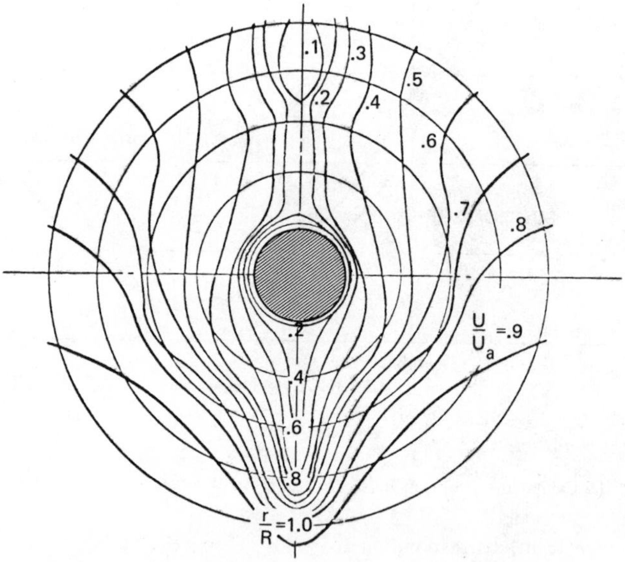


Fig. 8.10. Wake Diagram for Single-Screw Merchant Ship

merchant ship. The flow speed is seen to vary from over 90% of forward speed to less than 10%. As the propeller blade rotates, each section experiences a fluctuating inflow velocity. Figure 8.11(a) shows this variation as a function of angle, and Fig. 8.11(b) is a plot of the circumferential average velocity as a function of relative radius.

Torpedoes and many modern submarines have center-line propellers for which velocity inflows are more symmetric than for surface ships. Figure 8.12 shows a wake diagram for a typical torpedo, the only asymmetry being that caused by the four fins. While the circumferential variation is much less, the radial variation is similar to that for a merchant ship.

Operation of a propeller in a non-uniform wake differs drastically from operation in a uniform flow. Although all the effects interact, it is instructive to consider wake action as the superposition of three independent effects:

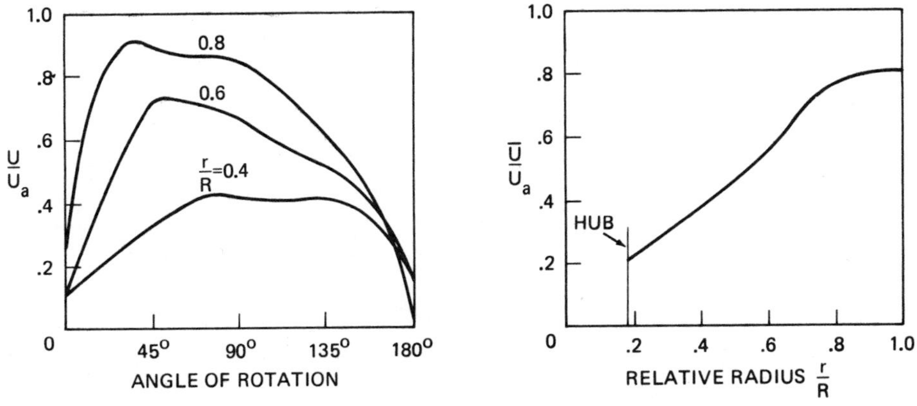


Fig. 8.11. Inflow Velocities Corresponding to Fig. 8.10

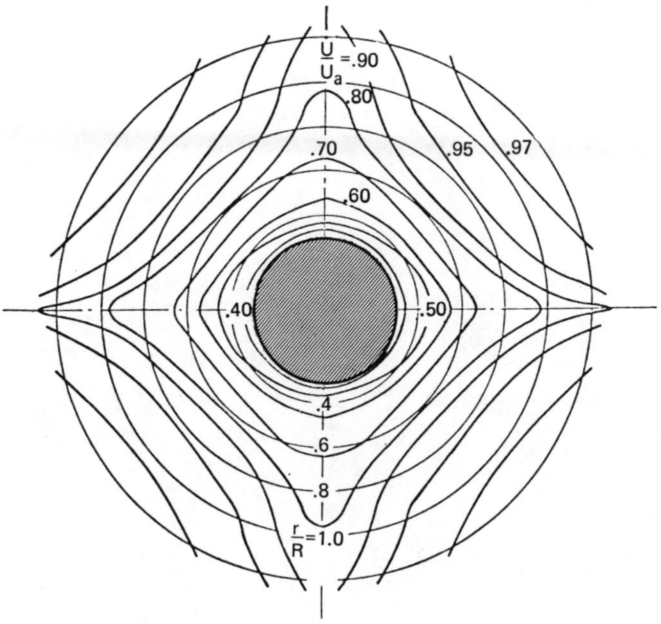


Fig. 8.12. Torpedo Wake Diagram

1) radial variation of circumferential inflow averages,
2) circumferential mean flow variations, and
3) turbulent fluctuations.

Of these, circumferential variations have by far the greatest effect on cavitation noise characteristics.

**Effect of Radially Varying Inflow**

The most obvious effect of a radially varying inflow is to alter velocity vectors of the inboard sections. Instead of the effective advance velocity being $U_a$, as in Fig. 8.7, it is the local circumferential average, as shown in Fig. 8.11(b). The effect on the magnitude of the resultant inflow velocity is small, since the rotational component is relatively large. By far the more important effect is to change the angle of attack.

Propeller designers have long recognized the effect of a radial wake on section angles of attack; not until the mid 1940's was it also realized that optimum load distributions are different. Application of momentum theory to wake operation leads to the conclusion that the optimum actuator-disk propeller is the one that tends to fill in the momentum deficiency of the wake. Such a propeller would be heavily loaded in its inboard sections and virtually unloaded near the blade tips. Its diameter would equal that of the wake. Lane (1952) applied the Betz-Prandtl blade-element theory to wake-operating finite-bladed propellers much as Goldstein had applied it to propellers in uniform flows. He confirmed that the optimum loading function is shifted toward the inboard sections, and that an optimum wake-operating propeller has a smaller diameter than one designed for uniform conditions. Propellers embodying these principles have been designed for torpedoes at the Garfield Thomas Water Tunnel at the Pennsylvania State University. As shown in Fig. 8.13, they have a large number of relatively stubby blades.

Fig. 8.13. Modern Torpedo Propeller Designed for Radially Varying Inflow, courtesy Garfield Thomas Water Tunnel

While design for a radial wake tends to reduce susceptibility to blade-surface and tip-vortex cavitation by unloading the tip sections, the shift to high inboard loading increases the strength of the hub vortex. In early designs the trend was carried too far, creating a strong hub vortex that not only cavitated prematurely but also caused a reduction of overall propulsive efficiency due to the accompanying severe pressure drop at the center of the tail cone. Later designs have compromised between dictates of momentum theory and the necessity of limiting hub vorticity.

**Effects of Circumferential Variations**

It is circumferential wake variations that are responsible for most of the deleterious effects of wake operation. As discussed above, variations of inflow velocity cause large variations of angle of attack. As a result of these variations, each blade element produces a varying amount of lift, resulting in significant fluctuations of thrust and torque during each revolution of the propeller. Oscillating components as high as 10% of average values are quite typical for single-screw merchant ships. It is these oscillating components which shake the hull and cause severe vibration. Such fluctuating forces also produce tonal sound radiation, as will be discussed in Chapter 9.

**Effect on Cavitation**

Compared to operation in uniform inflows, wake operation causes dramatic increase of critical inception indices and strong amplitude modulation of cavitation noise spectra. The effect of operating in a circumferentially varying wake is similar to, though not exactly equivalent to, operating a propeller with variable advance ratio. As shown in Fig. 8.9, the inception index is a strong function of the advance ratio. The index for a wake-operating propeller may equal that for the most extreme operating condition occurring as the blade rotates.

Consider the propeller whose uniform inflow characteristics are represented by Figs. 8.8 and 8.9. This propeller is designed to operate at a nominal advance ratio, $J$, of about 0.9, for which its critical tip cavitation index is about 0.5. When operating in a ship's wake, the swings in blade angle of attack may be equivalent to operation between $J$'s of 0.4 and 1.2, and the critical inception index may then be as high as 3.5 to 4. If the operating cavitation parameter were 2, each blade would be free of cavitation at all times except for the very short period when the angles of attack were equivalent to operation at $J < 0.6$. The resultant burst of cavitation noise would be very short-lived, sounding like a high-pitched click. Since one blade invariably cavitates sooner than the others, the bursts would first occur once per revolution. As the other blades join, the bursts would become more frequent, finally occurring at *blade rate*, i.e., the number of blades times rotational frequency. If the speed were increased and the cavitation index lowered still further, the point would be reached where cavitation noise would be continuous, since at least one blade would be cavitating at all times. However, the resultant spectrum would be strongly modulated at blade-rate frequency. Since, as mentioned above, one blade invariably cavitates more than the others, there is also a superimposed shaft-rate modulation. It is this shaft-rate modulation that can be detected by the human ear and which enables an experienced sonar operator to determine the propeller rpm and thereby often classify the target.

The effect of wake operation on cavitation inception is so dramatic that the critical inception index usually depends more on the wake than on the design of the propeller. Thus, for severe wakes, such as that shown in Fig. 8.10, stall is likely to occur when the blade passes behind the stern post. At this point one would expect a critical index of 3 to 6 independent of propeller design. On the other hand, critical indices of 1 to 2 are common for moderate wakes such as that of Fig. 8.12. Only under practically uniform flow conditions will values below 1 be achieved.

These generalizations are summarized in Fig. 8.14, which can be used to predict the likelihood of propeller cavitation based merely on the tip cavitation parameter, $K_t$, and a general evaluation of the nature of the wake.

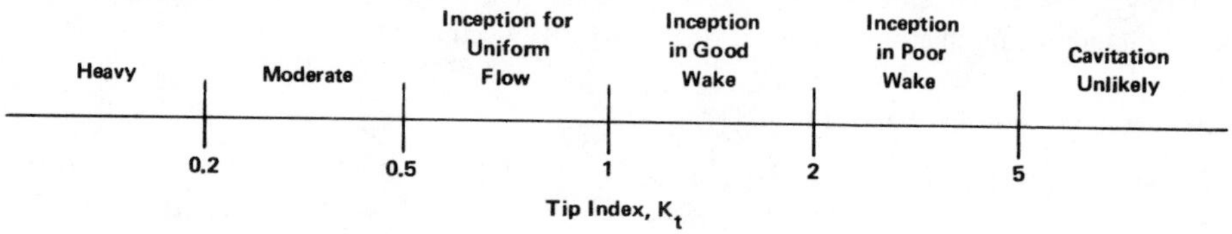


Fig. 8.14. Qualitative Cavitation Relationships to Tip Index

### Low-Frequency Cavitation Tonals

As reported by Aleksandrov (1962), low-frequency spectra of cavitating ship propellers are usually dominated by tonal components at harmonics of the rotational frequency, blade-rate harmonics being strongest. Since ship propellers generally operate at from 60 to 350 rpm and have from three to six blades, the fundamental repetition frequencies of this type of sound vary from 1 to 18 Hz. The strongest components are generally harmonics between 10 and 70 Hz. This direct radiation of tones occurs at the same frequencies as modulation of the cavitation continuum, and Aleksandrov attributed it to radiation by the aggregate of cavitation bubbles. If one considers the total void volume of cavitation bubbles on a blade at any one time to act as a single volume, then fluctuations of this volume caused by operation at varying angles of attack can be expected to radiate sound directly by the monopole mechanism described in Chapter 4 for pulsating bubbles.

It is now clear why cavitation is such a dominant noise source. Not only does collapse of many individual bubbles produce a continuous spectrum that extends from as low as 50 or 100 Hz to over 50 kHz, but also pulsations of the aggregate volume of cavitation radiate strong tonals at frequencies below 70 Hz.

## 8.5 Submarine Propeller Cavitation

During World War II passive sonars were used to detect submarines at frequencies above 1 kHz, often above 10 kHz. At these frequencies submarines were virtually undetectable when not cavitating and easily detectable when cavitating. Differences in noise levels between the two conditions were greater than 40 dB. Although cavitation inception was recognized as the limit to quiet operation, inception speeds at periscope depth were generally as low as 3 to 5 kts.

One reason for the poor cavitation performance of submarines was that their propellers had been designed for and tested in uniform inflow conditions. Submarines in WWII had twin screws and propeller diameters were the largest that would just miss scraping the hull. Consequently, tip sections passed through the region of the hull boundary layer where flow velocities were very low. The resultant angles of attack were high enough to cause local blade stall and consequent high inception cavitation indices.

Figure 8.15 shows typical noise data for WWII submarines plotted as a function of speed in m/sec divided by the square root of effective depth, given by the actual depth plus 9 m. Since cavitation of submarine propellers occurs when the tips are passing through a region of low forward speed, the appropriate tip cavitation index is that for rotating rods given by Eq. 8.3. This can be expressed in terms of the depth of submergence by

$$K_t \doteq \frac{2}{3} \frac{h + 9}{\left(\frac{N}{100}\right)^2 D^2}, \qquad (8.28)$$

where $h$ is the depth of the propeller tip below the surface in meters, $D$ is the propeller diameter in meters and $N$ is the rotational speed in rpm.* Utilizing Eq. 8.21 for the advance ratio, $K_t$ can also be expressed in terms of the forward speed by

$$K_t \doteq 1.85 \frac{h + 9}{U_a^2} J^2, \qquad (8.29)$$

where $U_a$ is in m/sec.* For the submarines represented in Fig. 8.15, $J \doteq 0.8$ and the critical

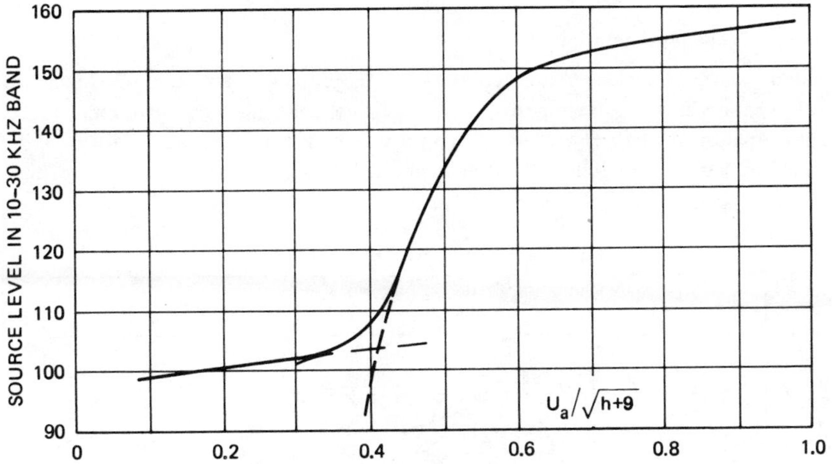


Fig. 8.15. High-Frequency Noise of World War II U.S. Submarines, as Measured by Strasberg and Sette (1944)

*For readers who are more at home with English units, Eq. 8.28 can be written:

$$K_t \doteq 2.2 \frac{h + 30}{\left(\frac{N}{100}\right)^2 D^2}, \qquad (8.28a)$$

where both $h$ and $D$ are measured in feet. When $U_a$ is expressed in kts and $h$ in ft, Eq. 8.29 becomes

$$K_t \doteq 2.1 \frac{h + 30}{U_a^2} J^2. \qquad (8.29a)$$

inception value of the speed/$\sqrt{\text{depth}}$ ratio of 0.4 corresponds to a tip index of about 6. Model tests of submarine propellers in uniform inflows corresponding to mean flow conditions predicted cavitation inception at speeds two to three times those actually observed. On the other hand, tests of a submarine propeller in still water, corresponding to boundary-layer operation, yielded an inception tip index of 6, confirming that cavitation was indeed controlled by the most extreme part of the wake.

Following WWII, in converting WWII Fleet submarines to modernized Guppy types, propeller diameters were reduced, and a significant increase in the speed for cavitation inception was achieved. Nuclear submarines have entirely different tail configurations and many have single center-line screws. Cavitation inception speeds of these submarines are therefore much higher than those that were typical during WWII.

Figure 8.16 shows several typical submarine cavitation spectra measured during WWII in which it is seen that the peak moves to lower frequencies as speed increases, as would be expected from the discussion of cavitation spectra in Section 7.5. The *anomalous depth effect* discussed in Section 8.2 and predicted by Eq. 8.11 is confirmed by measurements of submarine noise as a function of depth shown in Fig. 8.17.

## 8.6 Surface Ship Radiated Noise

### Importance of Propeller Cavitation

Radiated spectra of surface ships are dominated by propeller cavitation noise except when the ships are operating at very slow speeds. This is readily confirmed by calculating the operating tip-cavitation parameter from Eq. 8.28. A typical merchant ship having a length of about 200 m may have a 7 m diameter propeller operating at about 100 rpm, yielding a tip index of the order of

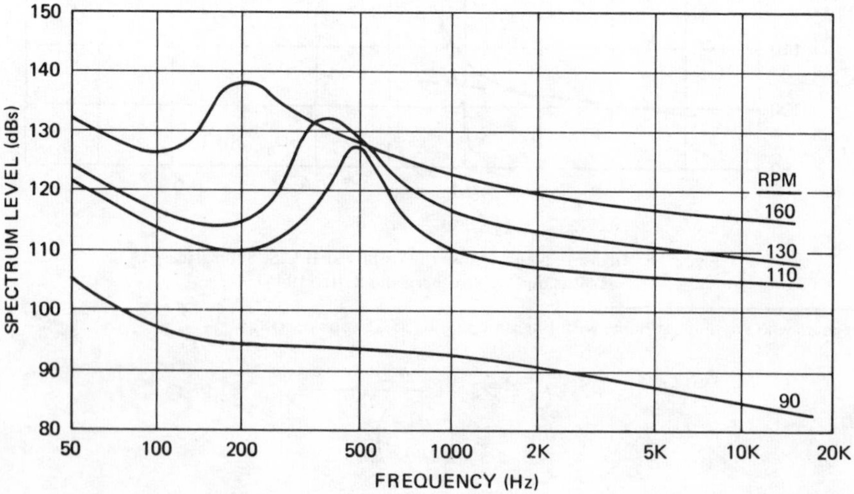


Fig. 8.16. Measured Submarine Cavitation Spectra, after Strasberg and Sette (1944)

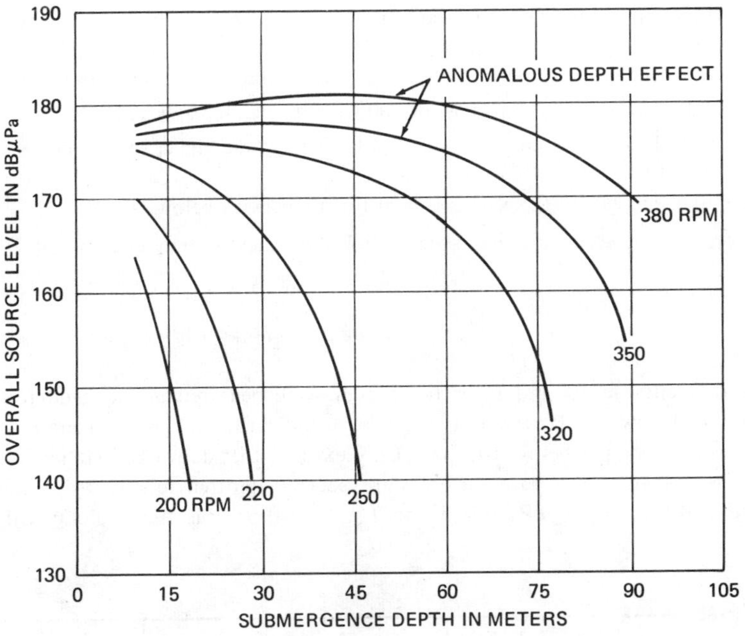


Fig. 8.17. Effect of Depth on WWII Submarine Propeller Cavitation Noise

0.2, close to a factor of 20 lower than the likely inception value of 3 to 4. Thus, a merchant ship near its normal cruise speed usually operates at a speed about four times that for which the first traces of cavitation occur.

The statement made here that merchant ships operate at speeds as much as four times cavitation inception speed is at variance with the claim usually made by naval architects that this ratio is less than two. Naval architects are concerned with the effects of cavitation on performance and usually quote inception speeds based on open-water tests, for which the inception tip index would be less than 1. However, when treating radiated noise characteristics the pertinent inception speed is that for which the first traces of cavitation occur as blades pass behind the stern post. As discussed in Section 8.4, the tip index is almost always higher than 3 for surface ships having asymmetrical wakes of the type shown in Fig. 8.10.

Other characteristics of surface ship noise that confirm the dominance of propeller cavitation are strong modulation of the broadband spectrum at shaft and blade frequencies and the radiation of low-frequency tonals at harmonics of these frequencies. These features are discussed later in the present section.

**World War II Noise Data**

The only sources of extensive data on surface ship radiated noise spectra are measurements made during WWII, reported in a compendium issued by the U.S. Office of Scientific Research and Development (O.S.R.D.) in 1945 and declassified in 1960. Measurements were made on American,

Canadian and British ranges. Results reported for a British cruiser and passenger vessel are presented in Figs. 8.18 and 8.19. Measurements were made on the botton in 40 m deep water at Innellan, Scotland. The data have been converted into source levels at 1 m relative to 1 $\mu$Pa by a process which may introduce errors of up to 3 dB.

Many of the surface ships ranged in the early 1940's showed the following typical trends:

a) sound in the mid-frequency range of 500 to 1000 Hz increases as $U^5$ to $U^6$,

b) the spectral slope is about -5.5 to -6 dB/octave at the higher speeds and as much as -7 to -8 dB/octave at low speeds, and

c) the rate of increase with speed is greater for frequencies below 100 Hz.

For ships proceeding at near cruise speeds. WWII results for frequencies over 100 Hz can be written

$$L_s = L_S' + 20 - 20 \log f \qquad (f \geqslant 100) \; , \tag{8.30}$$

where $f$ is frequency in Hz and $L_S'$ is the overall level measured in the band from 100 Hz to 10 kHz. Spectra below 100 Hz are quite variable, as indicated by Figs. 8.18 and 8.19. Near cruise speed, the radiated power below 100 Hz usually exceeds that above 100 Hz by from 2 to 8 dB. Figure 8.20 represents the average surface ship spectrum plotted relative to overall level in the band above 100 Hz, i.e., in dBs relative to $L_S'$. Shown in this figure along with the average

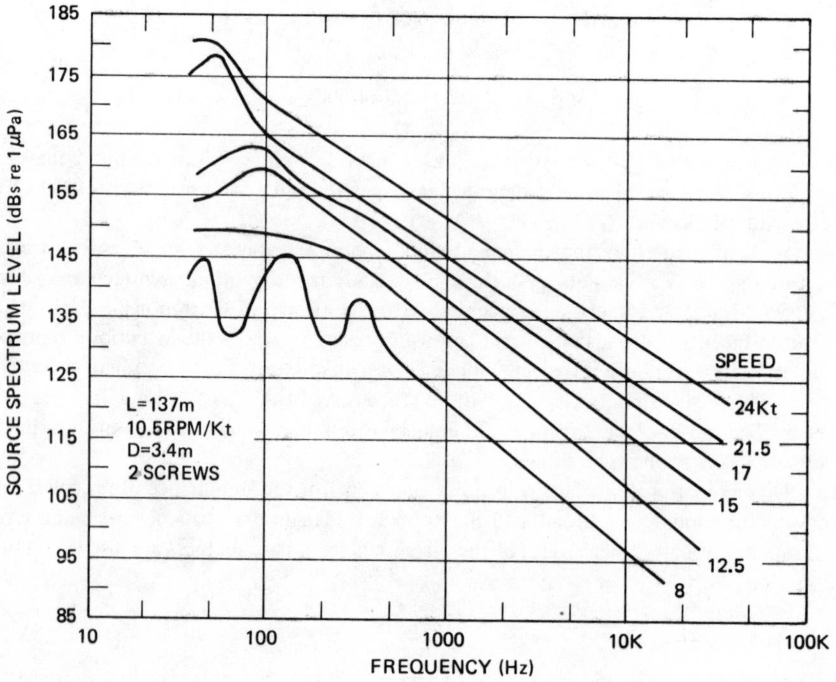


Fig. 8.18. Radiated Noise of British Cruiser *Cardiff*, as Measured in WWII

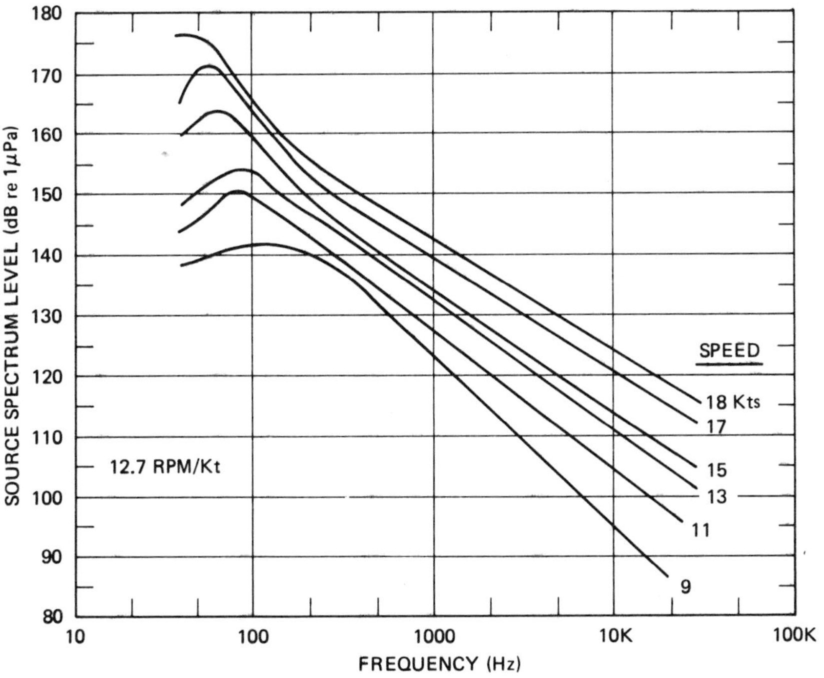


Fig. 8.19. Radiated Noise of Passenger Ship *Astrid*, as Measured during WWII

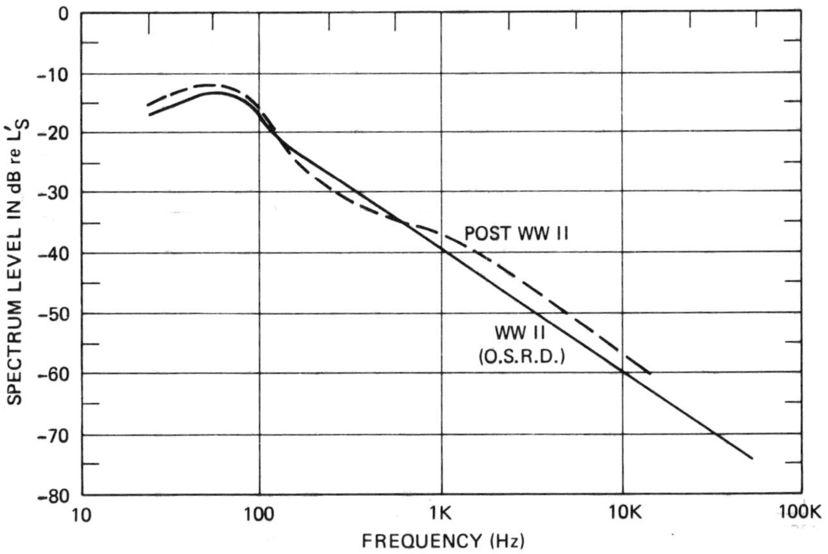


Fig. 8.20. Average Relative Spectra of Surface Ships

spectrum from WWII is the average curve from a number of post-war measurements of freighters and tankers which shows more structure than the WWII average and deviates from Eq. 8.30 by from 1 to 3 dB over much of the spectrum.

**Dependence on Speed**

Many measurements made during WWII were at speeds that are about half those of modern ships, although a few measurements of naval ships extended beyond 15 kts. Figure 8.21 summarizes data on speed dependence of the overall level, $L'_S$, for measurements of ships from 8 to 24 kts. The trend curve that has been drawn through the data fits the equation

$$L'_S = 170 + 53 \log \frac{U_a}{10\ kt} , \qquad (8.31)$$

where 10 kts is taken as the reference speed, or

$$L'_S = 179 + 53 \log \frac{U_a}{15\ kt} \qquad (8.32)$$

in terms of the level at 15 kts. Average values for several ships vary by ±4 dB from the trend curve.

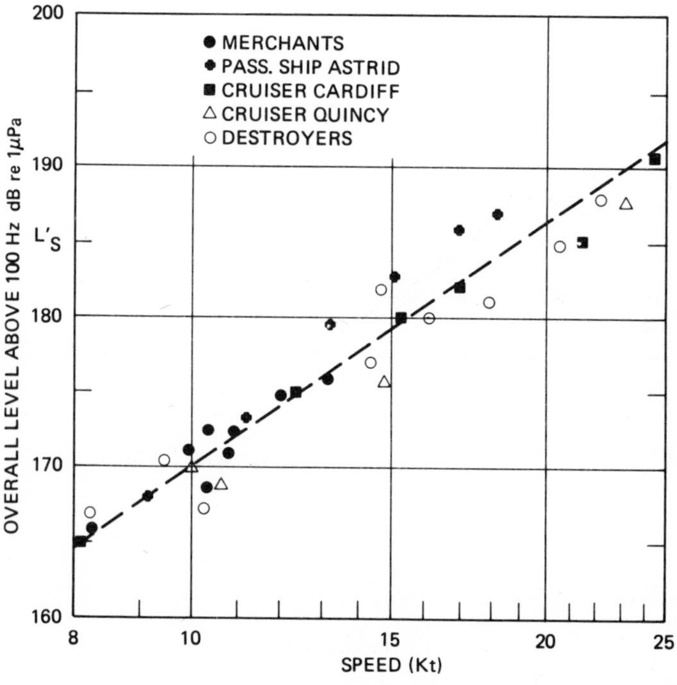


Fig. 8.21. Speed Dependence of Overall Radiated Level of Surface Ships, as Measured during WWII

### Estimation Formulas

The trends shown in Fig. 8.21 and represented by Eqs. 8.31 and 8.32 are somewhat contaminated by the fact that faster ships are generally larger than slower ones. Thus, the two factors of size and speed are both involved in the trend curve. That size is important was revealed by WWII data on battleships and aircraft carriers, which invariably were found to be about 10 dB noisier than smaller ships at the same speeds. Several formulas using tonnage as an indicator of size were developed during WWII. Two of the more popular ones may be expressed in terms of overall level above 100 Hz, $L'_S$, by

$$L'_S \doteq 112 + 50 \log \frac{U_a}{10\ kt} + 15 \log DT \tag{8.33}$$

and

$$L'_S \doteq 134 + 60 \log \frac{U_a}{10\ kt} + 9 \log DT\ , \tag{8.34}$$

where $DT$ is the displacement tonnage. These two formulas give similar results for ships of the types at sea in WWII. However, some modern supertankers are more than 20 times as large and the differences between levels predicted by the two formulas can be as much 10 dB for ships of this size. For this reason the author recommends that these formulas not be used for ships of over 30,000 tons.

Formulas developed in Section 8.2 for blade-surface cavitation noise indicate that propeller cavitation noise power should be proportional to total number of blades cavitating and to propeller diameter, and is a function of tip speed, the dependence on tip speed being strongest. Ship size or tonnage would not be expected to enter the equation except to the extent that the product of number of blades and diameter is usually bigger for larger ships. When data from WWII are examined, there is found to be a clear trend with tip speed and number of blades and none with any other variable. Noise data for ships over 100 m length can be represented by

$$L'_S \doteq 175 + 60 \log \frac{U_t}{25\ m/s} + 10 \log \frac{B}{4} \tag{8.35}$$

over the range of tip speeds from about 15 to 50 m/sec.* The apparent trends with tonnage that were expressed in Eqs. 8.33 and 8.34 are now attributable to the fact that heavier vessels usually require higher propeller loading, i.e., higher values of tip speed per knot and more blades. Equations 8.31, 8.32 and 8.35 yield similar levels for four-bladed propellers having advance ratios

*With $U_t$ expressed in ft/sec, Eq. 8.35 becomes:

$$L'_S \doteq 180 + 60 \log \frac{U_t}{100\ fps} + 10 \log \frac{B}{4}\ , \tag{8.35a}$$

where $L'_S$ is the overall level above 100 Hz in dB relative to 1 μPa at a reference distance of 1 yd.

of the order of 0.85. For ship propellers with lower advance ratios, Eqs. 8.31 and 8.32 may be expected to underestimate the noise radiated. Thus, data from battleships and aircraft carriers are better represented by Eq. 8.35 than by Eqs. 8.31 and 8.32. Their relatively high levels are partly explained by the large number of blades cavitating (8 to 12) and by operation at advance ratios lower than 0.85. Figure 8.22 is a plot of overall noise as a function of tip speed, as given by Eq. 8.35. Individual ships can be expected to differ from the curve by ±5 dB.

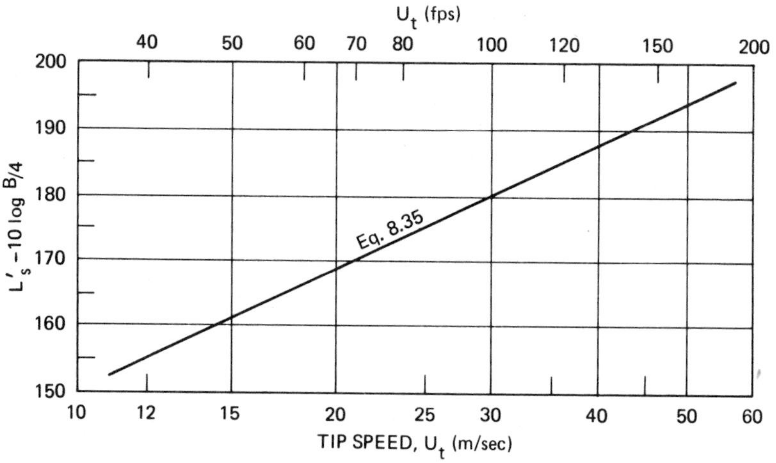


Fig. 8.22. Dependence of Overall Noise Level on Propeller Tip Speed, Based on Data from WWII

## Acoustic Efficiencies of Surface Ships

It is instructive to calculate the acoustic conversion efficiency for surface ship propeller cavitation. From Fig. 8.21 and Eq. 8.31, the overall level above 100 Hz for a 12-kt ship of WWII vintage would be about 174 dB re 1$\mu$Pa, and the overall level for the entire spectrum therefore about 178 dB re 1$\mu$Pa. This source level implies about 2.5 W acoustic power radiated over a hemisphere. Assuming 3000 hp, the propulsion power would be close to 2.5 MW, resulting in an acoustic conversion efficiency of about $1 \times 10^{-6}$. Calculations for a number of specific ships of various types indicate that from 0.3 to 5 W of acoustic power is radiated per MW of mechanical power. Thus, within ±6 dB the acoustic conversion efficiency for propeller cavitation is $1.5 \times 10^{-6}$.

## Modulation Effects

As discussed in Section 8.4, circumferential wake variations cause strong amplitude modulation effects at blade passage frequency, and slight physical differences between blades produce modulation at the shaft rotational frequency. These modulations give a very distinctive characteristic to surface ship noise and enable experienced sonar operators to classify targets by measuring the turn count and thereby determining propeller rpm.

Shaft and blade modulation frequencies for merchant ships are now significantly higher than they were during WWII. Thirty years ago most merchant ships had three- or four-bladed propellers and operated at from 60 to 100 rpm. Shaft modulation frequencies were generally between 1.0 and 1.6 Hz and blade frequencies were from 3.5 to 6.5 Hz. Today, typical merchant propellers have four, five or six blades and operate at from 75 to 135 rpm; shaft frequencies range from 1.3 to 2.2 Hz, and blade frequencies are typically 6 to 12 Hz.

**Tonal Spectra**

Dominance of low-frequency spectra by cavitation tonals at multiples of blade-rate frequency, as originally reported by Aleksandrov (1962), has recently been confirmed by Morris (1975) for a supertanker and by unpublished data obtained during a merchant ship noise study conducted under the auspices of the U.S. Naval Oceanographic Office (N.O.O.). Morris measured narrowband spectra from the *CHEVRON LONDON* at ranges of 75 to 250 nautical miles, finding strong tonals at multiples of 6.8 Hz with those from 40 to 70 Hz generally being strongest. Source levels of these tonals were estimated to be as high as 190 dB $\mu$Pa. Spectrograms obtained during N.O.O.'s measurements of a number of freighters, bulk carriers and tankers also showed strong tonals at multiples of blade frequency, the sixth to ninth harmonics being most prominent. In several instances, high harmonics of shaft-rate frequency were also observed, indicating shaft-rate modulation of blade-frequency tonals.

**Merchant Ship Trends**

Cargo vessels and tankers that operated during WWII were generally between 90 and 170 m long (300 to 560 ft), displaced less than 20,000 tons and were powered by engines of under 8,000 hp. Ten to 12 kts were typical speeds and propeller tip speeds of 17 to 29 m/sec (55 to 95 fps) were most common. Since most of the world's shipyards had been destroyed, the only new types of ships built during the first decade after the war were a few advanced classes built in the U.S. Beginning in about 1960, as new European and Japanese shipbuilding facilities became available, the process of replacing WWII ships began. Many of these new ships are of sizes and speeds not known before. Previously 15,000 hp delivered to a single shaft had been the maximum; today powers between 32,000 and 42,000 hp per shaft are common. Previously 20,000 tons was considered very large; today many ships exceed 100,000 tons. Previously lengths under 180 m were usual; today lengths of 180 to 370 m (600 to 1200 ft) are typical. The average installed power of all ships at sea has increased from 3000 hp to 9000 hp.

The greatest changes have occurred in oil tankers, bulk carriers and container ships. The most common tankers built in the U.S. during WWII and used for many years afterwards, the T-2 class, were about 160 m (525 ft) long, were rated at about 17,000 deadwt tons, traveled at 14 to 16 kts and were usually powered by 7500 hp turbines. Today's tanker fleet has the capacity of over 20,000 T-2 tankers, a single giant supertanker being equivalent to from 15 to 20 of them. Typical propulsion powers are from 20,000 to 40,000 hp. However, speeds have changed little: 14 to 16 kts is still typical.

Bulk carriers are a relatively new type of ship, built since about 1950. They are similar in construction to oil tankers but are generally intended only for dry bulk cargoes. They are smaller than the largest tankers, two thirds of them being between 15,000 and 70,000 deadwt tons. Bulk carriers and tankers are quite similar in their underwater conformation and therefore have similar acoustic properties. Taken together, tankers and bulk carriers today number over 9000, have a capacity of nearly 400 million deadwt tons, and are powered by over 100 million hp of propulsion machinery. The two classes account for over 80% of cargo capacity at sea at any one time and about 60% of installed propulsion power.

Containerships are the newest class of merchant ships. These are ships that carry cargo in freight containers stacked on deck. Some are older freighters converted to this purpose; many are especially designed ships built in the last ten years. Most of these newly built ships travel at speeds in excess of 20 kts, a few at over 30 kts. About 50 of the largest ones have multiple propellers and are powered by from 45,000 to 120,000 hp. These are the new queens of the sea, replacing the large passenger liners that have been retired in recent years.

While there are very few underwater noise measurements of modern ships, it seems likely that noise levels have risen significantly from WWII values. Average ship speeds are today about 50% above those of WWII. The trend shown in Fig. 8.21 would predict about a 9 dB rise in the noise radiated by an average ship. Information on typical propeller diameters and rpm's shows that tip speeds are now commonly between 30 and 45 m/sec (100 to 150 fps), about 60% higher than in WWII. In accordance with Eq. 8.35, this increase in tip speed would imply a noise increase of as much as 12 dB. The only mitigating factor might be improvement of the inception index, which could reduce these estimates by 3 to 5 dB. It therefore seems likely that the average noise radiated by individual ships currently at sea is between 5 and 8 dB higher than that common at the end of WWII.

## 8.7 Ship-Generated Ambient Noise

### Recognition of Ships as Sources of Ambient Noise

As discussed in Section 4.4, ambient noise curves developed during WWII were plotted only as a function of sea state and/or wind speed. These curves were intended for use only above 500 Hz since the investigators recognized that ship noise contaminated their low-frequency data. Nevertheless, others extrapolated the curves to lower frequencies and were then surprised when measurements made below 200 Hz showed very little dependence on wind speed or sea state.

During the decade of the 1950's ambient noise measurements were made down to as low as 10 Hz at several deep-water sites in the Atlantic. As reported by Walkinshaw (1960), data above 300 Hz correlated well with wind and weather but levels below about 200 Hz were virtually independent of these factors. Walkinshaw attributed the low-frequency spectrum to noise from distant shipping. In his classic survey article, Wenz (1962) also attributed the non-wind-dependent spectrum in the range of 10 to at least 100 Hz to *traffic noise*, which he defined as noise from distant shipping. The dominance of noise from distant ships has been confirmed by measurements by Axelrod et al (1965) of vertical arrival angles which show that below 200 Hz the major contributions are carried by ray paths that are within 20° of horizontal. Diurnal variations of noise levels at some locations have been attributed to local shipping patterns.

It is now well accepted within the underwater sound community that distant shipping accounts for ambient noise between 20 and 200 Hz in most deep-water, open-ocean areas and in highly traveled seas such as the Baltic and Mediterranean. Only in areas remote from shipping or protected from long-range sounds, such as the South Pacific and southern half of the Indian Ocean, does sea noise dominate throughout the spectrum as represented in Fig. 4.8. Figure 8.23 presents the author's estimate of the shipping contribution to low-frequency ambient noise for four levels of ship noise dependent on the acoustic proximity of shipping.

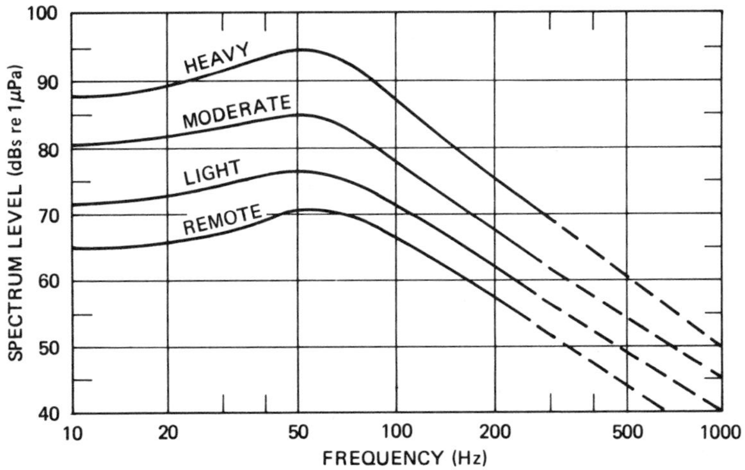


Fig. 8.23. Estimated Spectra Representing Shipping Contribution to Deep-Water Ambient Noise as Function of Shipping Concentration

**Reverberant Room Theory of Ambient Noise**

Accurate calculation of the contribution of ships to local ambient noise levels requires detailed knowledge of shipping distributions, of long-range sound propagation and of ship spectra. None of these is usually available. Nevertheless, lacking information for detailed calculations, one can derive the salient characteristics of ambient noise originating from ships by treating the ocean as a semi-reverberant volume, much as one would calculate the pressure spectrum from a number of sound sources in room acoustics. The ocean acts like a room in that sound rays change direction at least three times in 100 km because of refractive effects. Reverberant sound will dominate as long as the loss per mean free path is small and there are no dominant sources close to the receiver. These conditions are satisfied in the deep ocean for frequencies below 500 Hz, provided there are no ships closer than about 50 km.

Young (1959) has shown that, when the number of reflections is large, the spatially averaged energy density for steady sources can be expressed by

$$\langle E \rangle = \frac{\overline{p^2}}{\rho_o c_o^2} = \frac{\ell W}{\bar{a} c_o V}, \tag{8.36}$$

where $\ell$ is the mean free path between direction reversals, $\bar{a}$ is the mean reflection loss in nepers, $W$ is the source power and $V$ is the total volume of the reverberant space. The volume is the product of the surface area, $S$, and the effective average water depth, $H$. The other terms require more explanation. The coefficient, $\bar{a}$, represents the dissipative loss per reflection. In underwater sound, it is more usual to deal with the average attenuation, $\alpha$, expressed in dB per unit distance. If we take $\alpha_T$ to include boundary reflection losses as well as volume absorption, then $\overline{a}$ can be related to $\alpha_T$ by

$$\overline{a} = \alpha_T \ell (10 \log e)^{-1} = \frac{\alpha_T \ell}{4.34} , \tag{8.37}$$

where the last factor is required to convert dB into nepers.

Combining Eqs. 8.36 and 8.37 and expressing $V$ by $SH$, the mean square sound pressure can be related to the average source spectrum of merchant ships by

$$\overline{p^2} = 8.68 \frac{\theta_e \delta}{\alpha_T H} \overline{p_s^2(1)} , \tag{8.38}$$

where $\delta$ is the number of ships per unit area and $\theta_e$ is a factor incorporated in the analysis to take into account the fact that only rays that radiate in a fairly narrow range of angles near grazing contribute to the reverberant field.

Expressing the ambient sound pressure as a level, $L_n$, in dB and the average source level per ship by $L_s$, the ambient level is then related to the source level by

$$L_n = L_s + 10 \log \theta_e - 10 \log \alpha_T H + 10 \log \delta + 9.5 . \tag{8.39}$$

The noise is therefore a function of at least four factors. Equation 8.39 can be better written for order-of-magnitude calculations in terms of ship densities, $\delta°$, expressed in terms of numbers of ships per 1° square. On average, the area of a 1° square is about $10^{10}$ m². Assuming $\theta_e$ to be 1/3 radian, Eq. 8.39 becomes

$$L_n \doteq L_s - 95 + 10 \log \delta° + 10 \log \frac{1}{\alpha_T H} . \tag{8.40}$$

This equation serves to explain most observed trends. Thus, the spectral shape of ship-dominated ambient noise should be controlled by the average spectral shape of merchant ships, as modified by frequency dependence of the attenuation term. As reported by Wenz (1962), and more recently by Perrone (1969, 1970, 1974), ambient spectra below 100 Hz do indeed have shapes similar to ship noise spectra shown in Fig. 8.20. Above 100 Hz the shipping contribution decreases somewhat faster than that shown in Fig. 8.20 due to increased absorption. Equation 8.40 also explains geographical variations and long-term trends and forms a basis for understanding spatial and temporal fluctuations.

### Geographical Variations

Figure 8.23 reveals about 25 dB variation in traffic noise between areas remote from shipping and those near busy shipping lanes. While the average ship density over all ocean areas is estimated to be about 0.4 ships per 1° square, the number varies from as low as 0.02 in the South Pacific and other remote areas to over 1 for the North Atlantic and as high as 5 to 10 near the coast of Europe. Thus, this factor alone can account for as much as 25 dB of geographical variability.

Propagation differences can also account for 5 to 10 dB differences in shipping noise. In some areas, sound transmission is primarily by refractive paths that do not interact directly with the surface or bottom. In such cases, $\alpha_T$ equals that due to volume absorption alone, for which a value of 0.2 dB per 100 km is representative. Assuming an ocean depth of 4 km, the term involving $\alpha_T H$ would add 20 dB. On the other hand, if the water depth is not sufficient to support refractive transmission, losses will occur at each bottom and surface interaction. Experimental data for this type of propagation generally show between 0.05 and 0.2 dB loss relative to cylindrical spreading in a distance equal to the water depth, giving an average value of the transmission term in Eq. 8.40 of only about 10 dB and resulting in lower ambient levels for the same shipping density.

**Importance of Coastal Shipping**

Even at locations remote from the edges of an ocean basin, low-frequency ambient noise is often dominated by coastal shipping. The reason is that sound propagates especially well from sources located in relatively shallow water at the edge of a deep basin. As the sound rays propagate seaward, each bounce from the sloping bottom reduces the angle by twice the bottom slope angle. Rays that would otherwise interact with the bottom and/or surface become deep channel rays that propagate with minimum loss. This is equivalent both to increasing the angle $\theta_e$ and to assuring that propagation occurs with minimum $\alpha_T$.

The existence of the *coastal region enhancement effect* was demonstrated by Northrop et al (1968) using explosive charges. They found that sounds from such charges exploded off the California coast were received by deep hydrophones over 3000 miles away at a level at least 15 dB higher than that from similar sources over a flat bottom. Since the slope acts to channel the sound, Smith (1971) termed it the *megaphone effect*. A more complete explanation showing the importance of the bigradient sound-speed profile in channeling the sound was given by Smith and Jones (1972). More recently, Morris (1975) found that levels received when a supertanker proceeded toward port were enhanced 3 to 6 dB as it neared the coast. Other measurements show 6 to 10 dB to be more typical.

**Directional Characteristics**

The sound field in a truly reverberant room does not exhibit directional characteristics. However, the ocean is more like a long, highly-reverberant hallway than a room. Since shipping distributions are not uniform, and propagation is often more favorable in some directions than others, ambient noise at low frequencies may be expected to exhibit horizontal directionality of at least several dB and in many cases of more than 10 dB. This is very much a local effect dependent on location of ships at basin edges as well as on depth of the receiver and on sound velocity profile. Its calculation requires detailed knowledge of shipping distribution as well as sound propagation.

Vertical directionality depends somewhat on receiver depth and type of propagation. However, low-frequency ambient noise normally arrives within ±20° of horizontal.

**Temporal Fluctuations**

Transmission from near-surface sources to distant receivers is very much a function of the speed of sound at the surface relative to that near the bottom. If the sound speed is lower at the surface, sound can be transmitted without bottom interaction; if it is higher, all rays may strike the bottom. As discussed earlier in this section, the difference in the effective value of the absorption coefficient in these two cases is often of the order of a factor of 10, resulting in 10 dB difference in low-frequency ambient levels. There are many places where the warming of the surface waters in summer is sufficient to change refractive transmission to bottom interacting transmission. In these areas, seasonal variations of ambient noise may be expected to exceed 5 dB.

Wenz (1972) reported diurnal fluctuation at a number of coastal locations. This is probably due more to changes in nearby shipping patterns than to distant shipping effects. Port arrival and departure times tend to cluster around certain hours, which could cause peaking of local traffic interference at any coastal location close to a busy port. Wenz found that diurnal fluctuation may be only a dB or two in remote areas, but that 5 to 6 dB is quite common for coastal locales, and that in some locations, such as that illustrated by Fig. 8.24, fluctuation ,due to local shipping regularly exceeds 20 dB.

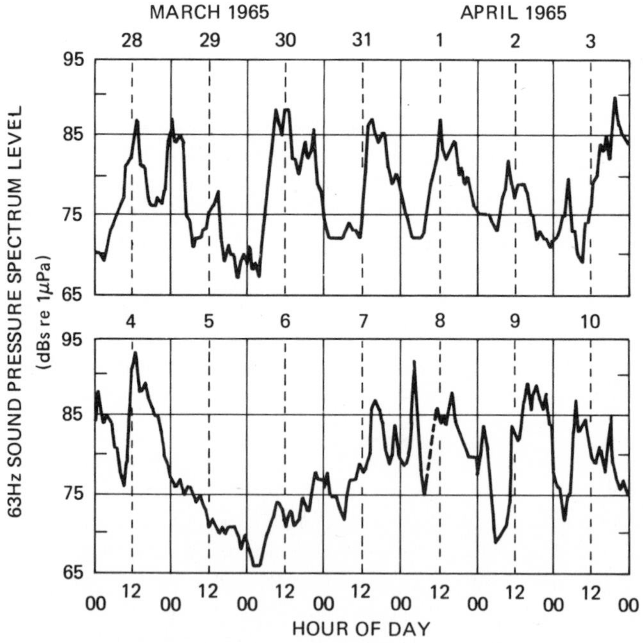


Fig. 8.24. Fluctuations of Low-Frequency Ambient Noise at a Coastal Location, from Wenz (1972)

In addition to seasonal effects due to changes of the surface sound speed and diurnal effects due to local ship patterns, there are short-term fluctuations. These are of the order of minutes and are analogous to the scintillation of starlight. Transmission of sound is itself a fluctuating phenomenon, variations occurring with both time and position. As individual ships move across the ocean surface, they move into and out of regions of exceptionally good transmission. Dyer (1970, 1973) showed that the standard deviation for multipath transmission is of the order of 5 dB, and that the value for ship-generated ambient noise depends on the density of shipping, array beam width and analysis frequency band. Typical values of the standard deviation when measuring with omnidirectional phones and one-third-octave bandwidths are 1.5 to 2.5 dB for the distant shipping component alone. When data are contaminated by nearby ships, as in Fig. 8.24, standard deviations are much larger.

It is common practice in the underwater sound community to assume a log-normal distribution of ambient noise values. While this offers a reasonable fit to the central distribution, a Gaussian function does not properly represent the tails. Dyer (1973) concluded that the actual distribution is closer to a Rayleigh distribution, which is similar to Gaussian but with truncated tails.

### Long-Term Trends

One of the more important conclusions that follows from this analysis of shipping noise is that low-frequency ambient noise levels must have risen significantly in the past quarter century. In the 25 years following 1950, the total number of ships has more than doubled. With increased efficiencies of port handling facilities, the number of ships at sea has increased even more. This factor alone would account for a 3 to 5 dB increase of ambient noise originating from shipping. In addition, as discussed in the previous section, increases of average ship speed, propulsion power and propeller tip speed all lead to the conclusion that the average ship produces at least 6 dB more noise. Combining all these factors, one must conclude that in the past 25 years ambient noise has probably risen about 10 dB in those areas where shipping noise dominates. Furthermore, ship noise must now have become a dominant factor in some areas where it did not previously control. Unfortunately, measurements made at the same location a decade or more apart have not appeared in the literature, so this conclusion cannot be supported with experimental data. However, in view of the nearly tenfold increase of the horsepower of propulsion plants in ships at sea, it would indeed be remarkable if the noise due to ships had not increased close to 10 dB.

This trend is not expected to continue at so rapid a pace. Over the next 25 years, the number of ships may be expected to increase only about 50%, and the noise per ship by only a few dB. Thus, the increase of low-frequency ambient noise levels due to ships may be only about 5 dB during the next quarter century.

## REFERENCES

Sections 8.1-8.4

Aleksandrov, I.A., Some cavitation characteristics of ship propellers, *Sov. Phys.-Acoustics, 7*, 67-69, 1961.

Aleksandrov, I.A., Physical nature of the rotation noise of ship propellers in the presence of cavitation, *Sov. Phys.-Acoustics, 8*, 23-28, 1962.

Boswell, R.J., Design, Cavitation Performance, and Open-Water Performance of a Series of Research Skewed Propellers, *N.S.R.D.C. Rept. 3339*, March 1971 (AD 732511).

Burrill, L.C., Sir Charles Parsons and cavitation, *Trans. Inst. Mar. Engin., 63*, 149-167, 1951.

Burrill, L.C., The phenomenon of cavitation, *Int. Shipbuilding Progress, 2*, 503-511, 1955.

Burrill, L.C. and Emerson, A., Propeller cavitation: tests on 16-inch models in the King's College cavitation tunnel, *Northeast Coast. Inst. Engin. and Shipbuilders, 70*, 121, 1953; also, *Int. Shipbuilding Progress, 10*, 119-131, 1963.

Eisenberg, P., On the Mechanism and Prevention of Cavitation, *D.T.M.B. Rept. 712*, July 1950.

Emerson, A. and Sinclair, L., Propeller cavitation: systematic series tests on 5- and 6-bladed model propellers, *Trans. Soc. Naval Arch. and Mar. Engin., 75*, 224-267, 1967.

Flamm, O., The scientific study of naval architecture in Germany, *Trans. Inst. of Naval Arch., 53*, 207-216, 1911.

Goldstein, S., On the vortex theory of screw propellers, *Proc. Roy. Soc. (London), A123*, 440-465, 1929.

Huse, E., Propeller-hull-vortex cavitation, *Int. Shipbuilding Progress, 19*, 111-125, 1972.

Lane, F., Optimum single propellers in radially varying, incompressible inflow, *J. Appl. Mech., 19*, 252-256, 1952.

Lerbs, H.W., "On the Development of the Theory of Marine Propulsion," Paper 7 of *Symposium on Naval Hydrodynamics*, Nat. Acad. of Sciences, Nat. Res. Council Publ. 515, Washington, 1956 (pp. 155-179).

Lesunovskii, V.P. and Khokha, Yu V., Characteristics of the noise spectrum of hydrodynamic cavitation on rotating bars in water, *Sov. Phys.-Acoustics, 14*, 474-478, 1968.

McCormick, B.W., Jr., Eisenhuth, J.J. and Lynn, J.E., A Study of Torpedo Propellers - Part 1, Theory, *Ord. Res. Lab. Rept. 16597-5*, March 1956.

Mellen, R.H., Ultrasonic spectrum of cavitation noise in water, *J.A.S.A., 26*, 356-362, 1954.

Morgan, W.B. and Lichtman, J.Z., "Cavitation Effects on Marine Devices," in *Cavitation State of Knowledge*, A.S.M.E., 1969 (pp. 195-241).

Robertson, J.M., Water tunnels for hydraulic investigations, *Trans. A.S.M.E., 78*, 95-104, 1956.

Ross, D. and McCormick, B.W., Jr., "Effect of Air Content on Cavitation Noise," report to *Eighth American Towing Tank Conference*, Oct. 1948; also, A Study of Propeller Blade-Surface Cavitation Noise, *Ord. Res. Lab. Rept. 7958-115*, Oct. 1948.

Theodorsen, T., *Theory of Propellers*, McGraw-Hill, New York, 1948.

Van de Voorde, C.B., A full scale model correlation investigation on propeller cavitation, *Int. Shipbuilding Progress, 8*, 255-266, 1961.

van Gent, W. and van Oossanen, P., Influence of wake on propeller loading and cavitation, *Int. Shipbuilding Progress, 20*, 279-321, 1973.

van Manen, J.D., The effect of cavitation on the interaction between propeller and ship's hull, *Int. Shipbuilding Progress, 19*, 3-20, 1972.

van Oossanen, P., A method for minimizing the occurrence of cavitation on propellers in a wake, *Int. Shipbuilding Progress, 18*, 321-333, 1971.

von Mises, R., *Theory of Flight*, McGraw-Hill, New York, 1945 (Chapters 11 and 12).

## Sections 8.5 and 8.6

Dorman, W.J. and de Koff, D.L., Characteristics of recent large container ship designs, *Marine Technology, 8*, 453-464, 1971.

Dow, M.T., Emling, J.W., Knudsen, V.O., "Survey of Underwater Sound; Report No. 4, Sounds from Surface Ships," *O.S.R.D., Div. 6.1, N.D.R.C. Rept.*, June 1945 (Declassified Aug. 1960).

Kopec, B.M., The ships of the US-flag intermodal fleet, *Proc. U.S. Naval Inst., 101*, No. 5, 213-230, 1975.

Knudsen, V.O., Alford, R.S. and Emling, J.W., "Survey of Underwater Sound; Report No. 2, Sounds from Submarines," *O.S.R.D., Div. 6.1, N.D.R.C. Rept.*, 1943 (Declassified).

Morris, G.B., Preliminary Results on Seamount and Continental Slope Reflection Enhancement of Shipping Noise, *Marine Phys. Lab. Rept. SIO Ref. 75-34*, Nov. 1975.

"Principles and Applications of Underwater Sound," Vol. 7, *Summary Tech. Rept. of Div. 6, N.D.R.C.*, 1946 (Chapter 12).

Ross, D., Trends in Merchant Shipping (1969-1980), *Tetra Tech, Inc. Rept. SD-449-75-1*, April 1975.

Strasberg, M. and Sette, W.J., Measurements of Propeller Noise on Three Submarines of the SS 212 Class, *D.T.M.B. Rept. R-205*, 1944.

Urick, R.J., *Principles of Underwater Sound for Engineers*, McGraw-Hill, New York, 1967 (Chapter 10).

*Jane's Flighting Ships.*

*Jane's Freight Containers.*

*Lloyd's Register of Shipping*, Statistical Tables, pub. annually.

"A Statistical Analysis of the World's Merchant Fleets," publ. annually by the U.S. Dept. of Commerce, Maritime Administration.

"Acoustic Torpedoes," Vol. *22, Summary Tech. Rept. of Div. 6, N.D.R.C.*, 1946 (Section 3.2).

## Section 8.7

Axelrod, E.H., Schoomer, B.A. and Von Winkle, W.A., Vertical directionality of ambient noise in the deep ocean at a site near Bermuda, *J.A.S.A., 37*, 77-83, 1965.

Arase, E.M. and Arase, T., Correlation of ambient sea noise, *J.A.S.A., 40*, 205-210, 1966.

Arase, E.M. and Arase, T., Ambient sea noise in the deep and shallow ocean, *J.A.S.A., 42*, 73-77, 1967.

Dyer, I., Statistics of sound propagation in the ocean, *J.A.S.A., 48*, 337-345, 1970.

Dyer, I., Statistics of distant shipping noise, *J.A.S.A., 53*, 564-570, 1973.

Frosch, R.A., How to make an ambient noise in the ocean, Paper C1, 59th Meeting A.S.A., *J.A.S.A., 32*, 915, 1960; also, *Hudson Labs. Contrib. 81*, 1960.

Knudsen, V.O., Alford, R.S. and Emling, J.W., "Survey of Underwater Sound; Report No. 3, Ambient Noise," *O.S.R.D., Div. 6.1, N.D.R.C. Rept. 1848*, 1944.

Morris, G.B., *op cit.*

Northrop, J., Loughridge, M.S. and Werner, E.W., Effect of near-source bottom conditions on long-range sound propagation in the ocean, *J. Geophys. Res., 73*, 3905-3908, 1968.

Perrone, A.J., Deep-ocean ambient noise spectra in the northwest Atlantic, *J.A.S.A., 46*, 762-770, 1969.

Perrone, A.J., Ambient noise spectrum level as function of water depth, *J.A.S.A., 48*, 362-370, 1970.

Perrone, A.J., Infrasonic and low-frequency ambient noise measurements on the Grand Banks, *J.A.S.A., 55*, 754-758, 1974.

Smith, P.W., Jr., Sound transmission in isogradient shallow water over a plane sloping bottom, Paper Q2, 80th Meeting A.S.A., *J.A.S.A., 49*, 96, 1971.

Smith, P.W., Jr. and Jones, J.P., Transmission into a basin having a bigradient sound-speed profile, Paper M5, 83rd Meeting A.S.A., *J.A.S.A., 52*, 137, 1972.

Talham, R.J., Ambient-sea-noise model, *J.A.S.A., 36*, 1541-1544, 1964.

Walkinshaw, H.M., Low-frequency spectrum of deep ocean ambient noise, Paper D1, 60th Meeting A.S.A., *J.A.S.A., 32*, 1497, 1960.

Wenz, G.M., Acoustic ambient noise in the ocean: spectra and sources, *J.A.S.A., 34*, 1936-1956, 1962.

Wenz, G.M., Review of underwater acoustics: noise, *J.A.S.A., 51*, 1010-1024, 1972.

Young, R.W., Sabine reverberation equation and sound power calculations, *J.A.S.A., 31*, 912-921, 1959.

## CHAPTER 9

## RADIATION BY FLUCTUATING-FORCE (DIPOLE) SOURCES

Sources that produce fluid volume fluctuations are dominant when they exist. There are many cases, however, in which they are absent and in which force fluctuations produce the strongest sounds. Fluctuating, or unsteady, forces occur as by-products of steady work-producing forces, as discussed in Chapter 1. When such forces cause a structure to vibrate, radiation occurs from flexural waves, as covered in Chapter 6. When forces are hydrodynamic in origin, sound is radiated directly into the fluid independent of any motion of a fluid boundary. This rigid-body, oscillating-force radiation is of dipole nature, as discussed in Section 3.4. The present chapter deals primarily with dipole-type radiation of sound by hydrodynamic fluctuating forces acting on rigid bodies. All lifting surfaces radiate sound in this way, and this mechanism accounts for much of the sound generated by hydraulic machines such as turbines, pumps and propellers as well as by fans, blowers and compressors.

### 9.1 Dipole Sound Sources

There are a number of ways in which dipole sound fields can be generated. Physically, the sources usually involve fluctuating forces or oscillating motion of a rigid body; mathematically, they can be expressed in terms of two equal out-of-phase monopole volume sources or by the spatial derivative of a monopole field.

**Acoustic Field of a Concentrated Force**

Just as large fluctuating-volume sources can be treated by summing the effects of many monopoles, so also sound radiation from large bodies experiencing fluctuating forces can be calculated by integrating the sound fields of elemental concentrated-force radiators. The sound field of a concentrated force varying arbitrarily with time was derived in Chapter 3. Since superposition may be assumed, any arbitrary force may be decomposed into harmonic components using Fourier's theorem as discussed in Section 1.5. Assuming a sinusoidally varying force, Eq. 3.31 for the radiated acoustic pressure due to a concentrated force becomes

$$\underline{p}' = \frac{\dot{\underline{F}} \cos\theta}{4\pi r c_o} e^{-ikr} = \frac{i\omega \tilde{\underline{F}}_o \cos\theta}{4\pi r c_o} e^{i(\omega t - kr)} \quad . \qquad (9.1)$$

This result is applicable only if the dimensions of the body or surface experiencing the force are small compared to an acoustic wavelength, and if the distance $r$ to the field point is large compared to a wavelength. The cosine radiation pattern is characteristic of a dipole.

The acoustic intensity of an elementary force dipole is given by

$$I(\theta) = \frac{\overline{p'^2}}{\rho_o c_o} = \frac{\omega^2 \overline{\tilde{F}^2}}{16\pi^2 r^2 \rho_o c_o^3} \cos^2\theta \ . \qquad (9.2)$$

Integrating over a sphere, the average intensity is

$$\overline{I} = I(0^o)\frac{1}{4\pi}\int_o^{2\pi}\int_o^{\pi} \cos^2\theta \sin\theta \, d\theta d\phi = \frac{1}{3} I(0) \ , \qquad (9.3)$$

from which it follows that the acoustic power is

$$W_{ac} = \frac{\omega^2 \overline{\tilde{F}^2}}{12\pi\rho_o c_o^3} \ . \qquad (9.4)$$

Comparing this expression to Eq. 4.17 for the power radiated by a monopole fluctuating-volume source, its dipole character is indicated by the cubic dependence on speed of sound, which implies a cubic dependence of radiation efficiency on Mach number.

**Oscillating Rigid Sphere**

As discussed in Chapter 3, it is the fluctuating surface-pressure field associated with a fluctuating force that radiates sound. Another way of producing fluctuating surface pressure is by oscillating motion of a rigid sphere, as depicted in Fig. 9.1. Consider a rigid sphere of radius $a_o$

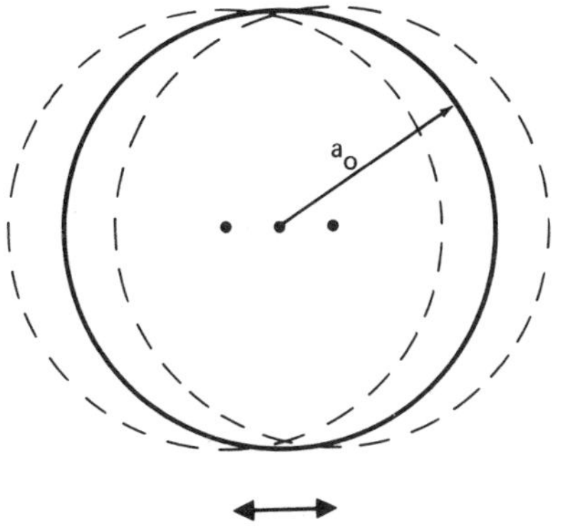


Fig. 9.1. Translational Oscillation of a Rigid Sphere

executing simple harmonic motion with peak speed $u_o$. The radial component of speed normal to the surface at each point on the sphere is given by

$$\underline{u}(\theta) = u_o \cos\theta \, e^{i\omega t} \, , \tag{9.5}$$

where $\theta$ is the angle between the radius vector and the direction of motion. Equating this surface velocity to the radial acoustic particle velocity and then solving for the far-field acoustic pressure, one finds

$$\underline{p}' \doteq - \frac{\omega\rho_o S_o u_o}{4\pi r} \left( \frac{ka_o}{2} \cos\theta \right) e^{i(\omega t - kr)} \, , \tag{9.6}$$

provided $ka_o << 1$.

The total power radiated by an oscillating sphere is

$$W_{ac} = \frac{1}{3} 4\pi r^2 \frac{\overline{p'^2(0)}}{\rho_o c_o} = \frac{(ka_o)^4}{24} \rho_o c_o S_o u_o^2 \, , \tag{9.7}$$

from which it follows that the radiation resistance, Eq. 3.2, is

$$R_r = \frac{W_{ac}}{\frac{1}{2} u_o^2} = \frac{1}{12} \rho_o c_o S_o (ka_o)^4 \, , \tag{9.8}$$

and the specific radiation resistance, Eq. 3.3, is

$$\sigma_r = \frac{R_r}{\rho_o c_o S_o} = \frac{1}{12} (ka_o)^4 \, . \tag{9.9}$$

This result is identical to that given by Eq. 3.18 for a first-order multipole, as derived from a general spherical source.

Not only do dipoles differ from monopoles in having cosine directional patterns, but also they differ in the nature of their near-field pressures. In the case of a pulsating volume source, a single expression for pressure decreasing with distance from the center applies at all locations outside the source. This is not the case for dipoles. A large fraction of the power that is required to oscillate a rigid sphere goes into a near-field hydrodynamic sloshing motion of the fluid that does not radiate as sound. For small $ka_o$ and small $kr$, the pressure near an oscillating rigid sphere is

$$\underline{p}_i' \doteq i \frac{\omega\rho_o S_o u_o}{4\pi r^2} \left( \frac{a_o}{2} \cos\theta \right) e^{i(\omega t - kr)} \, , \tag{9.10}$$

which, being inductive, decays as the square of the distance from the center of the sphere. Comparing Eq. 9.10 for the inductive field to Eq. 9.6 for the acoustic field, we find

$$\underline{p}_i' = \frac{\underline{p}'}{ikr} \, . \tag{9.11}$$

Hence, the inductive field lags the acoustic field by 90° at each radial distance. The total fluctuating pressure at any radius is the sum of the two components.

The reactive force associated with the fluid motion involved in the oscillation of a rigid sphere equals the integral of the component of the pressure in the direction of motion over the surface,

$$\underline{F}_x = \int_{S_o} \underline{p}_i'(a_o) \cos\theta \, dS \ . \tag{9.12}$$

Using Eq. 9.10 with $r = a_o$ for the surface pressure, and carrying out the indicated integration,

$$\underline{F}_x = i \frac{\omega\rho_o S_o u_o e^{i\omega t}}{8\pi a_o} \int_0^{2\pi} \int_0^{\pi} a_o^2 \cos^2\theta \sin\theta d\theta d\phi$$

$$= \frac{i}{6} \rho_o c_o (ka_o) S_o u_o e^{i\omega t} \ . \tag{9.13}$$

The reactive component of the radiation impedance equals the reactive force divided by the velocity. It follows that

$$X_r = \frac{F_x}{u_o e^{i\omega t}} = \frac{1}{6} \rho_o c_o S_o (ka_o) \ , \tag{9.14}$$

which is the reactance of a mass equal to one half of that displaced by the sphere.

For small $ka_o$ the radiation resistance given by Eq. 9.8 is small compared to the reactance and the impedance can be taken to be entirely reactive. It follows that the radiation efficiency is

$$\eta_{rad} = \frac{R_r}{|Z_r|} \doteq \frac{R_r}{X_r} = \frac{1}{2} (ka_o)^3 \tag{9.15}$$

in complete agreement with Eq. 3.23.

The equivalence of an oscillating rigid sphere and a fluctuating force as sound sources can be further demonstrated by expressing the acoustic field of an oscillating sphere in terms of the force required to keep it in motion. This force is composed of two terms: the reactive force of the medium, as given by Eq. 9.13, and the force required to accelerate its mass. Assuming that the sphere has the same density as the fluid, the total force is

$$\underline{\widetilde{F}} = \underline{F}_x + m\dot{u} = \underline{F}_x + i\omega\rho_o \left( \frac{4}{3} \pi a_o^3 \right) u_o e^{i\omega t} \ , \tag{9.16}$$

from which it follows that

$$\underline{\widetilde{F}} = i\rho_o c_o S_o \left( \frac{ka_o}{2} \right) u_o e^{i\omega t} \ . \tag{9.17}$$

Equation 9.6 for the radiated pressure may be written

$$\underline{p}' \doteq \frac{i\omega\tilde{F}}{4\pi r c_o} \cos\theta \; e^{-ikr} \; , \qquad (9.18)$$

which is equivalent to Eq. 9.1. Thus, the two source expressions are equivalent, provided the wavelength is large compared to the diameter of the sphere.

**Spheres Pulsating Out of Phase**

Dipole sound patterns are also generated by two equal out-of-phase monopoles separated by a distance small compared to a wavelength, as was developed in Section 4.5. If each of the pulsating spheres comprising the dipole has source strength given by

$$\underline{Q} = Q_o \, e^{i\omega t} \; , \qquad (9.19)$$

and their centers are separated by $d$, then from Eq. 4.75

$$\underline{p}' = i \frac{kQ_o d}{4\pi r} \cos\theta \; e^{-ikr} = - \frac{\omega^2 Q_o d}{4\pi r c_o} \cos\theta \; e^{i(\omega t - kr)} \; , \qquad (9.20)$$

where $\cos\theta$ replaces $\sin\theta$ because of the present choice of the dipole axis as the reference for $\theta$ rather than a perpendicular.

The product $Q_o d$ is the magnitude, or strength, of the dipole, represented by $D_o$ in the following equations. Comparing Eq. 9.20 to Eqs. 9.1 and 9.6, dipole strength can be related to the strength of a fluctuating force and to the size and velocity of an oscillating sphere by

$$D_o \equiv Q_o d = \frac{\tilde{F}_o}{i\omega} = \rho_o S_o u_o \frac{a_o}{2} \; . \qquad (9.21)$$

General expressions for the acoustic pressure, intensity and power of dipoles are

$$\underline{p}' = - \frac{\omega^2 D_o}{4\pi r c_o} \cos\theta \; e^{i(\omega t - kr)} \; , \qquad (9.22)$$

$$I = \frac{\overline{p'^2}}{\rho_o c_o} = \frac{\omega^4 D_o^2}{32\pi^2 r^2 \rho_o c_o^3} \cos^2\theta \; , \qquad (9.23)$$

and

$$W_{ac} = \frac{4}{3} \pi r^2 I(0) = \frac{\omega^4 D_o^2}{24\pi \rho_o c_o^3} \; . \qquad (9.24)$$

All of these expressions written in terms of dipole strength reduce to the corresponding equations in terms of force or velocity flux, using the relations of Eq. 9.21.

**Dipole Fields from Monopole Fields**

The complete pressure field of a dipole, including both inductive and acoustic components, can be expressed as a spatial derivative of a monopole pressure field. Using Eq. 4.15 for the pressure field of a monopole,

$$dp_o' = \frac{\partial p_o'}{\partial x} dx = \frac{\partial p'}{\partial r} \frac{\partial r}{\partial x} dx = \frac{i\omega Q_o e^{i\omega t}}{4\pi} \frac{\partial}{\partial r} \left(\frac{e^{-ikr}}{r}\right) \left(\frac{\partial r}{\partial x}\right) dx$$

$$= \frac{i\omega Q_o}{4\pi r} \left(-\frac{1}{r} - ik\right) \left(\frac{\partial r}{\partial x}\right) e^{i(\omega t - kr)} dx \ . \qquad (9.25)$$

Interpreting $\partial r/\partial x$ as $\cos\theta$ and equating $dx$ to the separation of the poles, $d$, we find

$$dp_o' = \frac{\omega^2 Q_o d}{4\pi r c_o} \left(1 - \frac{i}{kr}\right) \cos\theta \ e^{i(\omega t - kr)} \ , \qquad (9.26)$$

which is the negative of the complete dipole pressure field obtained by adding the acoustic component, Eq. 9.20, to the inductive component, Eq. 9.11.

This relation between dipole pressure fields and monopole fields can be generalized. Quadrupole fields can be obtained from derivatives of dipole fields, or from second derivatives of monopole fields. Higher order fields are produced by higher order derivatives.

## 9.2 Propeller Blade Tonals

Blade tonal radiation from non-cavitating propellers and from fans, compressors, turbines and pumps is an important noise source. The initial analysis of this problem by Gutin (1936) was concerned with sound radiation by a rotating static force distribution, i.e., sound radiation by a finite-bladed impeller in a uniform inflow, for which thrust and torque are constant. As discussed in Section 3.5, Gutin found that the sound radiated depends very strongly on both the number of blades and tip Mach number. At the low Mach numbers of marine propellers and of most hydraulic machinery Gutin noise is negligible compared to that generated as a result of force fluctuations; further discussion of his analysis will therefore be omitted. Readers interested in this subject are referred to Blokhintsev (1946) and to Richards and Mead (1968).

### General Oscillating Hydrodynamic Force

When oscillating force is generated in connection with fluid flows, it is useful to define an oscillating force coefficient, $\widetilde{C}_F$, analogous to the lift and drag coefficients defined by Eqs. 7.72 and 7.73. Thus, writing

$$\widetilde{C}_F \equiv \frac{\widetilde{F}_{rms}}{\frac{1}{2} \rho_o U_o^2 S} \ , \qquad (9.27)$$

the intensity and radiated power of a concentrated fluctuating force may be expressed by

$$I(\theta) = \frac{\rho_o U_o^3 S}{16 r^2} \left(\frac{f^2 S}{U_o^2}\right) \left(\frac{U_o}{c_o}\right)^3 \widetilde{C}_F^2 \cos^2\theta \qquad (9.28)$$

and

$$W_{ac} = \frac{\pi}{12} \rho_o U_o^3 S \left( \frac{f^2 S}{U_o^2} \right) \widetilde{C}_F^2 M^3 \quad . \tag{9.29}$$

These equations, which may be used in place of Eqs. 9.2 and 9.4, show dependence on the sixth power of the flow speed and on the square of a dimensionless frequency coefficient. Calculation of the sound power radiated by various types of oscillating force requires expressions for the oscillating force coefficient and for the dimensionless frequency.

Usually oscillating forces are unwanted by-products of steady work-producing forces. The mechanical power associated with a steady force can be written

$$W_{mech} = \frac{1}{2} \rho_o U_o^3 S C_F \quad . \tag{9.30}$$

Combining this expression with Eq. 9.29, the acoustic efficiency is

$$\eta_{ac} \equiv \frac{W_{ac}}{W_{mech}} = \frac{\pi}{6} \left( \frac{f^2 S}{U_o^2} \right) \left( \frac{\widetilde{C}_F}{C_F} \right)^2 M^3 C_F \quad . \tag{9.31}$$

**Noise from Oscillating Thrust**

As discussed in Section 8.4, operation of a propeller in a wake having circumferential variations results in oscillating components of thrust at multiples of the blade frequency, which are given by

$$f = mBn \quad . \tag{9.32}$$

Here $m$ is the order of the harmonic, $B$ the number of blades and $n$ the rotational speed in rps. Defining an rms oscillating thrust coefficient, $\widetilde{C}_T$, in a manner analogous to that of Eq. 8.18 for the steady thrust, by

$$\widetilde{C}_T \equiv \frac{\widetilde{T}_{rms}}{\rho_o n^2 D^4} \quad , \tag{9.33}$$

the intensity of directly radiated sound at the mth harmonic is then given from Eq. 9.2 by

$$I_m(\theta) \doteq \frac{m^2 B^2}{4 r^2 c_o^3} \rho_o n^6 D^8 \widetilde{C}_{T_m}^2 \cos^2 \theta \quad . \tag{9.34}$$

Thus, the intensity increases as the sixth power of tip rotational speed, as disk area, and as the square of number of blades, harmonic number and oscillating thrust coefficient. From Eq. 9.4 and the definition of the steady-state thrust coefficient given by Eq. 8.18, the acoustic conversion efficiency can be expressed by

$$\eta_{ac} = \frac{m^2 B^2}{3\pi^2 J} \frac{\widetilde{C}^2_{T_m}}{C_T} \left(\frac{\pi n D}{c_o}\right)^3 \tag{9.35}$$

For typical propeller tip speeds of the order of 25 to 50 m/sec and oscillating thrust coefficients of 2 to 10% of that for the steady-state thrust, acoustic conversion efficiencies for direct radiation of blade-rate tonals are estimated to be between $10^{-10}$ and $10^{-8}$, well below that for propeller cavitation.

While not efficient radiators of blade tonal components at the low Mach numbers of marine propellers, blade-rate forces transmitted by propeller shafts are a dominant cause of hull vibration. When these vibratory forces coincide with low-frequency hull resonances of the types discussed in Sections 4.11 and 5.11, severe vibrations may occur. Not only are these vibrations harmful to men and machines but also they may radiate blade tonal components at higher levels than those radiated directly by the propeller.

## Factors Affecting Oscillating Thrust

Primarily because of the interest of naval architects in reducing shipboard vibrations and preventing propeller shaft fatigue failures, considerable effort has been devoted by a number of investigators to the development of methods of calculating propeller alternating thrust. The calculation of steady-state propeller forces for uniform inflow conditions is itself a complex problem for which no single method has proven to be clearly superior. Non-steady effects caused by wake operation make the problem even more untractable. As summarized by Stern and Ross (1964), the various published methods may be classified as either quasi-steady or unsteady and either two-dimensional or three-dimensional. In quasi-steady methods the forces on a propeller blade are calculated at each angular position as though the wake at that position existed over the entire 360°. In unsteady methods, unsteady airfoil theory developed by von Karman and Sears (1938) is used in deriving oscillating lift coefficients for blade elements. In two-dimensional analyses, induced velocity components due to helical trailing vortex sheets, cascade effects of other blades, tip vortices and other three-dimensional effects are ignored. Brown (1964) compared the various methods, finding, as shown in Fig. 9.2, that quasi-steady analysis is in good agreement with his three-dimensional unsteady theory when calculating the fundamental and second harmonic components while a two-dimensional unsteady method gives good results for the fourth and higher harmonics.

According to two-dimensional unsteady airfoil theory, the oscillatory lift experienced by an airfoil in a sinusoidal gust of amplitude $w_o$ is given by

$$\underline{\widetilde{C}}_L = 2\pi \frac{w_o}{U_o} e^{i\omega t} \underline{G}(\gamma) , \tag{9.36}$$

where

$$\gamma \equiv \frac{\omega s}{2U_o} \tag{9.37}$$

is called the *reduced frequency* of the gust. The phase angle of the function $\underline{G}(\gamma)$ depends upon the reference point on the airfoil. When expressed relative to the center as originally done by Sears (1949), the phase varies greatly, but Brown (1964) and Lowson (1970) have shown that the phase

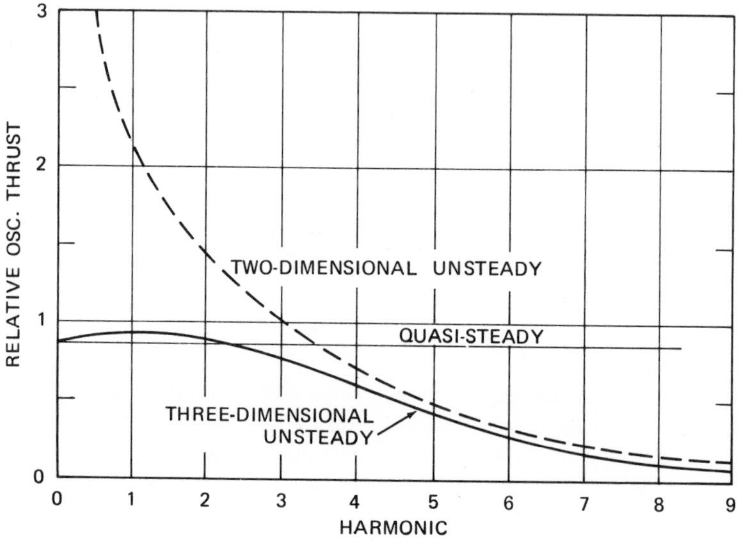


Fig. 9.2. Comparison of Computational Methods for Propeller Fluctuating Thrust, after Brown (1964)

angle varies by less than 45° over the entire frequency range when the leading edge is used as the reference point. As expressed by Brown,

$$\underline{G}_{LE}(\gamma) = \frac{e^{-i\gamma}}{i\gamma\left[K_o(i\gamma) + K_1(i\gamma)\right]} , \tag{9.38}$$

where $K_o$ and $K_1$ are modified Bessel functions of the second kind. This function is plotted in Fig. 9.3. For the high values of the reduced frequency typical of marine propellers, especially for the higher harmonics, Eq. 9.38 reduces to

$$\underline{G}_{LE}(\gamma) \doteq \frac{1}{\sqrt{2\pi\gamma}} e^{-i(\pi/4)} , \tag{9.39}$$

which relation is valid within 3% for $\gamma \geqslant 1$.

The procedure used when making unsteady airfoil calculations is to perform an harmonic analysis of the circumferential wake at each radial station. Since the component of the wake having periodicity equal to $m$ times $B$ is the only component causing the mth harmonic of the blade-rate oscillating thrust, the complex oscillating force is computed for this component at each radial station and then integrated over the radius.

It is apparent from this discussion that number of blades is a most important factor affecting oscillating thrust. Some wakes, such as that shown in Fig. 8.12, have strong components at certain

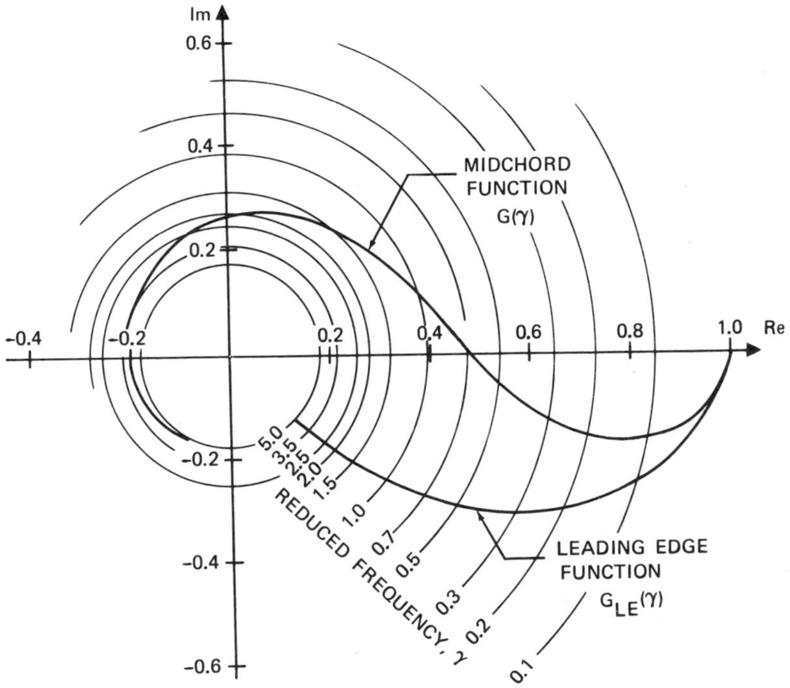


Fig. 9.3. Sears Function Relative to Midchord and to Leading Edge, after Brown (1964)

even harmonics. Selection of an odd number of blades may result in a much lower fluctuating force than would selection of an even number. In other cases, such as for the wake depicted in Figs. 8.10 and 8.11, there is little difference between four-, five- or six-bladed propellers.

Another factor affecting the fluctuating thrust is the shape of the leading edge. Cox and Morgan (1972) have demonstrated that skewing the leading edge tends to reduce the net force by causing the various radial sections to experience their forces out of phase with each other. Skewing also has the effect of increasing the section chord length, thereby increasing $\gamma$ and slightly reducing the oscillating force, as implied by Eq. 9.39.

Calculations of oscillating thrust for a given propeller show relatively small variations of $\widetilde{C}_T$ with advance ratio $J$. It follows from Eq. 9.35 and Fig. 8.8 that somewhat lower acoustic efficiencies, i.e., lower blade tonals, will be achieved if propellers are operated at advance ratios slightly lower than optimum from the point of view of efficiency.

### Propeller-Induced Hull Forces

In addition to direct excitation of hull vibrations by oscillating thrust transmitted through the propeller shaft and thrust bearing to the hull, the rotating pressure field associated with a propeller can induce oscillating forces on nearby hull plating, fins and/or struts. As previously discussed, direct radiation from rotating pressure fields is very small at the low Mach numbers of marine propellers. However, inductive near-field pressures can be significant and the forces experienced by nearby stationary surfaces can be large. In a summary of this subject, Breslin (1962) noted that important contributions to the inductive pressure field are made by both blade thickness and lift distributions and that propellers in non-uniform wakes produce larger forces. As confirmed by Tsakonas et al (1964), induced pressures and radiated sound both decrease markedly as tip clearances and/or number of blades are increased. The decrease of induced pressure fields experienced with increasing numbers of blades is a contributing factor in the present trend toward the use of five- and six-bladed propellers on modern high-power merchant ships.

Submarine and torpedo hulls also experience oscillating forces transmitted by propeller induction pressure fields. However, Chertock (1965) found these induced forces to be only of the order of 6 to 10% as large as those transmitted directly by the shaft. Tsakonas and Breslin (1965) also calculated the longitudinal force induced by a propeller on a prolate spheroid and found this force to vary inversely with the length-to-diameter ratio of the body. They noted that transverse forces induced in fins augment hull vibrations.

The importance of struts in transmitting oscillating forces to ship hulls was recognized by Lewis in the 1930's. More recently, Pinkus et al (1963) have calculated the force induced in a finite plate, representing an appendage, by a vortex distribution representing a blade moving past one end; and Lewis (1963, 1967) has reported on measurements of strut oscillating forces made in a water tunnel. Both studies show a very rapid decrease of induced force with increasing clearance, leading to the conclusion that this problem can be eliminated by giving attention to the spacing between propeller and stationary surfaces such as struts, fins and rudders.

### Blade-Vortex Interaction Noise

Occasionally marine propellers emit a sound that resembles what one would expect from repeated slaps occurring at blade frequency. It is believed that the source of such *blade-slap noise* is the passage of blades through a vortex. Vortices originating from the tips of lifting surfaces upstream of the propeller, or from the first propeller of a counterrotating pair, may pass through the propeller disk. Each time a blade comes close to a vortex it experiences a force much as from an abrupt gust. Each force pulse generates a sound pulse, resulting in pulses repeated at blade frequency. The phenomenon has been studied by Simons (1966) and Widnall (1971) in connection with helicopter blade-slap noise. They found that the sound radiated is not only a function of the strength of the vortex but also of its core size levels, being lower for larger cores.

### Shaft-Rate Components

Tonal components at shaft rate also occur in propeller spectra, though at much lower levels than blade tonals. Their presence implies modulation of the blade tonals at shaft rotational frequency. Such modulation would be expected to occur either if the blades were not mechanically identical and/or if their spacings were not exactly equal. Furthermore, even if blades and spacings were the same, forces experienced by the individual blades could differ somewhat since blade flexural vibrations do not occur identically. Expressing a modulated blade harmonic by

$$p = P\left(1 + \sum_j \alpha_j \cos j\omega t\right) \cos mB\omega t \tag{9.40}$$

leads to

$$p = \frac{P}{2} \sum_j \alpha_j \left[ \cos(mB + j)\omega t + \cos(mB - j)\omega t \right] , \qquad (9.41)$$

which series represents a family of tonals at multiples of the shaft rotational frequency.

**Rotor-Stator Interactions**

When center-line propellers are used on bodies of revolution such as torpedoes or submarines, the major cause of wake variation is the fins. In this case, oscillating forces may be considered to result from *rotor-stator interaction*. Similar rotor-stator interactions are also dominant sources of tonal noise from fans, compressors, pumps and turbines, and the subject has received considerable attention in connection with noise from such machinery.

Kemp and Sears (1953, 1955) applied unsteady airfoil theory developed by von Karman and Sears (1938) and Sears (1941) to the rotor-stator interaction problem, finding that potential interaction effects and viscous wake effects are often of the same order of magnitude. For close spacing of rotor and stator, potential interaction effects dominate. These forces, which are similar to appendage forces previously discussed, decrease quite rapidly with increased spacing. On the other hand, viscous effects caused by wakes from the first row interacting with the second row decay gradually with distance. Kemp and Sears found viscous effects to be proportional to the drag coefficient of the upstream airfoils. Later studies by Sharland (1964), Fincher (1966), Lowson (1968) and Morfey (1970) confirmed these conclusions. Mather et al (1971) reported that the levels of shaft-rate tonals are also influenced by rotor-stator interaction effects. Hanson (1973, 1974) found little difference in the spectra whether the stator precedes or follows the rotor.

Blade tonals give a distinctive character to rotor noise which is often quite annoying to humans. Mellin and Sovran (1970), Duncan and Dawson (1975) and others have proposed that unequal rotor and/or stator spacings be used in order to reduce blade-frequency tonals. Shaft-rate tonals are thereby increased and the total sound output remains the same, but the broadband characteristic of the resultant sound is more acceptable.

**Blade-Turbulence Interactions**

Not only do rotors interact with the wakes of upstream stators, producing blade and shaft rate tonals, but also they may interact with turbulent inflow velocity fluctuations and thereby produce a broadband noise spectrum. The importance of inlet turbulence was demonstrated by Sharland (1964), who found an 8 dB increase in noise from a fan operating in a turbulent inflow compared to its operation in a smooth flow. Further study of this noise source by Mani (1971) and Mugridge (1973) showed its importance for values of the Sears parameter, $\gamma$, defined by Eq. 9.37, up to about 10. Higher-frequency broadband noise is associated with boundary-layer turbulence and with turbulent eddies in blade wakes, as discussed in the next section.

## 9.3 Vortex Shedding Sounds

The turbulent wakes of most bodies contain relatively strong vortices which occur in certain geometric configurations and which account for a significant fraction of wake energy. Oscillating forces are produced in connection with the formation of vortex wakes. These forces are responsible for such diverse phenomena as noise in electrical power lines, vibration of radar antennas, fatigue failure of hydraulic turbine blades and collapse of tall smokestacks. They have been studied extensively by mechanical, civil and hydraulic engineers as well as by acousticians and aerodynamicists. In acoustics, oscillating forces on wires produce sounds known as *Aeolian tones*, and similar forces on blades produce components of fan, compressor, pump and propeller noise that are sometimes very strong and are known as *singing*.

Investigations of the subject of vortex shedding phenomena within each of the disciplines mentioned proceeded for many decades almost without interaction between them. Although articles on this subject have appeared for almost 100 years, it was not until the 1960's that Ross (1964) combined results from all the fields to develop a unified hydro-acoustic theory of vortex shedding sounds. The present section is based on that study as revised by more recent experimental and theoretical developments.

**Aeolian Tones**

As recounted by Richardson (1924), descriptions of *Aeolian harps* in which wind or the draft from a fire produces musical tones are given in a book published in the 17th century. Although the phenomenon had been known since the time of the Greeks, the first scientific investigation was that of Strouhal (1878) who found that frequency of the sound increases with wind speed and decreases with wire diameter. Thus, the dimensionless frequency $fD/U_o$ tends to remain constant. This factor is known as the *Strouhal number*, $S_N$, and is written

$$S_N \equiv \frac{fb}{U_o} , \tag{9.42}$$

where $b$ is a characteristic transverse dimension of the body. For cylinders, Strouhal found $S_N \doteq 0.185$. Rayleigh (1915) noted that vibrations of the wire occur in a plane perpendicular to the direction of the wind. He associated the motion with the vortex wake that had been observed in water, and also concluded that the Strouhal number must be a function of Reynolds number, finding that Strouhal's experimental results are given by

$$S_N \doteq 0.195 \left(1 - \frac{20}{R_N}\right) . \tag{9.43}$$

Many of the studies of vortex shedding have been concerned with determining the exact relationship between $S_N$ and $R_N$ for rigid cylinders. Figure 9.4 summarizes these results. For very low values of $R_N$, below about 40, a symmetric vortex pattern is frozen in space. Above this value vortices are shed alternately from one side and the other and the dimensionless frequency is about 0.12, increasing to 0.19 at $R_N = 200$. In the Reynolds number range from 200 to 200,000 the wake is turbulent, but a discrete vortex pattern persists and the Strouhal number is practically constant at $S_N = 0.20 \pm 0.01$. Above about $R_N = 2 \times 10^5$, the situation is unclear. From this value to $R_N \doteq 3 \times 10^6$, the wake is highly turbulent and whatever vortices occur do not seem to have a definite frequency. Relf and Simmons (1925) made wake hot-wire measurements and found a peak in the spectrum with $S_N > 0.4$ in this region. Similar results were reported by Delany and Sorensen (1953), Itaya and Yasuda (1961) and Bearman (1969). However, Fung (1958) and Blyumina and Fedyaevskii (1968) reported finding $S_N \doteq 0.20$ throughout. Above this region of weak discrete vorticity, stronger vortices again occur, and Roshko (1961) found $S_N \doteq 0.27$ for $R_N$ from $3 \times 10^6$ to $10^7$.

All of the results summarized above are presumably for rigid cylinders in a free environment. Any departures from ideal conditions may cause significant changes of observed Strouhal frequencies.

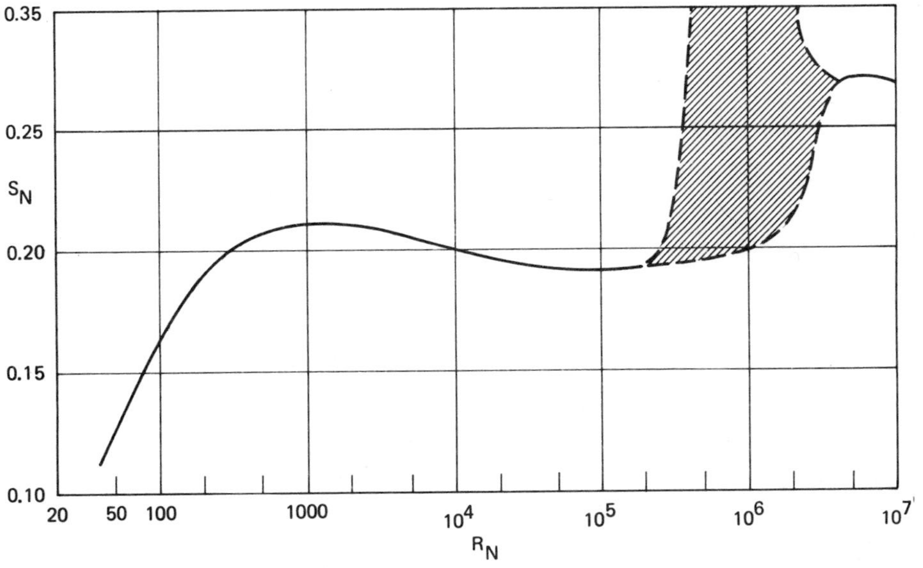


Fig. 9.4. Strouhal-Reynolds Number Relation for Circular Cylinders

**Vortex Wakes of Bluff Bodies**

Figure 9.5 shows a *vortex street* consisting of two rows of alternating vortices of strength $\Gamma$ in the wake of an elliptic cylinder of thickness $b$. The vortex rows are separated by $h$ and the distance between vortices in the same row is $a$. The vortices produce their own velocity field superimposed on the free stream velocity, $U_o$. The velocity induced at any vortex by all the other vortices is $u_s$. Von Karman and Rubach (1912) carried out a stability analysis of an infinite vortex street, finding

$$\frac{h}{a} = 0.28 \ . \tag{9.44}$$

Measurements of the spacing ratio of actual vortex streets are generally in fair agreement with this value, though ratios as high as 0.35 are not uncommon. Birkhoff (1953) has reasoned that, while $a$

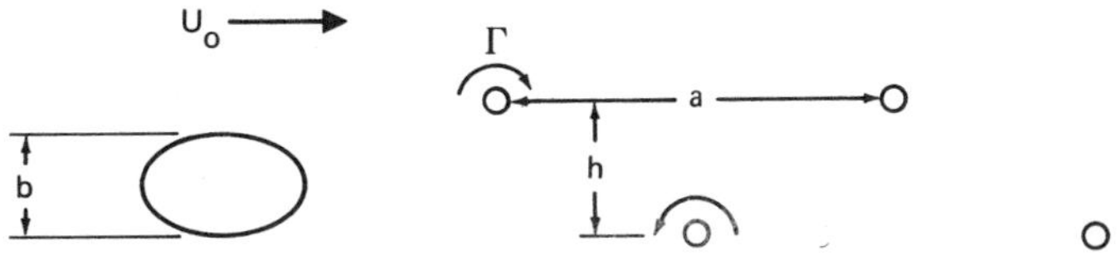


Fig. 9.5. Vortex Street Geometry

remains constant as the wake decays, $h$ increases due to the action of viscosity. Near the body, spacing ratios are usually close to that given by Eq. 9.44.

Von Karman and Rubach computed the induced velocity for an infinite vortex street, finding

$$u_s = \frac{\Gamma}{2a} \tanh \frac{\pi h}{a} \doteq \frac{\Gamma}{2\sqrt{2}\,a}\left[1 + \frac{\pi}{\sqrt{2}}\left(\frac{h}{a} - 0.281\right)\right] \doteq \frac{3\Gamma}{8a}\sqrt{\pi \frac{h}{a}} \, . \tag{9.45}$$

Assuming the spacing to be close to equilibrium,

$$\frac{u_s}{U_o} \doteq \frac{\Gamma}{2\sqrt{2}aU_o} \, . \tag{9.46}$$

The Strouhal number for the movement of vortices past a fixed point in the wake is

$$S_N = \frac{U_o - u_s}{a}\,\frac{b}{U_o} = \left(1 - \frac{u_s}{U_o}\right)\frac{b}{a} \doteq 0.28\left(1 - \frac{u_s}{U_o}\right)\frac{b}{h} \, , \tag{9.47}$$

showing that both relative wake width and induced velocity affect the observed frequency.

In some Reynolds number ranges, a significant fraction of the drag is associated with wake vortices. Von Karman and Rubach (1912) equated momentum carried downstream by vortices to form drag, $F_{D_F}$, finding

$$F_{D_F} \doteq \frac{\rho_o \Gamma h}{a}\left(U_o - 2u_s\right) + \frac{\rho_o \Gamma^2}{2\pi a} \, . \tag{9.48}$$

Defining a form drag coefficient similar to Eq. 7.73 and assuming equilibrium spacing, Eq. 9.48 leads to

$$C_{D_F} \equiv \frac{F_{D_F}}{\frac{1}{2}\rho_o U_o^2 b} \doteq 4\sqrt{2}\,\frac{h}{b}\,\frac{u_s}{U_o}\left(1 - 0.4\frac{u_s}{U_o}\right) . \tag{9.49}$$

Form drag is proportional to the relative wake width and Strouhal number varies inversely with this quantity. Krzywoblocki (1945) multiplied Eqs. 9.47 and 9.49, getting

$$S_N \cdot C_{D_F} \doteq 1.6\,\frac{u_s}{U_o}\left[1 - 1.4\frac{u_s}{U_o} + 0.4\left(\frac{u_s}{U_o}\right)^2\right] , \tag{9.50}$$

independent of relative wake width. This relation is plotted in Fig. 9.6. Roshko (1961) noted the inverse behavior of $S_N$ and $C_{D_F}$. Since the drag coefficient drops precipitously in the critical Reynolds number region around $3 \cdot 10^5$, he found an increase of Strouhal numbers in this region to be quite believable. However, if very little energy were to go into vortex streets in this region, then vortex strengths would be low and one would expect relative induced velocities to be low as

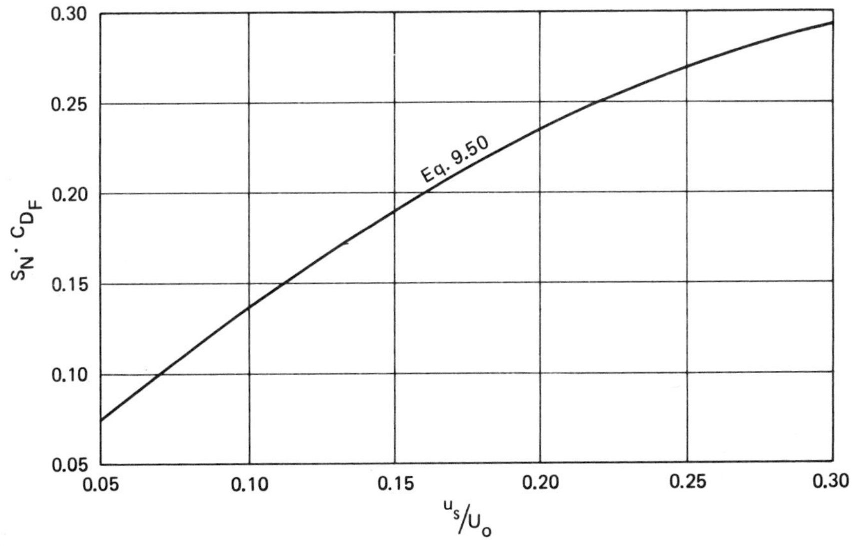


Fig. 9.6. Product of Strouhal Number and Form Drag Coefficient from Eq. 9.50

well. By Eq. 9.49, $C_{D_F}$ would decrease relatively more than $S_N$ would increase and the product would decrease in accordance with Fig. 9.6. Figure 9.7 is a plot of the product of $S_N$ and $C_D$ as a function of Reynolds number for vortex shedding from cylinders. Except in the critical regime, the product is close to constant at 0.22, implying that $u_s \doteq 0.18\ U_o$ and that vortex strength is practically constant outside that region.

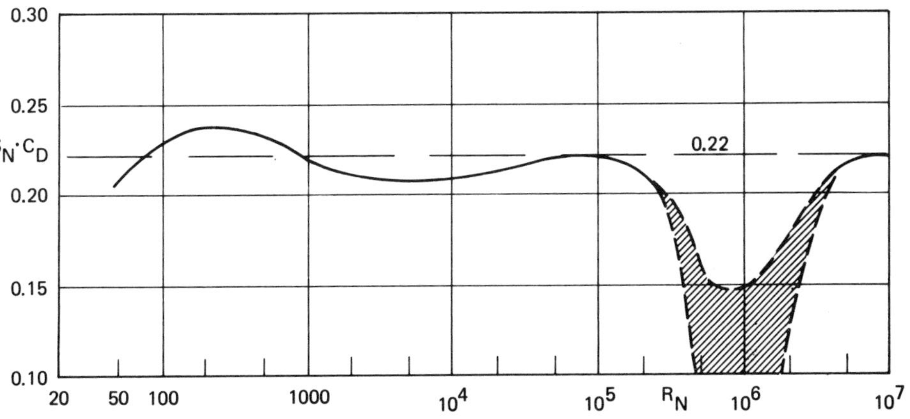


Fig. 9.7. Product of Strouhal Number and Drag Coefficient for Cylinders

These results for cylinders can be generalized to other bluff bodies, since nothing in the analysis was specific to circular or elliptic cylinders. Thus Fage and Johansen (1927, 1928) found that the Strouhal number for flat plates at large angles to a flow is constant at 0.15 over a wide range of angles provided $b$ is the projection of the plate normal to the flow. They also found $u_s \doteq 0.16\ U_o$. Roshko (1955) studied a wide variety of bluff bodies, finding

$$S_R \equiv \frac{fh'}{U_s} \doteq 0.165 \tag{9.51}$$

for a wide range of Reynolds numbers. The reference velocity $U_s$ in this relation is the velocity at the point of separation of the flow from the body and $h'$ is the theoretical distance between the separated free streamlines as determined downstream where they have become parallel. Abernathy (1962) studied separated flows from flat plates at various angles to a flow, finding

$$S_A \equiv \frac{fh''}{U_s} \doteq 0.155 \ , \tag{9.52}$$

where $h''$ is the measured separation between the centers of the shear layers. Bearman (1967) used separations of the vortex streets and free-streamline velocity, $U_s$, in defining a Strouhal number,

$$S_B \equiv \frac{fh}{U_s} \ , \tag{9.53}$$

which he found to be 0.18 for a wide variety of wakes. The three modified Strouhal numbers all use the free-streamline velocity, $U_s$, since this quantity is more fundamental than the flow speed.

### Oscillating Forces Associated with Vortex Wakes

Formation of vortices and motion of a vortex street away from the body shedding the vortices induce a time-varying velocity component in the flow field about that body and consequently a time-varying pressure field. The result is an oscillating force component practically perpendicular to the direction of flow, which force is a source of dipole sound as well as of vibrations of the body.

The instantaneous induced velocity field and force resulting from vortex street motion are dominated by the vortex closest to the body. It is therefore useful to calculate these quantities for the motion of a single vortex. Consider a vortex of strength $\Gamma$ moving with speed $U_o - u_s$ away from a cylinder of diameter $D$, as shown in Fig. 9.8. As explained by Milne-Thomson (1950), the effects of this vortex can be treated in terms of an image vortex located within the cylinder at radius $s_i$ given by

$$s_i = \frac{(D/2)^2}{s} = \frac{(D/2)^2}{\sqrt{x^2 + \left(\frac{h}{2}\right)^2}} \ . \tag{9.54}$$

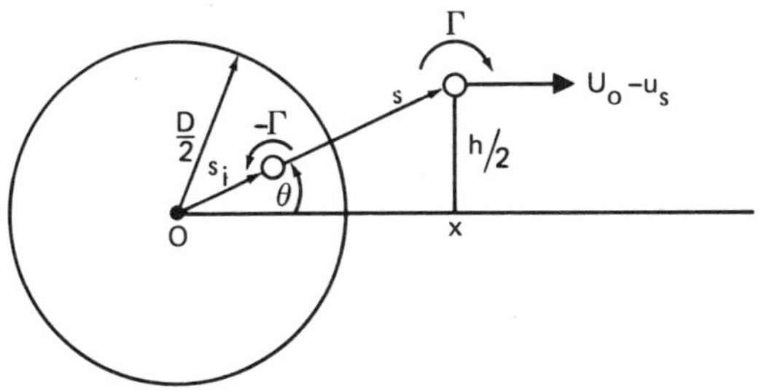


Fig. 9.8. Image Vortex for Vortex Outside a Cylinder

The lift component of the induced force at any instant is given by

$$F_{L_i} = -\rho_o \Gamma \dot{s}_i \cos\theta \ . \tag{9.55}$$

Taking the time derivative of Eq. 9.54, it follows that

$$F_{L_i} = \rho_o \Gamma (U_o - u_s) \frac{x^2 (D/2)^2}{\left[x^2 + \left(\frac{h}{2}\right)^2\right]^2} \ . \tag{9.56}$$

The maximum instantaneous lift that could be experienced would be that for a vortex at $x = D/2$, for which

$$\hat{F}_{L_i} = \frac{\rho_o \Gamma (U_o - u_s)}{\left[1 + \left(\frac{h}{D}\right)^2\right]^2} \ . \tag{9.57}$$

As the first vortex proceeds downstream, a second one of opposite sign is formed at $-h/2$ leading to a negative force equal to that given by Eq. 9.57. The rms oscillating lift for the fundamental component at shedding frequency is estimated to be approximately half of $\hat{F}_{L_i}$. From this fact and from Eq. 9.46 it follows that

$$\tilde{C}_L \doteq 2\sqrt{2} \frac{u_s}{U_o} \left(1 - \frac{u_s}{U_o}\right) \frac{a/D}{\left[1 + \left(\frac{h}{D}\right)^2\right]^2} \ . \tag{9.58}$$

Comparison with Eq. 9.49 shows that the oscillating lift coefficient due to a single vortex is closely related to the form drag coefficient, their ratio being

$$\frac{\tilde{C}_L}{C_{D_F}} \doteq \frac{\frac{1}{2}\left(\frac{a}{h}\right)}{\left[1 + \left(\frac{h}{D}\right)^2\right]^2} \left(1 - 0.6\,\frac{u_s}{U_o}\right) . \tag{9.59}$$

For circular cylinders at Reynolds numbers below $10^5$, the lateral separation distance $h$ can be taken as approximately equal to the diameter and $u_s/U_o \doteq 0.16$. It follows that the value of the rms oscillating lift coefficient calculated from Eq. 9.58 is about 40% of the form drag, which result is in agreement with an analysis originally published by Ruedy (1935).

Three factors not considered in deriving Eqs. 9.57-9.59 act to reduce the magnitude of the oscillating force. The first is that vortices do not form right at the cylinder, at $x = D/2$, as was assumed. Actually, vorticity is shed at this point into a parallel shear layer. As discussed by Abernathy and Kronauer (1962), such shear layers are unstable and break up into discrete vortices at downstream distances that depend on a number of external factors. Figure 9.9, based on Eq. 9.56, shows the decrease of induced force as a function of the downstream position of vortex formation. Thus, if the vortices were to form at a distance one diameter downstream, for which

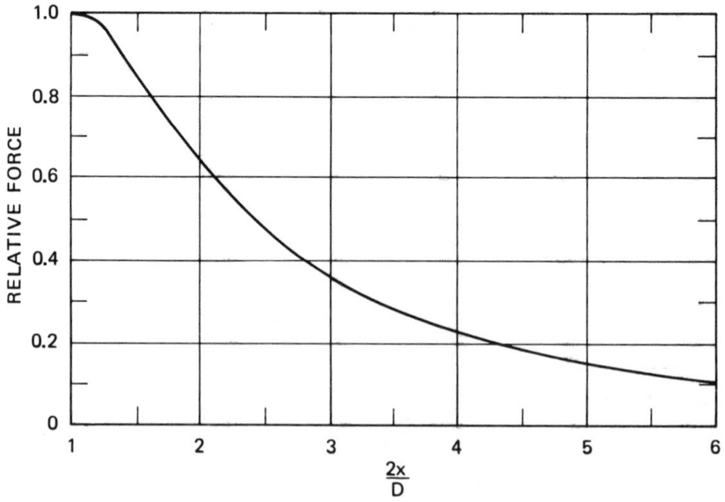


Fig. 9.9. Relative Induced Force as Function of Vortex Position in Fig. 9.8

$2x/D \doteq 3$, the force would be reduced to about one third of that previously calculated. Several investigators have reported that, when tests are run in low-turbulence flows at Reynolds numbers between 200 and 5000 and when care is exerted to prevent cylinder oscillation, formation distances to the first vortex are from 2 to 4 cylinder diameters. The corresponding oscillating force is only 5 to 15% of that for close vortex formation.

A second factor is reduction of the peak force due to induced velocities of all previously shed vortices. This amounts to about 15% and reduces the maximum possible oscillating lift from

40% of the form drag to about one third. Finally, the assumption of two-dimensionality is violated, as will be discussed below.

In view of the sensitivity of oscillating forces to the point of formation of the first vortex and to three-dimensional effects it is not at all surprising that experimental measurements of oscillating lift coefficients show a great deal of scatter. Confirmation of the above analysis is found in the fact that the highest measured values are about half the form drag. Thus, rms lift coefficients as high as 0.5 to 0.6 have been reported by Keefe (1962) and several other investigators. On the other hand, values under 0.1 were measured by Gerrard (1961) and Leehey and Hanson (1970) for Reynolds numbers between $10^3$ and $10^4$. Ballou (1967) confirmed that distance to vortex formation decreases markedly in the Reynolds number range between 4000 and 6000, corresponding to the observed increase of $\widetilde{C}_L$.

### Three-Dimensional Character of Vortex Wakes

The two-dimensional vortex street envisioned by von Karman and Rubach (1912) and other investigators consists of long straight vortices lined up parallel to the axis of the shedding bluff body; this is an idealization not usually found in practice. Flow visualization experiments of Hama (1957), Gerrard (1966), Koopmann (1967) and Berger and Wille (1972) have shown that under some conditions the vortices are shed in a regular manner but at angles of 10 to 30 degrees relative to the cylinder axis, while under other conditions the vortex lines are irregular as well as slanted.

Indications of the three-dimensional character of vortex patterns have also been found in measurements of oscillating pressures and velocities at different positions along a cylinder by Prendergast (1958) and el Baroudi (1960) and in flow pattern measurements by Humphreys (1960). These investigators found phase reversals occurring on the cylinder at lateral distances corresponding to 2 to 5 diameters. Vickery (1966) and Petrie (1974) reported that high levels of free-stream turbulence cause irregularity of vortex patterns for $R_N < 10^4$, for which shedding is normally regular.

Three-dimensionality of the vortex pattern reduces oscillating lift in two ways. Distortion results in lower local lift forces at each element of the cylinder, and phase shifts result in strong cancellation effects when the lift is integrated over the entire length. When slanted vortices are regular, as may occur for Reynolds numbers of 200 to 5000, this cancellation effect can be very strong. When they are irregular due to wake or stream turbulence, force cells each a few diameters long are produced and these add more or less randomly. Thus, Petrie found that in some cases turbulence increases the total oscillating lift. It is apparent that the wide range of measured oscillating lift coefficients that have been reported can be attributed to differences of experimental conditions and resultant differences of the three-dimensional vortex patterns.

### Effects of Vibration

Three-dimensional vortex patterns, either regular or irregular, are observed only in the wakes of rigid cylinders. As illustrated by Fig. 9.10, Koopmann (1967) and Griffin et al (1973) reported that the most dramatic effect of slight cylinder vibration is to straighten out the vortices so that near the cylinder they are essentially parallel to the cylinder axis. A second effect of cylinder motion is to assure that vortices form close to the body. Thus, in cases where the oscillating lift is relatively low due to three-dimensional vortex patterns and/or delayed vortex formation, a slight amount of cylinder vibration in synchronism with the vortex shedding may increase the oscillating lift coefficient by a large factor. It seems likely that some freedom to vibrate may have been involved in those experiments that produced exceptionally high values of $\widetilde{C}_L$.

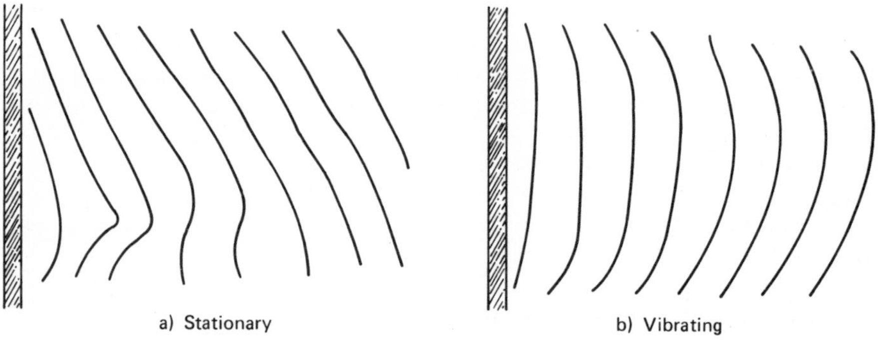


Fig. 9.10. Effect of Cylinder Vibration on Vortex Pattern, after Koopmann (1967)

Oscillations of the body shedding the vortices can also affect the shedding frequency. If a body is driven at a frequency within about ± 10% of the natural shedding frequency, vortices are shed at the cylinder vibration frequency.

The vibratory interaction of the body shedding the vortices with its vortex street explains many of the catastrophic effects of vortex shedding. For example, consider a tall thin structure in a wind. Normally the Strouhal frequency does not coincide with resonance frequencies of the structure; the structure remains rigid, the vortex pattern is irregular and the overall force is low. However, should the shedding frequency approach a resonance, the structure may start to vibrate. This vibration may cause the vortices to straighten, which increases the force and also the vibration up to the point at which the entire vortex pattern is straight and exerts maximum force. In this situation, the vibration amplitude may become so large as to cause structural failure. A similar phenomenon is involved in *singing*, which will be discussed later in this chapter.

**Effects of Sound Fields**

Many practical examples of vortex shedding occur in enclosed or partially enclosed spaces. In such cases, interactions of acoustic properties of the spaces with vortex shedding phenomena have been noted by a number of investigators. Parker et al (1966, 1967, 1968 and 1972) found that wind tunnel resonances affect both force amplitudes and frequencies associated with vortex wakes of airfoils. Graham and Maull (1971) and Cumpsty and Whitehead (1971) reported that acoustic resonances cause vortices to shed in a regular manner parallel to the cylinder axis in much the same manner as vibration of the cylinder.

Some investigators have suggested that acoustic feedback mechanisms play a central role in controlling vortex shedding processes in a manner similar to that found in the related phenomenon of edge tones. *Edge tones* are created when a fluid stream impinges on the edge of a flat plate. As analyzed by Richardson (1931), Curle (1953) and Powell (1953, 1961), acoustic feedback from the plate serves to stabilize one of many possible vortex patterns originating in the jet. It is generally agreed that this is not a dominant mechanism for vortex shedding from rigid bodies, but rather that sound fields may play a secondary role much like cylinder vibrations.

**Vortex Sounds from Cylinders**

Measurements of vortex shedding sounds by Yudin (1942), Gerrard (1955), Richardson (1957) and Etkin et al (1957) reveal a sixth-power dependence of acoustic power on flow speed and a cosine directionality pattern. As discussed in Section 9.1, both of these characteristics are typical of dipole radiation. Yudin (1944) assumed the oscillating force to be proportional to the drag coefficient and derived an expression for the acoustic power which was improved slightly by Blokhintsev (1946).

Most modern analyses are based on an expression derived by Phillips (1956) that includes three-dimensionality effects. Phillips started with Lighthill's equation and derived a general expression similar to Eq. 9.28 for the acoustic intensity at a point distant $r$ from a body experiencing a concentrated oscillating force. Expressing the normal cross-sectional area, $S$, by the product of the transverse dimension, $b$, and a spanwise length, $\ell$, as shown in Fig. 9.11, his result may be written

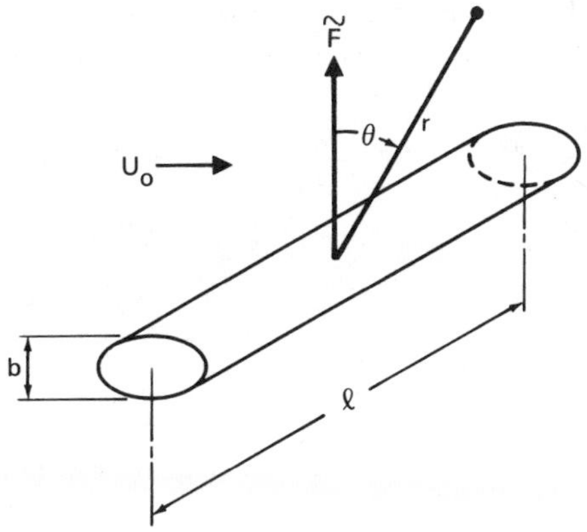


Fig. 9.11. Geometric Arrangement for Acoustic Calculation

$$I(\theta) = \frac{\rho_o U_o^3 \ell^2}{16r^2} \left(\frac{fb}{U_o}\right)^2 \left(\frac{U_o}{c_o}\right)^3 \tilde{C}_F^2 \cos^2\theta \ . \tag{9.60}$$

Phillips noted that this expression is only valid over a spanwise distance for which vortex shedding is coherent. For a cylinder of length $L$ he estimated that there would be $L/\ell$ coherent vortex shedding cells. Assuming that their phase angles are related randomly, Phillips summed the intensities, obtaining

$$I(\theta) = \frac{\rho_o U_o^3 \ell L}{16r^2} S_N^2 \tilde{C}_F^2 M^3 \cos^2\theta \tag{9.61}$$

for the total sound intensity from a body of length $L$ and

$$W_{ac} = \frac{\pi \rho_o U_o^3 \ell L}{12} S_N^2 \tilde{C}_F^2 M^3 \tag{9.62}$$

for the radiated power. An important result shown by Phillips' equation is the dependence of sound power on the coherence length. Thus, factors such as vibration and acoustic resonances that tend to straighten out the vortex pattern may increase the sound radiated more by increasing the correlation length, $\ell$, than by increasing the oscillating lift coefficient, $\tilde{C}_F$.

Ross (1964) rewrote Eqs. 9.61 and 9.62 by introducing the steady-state form drag coefficient, $C_{D_F}$, obtaining

$$I(\theta) = \frac{\rho_o U_o^3 S}{16r^2} \left(S_N C_{D_F}\right)^2 \left(\frac{\tilde{C}_F}{C_{D_F}}\right)^2 \left(\frac{\ell}{b}\right) M^3 \cos^2\theta \tag{9.63}$$

and

$$W_{ac} = \frac{\pi \rho_o U_o^3 S}{12} \left(S_N C_{D_F}\right)^2 \left(\frac{\tilde{C}_F}{C_{D_F}}\right)^2 \left(\frac{\ell}{b}\right) M^3 . \tag{9.64}$$

Based on the data shown in Fig. 9.7 and the relationship between oscillating lift and form drag previously discussed, Ross set $S_N C_{D_F} \doteq 0.22$ and $\tilde{C}_F \doteq 1/3\ C_{D_F}$, obtaining

$$I(\theta) \doteq 3.4 \times 10^{-4} \frac{\rho_o U_o^3 S}{r^2} \frac{\ell}{b} M^3 \cos^2\theta \tag{9.65}$$

and

$$W_{ac} \doteq (1.4 \times 10^{-3})\, \rho_o U_o^3 S \frac{\ell}{b} M^3 . \tag{9.66}$$

As previously discussed, $\tilde{C}_F$ is sometimes much smaller than $1/3\ C_D$, in which case Eqs. 9.65 and 9.66 overestimate the radiated sound. The ratio of $\ell$ to $b$ may be as low as 2 for a rigid cylinder at moderate Reynolds numbers, or $\ell$ may almost equal $L$ for a cylinder free to vibrate.

Equation 9.64 can be used to estimate the acoustic conversion efficiency for vortex shedding. The mechanical power given by Eq. 9.30 can be written

$$W_{mech} = \frac{1}{2} \rho_o U_o^3 S C_D , \tag{9.67}$$

from which

$$\eta_{ac} = \frac{\pi}{6} \left(\frac{S_N^2 C_{D_F}^2}{C_D}\right) \left(\frac{\tilde{C}_F}{C_{D_F}}\right)^2 \frac{\ell}{b} M^3 . \tag{9.68}$$

If form drag dominates, then $C_{D_F} \doteq C_D$ and

$$S_N^2 C_{D_F} \doteq 0.053 \frac{b}{h} \tag{9.69}$$

over a wide range of values of the relative induced velocity. With this result, and setting $\widetilde{C}_F \doteq 1/3\ C_{D_F}$, Eq. 9.68 becomes

$$\eta_{ac} \doteq 3 \times 10^{-3} \frac{\ell}{h} M^3 , \qquad (9.70)$$

showing that in many situations the acoustic efficiency depends only on relative coherence length and Mach number.

Phillips (1956) found that the intensity measurements of Holle (1938) and Gerrard (1955) for Reynolds numbers of 200 to $3 \times 10^4$ confirm the sixth-power dependence of intensity on flow speed predicted by Eq. 9.61 and agree as to magnitude with this expression, provided the coherence length, $\ell$, is taken to be about 5 to 8 diameters. More recently, Leehey and Hanson (1970), measuring vortex-shedding sound from a wire in a low-noise, low-turbulence wind tunnel, found that intensity increases by about the ninth power of flow speed in the Reynolds number range between 3000 and 9000, for which they also found a dramatic increase of the fluctuating lift coefficient associated with changes of the vortex formation distance. A similar result has been reported by Rimsky-Korsakov (1975) based on results of noise measurements from rotating rods.

### Sounds from Rotating Rods

The vortex shedding frequency of each section of a rod rotating about its center is a function of radius of that section, and each section of about one diameter in length radiates independently. It follows that

$$I(\theta) \doteq \frac{4.8 \times 10^{-5}}{r^2} \rho_o U_t^3 bDM_t^3 \cos^2\theta \qquad (9.71)$$

and

$$W_{ac} \doteq (2.0 \times 10^{-4})\, \rho_o U_t^3 DbM_t^3 , \qquad (9.72)$$

and that

$$\eta_{ac} \doteq (1.2 \times 10^{-3})\, M_t^3 , \qquad (9.73)$$

where subscript $t$ refers to values computed at the tip. These equations apply to rods formed of bluff sections, such as cylinders. They must be modified when dealing with airfoil sections, as will be discussed next. Also, as noted by Ross (1964), they appear to overestimate the sound measured by Stowell and Deming (1936) and by Yudin (1944) by from 3 to 18 dB. Rimsky-Korsakov (1975) reported agreement with these results for rods having tip Reynolds numbers between $2 \times 10^4$ and $4 \times 10^5$, levels at smaller Reynolds numbers being as much as 15 dB lower.

### Vortex Wakes of Airfoils

Turbulent wakes of airfoils at low angles of attack contain discrete vortices that resemble von Karman vortex streets of bluff bodies. Unlike bluff bodies, however, no simple relation exists between body dimensions and shedding frequency. The reason for this is that wake widths depend on both development of the boundary layer over the section and detailed trailing edge geometry.

Thus, Tyler (1928) and Lehnert (1937), defining Strouhal number in terms of airfoil thickness, found measured values to be strong functions of Reynolds number. Taneda (1958) found the variation to be as $R_N^{1/2}$ for flat plates having negligible trailing edge thicknesses. Gongwer (1952) recognized that the appropriate dimension should be the separation distance of the vortex sheets. He added the boundary-layer momentum thickness, $\theta$, to the trailing edge thickness, $e$, finding

$$\frac{f(e+\theta)}{U_o} \doteq 0.185 \quad . \tag{9.74}$$

The effect of trailing edge shape on the strength of the oscillating lift associated with vortex wakes has been studied by a number of groups in connection with design of hydraulic turbine and propeller blades for minimum noise. Three factors apparently influence the force: width of the street determines strength of the individual vortices and shedding frequency, in accordance with Eqs. 9.45 and 9.75; distance of point of formation of vortices from the trailing edge strongly affects force amplitude; and sharpness of the trailing edge controls its susceptibility to vibration, which vibration would be expected to increase the oscillating force by the mechanism previously discussed. Figure 9.12 summarizes results published by Donaldson (1956), Ippen et al (1960),

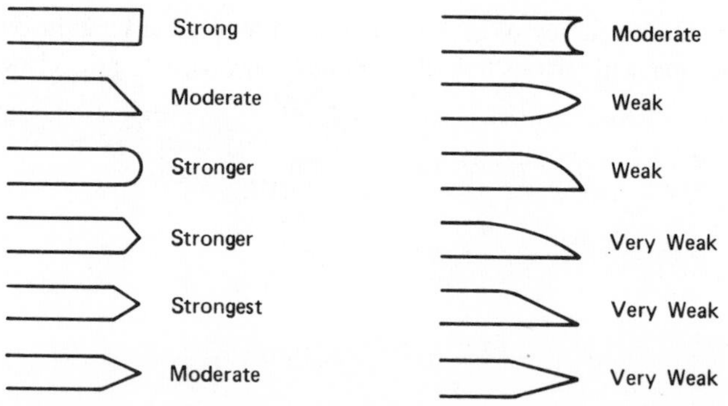


Fig. 9.12. Evaluation of Trailing Edges from Flat Plate Oscillating Force Measurements

Heskestad and Olberts (1960) and Toebes and Eagleson (1961) which confirm our expectation that an edge with strong vortices formed close to the tip experiences maximum force, and an edge which produces a narrow vortex wake is most desirable.

The peak oscillating pressure produced at the trailing edge of an airfoil has been shown by Blake (1975) to occur at the point where the streamline representing the center of the vortex street leaves the airfoil, as assumed by von Karman and Sears (1938). In many cases this is right at the tail, but it can be somewhat upstream. It follows that peak sound is radiated from near the trailing edge and not from the wake.

### Vortex Sounds from Rotating Blades

There have been no conclusive experiments in which airfoil vortex sounds were measured simultaneously with appropriate hydrodynamical characteristics of the wake. Ross (1964) suggested that Eqs. 9.65, 9.66 and 9.70-9.73, which were derived for bluff bodies, might apply unchanged to more streamlined sections. However, there is reason to believe that only a small fraction of the wake energy of airfoils occurs as discrete vortices and that the induced velocity, $u_s$, is therefore a smaller fraction of the flow speed. If this is the case, then the product of $S_N$ and $C_{D_F}$ should be somewhat smaller than for cylinders. Also, vortices may form relatively far downstream, thereby reducing the ratio of $\tilde{C}_L$ to $C_{D_F}$. For these reasons, the author believes that equations developed for bluff sections overestimate noise levels for airfoils and for rotating blades having airfoil sections by about 10 dB.

## 9.4 Noise from Fans and Blowers

### Noise Mechanisms

Noise spectra of fans and blowers are almost entirely produced by the oscillating-force mechanisms discussed in the previous two sections. Spectra of fans include both tonal and broadband components. Tonal components occur at multiples of blade passage frequency and are caused by flow assymmetries and rotor-stator interactions. Sources of broadband noise include wake vortex shedding, boundary-layer turbulence and blade operation in turbulent inflows. While there is good agreement throughout the literature on causes of tonal radiation, considerable controversy exists as to whether vortex shedding or boundary-layer turbulence is the dominant source of broadband noise when rotors operate under non-turbulent inflow conditions. Thus, Wells and Madison (1957) and Rimsky-Korsakov (1975) mentioned only vortex shedding, and Mugridge and Morfey (1972, 1973) discussed only boundary-layer turbulence. Sharland (1964) calculated levels from both sources and concluded that noise from vortex shedding is from 3 to 10 dB stronger than noise from boundary-layer turbulences. He also demonstrated that under turbulent inflow conditions blade interaction with incoming turbulence is the dominant broadband mechanism. Barry and Moore (1971) have noted that high shaft-rate harmonics caused by blade-to-blade variations also contribute to high-frequency broadband fan spectra.

### Spectra

The relative importance of tonal and broadband spectra versus overall spectrum shape depends strongly on the type of fan or blower. Fans are divided into two categories: axial and centrifugal. *Axial-flow fans*, often referred to as *propeller fans*, may operate against little or no static pressure, may be in housings or may be free standing. *Centrifugal fans and blowers* impart a radial motion to the fluid and operate against a significant static pressure drop. They operate at lower tip speeds and usually have more blades than axial-flow units. (Rotary positive displacement blowers, used to deliver small volumes of gas against high pressures, are not classed as fans.)

Blade passage frequencies of axial flow and centrifugal machines are generally in the same range, since axial machines have fewer blades but operate at higher rpm's. Typically, the fundamental blade frequency lies between 100 and 350 Hz. Some centrifugal blowers operate at speeds as high as 12,000 rpm and have blade tonals above 2 kHz. Blade tonals are usually the strongest components of the spectrum, being only about 4 to 8 dB lower than the overall level. Above the blade frequency, the spectra from centrifugal machines decrease quite markedly while those of axial-flow units are relatively flat. Figure 9.13 compares average octave-band spectra of the two types of fans. Exceptions to these spectra occur when excitation frequencies coincide with duct resonances, in which case strong peaks occur well above the blade fundamental.

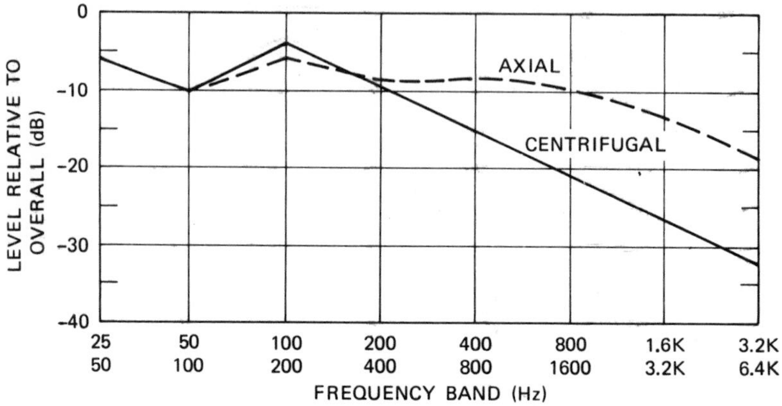


Fig. 9.13. Average Relative Spectra of Axial and Centrifugal Fans

## Noise Levels

Intensities from all of the fluctuating-force noise mechanisms discussed in the previous two sections were shown to vary as the sixth power of speed. Yet measurements of fan noise by Peistrup and Wesler (1953), Goldman and Maling (1959) and Sharland (1964) all show weaker dependence on speed, fifth power being typical. There are two major reasons for the discrepancy. First, blade tonals depend on inflow assymmetries caused by upstream stators and other structures. Such wakes tend to become less severe with increasing Reynolds number, thus causing $\widetilde{C}_L$ to decrease slightly with increasing speed. Secondly, the third-power dependence on Mach number found in Eq. 9.28 is valid only when acoustic wavelengths are large compared to the body experiencing the oscillating force, i.e., $kD < 1$. Lowson (1970) has shown that for $kD > 2$ the expressions previously derived for noise from fluctuating-force sources should be divided by 2 $kD$, where

$$kD = \frac{2\pi mBnD}{c_o} = 2mBM_t \quad . \tag{9.75}$$

It follows that at high frequencies and/or high tip speeds fan noise attributable to fluctuating forces should vary at a rate no greater than the fifth power of rotational speed.

Empirical scaling formulas given by Goldman and Maling (1955), Wells and Madison (1957) and Allen (1957) all agree on the fifth-power dependence of noise of a given fan on rpm. Taking into account the approximate cubic dependence of mechanical power on speed, it follows that the acoustic efficiency of a given fan varies as the square of its rpm. However, as noted by Beranek et al (1955), when fans operate near full speed, the acoustic efficiency is nearly constant. Within about ± 5 dB, they found

$$\eta_{ac} \doteq 1.5 \times 10^{-6} \tag{9.76}$$

for a number of *centrifugal fans* rated between 1 and 50 hp. Peistrup and Wesler found the acoustic efficiencies of *axial-flow fans* to be somewhat higher, being given by

$$\eta_{ac} \doteq 10^{-5} \ . \tag{9.77}$$

The difference is primarily attributable to higher operating tip Mach numbers of axial flow units.

Equations 9.76 and 9.77 give average values of acoustic conversion efficiencies for the two major classes of fans. As noted, fans with higher than normal tip speeds will be noisier and those with lower tip speeds will generally be quieter than the average. The importance of tip speed in controlling fan noise was recognized by Zinchenko (1957) who presented a formula for noise levels of centrifugal blowers as a function only of tip speed. This can be written

$$PWL \doteq 115 + 55 \log \frac{U_t}{100 \ m/s} \ , \tag{9.78}$$

where $PWL$ is acoustic power level in dB relative to $10^{-12}$ W.

A relation for centrifugal fan noise as a function only of horsepower was given by Beranek et al (1955) as

$$PWL \doteq 90 + 10 \log hp \ . \tag{9.79}$$

Allen (1957) found that fans make more noise when they operate against a higher static pressure, and Heidmann and Feiler (1974) found a strong correlation with temperature rise of the gas being moved. Thus, Allen suggested

$$PWL \doteq 86 + 10 \log hp + 10 \log \Delta p \tag{9.80}$$

for centrifugal fans, where $\Delta p$ is measured in cm of water, and Heidmann and Feiler's results can be expressed by

$$PWL \doteq 91 + 10 \log hp + 10 \log \Delta\theta \ , \tag{9.81}$$

where $\Delta\theta$ is temperature rise in degrees Centigrade. Other factors that affect fan noise include rotor-stator spacing and blade skew of axial fans and impeller clearance and blade slope of centrifugal fans, as discussed by Neise (1976).

**Positive Displacement Blowers**

Rotary positive displacement blowers of the Roots type are used extensively as scavenging blowers to supply air to two-stroke-cycle diesel engines. They consist of two, three or four intermeshing rotors that force air through a semicircular casing. In many instances they are the predominant source of engine room noise, as reported by Zinchenko (1957). Spectra from these units are dominated by harmonics of the rotor meshing frequency, given by twice the product of the rotational speed and the number of rotors. This may be as low as 30 Hz or as high as 400 Hz. While the fundamental is usually the strongest component, Priede (1966) found that each blower has bands of frequencies for which higher harmonics are enhanced; these bands appear to be related to cavity resonances of the unit. Priede also concluded that rotor tip speed and number of rotors are controlling parameters.

Rotary blowers are extremely noisy. Power levels of over 120 dB re $10^{-12}$ W are common and even levels as high as 140 dB are sometimes experienced. The noise is especially unpleasant since it is dominated by tonal components. Zinchenko suggested the use of large, low-speed units in order to lower the dominant frequencies and thereby reduce annoyance. He also proposed the use of multiple reflection intake mufflers to achieve at least 25 dB of noise reduction above 500 Hz.

## 9.5 Propeller Singing

Marine propellers sometimes emit strong tones between 100 and 1000 Hz. Known as *propeller singing*, this phenomenon has been recognized for about 50 years. Similar singing phenomena have also been observed in hydraulic turbines. The sound is sometimes so intense as to be very annoying, and blade vibrations associated with it are often strong enough to produce fatigue failure. For these reasons, early efforts by engineers were primarily aimed at eliminating the problem when it occurred, and more recent scientific investigations have been motivated by the desire to design blades that avoid singing altogether.

A notable characteristic of singing is its dependence on otherwise unimportant features. It is not uncommon for one propeller of a set of seemingly identical propellers to sing while others in the set do not. Most often only one blade of a propeller actually sings, and this occurs only during part of its revolution. Occasionally two blades sing, but at somewhat different frequencies. Since small physical differences determine whether or not a blade will sing, it is not surprising that the literature contains many apparently conflicting cures for this problem. Thus, sharpening of leading edges, sharpening of trailing edges and blunting of trailing edges have all been reported to eliminate singing in specific instances.

Early papers of Gutsche (1937), Hunter (1937), Kerr et al (1940) and Hughes (1945) attributed singing to a wide variety of possible causes, including cavitation, hammer-like blows of wake variations, stalling, shaft-bearing friction, and vortex shedding. Work (1951) described singing as "vibration of propeller blades excited by hydrodynamic forces." Gongwer (1952), Gutsche (1957) and Krivtsov and Pernik (1957) all confirmed the dominance of vortex shedding and it is now recognized that vortex shedding causes most cases of blade singing. Thus, Burrill (1946-1949) and Hughes (1949) found coincidence of singing frequencies with resonance frequencies of blade vibrations; Lankester and Wallace (1955) found that propeller sounds emitted in the absence of singing have a broad peak about an octave wide in the same region of the frequency spectrum where singing occurs; and Van de Voorde (1960) correlated singing susceptibility with trailing edge shape.

Current understanding of blade singing is based on the description of vortex shedding phenomena given in a previous section. Under normal operating conditions, each section of a propeller blade has a vortex wake, frequencies of which differ from section to section because of radial variations of both relative flow speed and trailing edge thickness. The sound emitted therefore covers a bandwidth of about a half octave to an octave and the intensity is within 10 dB of that given by Eq. 9.71. Each blade also has a large number of resonant vibrational frequencies, a few of which involve in-phase vibration of at least a quarter of the blade trailing edge. It is these vibrational modes that are excited most easily by forces applied along the trailing edge. If one of these easy-to-excite vibrational modes lies within the band of vortex shedding frequencies, then the trailing edge may start to vibrate. Vortices in the immediate vicinity would then also shed at this frequency, increasing the coherence length and consequently increasing both force and vibrational amplitude. The process would continue to build up until a large part of the blade would be participating and at this point certain non-linear effects would limit the motion. Ross (1964) estimated the intensity from singing by assuming that about 25% of a blade participates in the radiation, finding

$$I(\theta) \doteq \frac{3 \times 10^{-6}}{r^2} \rho_o U_t^3 D^2 M_t^3 \cos^2 \theta \ . \tag{9.82}$$

Figure 9.14 shows the vortex pattern of a blade during singing, the vortices having been made visible by cavitation.

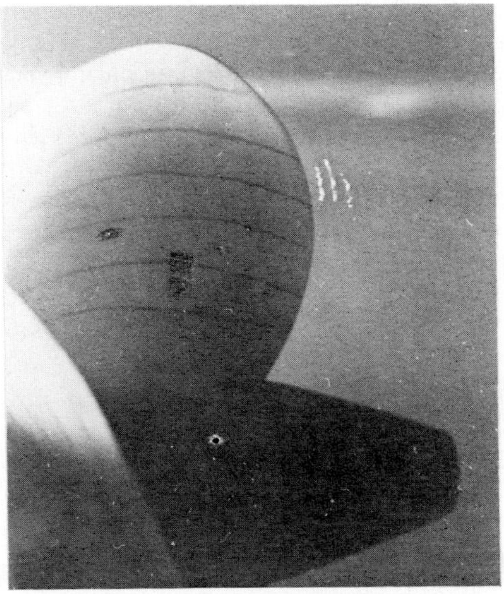

Fig. 9.14. Singing Propeller, as Photographed in Water Tunnel at Hamburg Shipbuilding Research Establishment

With this understanding of singing it is now clear why singing is such a critical phenomenon. Only a few vibrational modes of a blade can be readily excited by trailing edge excitation. One of these must coincide with a vortex shedding frequency. Any change of a blade that either changes natural frequencies or vortex shedding frequencies will probably eliminate singing. In this connection, it should be noted that blades with relatively straight trailing edges are more prone to singing than those with curved edges.

In a study of singing carried out in a water tunnel, Cumming (1965) found that the range of operating conditions over which singing is encountered is smaller than that for which singing can be maintained once it has started. He also confirmed that only a small fraction of blade vibrational modes is likely ever to be involved.

Apparently singing requires appreciable vibrational amplitudes. Therefore, one way to avoid singing is to reduce the resonant response by building blades of a high damping alloy or incorporating vibration damping treatments of the type described in Section 5.9. Arnold et al (1961) and Eagleson et al (1964) have developed theories for singing that include non-linear effects and demonstrate the importance of damping. Hughes (1949) noted that cavitation bubbles on a blade act to increase the damping by absorbing vibrational energy. This explains the rather common observation that singing ceases when cavitation becomes pronounced.

While very annoying when it occurs, singing is readily curable. Anti-singing trailing edges such as those described by Van de Voorde (1960) and Eagleson et al (1964) can be used and/or blades can be damped.

## 9.6 Flow-Excited Cavity Resonances

Another example of vortex sound that can attain very high levels and also cause fatigue failure is that of *flow-excited cavity resonances*. As discussed in Section 4.9, when certain conditions are met, vortices shed by flow past a cavity mouth may excite resonances of the cavity which act to further strengthen the vortex pattern and thereby produce intense pressures. The phenomenon is similar to singing in that a vortex motion is strengthened by a vibratory motion. Instead of a solid body the vibration is provided by a confined fluid, and instead of being relatively rare the phenomenon is quite common. An example is sound made by blowing across the mouth of a coke bottle.

Relations governing the frequency of vortex formation for rectangular cutouts are less straightforward than for cylinders. One complicating factor is that several vortices may exist in the mouth of a cavity. Another is that thickness of the boundary layer plays an important role in frequency of vortex formation. Figure 9.15 shows a rectangular cutout of length $L$ and depth $h$, showing that

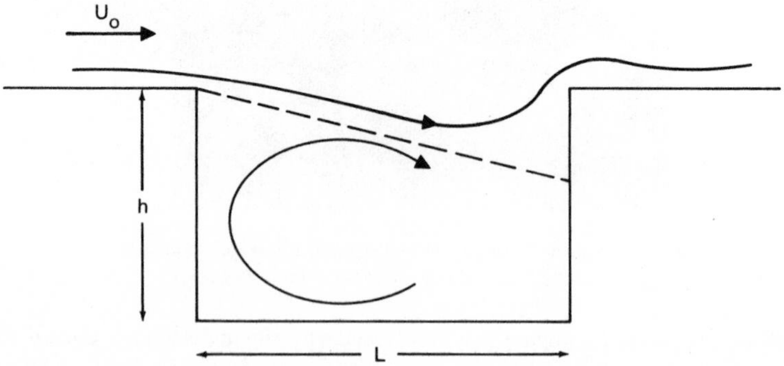


Fig. 9.15. Flow Past a Rectangular Cutout

a shear layer is produced between the outside and inside flows. This shear layer is unstable. According to Dunham (1962) and East (1966), the Strouhal number for vortex development obeys a relation of the form

$$S_N \equiv \frac{fL}{U_o} \doteq m \frac{\overline{u}_v}{U_o} \frac{L}{L - L_v} , \tag{9.83}$$

where $m$ is the number of simultaneous vortices, $\bar{u}_v$ is the average travel speed of a vortex in the shear layer, and $L_v$ is the formation distance of the first vortex. $S_N$ values of 0.3 to 0.6 are common.

East has shown that strong acoustic coupling exists when the frequency also satisfies the relation

$$\frac{fh}{c_o} \doteq \frac{0.25}{1 + \frac{2}{3}\frac{L}{h}} \qquad (9.84)$$

This may readily occur for flow of air past a cavity. In water, however, acoustic coupling can only be a factor if the cavity is very deep or $m$ very large. In water, coupling usually occurs with flexural resonances of the cavity walls, as explained by Dunham and discussed in Section 4.9.

Ingard and Dean (1958) measured intensity of sounds emitted by cavity resonators excited by vortex flows. They found that the sound at resonance increases as $U_o^5$. This compares with $U_o^2$ calculated by Blokhintsev (1945). However, Blokhintsev assumed very low level interaction of cavity resonances with vortex formation processes, as would occur at very low speeds, while the Ingard and Dean results are for strong coupling.

Several instances of very strong vortex-excited cavity resonances have been reported, the pressures in some cases being sufficient to cause fatigue cracking of tank walls. Cures are relatively simple, changing the shape of the mouth being the most obvious. If the opening is large enough, vanes can be used to break up the flow. Vortex generators similar to flow spoilers on aircraft wings can also be used to change the nature of the turbulent flow approaching the opening.

## REFERENCES

### Sections 9.1and 9.2


Blokhintsev, D.I., *Acoustics of Nonhomogeneous Moving Media* (in Russian), Leningrad, 1946; trans. in *N.A.C.A. Tech. Memo. 1399*, 1956 (Chapter 3).

Breslin, J.P., "Review and Extension of Theory for Near-Field Propeller-Induced Vibratory Effects," in *Proc. Fourth Symposium on Naval Hydrodynamics*, O.N.R., ACR-92, Washington, 1962 (pp. 603-640).

Breslin, J.P., Theoretical and experimental techniques for practical estimation of propeller-induced vibratory forces, *Trans. Soc. Naval Arch. and Mar. Engin., 78*, 23-40, 1970.

Brown, N.A., Periodic Propeller Forces in Nonuniform Flow, *M.I.T. Dept. of Naval Arch. and Mar. Engin. Rept. 64-7*, June 1964 (AD 605398).

Chandrashekhara, N., Tone radiation from axial flow fans running in turbulent flow, *J. Sound and Vibr., 18*, 533-543, 1971; *19*, 133-146, 1971.

Chertock, G., Forces on a submarine hull induced by the propeller, *J. Ship Res., 9*, 2, 122-130, 1965.

Cox, G.G. and Morgan, W.B., The use of theory in propeller design (of skewed propellers), *Marine Technology, 9*, 419-429, 1972.

Curle, N., The influence of solid boundaries upon aerodynamic sound, *Proc. Royal Soc. (London), A231*, 505-514, 1955.

Duncan, P.E. and Dawson, B., Reduction of interaction tones from axial flow fans by non-uniform distribution of the stator vanes, *J. Sound and Vibr., 38*, 357-371, 1975.

Fincher, H.M., Fan noise: the effect of a single upstream stator, *J. Sound and Vibr., 3*, 100-110, 1966.

Fitzpatrick, H.M. and Strasberg, M., "Hydrodynamic Sources of Sound," Paper 10 in *Symposium on Naval Hydrodynamics*, Nat. Acad. of Sci., Nat. Res. Council Publ. 515, Washington, 1956 (pp. 264-280); also, *D.T.M.B. Rept. 1269*, Jan. 1959.

Goldstein, M., Unified approach to aerodynamic sound generation in the presence of solid boundaries, *J.A.S.A., 56*, 497-509, 1974.

Griffiths, J.W.R., The spectrum of compressor noise of a jet engine, *J. Sound and Vibr., 1*, 127-140, 1964.

Gutin, L. Ya., On the sound field of a rotating propeller, *J. Tech. Phys. (U.S.S.R.), 6*, 899-909, 1936; trans. in *N.A.C.A. Tech. Memo. 1195*, 1948.

Hadler, J.B., Ruscus, P. and Kopko, W., "Correlation of Model and Full-Scale Propeller Alternating Thrust Forces on Submerged Bodies," in *Proc. Fourth Symposium on Naval Hydrodynamics*, O.N.R., ACR-92, Washington, 1962 (pp. 641-675).

Hadler, J.B. and Cheng, H.M., Analysis of experimental data in way of propeller plane of single and twin-screw ship models, *Trans. Soc. Naval Arch. and Mar. Engin., 73*, 287-414, 1965.

Hanson, D.B., Unified analysis of fan stator noise, *J.A.S.A., 54*, 1571-1591, 1973.

Hanson, D.B., Spectrum of rotor noise caused by inlet guide vane wakes, *J.A.S.A., 55*, 1247-1251, 1974.

Homicz, G.F. and George, A.R., Broadband and discrete frequency radiation from subsonic rotors, *J. Sound and Vibr., 36*, 151-177, 1974.

Jacobs, W.R., Mercier, J. and Tsakonas, S., Theory and measurements of the propeller-induced vibratory pressure field, *J. Ship Res., 16*, 124-139, 1972.

Kemp, N.H. and Sears, W.R., Aerodynamic interference between moving blade rows, *J. Aero. Sci., 20*, 585-598, 1953.

Kemp, N.H. and Sears, W.R., The unsteady forces due to viscous wakes in turbomachines, *J. Aero. Sci., 22*, 478-483, 1955.

Lewis, F.M., Propeller vibration forces, *Trans. Soc. Naval Arch. and Mar. Engin., 71*, 293-326, 1963.

Lewis, F.M., "Hull Vibration of Ships," in *Principles of Naval Architecture*, J.P. Comstock (Ed.), Soc. Naval Arch. & Mar. Engin., New York, 1967 (pp. 718-751).

Lowson, M.V., Reduction of compressor noise radiation, *J.A.S.A., 43*, 37-50, 1968.

Lowson, M.V., Theoretical analysis of compressor noise, *J.A.S.A., 47*, 371-385, 1970; also, *N.A.S.A. Contractor Rept. CR-1287*, March 1969.

Mani, R., Noise due to interaction of inlet turbulence with isolated stators and rotors, *J. Sound and Vibr., 17*, 251-260, 1971.

Mather, J.S.B., Savidge, J. and Fisher, M.F., New observations on tone generation in fans, *J. Sound and Vibr., 16*, 407-418, 1971.

Mellin, R.C. and Sovran, G., Controlling the tonal characteristics of the aerodynamic noise generated by fan rotors, *J. Basic Engin., 92D*, 143-154, 1970.

Morfey, C.L., "A Review of the Sound-Generating Mechanisms in Aircraft-Engine Fans and Compressors," in *Aerodynamic Noise*, H.S. Ribner (Ed.), Univ. of Toronto Press, Toronto, 1968 (pp. 299-329).

Morfey, C.L., Sound generation in subsonic turbomachinery, *J. Basic Engin., 92D*, 450-458, 1970.

Morfey, C.L., Rotating blades and aerodynamic sound, *J. Sound and Vibr., 28*, 587-617, 1973.

Morse, P.M. and Ingard, K.U., *Theoretical Acoustics*, McGraw-Hill, New York, 1968 (Sections 7.3, 7.4 and 11.3).

Mugridge, B.D. and Morfey, C.L., Sources of noise in axial flow fans, *J.A.S.A., 51*, 1411-1426, 1972.

Mugridge, B.D., "Broadband Noise Generation by Airfoils and Axial Flow Fans," in *Aeroacoustics: Fan, STOL, and Boundary Layer Noise; Sonic Boom; Aeroacoustic Instrumentation*, H.T. Nagamatsu (Ed.), Vol. 38 of *Progress of Astronautics and Aeronautics Series*, M.I.T. Press, Cambridge, Mass., 1974 (pp. 3-14).

Phillips, O.M., The intensity of Aeolian tones, *J. Fluid Mech., 1*, 607-624, 1956.

Pinkus, O., Lurye, J.R. and Karp, S., The unsteady forces due to propeller-appendage interaction, *J. Appl. Mech., 30*, 279-287, 1963; also in *Proc. Fourth Symposium on Naval Hydrodynamics*, O.N.R., ACR-92, Washington, 1962 (pp. 677-710).

Richards, E.J. and Mead, D.J. (Ed.), *Noise and Acoustic Fatigue in Aeronautics*, Wiley, London, 1968 (Chapters 5, 9 and 10).

Sears, W.R., Some aspects of non-stationary airfoil theory and its practical application, *J. Aero. Sci., 8*, 104-108, 1941.

Sharland, I.J., Sources of noise in axial flow fans, *J. Sound and Vibr., 1*, 302-322, 1964.

Simons, I.A., Some aspects of blade/vortex interaction on helicopter rotors in forward flight, *J. Sound and Vibr., 4*, 268-281, 1966.

Sretenskii, L.N., Sound radiation by a rotating dipole, *Sov. Phys.-Acoustics, 2*, 89-94, 1956.

Stern, R. and Ross, D., The Calculation of Alternating Forces of Wake-Operating Propellers, *Bolt Beranek and Newman, Inc. Rept. 1133*, July 1964.

Tsakonas, S., Braslin, J.P. and Jen, N., Pressure field around a marine propeller operating in a wake, *J. Ship Res., 6*, 4, 11-25, 1963; also, *Stevens Inst. Technol. Davidson Lab. Rept. 857*, 1962.

Tsakonas, S., Chen, C.Y. and Jacobs, W.R., Acoustic radiation of a cylindrical bar and an infinite plate excited by the field of a ship propeller, *J.A.S.A., 36*, 1569-1588, 1708-1718, 1964; also, *Stevens Inst. Technol. Davidson Lab. Rept. 888*, July 1963.

Tsakonas, S. and Breslin, J.P., Longitudinal blade-frequency force induced by a propeller on a prolate spheroid, *J. Ship Res., 8*, 4, 13-22, 1965.

Tsakonas, S. and Jacobs, W.R., Unsteady lifting-surface theory for a marine propeller of low pitch angle with chordwise load distribution, *J. Ship Res., 9*, 79-101, 1965; also, *Stevens Inst. Technol. Davidson Lab. Rept. 994*, Jan. 1964.

Tsakonas, S., Breslin, J.P. and Miller, M., Correlation and application of an unsteady flow theory for propeller forces, *Trans. Soc. Naval Arch. and Mar. Engin., 75*, 158-193, 1967.

van Gent, W., and van Oossanen, P., Influence of wake on propeller loading and cavitation, *Int. Shipbuilding Progress, 20*, 279-321, 1973.

von Karman, T. and Sears, W.R., Airfoil theory for non-uniform motion, *J. Aero. Sci., 5*, 379-390, 1938.

Widnall, S., Helicopter noise due to blade-vortex interaction, *J.A.S.A., 50*, 354-365, 1971.

Wright, S.E., Sound radiation from a lifting rotor generated by asymmetric disk loading, *J. Sound and Vibr., 9*, 223-240, 1969.

Wright, S.E., Discrete radiation from rotating periodic sources, *J. Sound and Vibr., 17*, 437-498, 1971.

Yudin, E. Ya., On the vortex sound from rotating rods, *J. Tech. Phys. (U.S.S.R.), 14*, 561-565, 1944; trans. in *N.A.C.A. Tech. Memo. 1136*, 1947.

## Section 9.3

Abernathy, F.H., Flow over an inclined flat plate, *J. Basic Engin., 84D*, 380-388, 1962.

Abernathy, F.H. and Kronauer, R.E., The formation of vortex streets, *J. Fluid Mech., 13*, 1-20, 1962.

Ballou, C.L., Investigation of the Wake Behind a Cylinder, *M.I.T. Acoustics and Vibr. Lab. Rept. 76028-2*, 1967.

Bearman, P.W., On vortex street wakes, *J. Fluid Mech., 28*, 625-641, 1967.

Bearman, P.W., On vortex shedding from a circular cylinder in the critical Reynolds number range, *J. Fluid Mech., 37*, 577-585, 1969.

Berger, E. and Wille, R., Periodic flow phenomena, *Ann. Rev. Fluid Mech., 4*, 313-340, 1972.

Birkhoff, G.D., Formation of vortex streets, *J. Appl. Phys., 24*, 98-103, 1953.

Birkhoff, G.D. and Zarantonello, E.H., *Jets, Wakes and Cavities*, Academic Press, New York, 1957 (Chapter 13).

Blake, W.K., Aerodynamic pressures on vortex-shedding struts, Paper U7, 90th Meeting A.S.A., *J.A.S.A., 58*, S37, 1975.

Blokhintsev, D.I., *op. cit.* Chapter 4.

Blyumina, L.K. and Fedyaevskii, K.K., Periodic shedding of vortices from the surface of a cylinder and the forces caused by these vortices for supercritical flow conditions, *Fluid Dynamics, 3*, 3, 67-70, 1968.

Chen, Y.N., Fluctuating lift forces of the Karman vortex streets on single circular cylinders, *J. Engin. for Industry, 94B*, 603-622, 1972.

Cumpsty, N.A. and Whitehead, D.S., The excitation of acoustic resonances by vortex shedding, *J. Sound and Vibr., 18*, 353-369, 1971.

Curle, N., The mechanics of edge tones, *Proc. Royal Soc. (London), A216*, 412-424, 1953.

Delany, N.K. and Sorensen, N.E., Low-Speed Drag of Cylinders of Various Shapes, *N.A.C.A. Tech. Note 3038*, 1953.

Dittrich, W., Radiation from aerodynamic dipole sources, *Acustica, 29*, 79-85, 1973 (in German).

Donaldson, R.M., Hydraulic-turbine runner vibrations, *Trans. A.S.M.E., 78*, 1141-1147, 1956.

el Baroudi, M.Y., Measurement of Two-Point Correlations of Velocity Near a Circular Cylinder Shedding a Karman Vortex Street, *Univ. of Toronto Inst. of Aero. Tech. Note 31*, Jan. 1960.

Etkin, B., Korbacher, G.K. and Keefe, R.T., Acoustic radiation from a stationary cylinder in a fluid stream, *J.A.S.A., 29*, 30-36, 1957; also, *Univ. of Toronto Inst. of Aero. Rept. 39*, May 1956.

Fage, A. and Johansen, F.C., On the flow of air about an inclined flat plate, *Proc. Royal Soc. (London), A116*, 170-197, 1927; also, *Aero, Res. Com. R. and M. 1104*, 1927.

Fage, A. and Johansen, F.C., The structure of vortex sheets, *Phil. Mag., 5*, 417-441, 1928; also, *Aero. Res. Com. R. and M. 1143*, 1927.

Fung, Y.C., Fluctuating lift and drag acting on a cylinder in a flow at supercritical Reynolds numbers, *Shock and Vibration Bulletin, 2*, 147-170, Dec. 1958; also, *J. Aero. Sci., 27*, 801-814, 1960.

Gerrard, J.H., Measurements of the sound from circular cylinders in an air stream, *Proc. Phys. Soc. London, 64B*, 453-461, 1955.

Gerrard, J.H., An experimental investigation of the oscillating lift and drag of a circular cylinder shedding turbulent vortices, *J. Fluid Mech., 11*, 244-256, 1961.

Gerrard, J.H., Three-dimensional structure of vortex wakes of circular cylinders and bluff bodies, *J. Fluid Mech., 25*, 143-164, 401-413, 1966.

Goldstein, S. (Ed.), *Modern Developments in Fluid Dynamics*, Vol. 2, Clarendon Press, Oxford, 1938 (Chapter 13).

Gongwer, C.A., A study of vanes singing in water, *J. Appl. Mech., 19*, 432-438, 1952.

Graham, J.M.R. and Maull, D.J., The effects of an oscillating flap and an acoustic resonance on vortex shedding, *J. Sound and Vibr., 18*, 371-380, 1971.

Griffin, O.M., Skop, R.A. and Koopmann, G.H., The vortex-excited resonant vibrations of circular cylinders, *J. Sound and Vibr., 31*, 235-249, 1973.

Hama, F.R., Three-dimensional vortex pattern behind a circular cylinder, *J. Aero. Sci., 24*, 156-158, 1957.

Heskestad, G. and Olberts, D.R., Influence of trailing-edge geometry on hydraulic-turbine-blade vibration resulting from vortex excitation, *J. Engin. for Power, 82A*, 103-110, 1960.

Holle, W., Frequency and intensity measurements of vortex tones, *Akust. Zeits., 3*, 321-331, 1938 (in German).

Humphreys, J.S., On a circular cylinder in a steady wind at transition Reynolds numbers, *J. Fluid Mech., 9*, 603-612, 1960.

Itaya, S. and Yasuda, Y., Experiments on Strouhal's number, *Bul. Japan Soc. Mech. Engin., 4*, 274-277, 1961.

Keefe, R.T., Investigation of the fluctuating forces acting on a stationary circular cylinder in a subsonic stream and the associated sound field, *J.A.S.A., 34*, 1711-1714, 1962; also, *Univ. of Toronto Inst. of Aero. Rept. 76*, Sept. 1961.

Koopmann, G.H., The vortex wakes of vibrating cylinders at low Reynolds numbers, *J. Fluid Mech., 28*, 501-512, 1967.

Krzywoblocki, M.Z., Investigation of the wing-wake frequency with application of the Strouhal number, *J. Aero. Sci., 12*, 51-62, 1945.

Leehey, P. and Hanson, C.E., Aeolian tones associated with resonant vibration, *J. Sound and Vibr., 13*, 465-483, 1970; also, *M.I.T. Acoustics and Vibr. Lab. Rept. 76234-4*, June 1969.

Lehnert, R., Acoustic measurements of vortex streets behind cylinders and flat plates, *Physik. Zeits., 38*, 476-498, 1937 (in German).

Marris, A.W., A review on vortex streets, periodic wakes and induced vibration phenomena, *J. Basic Engin., 86D*, 185-196, 1964.

McGregor, D.M. and Etkin, B., Investigation of the fluctuating pressures on a circular cylinder in an airstream, *Phys. of Fluids, 1*, 162-164, 1958.

Milne-Thomson, L.M., *Theoretical Hydrodynamics*, 2nd Edit., Macmillan, New York, 1950 (Chapter 13).

Parker, R., Resonance effects in wake shedding from parallel plates, *J. Sound and Vibr., 4*, 62-76, 1966; *5*, 330-343, 1967; *6*, 302-309, 1967; *7*, 371-379, 1968.

Parker, R., The effect of the acoustic properties of the environment on vibration of a flat plate subject to direct excitation and to excitation by vortex shedding in an airstream, *J. Sound and Vibr., 20*, 93-112, 1972.

Parker, R. and Llewelyn, D., Flow induced vibration of cantilever-mounted flat plates in enclosed passage, *J. Sound and Vibr., 25*, 451-463, 1972.

Petrie, A.M., Effect of free-stream turbulence on vortex shedding in the wakes of cylinders in cross flow, *J. Sound and Vibr., 34*, 287-290, 1974.

Phillips, O.M., The intensity of aeolian tones, *J. Fluid Mech., 1*, 607-624, 1956.

Powell, A., On edge tones and associated phenomena, *Acustica, 3*, 233-243, 1953.

Powell, A., On the edge tone, *J.A.S.A., 33*, 395-409, 1961.

Powell, A., Theory of vortex sound, *J.A.S.A., 36*, 177-195, 1964.

Prendergast, V., Measurement of Two-Point Correlations of the Surface Pressure on a Circular Cylinder, *Univ. of Toronto Inst. of Aero. Tech. Note 23*, July 1958.

Rayleigh, Lord, Aeolian tones, *Phil. Mag., 29*, 433-444, 1915; in *Collected Works*, Vol. 6, Dover, New York, 1964 (pp. 315-325).

Relf, E.F., On the sound emitted by wires of circular section when exposed to an air current, *Phil. Mag., 42*, 173-176, 1921.

Relf, E.F. and Simmons, L.F.G., The frequency of the eddies generated by the motion of circular cylinders through a fluid, *Phil. Mag., 49*, 509-511, 1925; also, *Aero. Res. Com. R. and M. 917*, 1924.

Richardson, E.G., Aeolian tones, *Proc. Phys. Soc. London, 36*, 153-167, 1924.

Richardson, E.G., Edge tones, *Proc. Phys. Soc. London, 43B*, 394-404, 1931.

Richardson, E.G., The flow and sound field near a cylinder towed through water, *Appl. Sci. Res., A7*, 341-350, 1957.

Rimsky-Korsakov, A.V., Aerodynamic noise sources, *J. Sound and Vibr., 43*, 199-209, 1975.

Roshko, A., On the Development of Turbulent Wakes from Vortex Streets, *N.A.C.A. Tech. Rept. 1191*, 1954.

Roshko, A., On the wake and drag of bluff bodies, *J. Aero. Sci., 22*, 124-132, 1955; also, *N.A.C.A. Tech. Note 3169*, July 1954.

Roshko, A., Experiments on the flow past a circular cylinder at very high Reynolds number, *J. Fluid Mech., 10*, 345-356, 1961.

Ross, D., Vortex-Shedding Sounds of Propellers, *Bolt, Beranek and Newman Inc. Rept. 1115*, March 1964.

Ruedy, R., Vibrations of power lines in a steady wind, *Canadian J. Res., 13*, 82-92, 1935.

Sallet, D.W., On the spacing of Karman vortices, *J. Appl. Mech., 36*, 370-372, 1969.

Stowell, E.Z. and Deming, A.F., Noise from rotating cylindrical rods, *J.A.S.A., 7*, 190-198, 1936; also, *N.A.C.A. Tech. Note 519*, 1935.

Strouhal, V., Über eine besondere Art der Tonerregung, *Annalen der Physik u. Chemie, 5*, 216-251, 1878.

Tam, C.K.W., Discrete tones of isolated airfoils, *J.A.S.A., 55*, 1173-1177, 1974.

Taneda, S., Oscillation of the wake behind a flat plate parallel to the flow, *J. Phys. Soc. Japan, 13*, 418-425, 1958.

Toebes, G.H. and Eagleson, P.S., Hydroelastic vibrations of flat plates related to trailing edge geometry, *J. Basic Engin., 83D*, 671-678, 1961; also, *M.I.T. Hydro. Lab. Tech. Rept. 36*, April 1960.

Tyler, E., Vortices behind aerofoil sections and rotating cylinders, *Phil. Mag., 5*, 449-463, 1928.

Vickery, B.J., Fluctuating lift and drag of a long cylinder of square cross-section in a smooth and in a turbulent stream, *J. Fluid Mech., 25*, 481-494, 1966.

von Karman, T. and Rubach, H., On the mechanisms of lift and drag, *Physik. Zeits., 13*, 49-59, 1912 (in German).

von Karman, T. and Sears, W.R., *op. cit.* (1938).

Wille, R., Karman vortex streets, *Advances in Fluid Mech., 6*, 273-287, 1960.

Yudin, E.Y., Investigation of Vortex Sound, *Central Aero. Hydro. Inst. Rept.*, 1942 (in Russian).

Yudin, E.Y., On the vortex sound from rotating rods, *J. Tech. Phys. (U.S.S.R.), 14*, 561, 1944; trans. in *N.A.C.A. Tech. Memo. 1136*, 1947.

## Section 9.4

Allen, C.H., Noise from air-conditioning fans, *Noise Control, 3*, 1, 28-34, 1957.

Barry, B. and Moore, C.J., Subsonic fan noise, *J. Sound and Vibr., 17*, 207-220, 1971.

Beranek, L.L., Kamperman, G.W. and Allen, C.H., Noise of centrifugal fans, *J.A.S.A., 27*, 217-219, 1955.

Goldman, R.B. and Maling, G.C., Noise from small centrifugal fans, *Noise Control, 1*, 6, 26-29, 50, 1955; *4*, 248, 1959.

Heidmann, M.F. and Feiler, C.E., "Noise Comparisons from Full-Scale Fan Tests," in *Aeroacoustics: Fan, STOL, and Boundary Layer Noise; Sonic Boom; Aeroacoustic Instrumentation*, H.T. Nagamatsu (Ed.), Vol. 38 of *Progress in Astronautics and Aeronautics Series*, M.I.T. Press, Cambridge, Mass., 1974 (pp. 15-34).

Jeannon, J.M. and Cockrell, D.J., Acoustic radiation of rotary positive displacement machinery, *J. Sound and Vibr., 39*, 181-193, 1975.

Lowson, M.V., *op. cit.* (1970).

Maling, G.C., Dimensional analysis of blower noise, *J.A.S.A., 35*, 1556-1564, 1963.

Mugridge, B.D. and Morfey, C.L., *op. cit.* (1972).

Mugridge, B.D., *op. cit.* (1973).

Neise, W., Application of similarity laws to the blade passage sound of centrifugal fans, *J. Sound and Vibr., 43*, 61-75, 1975.

Neise, W., Noise reduction in centrifugal fans: a literature survey, *J. Sound and Vibr., 45*, 375-403, 1976.

Parmakian, J., "Vibration and Noise in Hydraulic Turbines and pumps," in *Vibrations in Hydraulic Pumps and Turbines, Proc. Inst. Mech. Engin., 181, 3A*, 74-83, 1966.

Peistrup, C.F. and Wesler, J.E., Noise of ventilating fans, *J.A.S.A., 25*, 313-321, 1953.

Priede, T., "Rotary Positive Displacement Blower Noise," Paper 11 in *Noise from Power Plant Equipment, Proc. Inst. Mech. Engin., 181(3C)*, 90-105, 1966; also, Paper F62, *Fifth International Congress on Acoustics*, Liege, Belgium, 1965.

Richards, E.J. and Mead, D.J. (Ed.), *op. cit.* Chapter 10.

Rimsky-Korsakov, A.V., *op. cit.* (1975).

Sharland, I.J., *op. cit.* (1964).

Simpson, H.C., Clark, T.A. and Weir, G.A., A theoretical investigation of hydraulic noise in pumps, *J. Sound and Vibr., 5*, 456-488, 1967; *6*, 281-282, 1967.

Smith, M.J.T. and House, M.E., Internally generated noise from gas turbine engine, *J. Engin. for Power, 89A*, 177-190, 1967.

Wells, R.J. and Madison, R.D., "Fan Noise," Chapter 25 of *Handbook of Noise Control*, C.M. Harris (Ed.), McGraw-Hill, New York, 1957.

Wright, S.E., The acoustic spectrum of axial flow machines, *J. Sound and Vibr., 45*, 165-223, 1976.

Zinchenko, V.I., *Noise of Marine Diesel Engines*, Sudpromgiz, Leningrad, 1957 (in Russian); digested in *Bolt, Beranek and Newman Inc. T.I.R. 61*, July 1962 (Chapter 2).

## Sections 9.5 and 9.6

Arnold, L., Lane, F. and Slutsky, S., Propeller Singing Analysis, *Gen. Appl. Sci. Labs. Inc. Tech. Rept. 221*, Jan. 1961 (AD 257424).

Blokhintsev, D.I., Excitation of resonators by a stream of air, *J. Tech. Phys. (U.S.S.R.), 15*, 63-68, 1945; trans. in *D.T.M.B. Trans. 270*, 1957.

Brown, A.E., Experimental study of singing vanes, *Acustica, 10*, 380-384, 1960.

Burrill, L.C., Marine Propeller blade vibrations, *Trans. N.E. Coast Inst. Engin. and Shipbuilders, 62*, 249-270, 1946; *63*, 119-138, 1947; *65*, 301-314, 1949.

Cumming, R.A., A Preliminary Study of Vortex-Induced Propeller-Blade Vibrations and Singing, *D.T.M.B. Rept. 1838*, Sept. 1965.

Dunham, W.H., "Flow-Induced Cavity Resonance in Viscous Compressible and Incompressible Fluids," in *Proc. Fourth Symposium on Naval Hydrodynamics*, O.N.R., ACR-92, Washington, 1962 (pp. 1057-1081).

Eagleson, P.S., Noutsopolous, G.K. and Daily, J.W., The nature of self-excitation in the flow-induced vibration of flat plates, *J. Basic Engin., 86D*, 599-601, 1964; also, *M.I.T. Hydro. Lab. Rept. 58*, Feb. 1963.

East, L.F., Aerodynamically induced resonance in rectangular cavities, *J. Sound and Vibr., 3*, 277-287, 1966.

Gongwer, C.A., *op. cit.* (1952).

Gutsche, F., The singing of ship propellers, *V.D.I. Zeits, 81*, 882-883, 1937; and *Schiffbau, 38*, 110-113, 1937; trans. in *D.T.M.B. Trans. 123*, 1943.

Gutsche, F., Resonant frequencies and vibrations of ship propellers, *Schiff u. Hafen, 9*, 166-175, 1957 (in German).

Hughes, G., On singing propellers, *Trans. Inst. Naval Arch., 87*, 185-208, 1945.

Hughes, W.L., Propeller blade vibrations, *Trans. N.E. Coast Inst. Engin. and Shipbuilders, 65*, 273-300, 1949.

Hunter, H., Singing propellers, *Trans. N.E. Coast Inst. Engin. and Shipbuilders, 53*, 189-222, 1937; also, *J. Amer. Soc. Naval Engin., 49*, 258-262, 1937.

Ingard, U. and Dean, L.W., "Excitation of Acoustic Resonators by Flow," in *Proc. Second Symposium on Naval Hydrodynamics*, O.N.R., ACR-38, Washington, 1958 (pp. 137-150).

Kerr, W., Shannon, J.F. and Arnold, R.N., The problem of the singing propeller, *Proc. Inst. Mech. Engin., 144*, 54-76, 1940.

Krishnamurty, K., Acoustic Radiation from Two-Dimensional Rectangular Cutouts in Aerodynamic Surfaces, *N.A.C.A. Tech. Note 3487*, 1955.

Krivtsov, Y.V. and Pernik, A.J., The singing of propellers, *Sudostroeniye, 7*, 10, 1957; trans. in *D.T.M.B. Trans. 281*, 1958.

Kubanskii, P.N., On the theory of vortex formations in the vicinity of a resonator subjected to streaming air, *Sov. Phys.-Acoustics, 5*, 331-338, 1959.

Lankester, S.G. and Wallace, W.D., Some investigations into singing propellers, *Trans. N.E. Coast Inst. of Engin. and Shipbuilders, 71*, 291-318, 1955.

Roshko, A., Some Measurements of Flow in a Rectangular Cutout, *N.A.C.A. Tech. Note 3488*, 1955.

Ross, D., *op. cit.* (1964).

Van de Voorde, C.B., The singing of ship propellers, *Int. Shipbuilding Progress, 7*, 451-455, 1960.

Work, C.E., Singing propellers, *J. Amer. Soc. Naval Engin., 63*, 319-331, 1951.

# CHAPTER 10

# MECHANICAL NOISE SOURCES

The noise sources described in Chapters 3, 4, 7, 8 and 9 have been predominantly hydrodynamic. The present chapter discusses basic mechanisms by which mechanical sources generate structure-borne vibrations, the transmission and radiation of which were covered in Chapters 5 and 6. Phenomena such as mechanical unbalance, electromagnetic force fluctuation, impact and friction are often the mechanisms whereby noise is generated by turbines, motors, transformers, gears and reciprocating machines.

No useful mechanical process can occur without generating vibration. Small unsteadinesses associated with work-producing forces and torques produce vibrations which are ultimately transmitted to radiating surfaces and are therefore sources of noise. We are concerned here with the production of these vibrations. Although most data available on machinery noise are for airborne noise levels, the same functional relations may be expected to apply for underwater sound.

## 10.1 Mechanical Unbalances

Motions in machines are either rotating or reciprocating. Each generates a different type of mechanical unbalance.

### Rotational Unbalances

All rotational systems have slight amounts of static and dynamic mechanical unbalance due to imperfection of materials or construction, load and thermal distortions and/or bearing misalignments. As discussed by Klyukin (1961), *static unbalance* can be represented by a displacement of the center of gravity of a rotor from the center of rotation, and *dynamic unbalance* can be represented by two unbalanced masses lying in separate transverse planes. The resultant fluctuating force and moment are both proportional to the square of the *angular speed*, $\omega = 2\pi n$, where $n$ is rotational speed in rps. Unbalance forces and moments are transmitted through bearings to the frame and foundation. Since vibratory velocities are proportional to the forces causing them and acoustic pressures are proportional to vibratory velocities of radiating surfaces, it follows that for a given machine the sound power radiated from mechanical unbalances increases as the fourth power of rotational speed. Thus,

$$W_{ac} \sim p^2 \sim (\Delta F)^2 \sim (m\omega^2)^2 \sim m^2 n^4 \ . \qquad (10.1)$$

Since the useful mechanical power of a rotational machine increases as the cube of its rotational speed, it follows that for a given machine

$$\eta_{ac} \equiv \frac{W_{ac}}{W_{mech}} \sim \frac{n^4}{n^3} \sim n \ . \qquad (10.2)$$

This result can also be expressed by

$$PWL = A + 13.3 \log hp \quad , \tag{10.3}$$

where the constant $A$ depends on type of machine, amount of unbalance, foundation system, degree of isolation and nature of radiating surface, and $hp$ is the horsepower which the machine is capable of delivering at the speed at which it is being operated. Although derived for unbalance forces of a single machine, Eq. 10.3 has been found to be generally applicable for centrifugal pumps and other types of rotating machinery. Individual machines vary considerably from one another due to differences in degree of balance.

Radiated spectra attributable to rotational unbalances are dominated by single tones at rotational frequencies, the bandwidths of which are determined by stability of the power source and of the rotational speed. Slight motions within the bearings distort the normal sine wave and cause strengthening of alternate cycles, thus producing weak second harmonics as well as tones at subharmonics. In addition, rotational unbalances may modulate other spectral components such as blade-rate tonals of fans and pumps and contact frequencies of gears. The result is radiation of high-order harmonics of shaft frequency centered around these other components.

**Reciprocating Unbalances**

Machines characterized by reciprocating motions of pistons in cylinders that transmit forces to crank shafts through connecting rods generally create large unbalance forces and moments. Entire texts such as that of Biezeno and Grammel (1954) are devoted to calculation of the forces and moments produced by these machines and to methods of reducing such unbalances. Reciprocating unbalance forces and moments occur at low-order harmonics of crank rotational speed. As noted by Lewis (1961), different physical arrangements and cylinder phase angles produce different strengths of the various harmonics, and some of the stronger components may be balanced by judicious placement of counterweights.

Figure 10.1 depicts a single cylinder of a reciprocating machine showing attachment of a piston to a crank shaft by means of a connecting rod. Variations of cylinder gas pressure, of

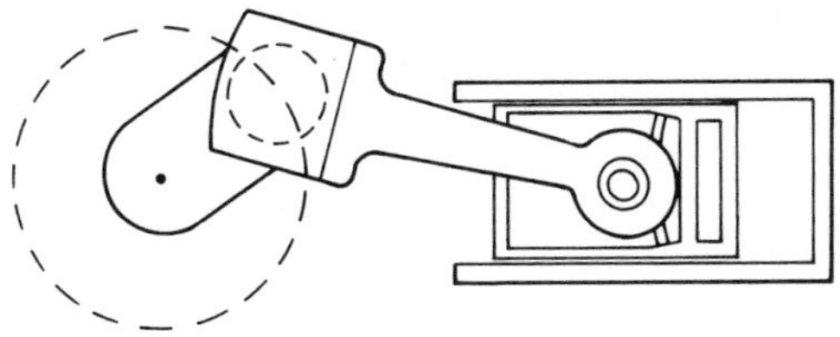

Fig. 10.1. Single Cylinder of Reciprocating Machine

inertial forces of the moving parts and of the crank angle cause cyclical fluctuations of torques and forces. These can be smoothed by using multiple cylinders with their connection points to the crank shaft equally spaced around a circle. However, their longitudinal spatial separation results in net fluctuating moments applied to the foundation.

A number of different arrangements have been developed for multiple cylinder units, including in-line, vee, opposed-piston and radial. Each of these has advantages and disadvantages; the radial arrangement is probably best from the point of view of static and dynamic balance. However, although dynamic unbalance is often an important source of annoying low-frequency vibrations, it is seldom a dominant noise source of reciprocating machinery.

## 10.2 Electromagnetic Force Fluctuations

Most modern electrical equipment and machinery used on ships are relatively quiet compared to other types of machinery. Electric motors are seldom as noisy as the pumps, compressors and blowers they drive, though they may occasionally be notable noise sources. In the 1930's, however, motor noise was often severe, and extensive research on this subject was carried out at that time. The present brief discussion is included because failure to recognize and understand electromagnetic force fluctuations could result in return to the earlier situation.

### Magnetostriction

When most materials are magnetized, they change dimensions slightly due to re-alignment of elementary magnets. The iron cores of a.c. magnetic systems experience such dimensional changes during each half cycle of voltage. Consequently, their surfaces vibrate at twice power-line frequency. Due to non-linear and hysteresis effects vibration is not a pure sinusoid but contains higher-order harmonics. The resultant spectra consist of several harmonics of twice the power-line frequency; the fundamental is usually strongest, producing *transformer hum*. If a resonant frequency of the housing should coincide with one of the harmonics, then that frequency will also radiate strongly.

Articles on the causes and cures of transformer magnetostrictive vibrations and noise have been written by Churcher and King (1940), Swaffield (1942), King (1957, 1965), Thompson (1963) and Wilkins (1966). They agree that noise increases with flux density and weight of iron and that the best material is 6% silicon iron in hot-rolled laminations. Thompson has also found that deviations from uniform lamination thickness increase noise. Although magnetostrictive vibrations also occur in rotating a.c. machinery, Alger (1954), Fehr and Muster (1957) and Campbell (1963) have found that this effect is small compared to vibrations at the same frequencies caused by magnetic force variations.

### Magnetic Force Variations

Two distinct types of magnetic force fluctuation occur in a.c. motors. Low-frequency noise similar to transformer hum occurs at twice the line frequency and is independent of rotational speed. High-frequency noise occurs at frequencies related to rotor speed and to the number of armature segments, or teeth.

*Low-frequency vibrations and noise* arise from fluctuations of the radial attractive force between stator and rotor. This force is proportional to the square of the instantaneous flux density and so goes through a complete zero-maximum-zero cycle twice during each voltage cycle. In this respect it is similar to magnetostrictive hum. Formulas for the noise produced at twice power-line frequency have been developed by Alger (1954), who found that noise decreases significantly with increasing number of poles. Since the speeds of a.c. machines are also reduced by using large numbers of poles, slow-speed motors are much quieter than those rotating at close to power-line frequency. Although fundamental low-frequency vibration of a.c. motors occurs at twice the line frequency, Robinson (1963) has shown that motion of the shaft in the bearings permits a side-to-side subharmonic vibration at half this frequency, i.e., at line frequency itself. Summers (1955) has found that because of slight asymmetries the hum component of two-pole a.c. induction motors is modulated at slip frequency, which is the frequency differential between line and rotational frequencies. For this reason, and because hum noise may be as much as 20 dB higher in these units, two-pole a.c. machines should be avoided in situations where motor noise might be significant.

*Rotor slot noise* occurs in d.c. as well as in a.c. machines and is due to the small flux variations that occur as the relative positions of the rotor teeth vary with respect to stator poles. The fundamental frequency of this type of noise is the number of rotor slots times the actual rotational frequency. In a.c. machines, two other strong components occur at the slot frequency plus and minus twice the line frequency. Thus,

$$f = Rn \overset{+}{\underset{o}{-}} 2\tilde{f} \tag{10.4}$$

where $R$ is the number of armature teeth, or rotor slots, $n$ is the rotational speed in rps, $\tilde{f}$ is line frequency and the symbol $\overset{+}{\underset{o}{-}}$ means plus, minus and zero. Muster and Wolfert (1956) have termed these high-order components *dissymmetry harmonics*, since their strengths are determined by stator as well as rotor dissymmetries. As noted by Lübcke (1956), structural resonances influence the relative strengths of the components. It seems clear that rotor slot noise can be minimized by the use of heavy, highly damped frames and by precision in manufacture. Skewing of slots to produce smoother flux transitions is also effective in reducing these components, especially in d.c. machines.

## 10.3 Impact Sounds

A number of machinery noise sources such as gears, engine valves and chain drives are characterized by repeated impacts of metal parts against other metal surfaces. Before considering specific sources, we will examine the general theory of impact sounds as developed and applied by Cremer (1950, 1953), Heckl and Rathe (1963) and Ungar and Ross (1965).

### Impact Vibratory Relations

Impacts are characterized by short impulsive excitations of structures, the period between successive pulses being long compared to the duration of each pulse. As depicted in Fig. 10.2, each

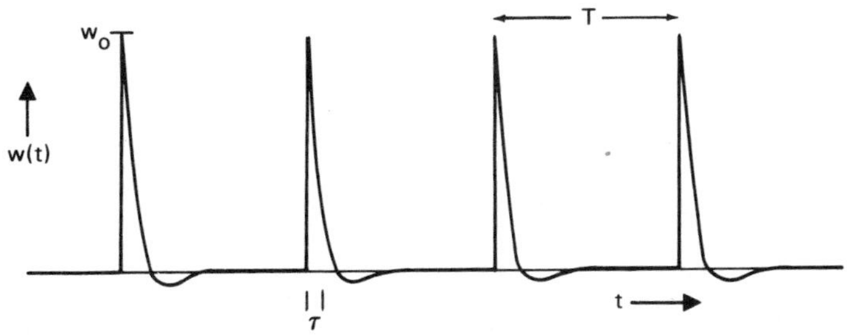


Fig. 10.2. Repeated Impacts

impact causes a rapid acceleration to an initial velocity, $w_o$, followed by a rapid decay prior to the next impact. The instantaneous velocity of each pulse may be represented by

$$w(t) = w_o \, e^{-t/\tau} \, . \tag{10.5}$$

Cremer assumed that the impacted structure takes on the velocity of the mass that strikes it, which represents an upper limit. The time constant, $\tau$, in which the velocity decays to $e^{-1}$ of its initial value is a function of the mass of the object relative to the impedance of the structure and also of the damping of the structure. In terms of $\tau$, the mean-square velocity is given by

$$\overline{w^2} = \frac{1}{T} \int_o^T w_o^2 \, e^{-2t/\tau} \, dt \doteq \frac{w_o^2 \tau}{2T} \, , \tag{10.6}$$

provided $T >> \tau$. From Eq. 5.124, the power transferred from the impacting body to the structure is given by

$$W_{vibr} = R_i \overline{w^2} = \frac{w_o^2 \tau}{2T} R_i \, , \tag{10.7}$$

where $R_i$ is the real part of the input impedance of the structure. Cremer equated this power to the kinetic energy carried by the impacting mass per unit time, namely,

$$W_{Kin} = \frac{E_{Kin}}{T} = \frac{m w_o^2}{2T} \, , \tag{10.8}$$

thereby finding

$$\tau \doteq \frac{m}{R_i} \, . \tag{10.9}$$

The spectrum of repeated pulses consists of a large number of tonals separated in frequency by the reciprocal of the repetition period, i.e.,

$$f_j = j \, \frac{1}{T} \, . \tag{10.10}$$

The amplitudes of these harmonics can be found from Fourier analysis, using Eq. 1.64, from which

$$w(\omega) \sim \frac{1}{T} \int_o^T w_o \, e^{-t/\tau} \, e^{-i\omega t} \, dt \doteq \frac{\tau w_o}{\sqrt{1 + (\omega\tau)^2}} \, . \tag{10.11}$$

The impact spectrum is therefore flat up to $\omega \doteq (3\tau)^{-1}$ and decreases at 6 dB/octave for $(\omega\tau > 3)$, as shown in Fig. 10.3. The actual vibration spectrum of a structure is this input spectrum multi-

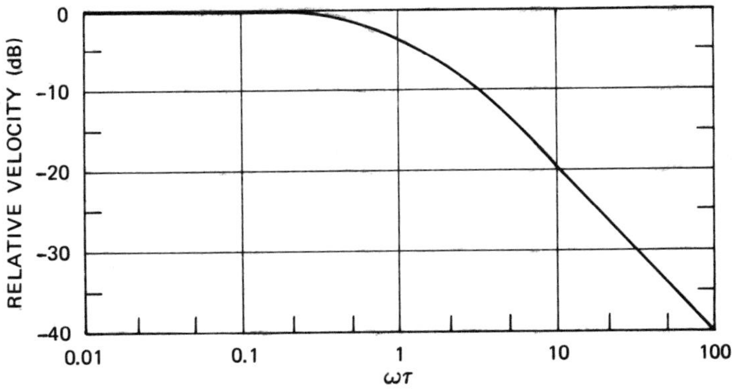


Fig. 10.3. Envelope of Spectrum for Repeated Impacts

plied by the structure's response spectrum. Therefore, highest vibratory and acoustic levels can be expected when harmonics of the impact frequency coincide with structural resonances. Because such coincidences are virtually unavoidable, use of structural damping to reduce resonant response is especially important in reducing impact noise.

**Gear Noise**

Gears are often important sources of machine noise. The two major causes of gear noise are tooth impacts and hobbing error. *Tooth impacts* produce tones at multiples of the tooth contact frequency. Usually the fundamental is strongest. Rosen (1961) measured noise spectra of two *planetary gear systems* composed of gears having straight teeth, which are called *spur gears*. He recorded as many as six harmonics, with the second harmonic strongest. Gear noise depends on the shape of the teeth as well as the accuracy with which they are machined. Except for resonance effects caused when tooth contact frequencies excite specific mechanical resonances of the web or casing, Rosen found that the noise is dependent only on the mechanical power being transmitted. From his tests, we can conclude that $\eta_{ac} \doteq 3 \times 10^{-6}$ for spur gears.

*Helical gears* are generally about 10 dB quieter than spur gears for the same power transmission. Attia (1969, 1970 and 1971) found that contact-frequency noise of helical gears decreases with increased pitch, but increases markedly if the number of teeth in contact at any one time is a whole number. He also found that *Novikov gears*, which use circular-arc tooth profiles, are 6 to 8 dB noisier than *involute helical gears*. Nakamura (1967) reported that gear noise increases with load, with peripheral speed for a given load and with use of thinner webs. He also found that under light loading conditions subharmonics of the contact frequency may be produced from abnormal meshing of every second or third tooth. Moeller (1957) and Attia (1969) have noted that proper lubrication is required to avoid excessive noise caused by friction between the teeth when under heavy load.

*Hobbing error* occurs because gears are cut on a machine that is itself driven by gears. If the gear drive of the cutting machine is not smooth, it will produce a wavy outer surface of the gear being cut, which waviness acts like a second set of gear teeth. Hobbing tones can be eliminated by honing or polishing the teeth after cutting, as discussed by Klyukin (1961). Klyukin also recommended use of heavy and/or damped rims and webs as well as operation at moderate load factors.

## 10.4 Piston-Slap Noise in Reciprocating Machinery

### Piston Slap

*Piston slap* refers to impact of a piston against a cylinder wall as a result of sidewise motion of the piston across the cylinder clearance space due to reversal of the direction of the cross-force component of connecting-rod force. As shown in Fig. 10.1, the connecting rod of a typical reciprocating machine moves from side to side relative to the primary line of piston motion. The direction of the cross-force component changes when this occurs. The piston, which has been riding against one cylinder surface, moves to the other side where it strikes the cylinder wall and causes an impact-type vibration. Piston slap also occurs when the connecting-rod force changes sign. Figure 10.4 shows an oscillogram taken from an accelerometer mounted on an engine cylinder. Each individual impact excites high-frequency resonant vibrations which decay prior to the next impact.

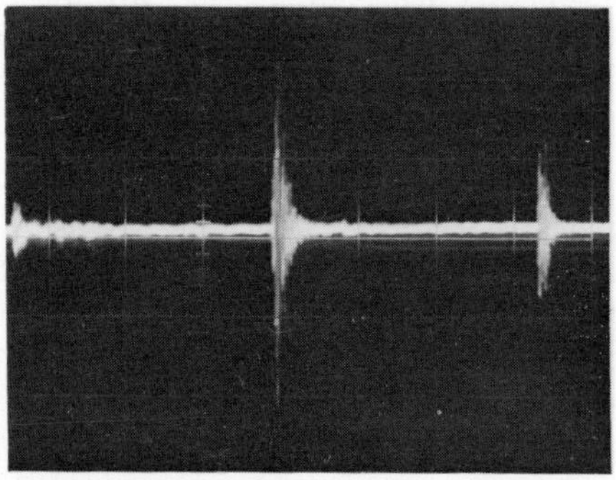

Fig. 10.4. Oscillographic Record of Piston Slap

Several piston slaps occur during each crank shaft revolution. Because they are not equally spaced, the fundamental repetition frequency is the crank rotational frequency. The resultant spectrum from each cylinder consists of numerous harmonically-spaced tonals whose envelope is described roughly according to Eq. 10.11 and Fig. 10.3. In a multiple-cylinder engine, the angular connections to the crank shaft are staggered to counter dynamic unbalances, as discussed in Section 10.1. As a result, harmonics that are multiples of the number of in-line cylinders are accentuated. These are called *firing-rate* tonals and occur in compressors as well as in diesels. The spectrum of a typical engine therefore consists of as many as 120 harmonics of the fundamental rotational frequency; those harmonics that are multiples of the firing rate and those that excite structural resonances are strongest.

Piston slap exists in most, though not all, reciprocating machines. It is sometimes eliminated by tight cylinder clearances and/or use of offset crankshafts and wristpins. Large, slow-speed (under 250 rpm) marine reciprocating and diesel propulsion engines usually incorporate articulated connecting rods, thereby eliminating piston cross forces and virtually eliminating piston slap. Rhombic drive mechanisms, such as that used in the Stirling engine, also eliminate cross forces.

### Significance of Piston Slap

It is generally recognized today that piston slap is a major mechanical noise source of most reciprocating compressors and of medium- and high-speed marine diesel engines and, furthermore, that it is a major cause of pitting erosion of cylinder liners, as noted by Joyner (1957). However, the importance of piston slap as an underwater sound noise source has been recognized only within the past 20 years. Prior to about 1955, the general assumption was that the dominant sources of diesel engine structural vibrations were mechanical unbalances and pulses associated with high cylinder pressures during combustion. In the U.S. in the late 1940's, *pancake diesels* having radial cylinder arrangements were selected for submarine installations, rather than the more usual in-line or vee arrangements, because it was thought that elimination of low-order unbalances would reduce underwater diesel noise. Modification of firing cycles was also investigated in order to reduce pressure pulses associated with combustion. Neither of these projects was successful; in fact, the pancake engines were found to be somewhat noisier than the engines they replaced.

Evidence of the dominance of another source was revealed by extensive noise and vibration tests carried out under Mercy (1955) at the Brooklyn Naval Shipyard. Mercy compared the noise and vibration of an engine when motorized with that when fueled and found very little change of either spectrum shape or amplitude. He then gradually dismantled the engine, finding the biggest decrease in noise and vibration when the pistons were removed. Similar results have been reported by Hobson (1960) and Griffiths and Skorecki (1964).

Mercy's finding that a motorized diesel produces almost the same spectrum as a fueled engine and the knowledge that spectra of reciprocating compressors are similar to those of naval diesels led Ross and Ungar (1965) to the conclusion that piston-slap noise described and analyzed by Zinchenko (1957) is the dominant source of noise of medium- and high-speed marine engines. Other studies such as those of Griffiths and Skorecki (1964) and Haddad and Pullen (1974) confirmed this conclusion. Measurements of diesel noise as a function of load, speed, piston clearance and type of connecting rod all conform to expectations based on piston impact analysis.

### Piston Impact Velocity

Detailed analyses of lateral piston motions in reciprocating machines have been made by Zinchenko (1957), Crane (1959), Griffiths and Skorecki (1964), Alvarez (1964) and Ungar and Ross (1965). These analyses, which differ only in small details, all consider inertia and gas pressure forces acting on a piston and calculate the cross component as a function of time. When the cross component passes through zero, the piston accelerates as it crosses the gap and arrives at the far wall with impact velocity, $w_o$.

Figure 10.5 depicts the geometry and forces involved in piston impact analyses. The various dimensions and angles shown in the figure are:

| | |
|---|---|
| $D$ | piston diameter, |
| $L$ | connecting-rod length, |
| $R$ | crank radius, |

| | |
|---|---|
| $S$ | piston stroke (= 2R), |
| $x$ | distance of lateral motion, |
| $y$ | piston position relative to center of stroke, |
| $\delta$ | piston clearance, |
| $\beta$ | connecting-rod angle, and |
| $\theta$ | crank angle. |

The instantaneous forces experienced by the piston are:

| | |
|---|---|
| $f_{CR}$ | connection-rod force, |
| $f_i$ | inertia force of the reciprocating mass in direction of piston motion, |
| $f_p$ | pressure force, and |
| $f_x$ | lateral force. |

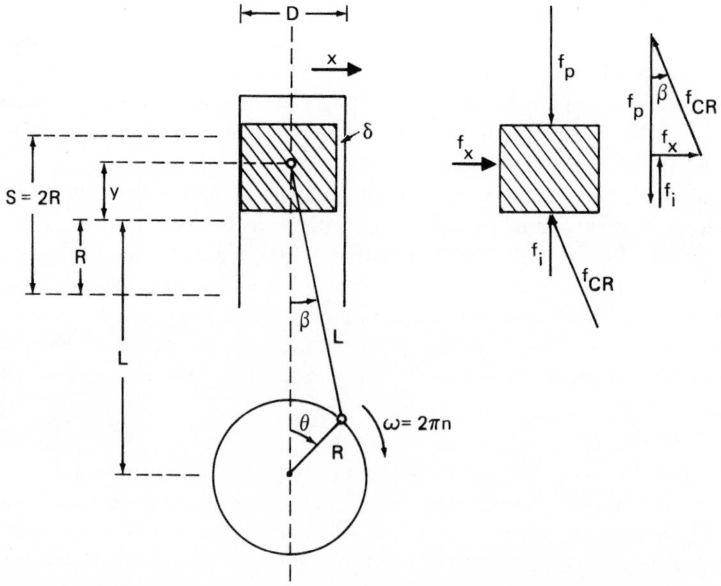


Fig. 10.5. Geometric and Force Diagrams for Piston Impact Analyses

When the piston rubs against a surface of the cylinder, the cylinder-wall normal force balances the lateral component of the connecting-rod force. But when the latter changes sign, either due to a change in the angle of the connecting rod or to a change in the sign of the connecting-rod force, the piston moves over to the other side of the cylinder. We are concerned here with the impulse of the resultant impact and the attendant noise and vibration.

From the force diagram of Fig. 10.5 we may write two scalar equations balancing the $y$ and $x$ force components:

$$f_p - f_i - f_{CR} \cos \beta = 0 \tag{10.12}$$

and

$$f_x = f_{CR} \sin \beta \ . \tag{10.13}$$

Solving for $f_{CR}$ from Eq. 10.12, Eq. 10.13 becomes

$$f_x = (f_p - f_i) \tan \beta \ . \tag{10.14}$$

The angle $\beta$ is related to the crank angle $\theta$ by

$$\sin \beta = \frac{R}{L} \sin \theta \ , \tag{10.15}$$

from which it follows that for small angles

$$\tan \beta = \frac{\sin \beta}{\sqrt{1 - \sin^2 \beta}} \doteq \frac{R}{L} \sin \theta \left(1 + \frac{1}{2}\left(\frac{R}{L}\right)^2 \sin^2 \theta\right) \ . \tag{10.16}$$

The piston position measured from mid stroke is given by

$$y = R \cos \theta - L(1 - \cos \beta) \ . \tag{10.17}$$

Assuming $R^2 << L^2$,

$$\frac{y}{R} \doteq \cos \theta - \frac{R}{4L}(1 - \cos 2\theta) \ . \tag{10.18}$$

For constant crank rotational speed, $\omega$, the inertia force associated with piston reciprocating motion is given by

$$f_i = - m_p \ddot{y} \doteq m_p R \omega^2 (\cos \theta + \frac{R}{L} \cos 2\theta) \ , \tag{10.19}$$

where $m_p$ is the effective mass of the piston and includes that fraction of the mass of the connecting rod that can be considered to move as part of the piston.

The cylinder pressure follows a cycle similar to that shown in Fig. 10.6. It is generally difficult to express the pressure by a meaningful analytical function; however, at times of piston lateral motion the piston pressure is either close to its maximum value or close to zero. We may therefore distinguish two kinds of impact: those in which cylinder pressure is important and $p \doteq p_m$, i.e., its value close to the peak of the pressure cycle, and those in which the cylinder pressure is virtually zero and inertia forces dominate.

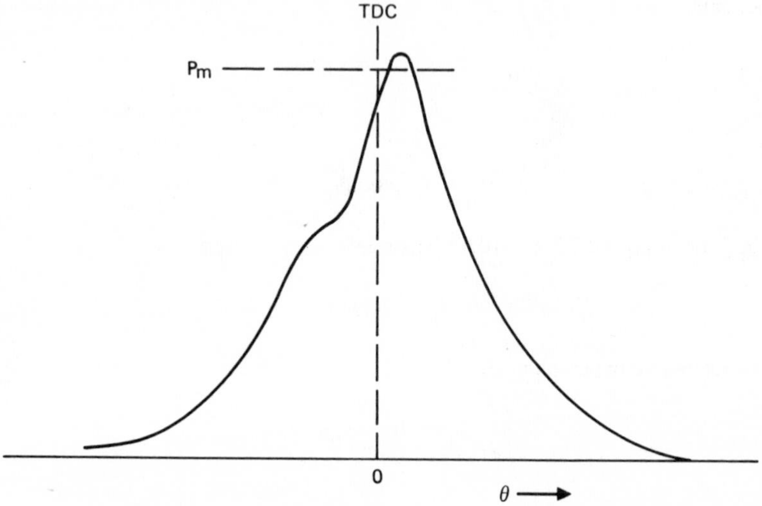


Fig. 10.6. Cylinder Pressure as Function of Crank Angle

For *pressure-controlled impacts*, which occur near the top-dead-center (TDC) position, the pressure force is

$$f_p \doteq \frac{\pi}{4} D^2 p_m = A_p p_m \tag{10.20}$$

and the inertia force can be approximated by

$$f_i \doteq m_p R \omega^2 \left(1 + \frac{R}{L}\right)\left(1 - \frac{L + 4R}{2L + 2R}\,\theta^2\right) . \tag{10.21}$$

Since $\theta$ is small, the inertia force is virtually constant during a pressure-controlled impact. Combining Eqs. 10.14, 10.16, 10.20 and 10.21 and assuming $\theta^2 << 1$, the cross force during a pressure-controlled impact near TDC is given by

$$f_x = (f_p - f_i) \tan\beta \doteq \left[A_p p_m - m_p R \omega^2 \left(1 + \frac{R}{L}\right)\right] \frac{R}{L}\,\theta . \tag{10.22}$$

Neglect of $\theta^2$ terms can be shown to introduce no more than a 5% error in the calculations for the range of parameters found in practice.

In those parts of the cycle for which the pressure forces are negligible, such as at bottom dead center (BDC) and during the scavenging stroke of a four-stroke engine, the cross force is controlled by the inertia force. Combining Eqs. 10.14, 10.16 and 10.19, the cross force during *inertia-controlled impacts* is

$$f_x = - f_i \tan\beta = - m_p R\omega^2 \frac{R}{L} \sin\theta \left(1 + \frac{1}{2}\left(\frac{R}{L}\right)^2 \sin^2\theta\right) \times$$
$$\left(\cos\theta + \frac{R}{L}\cos 2\theta\right) . \qquad (10.23)$$

Two types of sign reversal can occur in this equation. One type occurs at the top and bottom of the stroke when $\sin\theta$ changes sign by going through zero; the other occurs near 90° when the cosine term changes its sign. Because the two resultant motions cause similar impacts, we may estimate the force by calculating it at the point of reversal of the sign of $\sin\theta$. For this type, and neglecting terms involving the square of the angle relative to unity, the normal force is approximately

$$f_x \doteq \mp m_p R\omega^2 \frac{R}{L}\left(1 \pm \frac{R}{L}\right)\theta , \qquad (10.24)$$

where the top sign refers to impacts at the top of the stroke and the lower sign to those at the bottom. Neglect of higher powers of $\theta$ causes somewhat more error for inertia-dominated impacts than for impacts controlled by pressure. However, the author has carried out calculations retaining these extra terms and has shown them not to be significant.

The impact speed of the piston is calculated by integrating Newton's second law for motion across the gap. For inertia-controlled impacts at TDC or BDC,

$$m_p \ddot{x} \doteq \mp m_p R\omega^2 \frac{R}{L}\left(1 \pm \frac{R}{L}\right)\theta . \qquad (10.25)$$

It follows that

$$\dot{x} \doteq \mp R\omega \frac{R}{L}\left(1 \pm \frac{R}{L}\right)\frac{\theta^2}{2} \qquad (10.26)$$

and

$$x \doteq \mp \frac{R^2}{L}\left(1 \pm \frac{R}{L}\right)\frac{\theta^3}{6} . \qquad (10.27)$$

At the far wall $x = \delta$, the cylinder clearance, and the resultant angle, $\theta_i$, is

$$\theta_i \doteq \sqrt[3]{\frac{6\delta L}{R^2(1 \pm R/L)}} . \qquad (10.28)$$

The velocity at impact is thus

$$w_{o_i} \doteq R\omega \sqrt[3]{\frac{9}{2}\left(\frac{\delta}{R}\right)^2 \frac{R}{L}\left(1 \pm \frac{R}{L}\right)} . \qquad (10.29)$$

By a similar analysis, the velocity of the piston for a *pressure-controlled impact* is

$$w_{o_p} \doteq R\omega \sqrt[3]{\frac{9}{2}\left(\frac{\delta}{R}\right)^2 \frac{R}{L}\left(\frac{1-\alpha}{\alpha}\right)} , \qquad (10.30)$$

where

$$\alpha \equiv \frac{m_p R\omega^2}{A_p p_m} \qquad (10.31)$$

is the ratio of inertia to pressure forces during a pressure-controlled impact. As noted by Ungar and Ross (1965), this quantity is also the ratio to the peak piston pressure of the centrifugal force per unit area that the piston would exert if it were attached at the crank radius. This ratio is the critical parameter controlling the nature of the dominant impacts.

The parameter $\alpha$ can be shown to be a function of piston material, *linear piston speed*, $s \equiv 2nS$, and peak piston pressure, $p_m$. Thus, expressing the piston mass, $m_p$, by

$$m_p = \rho_p A_p H , \qquad (10.32)$$

it follows that

$$\alpha = \frac{\pi^2}{2} \frac{\rho_p}{p_m} \frac{H}{S} s^2 , \qquad (10.33)$$

where $H$ is the effective piston depth including a contribution from the connecting rod. Assuming $H$ to be about one third of the stroke,

$$\alpha \doteq \frac{5}{3} \frac{\rho_p s^2}{p_m} . \qquad (10.34)$$

Values of $\alpha$ for diesels generally lie between about 0.06 and 0.25.

The average ratio of the velocities for the two types of impact is

$$\gamma \equiv \frac{w_{o_p}}{w_{o_i}} \doteq \sqrt[3]{\frac{1-\alpha}{\alpha}} , \qquad (10.35)$$

which is also the ratio of crank angle travel during an impact controlled by inertia to crank angle travel during an impact controlled by pressure.

**Cylinder Wall Vibrations**

From our previous discussion of impact noise it follows that the energy transferred to the cylinder wall by each piston impact can be estimated from Eq. 10.8 using Eqs. 10.29 and 10.30 for impact velocities. The total power transferred is the product of the number of cylinders, $j$, the rotational frequency, $n$, and the vibrational energy associated with each cylinder per revolution. Distinction must be made between 2-stroke-cycle engines that fire every revolution and 4-stroke-cycle engines that intersperse scavenging strokes between power strokes and fire only every second revolution. From Eqs. 10.8, 10.29, 10.30 and 10.35,

$$W_{vibr} \doteq j \frac{2n}{spc} \frac{m_p R^2 \omega^2}{2} \left(\frac{9}{2}\right)^{2/3} \left(\frac{\delta}{R}\right)^{4/3} \left(\frac{R}{L}\right)^{2/3} \left(\gamma^2 + N_i\right) , \qquad (10.36)$$

where *spc* stands for *number of strokes per cycle* and $N_i$ is number of inertia-controlled impacts per complete cycle. The number of inertia-controlled impacts depends on the balance between inertia and gas forces. For 2-stroke-cycle engines there is always one impact at BDC where the sign of $\beta$ changes and sometimes two additional impacts at other angles. Four-stroke-cycle diesels have two impacts at BDC, one at TDC and either two or four additional impacts due to force reversals, as shown in Fig. 10.7. Thus, on average, $N_i \doteq 1.4\ spc$ and the vibratory power is approximately

$$W_{vibr} \doteq 1.7 j \alpha s p_m A_p \left(\frac{\delta}{S}\right)^{4/3} \left(\frac{R}{L}\right)^{2/3} \left(\frac{\gamma^2}{spc} + 1.4\right) . \qquad (10.37)$$

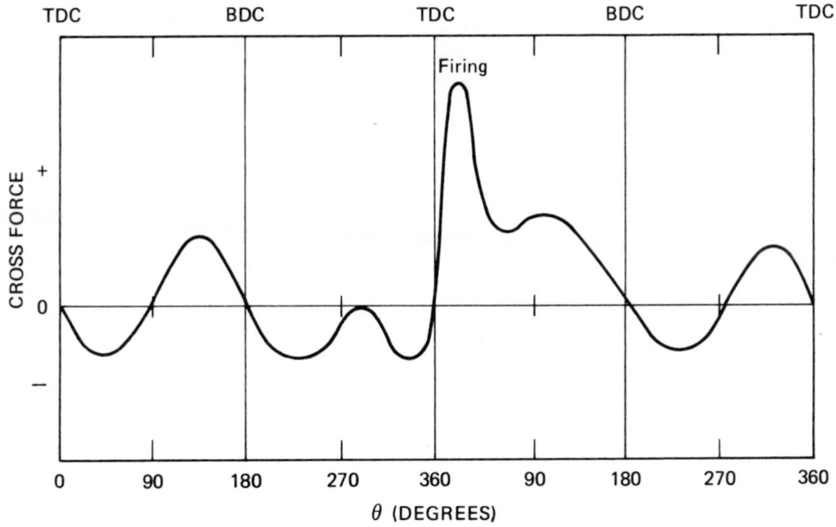


Fig. 10.7. Piston Cross Force during Full Cycle of a Four-Stroke Engine, after Zinchenko (1957)

Vibratory power due to inertia-controlled impacts for a given engine increases as the cube of piston speed; vibratory power due to pressure-controlled impacts increases approximately as the 5/3 power. It is now clear why piston-slap noise of a motorized diesel is almost as great as that of a fueled engine. When an engine is motorized, $\alpha$ is large and $\gamma^2$ small; this elimination of $\gamma^2$ from Eq. 10.37 generally decreases the vibratory power by less than a factor of two, i.e., by less than 3 dB.

The efficiency of conversion of mechanical power into vibratory power can be estimated by dividing Eq. 10.37 by an expression for the mechanical power of a fueled diesel. This power is given by

$$W_{mech} = \frac{2jn}{spc} A_p S\bar{p} = \frac{js}{spc} A_p \bar{p} \ , \tag{10.38}$$

where $\bar{p}$ is the *mean effective pressure.* Ungar and Ross (1965) have noted that under normal operating conditions $\bar{p}$ is usually close to one third of the peak cylinder pressure, $p_m$. It follows that the vibration conversion efficiency is approximately

$$\eta_{vibr} \doteq 5\alpha \left(\frac{\delta}{S}\right)^{4/3} \left(\frac{R}{L}\right)^{2/3} \left(\gamma^2 + N_i\right) \ . \tag{10.39}$$

Ungar and Ross found from examination of data on a number of marine engines that $\delta/S$ is of the order of $3 \times 10^{-3}$ and $R/L$ is usually about 0.25, from which $\eta_{vibr} \approx 10^{-3}$ for typical values of the parameters.

Ungar and Ross used the methodology of Section 6.4 and estimated that the radiation efficiency of airborne sound from typical engines is of the order to $10^{-4}$. Multiplying by the vibration conversion efficiency, they concluded that a typical 1000 hp engine would produce an airborne acoustic power level, *PWL*, of about 110 dB re $10^{-12}$ W. Variations of piston clearance, strokes per cycle, piston speed and engine material can cause deviations of at least ±10 dB about this mean value.

**Experimental Verification**

Oscillograms of the type shown in Fig. 10.4 and observation of multi-harmonic spectra are two indications that an impact phenomenon produces the dominant vibrations in most reciprocating machines. Evidence in support of piston slap as that phenomenon is found in experiments in which a single engine parameter is varied. Equation 10.37 for vibratory power is the basis for predictions of these variations. Substituting for $\alpha$ in Eq. 10.37 from Eq. 10.34, one obtains

$$W_{vibr} \doteq 18 j\rho_p n^3 S^2 D^3 \left(\frac{\delta}{D}\right)^{4/3} \left(\frac{R}{L}\right)^{2/3} \left(\frac{\gamma^2}{spc} + 1.4\right) \ . \tag{10.40}$$

This expression predicts noise dependence on number of cylinders, rotational speed, stroke, diameter, piston clearance, load, strokes per cycle and ratio of crank radius to length of connecting rod.

Zinchenko (1956, 1957) measured the airborne engine noise of over 60 Soviet diesels including some that differed only in number of cylinders. He verified the proportionality of noise to $j$ predicted by Eq. 10.40. The dependency of cylinder-wall vibration on piston clearance expected from Eq. 10.40 was confirmed by measurements made by Alvarez (1964). However, as shown in Fig. 10.8, Skobtsov et al (1962) found that airborne noise levels of diesels increase with piston clearance at about half the predicted rate.

Nowhere in the analysis is dependence of noise on load specifically included. Any changes due to load must therefore be secondary. Load can affect $\gamma$ slightly and differences of cylinder heating

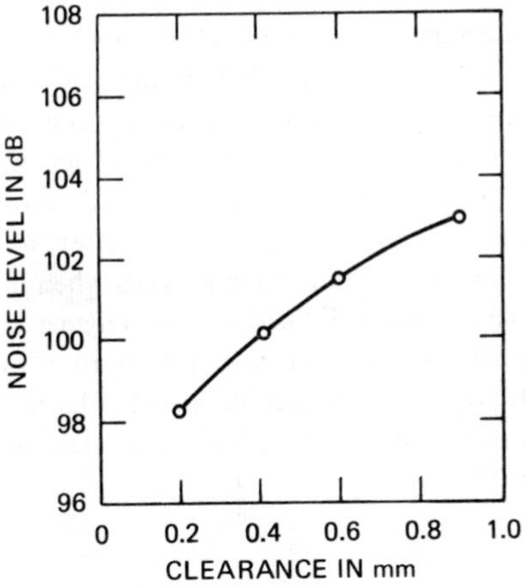


Fig. 10.8. Airborne Noise of a Diesel Engine as Function of Piston Clearance, after Skobtsov et al (1962)

due to load may affect piston clearances. As expected, data from six diesels reproduced in Fig. 10.9 show no consistent trend of noise with load.

It is well known that diesels are noisier when they first start up than after 15 or 20 minutes' operation. This can be explained by initial lack of an oil film and by the larger clearances

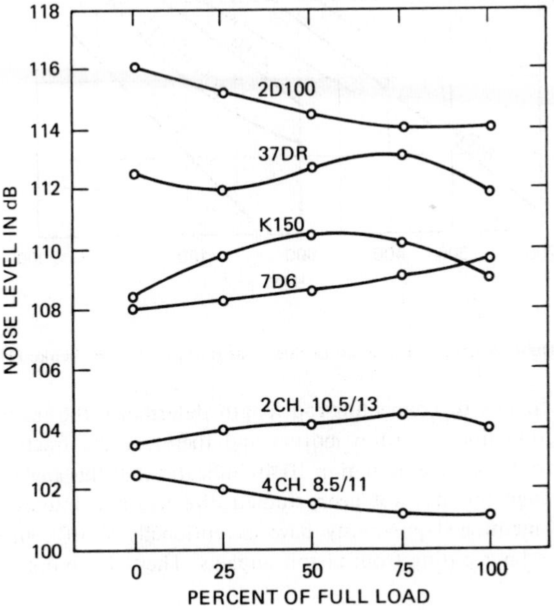


Fig. 10.9. Dependence of Noise on Load of Several Russian Diesels, after Zinchenko (1957)

characterizing a cold engine compared to a warm one. Both these factors cause more severe piston slap in a cold engine.

Equation 10.40 predicts only a slight dependence of piston-slap vibratory power on number of strokes per cycle. However, Eq. 10.38 indicates that mechanical power is reduced when *spc* is increased from two to four. Statistical analysis of Zinchenko's noise data shows that for the same horsepower rating four-stroke engines are indeed 2.5 to 3 dB noisier than two-stroke engines.

At very low speeds, for which inertia impacts produce less vibration than pressure impacts, Eq. 10.40 predicts that vibrations and noise will increase approximately as the square of the rotational speed (6 dB/ds). On the other hand, in the limit at high speeds when inertia impacts dominate, the dependence should be as the cube of speed (9 dB/ds). Most engines operate between these limits, though closer to the upper one. We would therefore expect that, on average, noise of a given engine would increase at a rate of 8 dB per double speed. Figure 10.10 shows data on seven Russian diesels confirming this expectation based on piston-slap analysis. Similar results were reported by Brammer and Muster (1975).

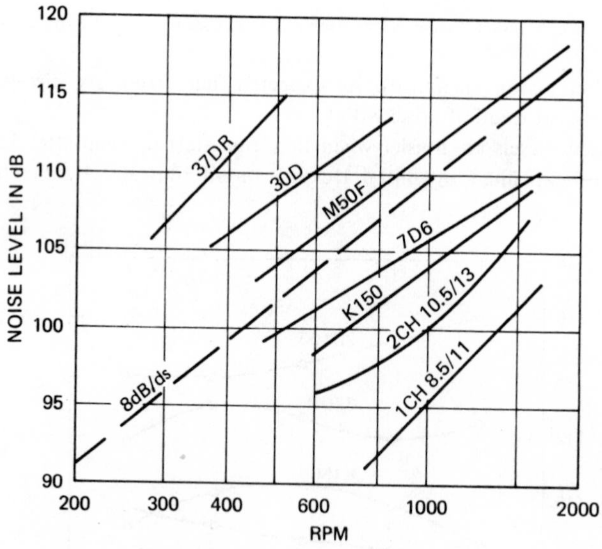


Fig. 10.10. Diesel Noise as a Function of Speed, as reported by Zinchenko (1957)

The ratio of crank radius to connecting-rod length determines the maximum angle of connecting-rod relative to direction of piston motion and therefore the fraction of connecting-rod force that contributes to cross force. Equation 10.40 indicates that this angle should play a role in piston-slap noise. Although this has not been studied directly, it is interesting to note that the radial *pancake* engines mentioned previously have exceptionally short connecting rods and experience severe cylinder liner pitting from piston impacts. They also produce exceptionally high noise levels.

Equation 10.40 predicts that vibratory power is proportional to density of piston material.

However, radiation analyses indicate that, other things being equal, radiation efficiency decreases with increasing material density. Ross and Ungar (1965) concluded that aluminum block engines should be somewhat noisier than those made of steel. In two cases in which aluminum and steel block models of the same engine were tested, Zinchenko (1956) found the aluminum engines to be 3 to 4 dB noisier.

In another confirmation of the dominance of piston impacts, Zinchenko measured the noise from two engines differing from the others only in having articulated connecting rods. He found engine noise in these cases to be 7 to 10 dB lower than for similar engines with single connecting rods.

### Empirical Noise Formulas

A number of empirical formulas for airborne noise levels of diesel engines have been developed from the noise data published by Zinchenko (1956, 1957). Since Zinchenko's sound pressure measurements were made relatively close to the engines, i.e., at 0.5 m, they do not actually reveal the fifth power dependence on linear dimensions predicted by the analysis, but rather seem to fit third to fourth power relations. Ross and Ungar (1965) found

$$SPL \doteq 94 + 10 \log j \left( \frac{\rho_{steel}}{\rho_{block}} \right) n^3 D^2 S^2 \quad . \tag{10.41}$$

An equally good fit to the data is given by

$$SPL = 91 + 10 \log j + 28 \log nD \quad , \tag{10.42}$$

which is shown in Fig. 10.11. Zinchenko's data can also be correlated with engine horsepower and rpm, as plotted in Fig. 10.12. A formula which represents these data is

$$SPL \doteq 86 + 10 \log \left( hp \frac{spc}{2} \right) + 18 \log \frac{N}{1000} \quad , \tag{10.43}$$

where $N$ is rotational speed in rpm. This formula indicates clearly that for the same rated power high-speed engines are generally noisier than slow-speed engines.

### Underwater Noise Implications

Although underwater noise measurements of marine diesels have not been published, Zinchenko's airborne noise measurements and the foregoing analyses of the basic mechanisms involved make certain conclusions clear. First, piston slap is a dominant source of underwater noise from marine reciprocating machines. Second, the selection of machines with low rpm's and low linear piston speeds will result in relatively low noise levels, as indicated by Eqs. 10.40 and 10.43 and Fig. 10.12. Third, if piston clearances are kept as small as is consistent with reasonable frictional wear, lower noise levels will be achieved. Fourth, tall machines with relatively long connecting rods are quieter than more compact ones incorporating short rods. Finally, slow-speed marine diesels and old-fashioned steam reciprocating engines are especially quiet since they not only operate at low speeds but also incorporate articulated connecting rods. In this connection, we note a recent trend in merchant ships in which medium-speed geared diesels are being used in some installations in place of slow-speed direct-drive engines. These medium-speed engines may be

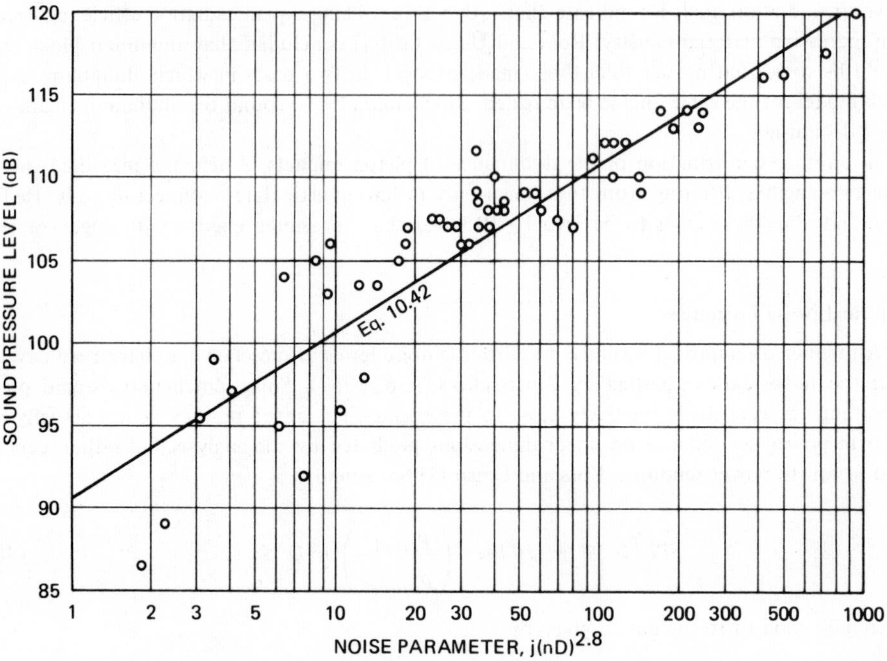


Fig. 10.11. Airborne Noise of Diesel Engines, as measured by Zinchenko (1956, 1957)

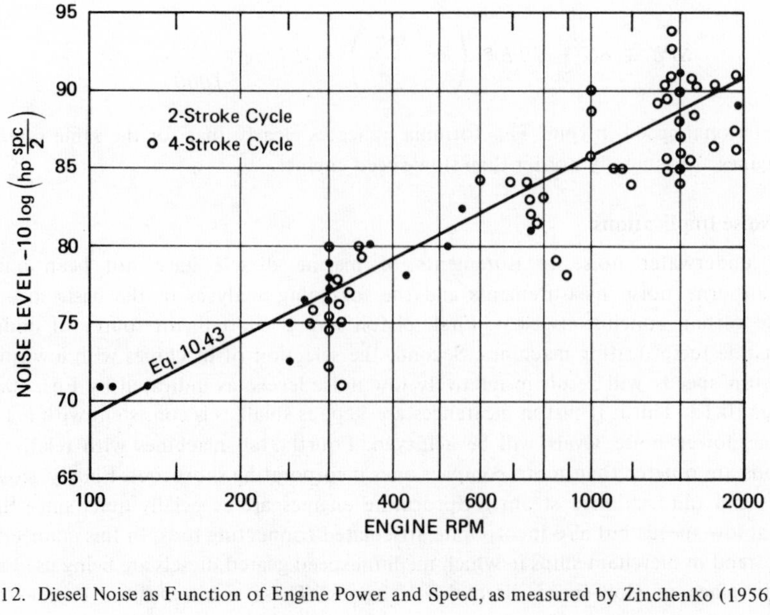


Fig. 10.12. Diesel Noise as Function of Engine Power and Speed, as measured by Zinchenko (1956, 1957)

expected to product as much as 20 dB more piston-slap noise since the speed factor implies about 10 to 12 dB higher levels and the replacement of the articulated connecting rod could add another 8 to 10 dB.

Equations 10.39 and 10.43 imply that for equal power two-stroke engines are quieter than four-stroke engines. However, this is true for the piston-slap component only. As discussed in Section 9.4, the fact that two-cycle engines use positive displacement scavenging blowers, which are quite noisy, may offset the 2 to 3 dB piston-slap advantage. In this connection, Hempel (1966, 1968) reported that turbocharging an engine has little effect on piston-slap noise, but that the turbocharger itself adds strong high-frequency components to the overall noise.

There are other noise sources that sometimes contribute significantly to the spectra of reciprocating machinery. Thus, combustion applies a sudden pulse to the cylinder structure similar to an impact. This source, which is dominant in many automotive engines, has been studied extensively by Goswami and Skorecki (1963), Austen and Priede (1965), Priede and Grover (1967) and Brammer and Muster (1975). These investigations have all reported that the rate of rise of cylinder pressure is a factor controlling combustion noise spectra above 500 Hz. Priede (1967) has also measured noise from fuel-injection equipment, finding that rapid changes of fluid pressure in fuel-injection pump elements excite pump camshaft vibrations in the 500 to 800 Hz range and that the injectors themselves produce noise above 2 kHz. Priede concluded that injector noise would only be noticeable at low engine speeds or on small engines. Finally, impact sounds associated with diesel valve mechanisms have been shown by Fielding and Skorecki (1966) to be occasional noise sources.

## 10.5 Bearing Noise

Bearings in rotating machinery both transmit and generate sonic vibrations. Of the two common types, *sliding bearings* more commonly transmit noise than generate it. Occasionally, when they become damaged or are poorly lubricated, sliding bearings generate high-pitched resonant vibrations that are both loud and annoying. More usually, noise generated by the oil pumps required to lubricate sliding bearings is much greater than that attributable to the bearings themselves.

*Ball bearings*, on the other hand, are often sources of tones that are related to both rotational speeds and resonances of the outer ring. Igarashi (1960, 1962 and 1964) found that the frequencies of outer ring resonances can be estimated from

$$f_m \doteq \frac{1}{2\pi} \frac{m(m^2 - 1)\kappa c_\ell}{\sqrt{1 + m^2 R^2}}, \qquad (10.44)$$

where $\kappa$ is the radius of gyration, $R$ the radius of the ring and $m$ is an integer. As speed changes, the distribution of intensity among these resonances changes, but the frequencies remain constant. Ring resonances are excited by impacts of the balls. Igarashi and Ruffini (1963) reported that such impacts are reduced significantly by axial preloading, and this has become common practice in situations where ball-bearing noise is deemed to be important.

Ball bearings sometimes produce subharmonic vibrations. As explained by Tamura and Taniguchi (1961), when the number of balls is small, a bearing may act like a spring whose spring constant varies cyclically with motion of the balls. The result is excitation of the retaining ring at a frequency equal to half of the product of the retainer speed times the number of balls.

Twenty years ago, bearings were considered to be important noise sources of electric motors. Today, with the development of precision manufacturing methods and axial preloading, bearings are only noisy when they are close to being worn out or when they are improperly installed.

## REFERENCES


Alger, P.L., The magnetic noise of polyphase induction motors, *Trans. Amer. Inst. Elect. Engin., 73* (III-A), 118-125, 1954.

Alger, P.L. and Erdelyi, E., Calculation of the magnetic noise of polyphase induction motors, *J.A.S.A., 28*, 1063-1067, 1956.

Alvarez, F.F., Noise and Vibration Problems of Reciprocating Machinery, *M.I.T. Dept. of Naval Arch. and Mar. Engin.*, M.S. Thesis, May 1964; results exerpted in *Bolt Beranek and Newman Rept. 1139*, July 1964.

Attia, A.Y., Noise of involute helical gears, *J. Engin. for Industry, 91B*, 165-171, 1969.

Attia, A.Y., Noise of gears of circular-arc tooth profile, *J. Sound and Vibr., 11*, 383-397, 1970.

Attia, A.Y., Effect of change of pitch on gear noise, *J. Sound and Vibr., 18*, 129-137, 1971.

Austen, A.E.W. and Priede, T., Noise of Automotive Diesel Engines: its Causes and Reduction, *Paper 1000A, Soc. of Automotive Engin.*, Jan. 1965.

Biezeno, C.B. and Grammel, R., *Engineering Dynamics: Vol. 4, Internal-Combustion Engines*, Blackie and Son, London, 1954.

Brammer, A.J. and Muster, D.F., Noise radiated by internal-combustion engines, *J.A.S.A., 58*, 11-21, 1975.

Campbell, J., Electric-motor noise, *Machine Design, 35*, 19, 139-158, Aug. 1963.

Churcher, B.G. and King, A.J., The limitation of transformer noise, *J. Inst. Elect. Engin., 87*, 539-569, 1940.

Crane, P.H.G., The Initiation of Diesel Engine Cylinder Liner Vibrations by Piston Transverse Motion, *G.B. Admiralty Res. Lab. Rept. R2/B10*, Aug. 1959.

Cremer, L., The Propagation of Structure-Borne Sound, *Dept. of Scientific and Indust. Res. (London) Sponsored Res. Rept. Ser. B.*, No. 1, 1950.

Cremer, L., Calculation of sound propagation in structures, *Acustica, 3*, 317-335, 1953.

Cremer, L., Heckl, M. and Ungar, E.E., *Structure-Borne Sound*, Springer-Verlag, New York, 1973 (Chapter 4).

Fearon, W., Waterside attack of diesel-engine cylinder liners, *J. Royal Naval Scientific Service, 19*, 22, 1964.

Fehr, R.O. and Muster, D.F., "Electric Motor and Generator Noise," Chapter 30 of *Handbook of Noise Control*, C.M. Harris (Ed.), McGraw-Hill, New York, 1957.

Fielding, B.J. and Skorecki, J., Identification of mechanical sources of noise in a diesel engine: sound emitted from the valve mechanism, *Proc. Inst. Mech. Engin., 181*, 437-451, 1966.

Goswami, D. and Skorecki, J., Some Vibration Experiments on a Single-Cylinder Diesel Engine, *A.S.M.E. Paper 63-WA-144*, Nov. 1963.

Griffiths, W.J. and Skorecki, J., Some aspects of vibration of a single cylinder diesel engine, *J. Sound and Vibr., 1*, 345-364, 1964.

Haddad, S.D. and Pullen, H.L., Piston slap as a source of noise and vibration in diesel engines, *J. Sound and Vibr., 34*, 249-260, 1964.

Heckl, M. and Rathe, E.J., Relationship between the transmission loss and the impact-noise isolation of floor structures, *J.A.S.A., 35*, 1825-1830, 1963.

Hempel, W., A contribution to knowledge of piston side movement, *Motortechnische Zeits., 27*, 1-6, 1966 (in German).

Hempel, W., Does Turbocharging Increase Diesel Engine Noise? - Observations on the Generation, Emission and Reduction of Diesel Engine Noise, *Paper 680406, Soc. of Automotive Engin.*, May 1968.

Hobson, A., Interim Report of Various Measurements of the Vibrations of Diesel Engines, *G.B. Admiralty Res. Lab. Rept. R4/93.20/D*, May 1960.

Igarashi, T., Noise of ball bearings, *Bul. Japan Soc. Mech. Engin., 3*(10), 220-227, 1960; *5*(17), 184-194, 1962; and *7*(25), 200-208, 1964.

Joyner, J.A., Reduction of pitting of diesel engine cylinder liners, *Trans. S.A.E., 65*, 337-348, 1957.

King, A.J., "Reduction of the Noise of Iron-Core Transformers and Chokes," Chapter 29 of *Handbook of Noise Control*, C.M. Harris (Ed.), McGraw-Hill, New York, 1957.

King, A.J., *The Measurement and Suppression of Noise*, Chapman and Hall, London, 1965 (Chapter 8).

Klyukin, I.I., *Control of Noise and Sonic Vibration in Ships*, Sudpromgiz, Leningrad, 1961; translation, U.S. Dept. of Commerce, Washington, 1963 (JPRS: 18,177,OTS63-21340) (Chapters 16-19).

Kohler, H.K., Pratt, A. and Thompson, A.M., "Dynamics and Noise of Parallel-Axis Gearing," Paper 14 of *Gearing in 1970, Proc. Inst. Mech. Engin., 184, 30*, 111-121, 1970.

Lewis, F.M., "Torsional Vibration in Reciprocating Machines." Chapter 38 of *Shock and Vibration Handbook*, C.M. Harris and C.E. Crede (Ed.), McGraw-Hill, New York, 1961.

Lübcke, E., Vibration problems in electrical machinery, *Acustica, 6*, 109-114, 1956 (in German).

Mercy, K.R., Analysis of the basic noise sources in the diesel engine, *A.S.M.E. Paper 55-OGP-4*, March 1955; also, *N.Y. Naval Shipyard, Materials Lab. Rept. NS 713-212*, April 1961.

Moeller, K.G.F., "Gear Noise" and "Bearing Noise," Chapters 23 and 24 of *Handbook of Noise Control*, C.M. Harris (Ed.), McGraw-Hill, New York, 1957.

Muster, D.F., "Balancing of Rotating Machinery," Chapter 39 of *Shock and Vibration Handbook*, C.M. Harris and C.E. Crede (Ed.), McGraw-Hill, New York, 1961.

Nakamura, K., Experimental studies about the effects of dynamic loads upon gear noise, *Bul. Japan Soc. Mech. Engin., 10*(37), 180-188, 1967; and *10*(41), 846-854, 1967.

Priede, T. and Grover, E.C., "Noise of Industrial Diesel Engines," Paper 2 of *Noise from Power Plant Equipment, Proc. Inst. Mech. Engin., 181, 3C*, 73-89, 1966.

Priede, T., Noise of diesel engine fuel injection equipment, *J. Sound and Vibr., 6*, 443-459, 1967.

Robinson, R.C., Line-frequency magnetic vibration of a.c. machines, *Trans. Amer. Inst. Elect. Engin., 81*(3), 675-679, 1963.

Rosen, M.W., The noises of two spur-gear transmissions, *Noise Control, 7*, 6, 11-19, 1961; also, *U.S. Naval Ord. Test Station Repts. NAVORD 6569 and 6594*, 1959.

Ross, D. and Ungar, E.E., On Piston Slap as a Source of Engine Noise, *A.S.M.E. Paper 65-OGP-10*, April 1965; also, *Bolt Beranek and Newman, Inc. Rept. 1139*, July 1964.

Ruffini, A.J., Bearing noise, *Machine Design, 35*, 11, 232-235; and *35*, 12, 158-166, 1963.

Skobtsov, Ye. A., Izotov, A.D. and Tuzov, L.V., *Methods of Reducing the Vibration and Noise of Diesel Engines*, Moscow, 1962 (in Russian).

Summers, E.W., Vibration in 2-pole induction motors related to slip frequency, *Trans. Amer. Inst. Elect. Engin., 74*, 69-72, 1955.

Swaffield, J., The causes and characteristics of transformer noise, *J. Inst. Elect. Engin., 89*, 212-224, 1942.

Taggart, R., Noise in reduction gears, *J. Amer. Soc. Naval Engin., 66*, 829-849, 1954; also, *BuShips Rept. 371-N-4*, May 1951.

Tamura, A. and Taniguchi, O., On the subharmonic vibration of order one-half caused by passing balls in a ball bearing, *Bul. Japan Soc. Mech. Engin., 4*(14), 193-200, 1961, and *4*(15), 482-488, 1961.

Thompson, J.E., Magnetostriction and transformer noise, *J. Inst. Elect. Engin., 9*, 72-74, 1963.

Ungar, E.E. and Ross, D., Vibrations and noise due to piston-slap in reciprocating machinery, *J. Sound and Vibr., 2*, 132-146, 1965; also, *Bolt Beranek and Newman, Inc. Rept. 1106*, April 1964.

Wilkins, J.T., "Noise in Transformers," Paper 3 of *Noise from Power Plant Equipment, Proc. Inst. Mech. Engin., 181, 3C*, 131-137, 1966.

Zinchenko, V.I., Effect of constructional factors on the noise of ships' engines, *Vestnik Mashinostroyeniya, 4*, 13-17, 1956 (translated).

Zinchenko, V.I., *Noise of Marine Diesel Engines*, Sudpromgiz, Leningrad, 1957; summarized in *Bolt Beranek and Newman, Inc. T.I.R. 61*, July 1962.

## APPENDIX A

## NOMENCLATURE

Underwater acoustics is a multi-discipline field involving concepts from fluid mechanics, aerodynamics, thermodynamics, electrical, mechanical and marine engineering and naval architecture, as well as acoustics. When possible, the author has selected symbols and abbreviations familiar to workers in each of these fields. In cases where this would cause confusion due to duplication preference has usually been given to acoustics.

Over 450 symbols and abbreviations used in this volume are listed here. Common symbols and abbreviations used in more than one chapter are given first. Nomenclature restricted to only one or two chapters is then listed by chapter. In most instances reference is made to the page, equation or figure where the symbol is first used and/or defined. A few symbols that occur only once in the text and are defined where they occur have been omitted.

### A.1 General Nomenclature

Roman Letters

| | | |
|---|---|---|
| $\vec{A}, \vec{B}$ | general vectors | p. 11 |
| $A, B, C$ | amplitudes; coefficients; constants | |
| $\underline{A}, \underline{B}, \underline{C}, \underline{D}$ | complex numbers; amplitudes; coefficients | |
| $A_i, B_i$ | vector components | p. 11 |
| $\underline{A}^*, \underline{B}^*$ | complex conjugates | Eq. 1.52 |
| $A_r$ | radial component of $\vec{A}$ | p. 14 |
| $a, b$ | coefficients; constants | |
| $\underline{a}, \underline{b}, \underline{c}, \underline{d}$ | complex coefficients | |
| $a$ | radius | |
| $a_o$ | radius of radiating body | p. 57 |
| $B$ | bulk modulus | Eq. 2.53 |
| $b$ | width or thickness | |
| $c$ | speed of wave propagation | Eq. 2.1 |
| $c_o$ | speed of sound in a fluid | Eq. 2.53 |
| $c_\ell$ | longitudinal wave speed in a solid | Eq. 5.1 |
| $c_s$ | shear wave speed in a solid | Eq. 5.2 |
| $D\_$ | substantial; material derivative | p. 24 |
| $D$ | diameter | |
| $D_o$ | dipole strength | p. 77 |
| $d\_$ | total derivative | |
| $d$ | distance; separation | |

Roman Letters (continued)

| | | |
|---|---|---|
| $E$ | energy | |
| $E_{ac}$ | acoustic (radiated) energy | Eq. 4.49 |
| $e$ | exponential | |
| $F, f, G$ | functions | |
| $\vec{F}$ | force | |
| $\underline{F}$ | complex value of force | |
| $F_o$ | force amplitude | |
| $f$ | frequency | |
| $\Delta f$ | bandwidth | |
| $f_i$ | component of force vector per unit volume | p. 48 |
| $f_o$ | resonance frequency | p. 63 |
| $G$ | shear modulus | Eq. 5.2 |
| $g, \vec{g}$ | acceleration of gravity | Eq. 2.36 |
| $H, h$ | depth; thickness | |
| $I$ | acoustic intensity | Eq. 2.69 |
| $i$ | $\sqrt{-1}$ | Eq. 1.54 |
| $i, j, k$ | index numbers | |
| $\hat{i}, \hat{j}, \hat{k}$ | unit cartesian vectors | Eq. 1.24 |
| $J_o, J_1$ | Bessel functions | |
| $j$ | integer | |
| $K$ | various parameters, coefficients | |
| $k$ | wave number | Eq. 2.8 |
| $\vec{k}$ | wave vector | Eq. 2.13 |
| $k_i$ | components of wave vector | Eq. 2.13 |
| $L$ | length | |
| $L_N, L_n$ | noise level (dB or dBs) | p. 10 |
| $L_S, L_s$ | source level (dB or dBs) | p. 7 |
| $\ell$ | turbulence scale length (eddy size) | p. 54 |
| $M$ | Mach number | Eq. 1.2 |
| $M'$ | acoustic Mach number | Eq. 2.67 |
| $m, n$ | index numbers; integers; exponents | |
| $m$ | mass | |
| $m_e$ | entrained mass | Eq. 4.13 |
| $N$ | number of | |
| $\hat{n}$ | unit vector normal to a surface | Eq. 1.47 |
| $n_i$ | direction cosines | Eq. 2.2 |
| $P$ | pressure amplitude | Eq. 2.75 |
| $P_A$ | static pressure in atmospheres | Eq. 4.40 |
| $p$ | pressure (instantaneous or rms) | |
| $p'$ | acoustic pressure | Eq. 2.19 |
| $p_o$ | ambient static pressure; local steady value of instantaneous pressure | Eq. 2.20 |
| $\underline{p}'_o$ | monopole pressure field | Eq. 4.58 |

Roman Letters (continued)

| | | |
|---|---|---|
| $Q$ | source stability; resonance sharpness | Eq. 1.18 and Eq. 5.138 |
| $Q$ | mass flux of a source | Eq. 3.27 |
| $Q_o$ | amplitude of mass flux | Eq. 4.1 |
| $q$ | mass flux per unit volume | Eq. 3.6 |
| $R$ | radius | |
| $R$ | resistance | |
| $R_i$ | input resistance | Eq. 5.116 |
| $R_r$ | radiation resistance | Eq. 3.1 |
| $r$ | radial coordinate; distance | |
| $\hat{r}$ | radial unit vector | p. 14 |
| $S$ | area (cross-section or surface) | |
| $S_o$ | mean area of radiating body | |
| $s$ | distance along a path | |
| $T$ | period of time | |
| $t$ | time | |
| $t'$ | retarded time | Eq. 2.6 |
| $U$ | fluid speed | |
| $U_o$ | flow speed | p. 54 |
| $u$ | instantaneous surface velocity; fluid speed | Eq. 4.2 |
| $u_i$ | component of fluid speed | p. 53 |
| $u_o$ | amplitude of surface velocity | Eq. 4.3 |
| $V$ | volume | |
| $V_o$ | equilibrium volume | Eq. 4.13 |
| $\vec{v}$ | particle velocity | p. 24 |
| $v_i$ | component of particle velocity | p. 26 |
| $\vec{v}'$, $v_i'$ | acoustic particle velocity | p. 26 |
| $\vec{v}_o$ | local steady value of $\vec{v}$ | p. 24 |
| $W$ | power | |
| $W_{ac}$ | acoustic (radiated) power | Eq. 1.1 |
| $W_{mech}$ | mechanical power | Eq. 1.1 |
| $W_{vibr}$ | vibratory power | Eq. 6.61 |
| $w$ | normal displacement of vibrating surface | p. 111 |
| $\dot{w}$ | vibratory velocity | p. 113 |
| $X, Y, Z$ | functions of x, y, z | Eq. 2.16 |
| $X$ | reactance | |
| $X_r$ | radiation reactance | Eq. 3.1 |
| $x, y, z$ | cartesian coordinates | |
| $x$ | general variable | |
| $Y$ | Young's modulus | Eq. 5.1 |

## Roman Letters (continued)

| | | |
|---|---|---|
| $\underline{Z}$ | impedance | |
| $\underline{Z}_i$ | input impedance | Eq. 5.114 |
| $\underline{Z}_r$ | radiation impedance | Eq. 3.1 |
| $\underline{z}_a$ | specific acoustic impedance | Eq. 2.68 |

## Greek Letters

| | | |
|---|---|---|
| $\alpha$, $\beta$ | coefficients; parameters | |
| $\alpha$ | absorption or dissipation coefficient | Eq. 2.94 |
| $\alpha_r$ | reflection coefficient | Eq. 2.105 |
| $\alpha_t$ | transmission coefficient | Eq. 2.108 |
| $\gamma$ | ratio of specific heats | Eq. 4.27 |
| $\nabla$ | gradient operator | Eq. 1.36 |
| $\nabla^2$ | Laplacian | Eq. 1.40 |
| $\partial\_$ | partial derivative | |
| $\delta_{ij}$ | Kronecker delta | p. 12 |
| $\eta$ | variable | |
| $\eta$ | loss factor | Eq. 2.90 |
| $\eta_{ac}$ | acoustic conversion efficiency | Eq. 1.1 |
| $\eta_{rad}$ | radiation efficiency; loss factor | Eq. 1.4 |
| $\eta_{vibr}$ | vibration conversion efficiency | Eq. 1.4 |
| $\theta$ | angle; phase angle | |
| $\theta$ | temperature | |
| $\theta_i$ | angle of incidence | Fig. 2.2 |
| $\lambda$ | wave length | Eq. 2.8 |
| $\mu$, $\mu'$ | total mass per unit length, area | p. 113 |
| $\nu$ | kinematic viscosity | Eq. 6.104 |
| $\pi$ | 3.14159 . . . | |
| $\rho$ | density | |
| $\rho'$ | acoustic density fluctuation | Eq. 2.22 |
| $\rho_o$ | fluid static (mean) density | |
| $\rho_s$ | density of structure material | p. 113 |
| $\Sigma$ | summation | |
| $\sigma_r$, $\sigma_x$ | specific radiation resistance, reactance | Eq. 3.3 |
| $\tau$ | time constant; time delay; decay time | |
| $\tau_{ij}$ | turbulent stress tensor | Eq. 3.14 |
| $\Phi$ | amplitude of potential | Eq. 2.64 |
| $\phi$ | potential | p. 14 |
| $\phi$ | angle; phase angle | |
| $\omega$ | angular frequency *($2\pi f$)* | Eq. 2.7 |

Abbreviations

| | | |
|---|---|---|
| *AG* | array signal-to-noise gain | p. 10 |
| *curl* | vector rotation operator | Eq. 1.38 |
| *dB* | decibel | p. 4 |
| *dBs* | dB spectrum (1 Hz band) | p. 8 |
| *div* | divergence operator | Eq. 1.37 |
| *cgs* | centimeter-gram-second system of units | |
| *a.c.* | alternating current | |
| *c.g.* | center of gravity | |
| *d.c.* | direct current | |
| *fps* | feet per second | |
| *grad* | gradient operator | Eq. 1.35 |
| *Hz* | Hertz (cycles per second) | |
| *hp* | horsepower | |
| *kt* | knot | |
| *MKS* | meter-kilogram-second system of units | |
| *N* | Newton (unit of force) | |
| *Pa* | Pascal ($N/m^2$) | |
| *PWL* | power level (dB) | Eq. 1.13 |
| *RP( )* | real part of | Eq. 2.10 |
| *rms* | root mean square | |
| *rpm* | revolutions per minute | |
| *rps* | revolutions per second | |
| *SPL* | sound pressure level (dB) | Eq. 1.11 |
| *TL* | transmission loss (dB) | Eq. 1.9 |
| *W* | Watt | |
| *WWII* | World War II | |

## A.2 Nomenclature by Chapter

Chapters 1-4

| | | |
|---|---|---|
| $a$ | ratio of $dp$ to $d\rho$ | Eq. 2.22 |
| $\bar{a}$ | array parameter | Eq. 4.99 |
| $\underline{c}$ | complex speed of sound | Eq. 2.90 |
| $D(\theta)$ | directivity function | Eq. 4.66 |
| $DF$ | directivity factor | Eq. 4.102 |
| $DI$ | directivity index (dB) | Eq. 4.107 |
| $DT$ | detection threshold (dB) | p. 10 |
| $e$ | electric voltage | p. 4 |
| $\vec{F}_g$ | gravitational force | Eq. 2.36 |
| $\vec{F}_p$ | force due to gradient of pressure | Eq. 2.37 |
| $f_c$ | effective center frequency of a filter | Eq. 1.17 |

Chapters 1-4 (continued)

| | | |
|---|---|---|
| $h_R$, $h_S$ | receiver and source depths | Fig. 4.12 |
| $I_o$ | reference intensity | Eq. 1.10 |
| $IL$ | intensity level (dB) | Eq. 1.10 |
| $K$ | spring constant for gas in a bubble | Eq. 4.26 |
| $k_o$ | wave number at resonance | p. 67 |
| $L$, $L'$ | array lengths | p. 83 |
| $M$ | momentum | Eq. 2.40 |
| $N$ | number of elements in an array | p. 83 |
| $N_{RD}$ | recognition differential (dB) | p. 10 |
| $P_i$ | incident pressure amplitude | Eq. 2.102 |
| $P_r$, $P_t$ | amplitudes of reflected and transmitted rays | Eq. 2.102 |
| $PTL$ | power transmission loss (dB) | Eq. 2.111 |
| $\bar{p}$ | pressure radiated by piston for $ka << 1$ | p. 90 |
| $\bar{p}_i$ | rms pressure inside pipe | Eq. 4.136 |
| $p_{ij}$ | instantaneous stress tensor | Eq. 3.9 |
| $p_o$ | reference sound pressure | Eq. 1.11 |
| $R$ | effective cross-sectional radius | Fig. 4.20 |
| $R$ | resistance to bubble motion | Eq. 4.25 |
| $\bar{r}$ | rms distance | Eq. 4.53 |
| $r_H$ | horizontal distance | Fig. 4.12 |
| $r_o$ | reference distance | p. 43 |
| $SE$ | signal excess (dB) | Eq. 1.23 |
| $SL$ | signal level (dB) | Eq. 1.19 |
| $S/N$ | signal-to-noise ratio (dB) | p. 10 |
| $T_o$ | oscillation period | Eq. 4.31 |
| $TA$ | transmission anomaly (dB) | Eq. 2.87 |
| $\bar{u}$ | rms fluctuating fluid velocity in pipe | Eq. 4.136 |
| $W_o$ | reference power | Eq. 1.13 |
| | | |
| $\beta$ | transmission parameter (Ch. 2) | Eq. 2.104 |
| $\beta$ | surface interference parameter (Ch. 4) | Eq. 4.54 |
| $\delta$ | logarithmic decrement | Eq. 4.32 |
| $\tau$ | time delay | Eq. 4.67 |
| $\theta$ | phase angle between acoustic pressure and particle velocity | Eq. 2.80 |
| $\theta_a$ | phase angle on surface of radiator | Eq. 4.5 |
| $\theta_o$ | angle of maximum radiation | Eq. 4.64 |
| $\theta_r$, $\theta_t$ | reflection, transmission angles | Fig. 2.2 |
| $\phi$ | array angle parameter | Eq. 4.89 |
| $\psi$ | phase angle between two sources | Eq. 4.57 |
| $\omega_o$ | resonance angular frequency $(2\pi f_o)$ | Eq. 4.28 |

Chapters 5 and 6

| | | |
|---|---|---|
| $B, B_p$ | bending rigidity of beam, plate | p. 113; Eq. 6.2 |
| $b$ | beam element width | p. 111 |
| $c_B$ | irrotational compressional wave speed of bulk solids | Eq. 5.3 |
| $c_f$ | boundary-layer wall friction coefficient | Eq. 6.103 |
| $c_\ell$ | longitudinal wave speed of solids | Eq. 5.1 |
| $c_p$ | plate wave speed | Eq. 5.9 |
| $c_s$ | shear wave speed | Eq. 5.2 |
| $D$ | boundary-layer velocity defect parameter (Sec. 6.6) | Eq. 6.102 |
| $E$-$B$ | Euler-Bernoulli | p. 116 |
| $\underline{F}_f$ | vibratory force transmitted to foundation | p. 143 |
| $\underline{F}_i$ | input force to mount generated by machine | p. 143 |
| $F_x$ | extensional force experienced by fiber of bending element | p. 111 |
| $F_z$ | normal force in bending | Fig. 5.5 |
| $f_c$ | coincidence frequency | p. 163 |
| $f_m$ | m-th order flexural resonance frequency | p. 124 |
| $H$ | vector potential for shear waves | Eq. 6.25 |
| $h$ | beam thickness; plate thickness | p. 120 |
| $h_p$ | plate thickness | Eq. 6.77 |
| $I$ | moment of inertia | p. 113 |
| $I'$ | mass moment of rotatory inertia | Eq. 5.20 |
| $I_i, I_t$ | intensity of incident and transmitted waves | Eq. 6.82 |
| $J_m$ | Lewis' coefficient for accession to inertia | Eq. 5.159 |
| $K$ | relative shear area | Eq. 5.23 |
| $K_p$ | relative shear area for plates | Eq. 6.3 |
| $k_B$ | beam flexural wave number | p. 177 |
| $k_c$ | wave number for coincidence | Eq. 6.35 |
| $k_c'$ | low-frequency approx. to wave number for coincidence | Eq. 6.58 |
| $k_f$ | wave number for flexural waves | p. 116 |
| $k_{f_o}$ | low-frequency approx. for flexural wave number | p. 126 |
| $k_o$ | wave number in fluid | p. 162 |
| $k_p$ | wave number for plate flexural waves | Eq. 6.76 |
| $k_s$ | wave number for shear waves | Eq. 6.25 |
| $k_t$ | effective hydrodynamic wave number (Sec. 6.6) | Eq. 6.119 |
| $L$ | beam length | p. 123 |
| $L_p$ | perimeter | Eq. 6.70 |
| $M$ | bending moment (Ch. 5) | p. 112 |
| $M_f$ | flexural wave Mach number | Eq. 6.38 |
| $m$ | order number of resonance; mode number | p. 124 |
| $N$ | number of modes | p. 142 |
| $n$ | mode number (circumferential) | Eq. 6.79 |
| $q_1$ | dynamic pressure of free-stream velocity | Eq. 6.116 |

Chapters 5 and 6 (continued)

| | | |
|---|---|---|
| $R_r'$ | radiation resistance per unit area | Eq. 6.77 |
| $u$ | x-component of boundary-layer velocity (Sec. 6.6) | p. 185 |
| $u'$ | fluctuating x-component of boundary-layer velocity (Sec. 6.6) | Eq. 6.114 |
| $u_c$ | convection velocity for boundary-layer fluctuations | p. 193 |
| $u_\theta$ | velocity at momentum thickness | p. 189 |
| $u_\tau^*$ | boundary-layer friction velocity | Eq. 6.96 |
| $v_f$ | flexural wave speed | Eq. 5.34 |
| $v_{f_h}, v_{f_\ell}$ | high- and low-frequency approx. to flexural wave speed | p. 118 |
| $W_i$ | input vibratory power | Eq. 5.116 |
| $w_o$ | vibratory displacement at source | p. 137 |
| $\dot{w}_o$ | input vibrational velocity | p. 137 |
| $X_r'$ | radiation reactance per unit area | Eq. 6.43 |
| $\underline{Y}_{i,f,s}$ | admittances of isolator, foundation and source (Sec. 5.9) | Eq. 5.149 |
| $\underline{Z}_{i\ell}$ | low-frequency estimate of input impedance | Eq. 5.115 |
| $\underline{Z}_{i,f,s}$ | impedances of isolator, foundation and source (Sec. 5.9) | p. 143 |
| $z$ | distance from neutral plane (Ch. 5) | Fig. 5.4 |
| $z$ | distance from wall in boundary layer (Sec. 6.6) | p. 185 |
| $z_o$ | displacement of neutral plane | Fig. 5.15 |
| $z_\tau$ | dimensionless distance from wall in boundary layer (Sec. 6.6) | Eq. 6.97 |
| | | |
| $\alpha'$ | relative rotatory inertia | Eq. 5.21 |
| $\bar{\alpha}$ | rotatory inertia relative to shear | Eq. 5.43 |
| $\beta$ | fluid loading factor | Eq. 6.45 |
| $\Gamma$ | shear parameter for flexural waves | Eq. 5.24 |
| $\Gamma_p$ | plate shear parameter | Eq. 6.4 |
| $\gamma$ | coefficient of bending wave exponential decay | p. 116 |
| $\delta$ | bending wave shear-frequency parameter | Eq. 5.42 |
| $\delta$ | boundary-layer thickness (Sec. 6.6) | p. 185 |
| $\delta^*$ | boundary-layer displacement thickness | Eq. 6.94 |
| $\epsilon$ | relative entrained mass | Eq. 5.17 |
| $\epsilon$ | roughness height in boundary-layer theory (Sec. 6.6) | p. 189 |
| $\eta_r$ | radiation loss factor | Eq. 6.47 |
| $\eta_s$ | structural loss factor | Eq. 6.48 |
| $\eta_T$ | total loss factor | Eq. 6.48 |
| $\theta$ | flexural angle in bending | Fig. 5.4 |
| $\theta$ | boundary-layer momentum thickness (Sec. 6.6) | Eq. 6.95 |
| $\theta_m$ | angle for maximum radiation | p. 172 |
| $\theta_o$ | trace matching angle | Fig. 6.4 |
| $\kappa$ | radius of gyration | Eq. 5.15 |
| $\lambda_c$ | wave length at coincidence | |
| $\lambda_c'$ | low-frequency calculated coincidence wave length | Eq. 6.68 |
| $\lambda_f$ | wavelength of flexural wave | Fig. 6.4 |

Chapters 5 and 6 (continued)

| | | |
|---|---|---|
| $\lambda_o$ | wave length in fluid | Fig. 6.4 |
| $\mu'_B$, $\mu_p$ | beam and plate masses per unit area | Eq. 6.76 |
| $\nu$ | plate curvature parameter | Eq. 6.78 |
| $\xi$ | extension | Fig. 5.4 |
| $\rho_s$, $\bar{\rho}_s$ | density of structure | p. 113 |
| $\sigma$ | Poisson's ratio | Eq. 5.4 |
| $\bar{\sigma}_r$ | specific radiation resistance for reverberant flexural wave field on plates | Eq. 6.69 |
| $\tau_o$ | extrapolated wall shear stress (Sec. 6.6) | Fig. 6.19 |
| $\tau_w$ | wall shear stress | Eq. 6.96 |
| $\Phi$ | phase shift of flexural waves | Eq. 5.80 |
| $\phi_m$ | modal amplitude | Eq. 5.134 |
| $\Omega$ | reference angular frequency | Eq. 5.36 |
| $\Omega_p$ | plate reference angular frequency | Eq. 6.9 |
| $\omega_c$ | coincidence angular frequency | Eq. 6.34 |
| $\omega'_c$ | low-frequency calculated angular frequency for coincidence | Eq. 6.45 |
| $\omega_m$ | angular frequency for m-th resonance | p. 124 |

Chapters 7-10

| | | |
|---|---|---|
| $A_p$ | piston cross-sectional area | Eq. 10.20 |
| $a$ | vortex core radius (Ch. 7) | p. 229 |
| $a$ | longitudinal separation of vortices (Ch. 9) | Fig. 9.5 |
| $\bar{a}$ | lift curve slope (Ch. 7) | Eq. 7.74 |
| $\bar{a}$ | mean reflection loss, in nepers (Ch. 8) | Eq. 8.36 |
| $a(0)$ | initial radius of growing or collapsing bubble | p. 206 |
| $a_c$ | bubble radius when collapse speed is maximum | Eq. 7.27 |
| $a_e$ | equilibrium radius for gas in a bubble | Eq. 7.17 |
| $a_m$ | minimum radius of a cavitation bubble | Eq. 7.20 |
| $a_o$ | maximum radius of a cavitation bubble | Eq. 7.10 |
| $B$ | number of blades | p. 258 |
| $b$ | thickness of airfoil, cylinder, etc. | Eq. 7.71 |
| $C_D$ | drag coefficient | Eq. 7.73 |
| $C_{D_F}$ | form drag coefficient | Eq. 9.49 |
| $C_F$ | force coefficient | Eq. 9.30 |
| $\widetilde{C}_F$ | fluctuating force coefficient | Eq. 9.27 |
| $C_L$ | steady-state lift coefficient | Eq. 7.72 |
| $\widetilde{C}_L$ | fluctuating lift coefficient | Eq. 9.36 |
| $C_p$ | pressure coefficient | Eq. 7.54 |
| $C_Q$ | torque coefficient | Eq. 8.19 |
| $C_T$ | steady-state thrust coefficient | Eq. 8.18 |
| $\widetilde{C}_T$ | fluctuating thrust coefficient | Eq. 9.33 |
| $c_f$ | boundary-layer wall friction coefficient | Eq. 7.58 |

Chapters 7-10 (continued)

| | | |
|---|---|---|
| $E_{Kin}, E_{Pot}$ | kinetic and potential energies | p. 207 |
| $e$ | airfoil trailing edge thickness | Eq. 9.74 |
| $\tilde{F}$ | fluctuating force | Eq. 9.1 |
| $F_D$ | drag force | Eq. 7.73 |
| $F_{D_F}$ | form drag | Eq. 9.48 |
| $F_L$ | lift force | Eq. 7.72 |
| $F_{L_i}$ | induced lift force | Eq. 9.55 |
| $\tilde{F}_o$ | magnitude of fluctuating force | Eq. 9.1 |
| $\tilde{f}$ | a.c. power-line frequency | Eq. 10.4 |
| $f_{CR}, f_i, f_p, f_x$ | piston forces (Sec. 10.4) | Fig. 10.5 |
| $G(\gamma)$ | Sear's function for airfoil gust response (Ch. 9) | Eq. 9.36 |
| $H$ | ocean depth (Sec. 8.7) | p. 281 |
| $H$ | effective piston depth (Sec. 10.4) | Eq. 10.32 |
| $h$ | lateral vortex spacing (Sec. 9.3) | Fig. 9.5 |
| $h$ | cavity depth (Sec. 9.6) | Fig. 9.15 |
| $I_f$ | intensity per 1 Hz band | Eq. 8.7 |
| $J$ | advance ratio | Eq. 8.21 |
| $j$ | number of engine cylinders (Sec. 10.4) | Eq. 10.36 |
| $K$ | cavitation parameter | Eq. 7.53 |
| $K_o, K_1$ | modified Bessel functions of second kind | Eq. 9.38 |
| $K_a$ | advance-speed cavitation parameter | Eq. 8.25 |
| $K_i$ | inception value of cavitation parameter | Eq. 7.55 |
| $K_t$ | tip cavitation parameter | Eq. 8.3 |
| $L_S'$ | overall source level above 100 Hz (dB) | p. 274 |
| $\ell$ | mean free path for sound waves in ocean (Sec. 8.7) | Eq. 8.36 |
| $M_t$ | tip Mach number | Eq. 9.71 |
| $m$ | order of harmonic | Eq. 9.32 |
| $m_p$ | effective piston mass (Sec. 10.4) | Eq. 10.19 |
| $N$ | rotational speed in rpm | Eq. 8.1 |
| $N_i$ | rotational speed for cavitation inception (Ch. 8) | Eq. 8.1 |
| $N_i$ | number of inertia impacts per cycle (Sec. 10.4) | Eq. 10.36 |
| $n$ | rotational speed in rps | Eq. 8.2 |
| $P$ | static pressure differential for bubble growth or collapse | Eq. 7.5 |
| $\overline{p}$ | effective average piston pressure (Sec. 10.4) | Eq. 10.38 |
| $p_g$ | partial pressure of gas in bubble | Eq. 7.16 |
| $p_i$ | pressure inside a bubble | Eq. 7.1 |
| $p_i'$ | inductive near-field pressure (Ch. 9) | Eq. 9.11 |
| $p_m$ | maximum piston pressure (Sec. 10.4) | Eq. 10.20 |
| $p_v$ | vapor pressure | Eq. 7.16 |
| $Q$ | equilibrium partial gas pressure (Ch. 7) | Eq. 7.19 |
| $Q$ | propeller torque (Ch. 8) | Eq. 8.13 |
| $R$ | number of armature (rotor) slots or teeth (Sec. 10.2) | Eq. 10.4 |

Chapters 7-10 (continued)

| | | |
|---|---|---|
| $R_N$ | Reynolds number | Eq. 7.56 |
| $S$ | piston stroke (Sec. 10.4) | Fig. 10.5 |
| $S_N$ | Strouhal number | Eq. 9.42 |
| $s$ | airfoil chord length (Ch. 7-9) | Eq. 7.71 |
| $s$ | piston linear speed (Sec. 10.4) | Eq. 10.33 |
| $s_i$ | image distance (Sec. 9.3) | Fig. 9.8 |
| $spc$ | strokes per cycle (Sec. 10.4) | Eq. 10.36 |
| $T$ | propeller thrust | Eq. 8.12 |
| $\widetilde{T}$ | fluctuating thrust | Eq. 9.33 |
| $T_c$, $T_g$ | time for bubble collapse and growth | p. 207 |
| $U_a$ | speed of advance | p. 261 |
| $U_s$ | free streamline velocity | Eq. 9.51 |
| $U_t$ | tip speed | Eq. 8.2 |
| $u_s$ | vortex sheet induced velocity (Sec. 9.3) | Eq. 9.45 |
| $W$ | weight of explosive in pounds (Sec. 7.10) | p. 243 |
| $W_N$ | Weber number | Eq. 7.57 |
| $w(t)$ | impact velocity (Ch. 10) | Eq. 10.5 |
| $w_i$ | propeller induced velocity (Ch. 8) | Fig. 8.7 |
| $w_o$ | gust amplitude (Ch. 9) | Eq. 9.36 |
| $w_o$ | peak value of impact velocity (Ch. 10) | Fig. 10.2 |
| $\alpha$ | angle of attack | Eq. 7.74 |
| $\alpha$ | ratio of inertia to pressure forces (Sec. 10.4) | Eq. 10.31 |
| $\alpha_o$ | angle of attack for zero lift | Eq. 7.74 |
| $\alpha_T$ | total effective absorption loss coefficient (Sec. 8.7) | Eq. 8.37 |
| $\beta$ | pitch angle (Ch. 8) | Fig. 8.7 |
| $\beta$ | connecting-rod angle (Sec. 10.4) | Fig. 10.5 |
| $\Gamma$ | circulation | Eq. 7.64 |
| $\gamma$ | Sear's reduced frequency parameter (Ch. 9) | Eq. 9.37 |
| $\delta$, $\delta^\circ$ | density of ships on ocean surface (Sec. 8.7) | Eq. 8.40 |
| $\delta$ | piston clearance (Sec. 10.4) | Fig. 10.5 |
| $\eta_i$, $\eta_p$ | propeller efficiencies (Ch. 8) | Eqs. 8.20, 8.23 |
| $\eta$ | viscosity | p. 209 |
| $\rho_p$ | density of piston material (Sec. 10.4) | Eq. 10.32 |
| $\sigma$ | surface tension | Eq. 7.1 |
| $\tau$ | thrust loading factor (Ch. 8) | Eq. 8.24 |
| $\tau_w$ | wall shear stress | Eq. 7.58 |
| $\Phi$ | hydrodynamic potential | Eq. 7.2 |
| $\phi$ | hydrodynamic pitch angle (Ch. 8) | Fig. 8.7 |
| $\omega$ | angular speed $(2\pi n)$ | Eq. 9.40 |

## A.3 Abbreviations Used in References

| | |
|---|---|
| *A.S.A.* | Acoustical Society of America |
| *A.S.M.E.* | American Society of Mechanical Engineers |
| *ASW* | Anti-Submarine Warfare |
| *C.I.T.* | California Institute of Technology |
| *D.T.M.B.* | David Taylor Model Basin |
| *J.* | Journal of |
| *M.I.T.* | Massachusetts Institute of Technology |
| *N.A.C.A.* | National Advisory Committee for Aeronautics |
| *N.A.S.A.* | National Aeronautics and Space Administration |
| *N.D.R.C.* | National Defense Research Committee |
| *N.S.R.D.C.* | Naval Ship Research and Development Center |
| *O.N.R.* | Office of Naval Research (U.S. Navy) |
| *O.S.R.D.* | Office of Scientific Research and Development |
| *R. and M.* | Reports and Memoranda |
| *S.A.E.* | Society of Automotive Engineers |
| *U.C.L.A.* | University of California at Los Angeles |
| *U.S.N.* | United States Navy |
| *op. cit.* | Work cited in references for *this chapter* |

# APPENDIX B

# DECIBEL ARITHMETIC

Decibels are especially useful when numbers representing physical quantities are being multiplied or divided. As indicated in Section 1.2, these operations are replaced by addition and subtraction. However, decibels are awkward to use when addition or subtraction of physical quantities is required. The method of accomplishing the indicated process depends on whether the signals are coherent or incoherent. Formulas for carrying out the several types of decibel addition and subtraction are given in this appendix.

### Addition and Subtraction of Coherent Signals

Consider two instantaneous acoustic pressures having the same frequency,

$$p_1' = p_1\sqrt{2}\cos(\omega t - \theta_1) \qquad (B.1)$$

and

$$p_2' = p_2\sqrt{2}\cos(\omega t - \theta_2)\ , \qquad (B.2)$$

where $p_1$ and $p_2$ are rms pressures. The corresponding sound pressure levels are

$$L_1 = 20 \log \frac{p_1}{p_o} \text{ and } L_2 = 20 \log \frac{p_2}{p_o} , \tag{B.3}$$

where $p_o$ is the reference pressure, as discussed in Section 1.2. The result of combining these signals is

$$L_T = 10 \log \frac{p_T^2}{p_o^2} , \tag{B.4}$$

where

$$p_T^2 = \overline{(p'_1 + p'_2)^2} = p_1^2 + p_2^2 + 4p_1p_2 \overline{\cos(\omega t - \theta_1)\cos(\omega t - \theta_2)}$$

$$= p_1^2 + p_2^2 + 2p_1p_2 \cos(\theta_1 - \theta_2) . \tag{B.5}$$

This result depends on the phase angle between the two signals. If they are equal and in phase, the result is 6 dB higher than either. If they are equal and exactly out of phase, the resultant pressure is zero. If they are not equal in magnitude, the maximum value of $L_T$ will always be less than 6 dB above the level of the stronger signal. Equation B.5 applies to subtraction as well as addition since these are equivalent processes but with different phase angles.

### Incoherent Addition

Most often the signals being considered are either broadband or of different frequencies, in which case the long-term average of the product of the cosines is zero. In this case,

$$L_T = 10 \log \frac{p_1^2 + p_2^2}{p_o^2} = 10 \log \left(10^{L_1/10} + 10^{L_2/10}\right) . \tag{B.6}$$

This is known as the *power sum* of two levels and can be extended to any number of incoherent sources.

A rapid method of making power summations can be derived from the above. Taking $L_1 \geqslant L_2$, Eq. B.6 can be written

$$L_T = 10 \log \frac{p_1^2}{p_o^2} \left(1 + \frac{p_2^2}{p_1^2}\right) = L_1 + 10 \log \left(1 + \frac{1}{10^{(L_1 - L_2)/10}}\right) . \tag{B.7}$$

It follows that unless $L_2$ is within 12 dB of $L_1$ the total level will be virtually unaffected. When $L_2$ is within 12 dB of $L_1$, Fig. B.1 can be used to obtain the power sum.

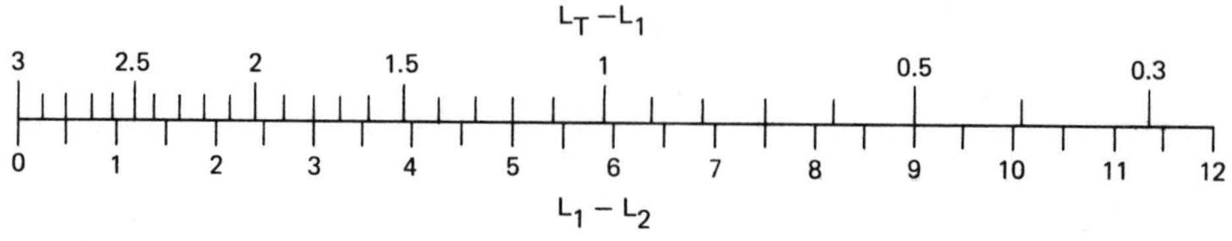


Fig. B.1. Power Sum of Two Incoherent Pressures

## Subtraction of Incoherent Sources

When one source, $L_1$, is turned off, the level will drop by an amount that will depend upon how close the level of the removed source was to the total from all sources. Solving Eq. B.7 for two incoherent sources for $L_2$ gives

$$L_2 = L_T - 10 \log \left[ \frac{10^{(L_T - L_1)/10}}{10^{(L_T - L_1)/10} - 1} \right] = L_T + 10 \log \left[ 1 - \frac{1}{10^{(L_T - L_1)/10}} \right] . \tag{B.8}$$

This result is graphed in Fig. B.2, where it can be seen that the remaining signal becomes lower as the secured source approaches the total. When the two sources are equal, the difference level is 3 dB lower than their sum, in agreement with Fig. B.1.

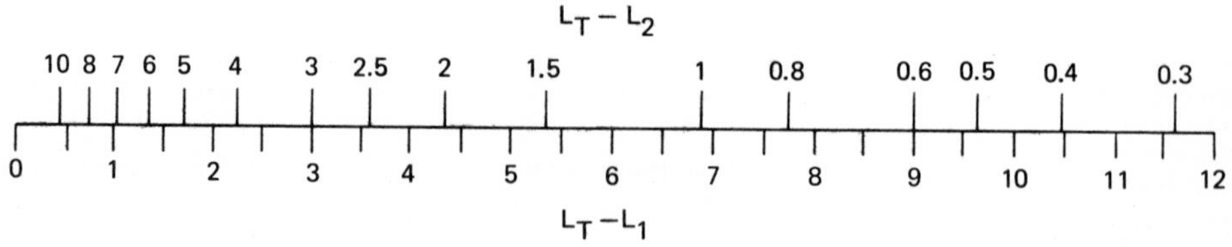


Fig. B.2. Incoherent Subtraction of Pressures

## AUTHOR INDEX


Abbott, I.H. 232, 235, 250
Abernathy, F.H. 304, 306, 321
Abramson, H.N. 115, 154
Ackeret, J. 239, 240, 250
Adams, R.D. 145, 147, 155
Adler, A.A. 154
Akulichev, V.A. 204, 220, 222, 246, 248, 252
Aleksandrov, I.A. 270, 279, 285
Alford, R.S. 69, 103, 113, 286, 287
Alfredson, R.J. 104
Alger, P.L. 328, 346
Allen, C.H. 314, 315, 324
Alvarez, F.F. 333, 340, 346
Andersson, G. 152, 157
Apfel, R.E. 204, 246
Arase, E.M. 287
Arase, T. 287
Arndt, L.K. 103
Arndt, R.E.A. 228, 250
Arneson, A.D. 103
Arnold, L. 317, 324
Arnold, R.N. 325
Arons, A.B. 243, 252
Attia, A.Y. 331, 346
Aupperle, F.A. 196, 199
Austen, A.E.W. 345, 346
Axelrod, E.H. 280, 287

Badilian, B. 222, 249
Bahl, S.K. 209, 246
Ball, J.W. 242, 250
Ballou, C.L. 307, 321
Bannister, R.W. 103
Bardyshev, V.I. 103
Barger, J.E. 204, 246
Barker, P.H. 103
Barnaby, S.W. 202
Baron, M.L. 99, 105
Barry, B. 313, 324
Bartberger, C.L. 44, 103
Bashta, T.M. 242, 250
Bearman, P.W. 300, 304, 321
Bebchuk, A.S. 249
Becker, G.W. 156
Benjamin, T.B. 246, 248
Benscoter, S.U. 154
Beranek, L.L. 18, 183, 198, 314, 315, 324
Berger, E. 307, 321
Bernd, L.H. 205, 246, 250
Bernoulli, D. 115, 116
Bethe, H.A. 252
Betz, A. 260, 268
Beyer, R.T. 43, 44, 246, 252
Biezeno, C.B. 327, 346
Birkhoff, G.D. 311, 321
Bishop, R.E.D. 153
Black, T.J. 192, 199
Blackstock, D.T. 44
Blaik, M. 244, 252
Blake, W.K. 151, 157, 193, 194, 196, 199, 312, 321
Blank, F.G. 175, 196
Blasingame, W. 155
Bleich, H.H. 99, 105
Blokhintsev, D.I. 56, 293, 309, 319, 321, 324
Blyumina, L.K. 300, 321
Bobber, R.J. 103
Bobrovnitskii, Yu.I. 155
Boguslavskii, Yu.Ya. 215, 220, 246, 248, 252
Bolt, R.H. 103, 163, 197
Bom, N. 71, 103
Borden, A. 229, 250
Bornhurst, W.J. 246
Boswell, R.J. 285
Brammer, A.J. 342, 345, 346
Brand, R.S. 196, 201
Brekhovskikh, L.M. 37, 44, 196
Breslin, J.P. 298, 319, 321
Brillouin, L. 150, 155
Brooke-Benjamin, T. 102
Brown, A.E. 325
Brown, N.A. 295, 296, 297, 319
Browning, D.G. 103
Budiansky, B. 118, 153, 154
Bull, M.K. 199
Burrill, L.C. 285, 316, 325

Campbell, J. 328, 346
Carter, A.H. 103
Chandrashekhara, N. 319
Chapman, R.B. 215, 246, 247
Chase, D.M. 194, 199
Chen, L.H. 105
Chen, Y.N. 321
Cheng, H.M. 320
Chertock, G. 98, 99, 105, 151, 157, 298, 319
Chetaev, D.N. 95, 103
Chida, I. 251
Christian, E.A. 244, 252
Churcher, B.G. 328, 346
Churchill, R.V. 18

Clark, T.A. 251
Clauser, F.H. 188, 199
Cockrell, D.J. 324
Cohen, H. 95, 104
Cole, R.H. 242, 252
Coles, D. 187, 199
Collar, A.R. 154
Copley, L.G. 98, 105
Corcos, G.M. 192, 196, 199
Corrsin, S. 191, 199
Cowper, G.R. 153
Cox, G.G. 297, 319
Cranch, E.T. 154
Crandall, S.H. 155
Crane, P.H.G. 94, 103, 333, 346
Crede, C.E. 155
Cremer, L. 103, 106, 110, 148, 153, 155, 158, 162, 163, 177, 184, 196, 197, 198, 329, 330, 346
Crighton, D.G. 54, 56, 197, 199
Crocker, M.J. 198
Cumming, R.A. 317, 325
Cumpsty, N.A. 308, 321
Curle, N. 56, 195, 199, 308, 319, 321

Daily, J.W. 228, 235, 247, 249, 250, 325
Dämmig, P. 198
Davies, H.G. 196, 199
Davies, P.O.A.L. 104
Davis, R. 154
Dawson, B. 299, 319
de Koff, D.L. 286
Dean, L.W. 104, 319, 325
Dean, R.B. 230, 250
Degrois, M. 222, 249
Delany, N.K. 300, 322
Deming, A.F. 311, 323
Denham, R.N. 103, 244, 245, 252
Derby, T.F. 156
Devin, C., Jr. 66, 67, 102
Dietrick, C.W. 157
Di Taranto, R.A. 155
Dittrich, W. 322
Donaldson, J.M. 101, 105, 180, 197
Donaldson, R.M. 312, 322
Dorman, W.J. 286
Dow, M.T. 286
Dowell, E.H. 196, 199
Duncan, M.E. 94, 103
Duncan, P.E. 299, 319
Dunham, W.H. 104, 318, 319, 325
Dyer, I. 56, 161, 195, 196, 197, 199, 285, 287

Eagleson, P.S. 312, 317, 318, 323, 325
East, L.F. 318, 319, 325
Eckhart, C. 44
Eisenberg, P. 246, 249, 285
Eisenhuth, J.J. 286
el Baroudi, M.Y. 307, 322
Eller, A. 215, 246
Ellis, A.T. 215, 246, 249
Elpiner, I.E. 249
Emerson, A. 285
Emling, J.W. 69, 103, 286, 287
Erdelyi, E. 346
Esipov, I.B. 252
Etkin, B. 309, 322
Euler, L. 25, 115, 116

Fabula, A.G. 193, 199, 200
Fage, A. 304, 322
Fahy, F.J. 151, 157
Fearon, W. 346
Fedyaevskii, K.K. 300, 321
Fehr, R.O. 328, 346
Feiler, C.E. 315, 324
Feit, D. 94, 102, 103, 104, 105, 153, 169, 171, 173, 176, 197
Ferry, J.D. 155
Feshbach, H. 98, 105
Ffowcs Williams, J.E. 56, 97, 104, 200
Fielding, B.J. 345, 346
Finch, R.D. 249
Fincher, H.M. 299, 319
Fischer, H.W. 199
Fisher, M.F. 320
Fitzpatrick, H.M. 56, 102, 103, 248, 319
Flamm, O. 285
Flynn, H.G. 246
Fortuin, L. 44
Franken, P.A. 197
Frankenfeld, K. 156
Franz, G.J. 68-71, 103
Frey, A.R. 18, 44, 102, 104, 153, 197, 198
Friedman, B. 252
Frosch, R.A. 287
Froude, R.E. 202
Fung, Y.C. 300, 322
Furduev, A.V. 103
Furduev, V.V. 104

Gaines, J.H. 154
Galloway, W.J. 205, 246
Garcia, R. 249
Gardner, S. 200
Gavigan, J.J. 68, 102
Geib, F.E., Jr. 192, 200
George, A.R. 320
Gerrard, J.H. 307, 309, 311, 322
Gershman, S.G. 103
Gilchrist, R.B. 192, 200
Gilmore, F.R. 209, 213, 246
Glauert, H. 250
Goldman, R.B. 314, 324
Goldstein, M. 56, 320
Goldstein, S. 250, 260, 268, 286, 322
Golubnichi, P.I. 249
Goncharov, V.D. 249
Gongwer, C.A. 312, 316, 322, 325

Gösele, K. 169, 174, 197
Goswami, D. 345, 346
Graham, J.M.R. 308, 322
Grammel, R. 327, 346
Greene, D.C. 198
Greenspon, J.E. 100, 105
Greenspon, J.R. 95, 103
Griffin, O.M. 307, 322
Griffiths, J.W.R. 320
Griffiths, W.J. 333, 346
Grootenhuis, P. 148, 155
Grover, E.C. 345, 347
Gutin, L. Ya. 56, 169, 171, 197, 293, 320
Gutsche, F. 316, 325

Haddad, S.D. 333, 346
Haddle, G.P. 194, 195, 200, 201
Hadler, J.B. 320
Hall, L.H. 200
Hallam, M.G. 156
Hama, F.R. 189, 200, 307, 322
Hamme, R.N. 155
Hammitt, F.G. 215, 247, 249
Hanson, C.E. 307, 311, 322
Hanson, D.B. 299, 320
Harrington, M.C. 104
Harris, C.M. 18, 155
Harrison, M. 220, 248
Hatsopoulos, G.N. 246
Heckl, M. 68, 99, 102, 103, 105, 153, 155, 169, 176, 177, 178, 184, 197, 198, 329, 346
Heidmann, M.F. 315, 324
Heindsman, T.E. 71, 103
Helmholtz, H. von 21, 30, 96, 97, 151
Hempel, W. 345, 346
Henshell, R.D. 154
Herrey, E.M.J. 103
Herring, C. 252
Heskestad, G. 312, 322
Hess, J.L. 105
Hickling, R. 213, 214, 246, 249
Hixson, E.L. 155
Hobson, A. 333, 346
Holl, J.W. 227, 228, 229, 237, 246, 250, 251
Hollander, A. 247
Holle, W. 311, 322
Holmer, C.I. 198, 199
Homicz, G.F. 320
Horton, C.W., Sr. 18, 103
House, M.E. 324
Howe, M.S. 197
Howlett, R. 222, 249
Hoyt, J.W. 200
Hsieh, D.-Y. 215, 246, 247
Hsieh, T. 228, 250
Huang, T.C. 115, 153
Hueter, T.F. 103
Hughes, G. 316, 325
Hughes, W.L. 316, 317, 325
Humphreys, J.S. 307, 322
Hunt, F.V. 44
Hunter, C. 209, 247
Hunter, H. 316, 325
Huse, E. 286

Iernetti, G. 247
Igarashi, T. 345, 347
Il'ichev, V.I. 220, 222, 248
Ingard, K.U. 18, 44, 50, 56, 94, 102, 104, 154, 197, 319, 320, 325
Ioffe, A.I. 248, 252
Ippen, A.T. 228, 250, 312
Itaya, S. 300, 322
Ivany, R.D. 215, 247
Izotov, A.D. 347

Jacobs, W.R. 320, 321
Jarman, P. 222, 249
Jeannon, J.M. 324
Jen, N. 321
Johansen, F.C. 304, 322
Johnson, D.C. 153
Johnson, V.E. 228, 250
Johnsson, C.A. 250
Jones, J.P. 283, 287
Jones, R.C. 104
Jorgensen, D.W. 194, 200, 231, 250
Joyner, J.A. 333, 347
Junger, M.C. 99, 102, 104, 105, 153, 155, 197

Kadykov, I.F. 193, 200
Kallas, D.H. 249
Kamiyama, S. 242, 250
Kamperman, G.W. 324
Kapustina, O.A. 102
Karelin, V.Y. 250
Karnovskii, M.I. 104
Karp, S. 320
Kautz, B.R. 198
Keefe, R.T. 307, 322
Kellogg, O.D. 105
Kemp, N.H. 299, 320
Kennard, E.H. 126, 152, 153, 154, 157
Kennedy, R.M. 194, 200
Kermeen, R.W. 227, 235, 237, 238, 250
Kerr, W. 316, 325
Kerwin, E.M., Jr. 147, 148, 155, 156, 169, 171
Khokha, Yu.V. 255. 257, 258, 286
Khoroshev, G.A. 214, 220, 242, 247, 248, 250
Kibblewhite, A.C. 244, 245, 252
King, A.J. 328, 346, 347
King, W.R., III 68, 102
Kinsler, L.E. 18, 44, 102, 104, 153, 197, 198
Kirkwood, J.G. 252
Kistler, A.L. 191, 199
Kline, S.J. 192, 195, 200
Kling, C.L. 247
Klyukin, I.I. 145, 150, 155, 156, 326, 332, 347

Knapp, R.T. 208, 215, 226, 247, 249, 250
Knudsen, V.O. 69-71, 103, 286, 287
Knyazev, A.S. 150, 156
Kobayashi, R. 247
Kohler, H.K. 347
Komarova, L.N. 178, 197
Koopmann, G.H. 307, 308, 322
Kopec, B.M. 286
Kopko, W. 320
Korbacher, G.K. 322
Korets, V.L. 246
Kornfeld, M. 249
Kozhelupova, N.G. 252
Kozyrev, S.P. 215, 247
Krishnamurty, K. 104, 325
Krivtsov, Y.V. 316, 325
Kronauer, R.E. 306, 321
Kruszewski, E.T. 118, 153
Krzywoblocki, M.Z. 302, 322
Kubanskii, P.M. 325
Kuhn, G.F. 151, 157
Kurtze, G. 148, 156, 163, 184, 197, 198
Kuttruff, H. 222, 249

Lagrange, J.L. 24
Laird, D.T. 95, 104
Lamb, Sir Horace 44, 105, 109, 206, 247
Lambert, R.F. 196, 199
Landahl, M.T. 192, 195, 200
Landweber, L. 157, 250
Lane, F. 268, 286, 324
Lankester, S.G. 316, 325
Laplace, P.S. 20-29, 97
Lauterborn, W. 102, 205, 247
Lawther, J.M. 150, 156
Lazan, B.J. 156
Lee, R. 56
Leehey, P. 200, 307, 311, 322
Lehman, A.F. 251
Lehnert, R. 312, 322
Leibowitz, R.C. 126, 152, 153, 154, 157
LeMéhaute, B. 252
Leonard, R.W. 154
Lerbs, H.W. 286
Lesunovskii, V.P. 220, 248, 255, 257, 258, 286
Levkovskii, Yu.L. 248
Lewis, F.M. 151, 157, 298, 320, 327, 347
Lichtman, J.Z. 249, 286
Lighthill, M.J. 18, 47, 56, 190, 195, 309
Lilley, G.M. 200
Lindsay, R.B. 44, 102, 104, 154
Llewelyn, D. 323
Loda, C.J. 104
Loughridge, M.S. 287
Lowson, M.V. 56, 295, 299, 314, 320, 324
Lübcke, E. 329, 347
Ludwieg, H. 187, 200
Ludwig, G.R. 195, 196, 200
Lurye, J.R. 320
Lyamshev, L.M. 180, 192, 193, 198, 200, 220, 248
Lyapunov, V.T. 177, 197
Lynn, J.E. 286
Lyon, R.H. 177, 197

Mabie, H.H. 133, 134, 154
Macaskill, R. 251
MacNeal, R.H. 100, 105, 131, 154
Madison, R.D. 313, 314, 324
Maestrello, L. 195, 200
Maga, L.J. 151, 157
Maidanik, G. 169, 171, 175, 176, 177, 178, 179, 194, 196, 197, 200
Maling, G.C. 314, 324
Mangiarotty, R.A. 56
Mangulis, V. 104
Mani, R. 299, 320
Manning, J.E. 178, 179, 197
Mao, M. 148, 156
Mark, W.D. 155
Marris, A.W. 322
Martin, A.I. 133, 154
Maslov, V.P. 155, 156
Mather, J.S.B. 299, 320
Mathews, A.T. 105
Maull, D.J. 308, 322
McCann, G.D. 131, 154
McCormick, B.W., Jr. 218, 239, 240, 248, 251, 255, 256, 258, 260, 286
McCormick, J.M. 105
McGoldrick, R.T. 152, 154, 157
McGraw, J.T. 250
McGregor, D.M. 322
McNown, J.S. 226, 251
McQuillin, R.J. 97, 105
Mead, D.J. 56, 149, 156, 198, 201, 293, 320, 324
Medwin, H. 44
Mellen, R.H. 220, 248, 255, 256, 286
Mellin, R.C. 299, 320
Mercier, J. 320
Mercy, K.R. 333, 347
Messino, D. 247
Meyer, E. 102
Miklowitz, J. 154
Miller, E.A. 251
Miller, M. 321
Milne-Thomson, L.M. 304, 323
Mindlin, R.D. 158, 161, 171, 197
Minnaert, M. 62, 65, 102
Mises, R. von 251, 286
Misra, P.N. 157
Mitchell, T.M. 215, 247
Moeller, K.G.F. 331, 347
Molloy, C.T. 93, 104
Moore, C.J. 313, 324
Morfey, C.L. 56, 104, 151, 157, 299, 313, 320, 324
Morgan, W.B. 251, 286, 297, 319
Morozov, V.P. 220, 248
Morris, G.B. 279, 283, 286, 287

Morse, P.M. 18, 44, 50, 56, 94, 95, 96, 98, 102, 104, 105, 151, 154, 157, 197, 320
Mugridge, B.D. 193, 200, 299, 313, 320, 324
Mühle, C. 68, 102
Murray, M.T. 105
Muster, D.F. 156, 328, 329, 342, 345, 346, 347
Myklestad, N.O. 155

Nakamura, K. 331, 347
Naudé, C.F. 249
Naugol'nykh, K.A. 44, 248, 252
Neise, W. 315, 324
Nelson, H.M. 121, 122, 142, 154, 155, 197
Neppiras, E.A. 210, 212-217, 220, 247
Nikiforov, A.S. 174, 176, 177, 197, 198
Nolle, A.W. 156
Noltingk, B.E. 210, 212-217, 220, 247, 249
Norrand, K. 152, 157
North, E.L. 105
Northrop, J. 283, 287
Noutsopolous, G.K. 325
Numachi, F. 251

Oba, R. 251
Oberst, H. 145, 147, 156
Officer, C.B. 19, 44
Olberts, D.R. 312, 322
Ol'shevskii, V.V. 220, 248
Olson, H.G. 247
Oossanen, P. van 251, 286, 321
Osborne, M.F.M. 218, 220, 248
Oshima, K. 228

Parker, R. 308, 323
Parkin, B.R. 227, 250, 251
Parsons, Sir Charles 202, 223, 285
Pearsall, I.S. 251
Peistrup, C.F. 314, 315, 324
Pernik, A.J. 316, 325
Perrone, A.J. 71, 103, 282, 287
Petrie, A.M. 307, 323
Phillips, O.M. 309, 310, 311, 320, 323
Piggott, C.L. 71, 103
Pinkus, O. 298, 320
Plakhov, D.D. 178, 184, 196, 198, 201
Plass, H.J., Jr. 114, 154
Plesset, M.S. 213, 214, 215, 246, 247, 249
Plett, E.G. 97, 104
Plunkett, R. 156
Pokrovskii, V.B. 251
Pond, H.L. 98, 99, 105
Poritsky, H. 209, 247
Powell, A. 195, 199, 201, 308, 323
Prandtl, L. 187, 201, 260, 268
Pratt, A. 347
Preiser, H.S. 249
Prendergast, V. 307, 323
Price, A.J. 198
Priede, T. 315, 324, 345, 346, 347
Protopopov, K.V. 249
Pullen, H.I. 333, 346

Rader, D. 148, 156
Rathe, E.J. 329, 346
Ray, J. 209, 246
Rayleigh, Lord 32, 44, 47, 49, 102, 109, 114, 154, 198, 206, 207, 208, 210, 215, 216, 247, 323
Relf, E.F. 300, 323
Reynolds, O. 53, 190, 201, 227, 240, 300, 307
Reynolds, W.C. 200
Richards, E.J. 56, 198, 201, 293, 320, 324
Richardson, E.G. 300, 308, 309, 323
Rimsky-Korsakov, A.V. 311, 313, 323, 324
Ripperger, E.A. 115, 154
Robertson, J.M. 187, 201, 203, 247, 286
Robinson, R.C. 329, 347
Rockwell, R.H. 150, 156
Rogers, C.B. 133, 134, 154
Roi, N.A. 252
Romanov, V.N. 177, 198
Roos, F.W. 201
Rosen, M.W. 331, 347
Roshko, A. 300, 302, 304, 323, 325
Ross, D. 147-149, 156, 157, 186-191, 201, 218, 248, 251, 255-260, 286, 295, 300, 310-312, 317, 321, 323, 325, 329, 333, 338, 340, 343, 347
Rouse, H. 226, 251
Rozenberg, L.D. 248, 249
Rschevkin, S.N. 102, 104
Rubach, H. 301, 302, 307, 323
Ruedy, R. 306, 323
Ruffini, A.J. 345, 347
Runstadler, P.W. 200
Ruscus, P. 320
Russell, W.T. 154
Russo, V.L. 152, 157
Ruzicka, J.E. 148, 149, 156
Rybak, S.A. 198

Safar, M.H. 247
Sallet, D.W. 323
Salosina, S.A. 192, 194, 200
Sarpkaya, T. 251
Savidge, J. 320
Schelkunoff, S.A. 104
Schenck, H.A. 98, 105
Schiller, K.K. 183, 198
Schlichting, H. 201
Schloemer, H.H. 193, 201
Schoomer, B.A. 287
Schraub, F.A. 200
Schubauer, G.B. 201
Schultz-Grunow, F. 201
Schweikert, D.G. 105
Sears, W.R. 295-299, 312, 320, 321, 324
Sebestyen, D. 249
Sen Gupta, G. 150, 156
Sette, D. 205, 247, 271, 272

Sette, W.J. 286
Shalnev, K.K. 231, 242, 249, 251
Shannon, J.F. 325
Sharland, I.J. 313, 314, 321, 324
Shenderov, E.L. 184, 198, 199
Sherman, C.H. 95, 103
Shima, A. 102
Simmons, L.F.G. 300, 323
Simons, I.A. 298, 321
Simpson, H.C. 251
Sinclair, L. 285
Sirotyuk, M.G. 205, 248, 249
Skobtsov, Ye.A. 340, 341, 347
Skop, R.A. 322
Skorecki, J. 333, 345, 346
Skudrzyk, E.J. 140, 141, 154-156, 158, 161, 162, 193-195, 198, 200, 201
Slutsky, S. 324
Smaryshev, M.D. 104
Smith, M.J.T. 324
Smith, P.W., Jr. 174, 198, 199, 283, 287
Smith, R.H. 103
Snay, H.G. 243, 252
Snowdon, J.C. 141, 154-156, 162, 198
Soliman, J.I. 156
Solosina, S.A. 200
Soloukin, R.I. 103
Sorensen, N.F. 300, 322
Sorokin, V.I. 104
Sovran, G. 320
Sretenskii, L.N. 321
Stenzel, H. 93, 104
Stern, R. 295, 321
Stokes, Sir G. 47, 49, 190, 209
Stowell, E.Z. 311, 323
Strasberg, M. 56, 62, 66, 68, 102, 103, 105, 204, 248, 271, 272, 286, 319
Strawderman, W.A. 192, 196, 200, 201
Strouhal, V. 300, 318, 323
Summerfield, M. 97, 104
Summers, E.W. 329, 347
Suvorov, L. 249
Swaffield, J. 328, 347
Sykes, A.O. 145, 156
Szechenyi, E. 178, 198

Tachmindji, A.J. 251
Taggart, R. 347
Talham, R.J. 287
Tam, C.K.W. 323
Tamm, K. 102
Tamura, A. 345, 347
Taneda, S. 312, 323
Taniguchi, O. 345, 347
Tartakovskii, B.D. 150, 156, 198
Taylor, K.J. 222, 249
Tchen, C.M. 201
Theodorsen, T. 260, 286
Thiruvengadam, A. 249
Thompson, A.M. 347
Thompson, J.E. 328, 347
Tillmann, W. 200
Timoshenko, S. 114, 115-117, 125, 128, 130, 152-155, 158-159, 161, 171-173
Toebes, G.H. 312, 323
Toms, B.A. 193, 201
Townsend, A.A. 201
Townsin, R.L. 151, 157
Traill-Nash, R.W. 154
Treaster, A.L. 250
Trent, H.M. 131, 155
Trilling, L. 213, 248
Tsakonas, S. 298, 320, 321
Tsokos, C.P. 105
Tulin, M.P. 251
Turner, B.A. 56
Tuzov, L.V. 347
Tyler, E. 312, 323

Ungar, E.E. 103, 145, 147, 149, 153, 155, 156, 157, 177, 184, 197, 198, 329, 333, 338, 340, 343, 346, 347
Urick, R.J. 18, 103, 104, 252, 286
Van de Voorde, C.B. 286, 316, 318, 325
van der Meulen, J.H.J. 228, 251
van der Walle, F. 228, 251
Van Driest, E.R. 193, 201
van Gent, W. 286, 321
van Manen, J.D. 286
van Oossanen, P. 251, 286, 321
van Wijngaarden, L. 221, 248
Varga, I.I. 249
Vecchio, E.A. 196, 201
Velikanov, A.M. 103
Venzke, G. 184, 199
Ver, I.L. 198, 199
Vickery, B.J. 307, 323
Victor, A.S. 103
Vinogradova, E.L. 104
Volterra, E. 154
von Doenhoff, A.E. 232, 235, 250
von Karman, T. 295, 299, 301, 302, 307, 311, 312, 321, 323, 324
von Mises, R. 251, 286
Von Winkle, W.A. 287
Vorotnikova, M.I. 103

Walkinshaw, H.M. 280, 287
Wallace, W.D. 316, 325
Wanderlingh, F. 205, 247
Wang, T.M. 154
Warburton, G.B. 99, 105, 154
Warren, W.E. 184, 199
Watson, E.E. 68, 102
Watters, B.G. 184, 198
Weaver, W., Jr. 154, 155
Wells, R.J. 313, 314, 324
Wenz, G.M. 71, 103, 280, 282, 284, 287
Werner, E.W. 287

Wesler, J.E. 314, 315, 324
West, C. 222, 249
Westervelt, P.J. 97, 105
Weston, D.E. 245, 252
Westphal, W. 169, 198
White, P.H. 194, 196, 199, 201
Whitehead, D.S. 308, 321
Widnall, S.E. 251, 298, 321
Wiley, C.A. 196, 201
Wilkins, J.T. 328, 347
Wille, R. 307, 321, 324
Williams, A.O., Jr. 103
Willmarth, W.W. 201
Winder, A.A. 104
Wislicenus, G.F. 228, 242, 250, 251
Wooldridge, C.E. 201
Work, C.E. 316, 325
Wright, D.V. 155
Wright, S.E. 321, 324

Yaneske, P.P. 163, 198
Yasuda, Y. 300, 322
Yennie, D.R. 243, 252
Young, D.H. 154, 155
Yound, J.E. 199
Young, J.O. 251
Young, R.W. 41, 42, 44, 104, 281, 287
Young, T. 107
Yousri, S.N. 151, 157
Yudin, E.Ya. 251, 309, 311, 321, 324

Zarantonello, E.H. 321
Zinchenko, V.I. 315, 316, 324, 333, 339-344

# SUBJECT INDEX

Absorption coefficient 37
Accordion mode vibrations 98-101
Acoustic arrays 22, 81-89, 93-94
Acoustic assumption 23
Acoustic cavitation 202
Acoustic continuity equation 26
Acoustic conversion efficiency 2-3, 278
Acoustic feedback 308
Acoustic intensity 5-7, 32-33, 35-36, 58
Acoustic Mach number 32, 43
Acoustic momentum equation 28-30
Acoustic particle speed 31-34
Acoustic potential 30-33
Acoustic reciprocity principle 180
Acoustic wave equation 23-31, 47-50
Active dampers 150
Actuator-disk propeller 262-264, 268
Advance ratio 262, 265, 269
Aeolian tones 300
Aerodynamic noise 51-56
Air-to-air transmission 181-184
Air-to-water transmission 40-42, 182
Airfoil in a sinusoidal gust 295-298
Airfoil vortex wakes 311-312
Ambient noise 3-4, 69-72, 243, 280-285
American Standards Association 3, 6
Anomalous depth effect 259-260, 272
Anti-singing trailing edges 318
Applied damping 145-149
Array signal-to-noise gain 10, 88
Arrays 22, 81-89, 93-94
Arrays as spatial filters 88-89
Arrays of directional sources 88
Arrays of flush-mounted hydrophones 194
Asymmetrical bubble collapse 215
Attenuation of structural vibrations 143-150
Axial-flow fans 313-315

Ball bearings 345
Bars, vibrations of 106-108
Beams, flexural vibrations of 100-101, 106-153, 183-184
Beam bending equations 110-116
Beam-plate systems 176-180
Bearings 345-346
Bending equations 110-116, 158-159
Bending rigidity 113, 158
Bending stiffness 113, 158
Bending vibrations of ship hulls 106, 150-153
Bernoulli's equation 224, 241
Bessel's equation 160-161
Bessel functions 50, 90-92, 95, 160-161, 296
Blade-element theory 260-262
Blade frequency 269-270, 293-299
Blade-rate modulation 269, 278-279
Blade-slap 298
Blade-surface cavitation 253-260, 264, 269
Blade tones 269-270, 293-299, 327
Blade-turbulence interaction 299
Blade-vortex interaction 298
Blending region of boundary layer 188
Blowers 288, 313-316
Bodies of revolution 98-99
Body cavitation 202, 223-229
Boiler explosions 203
Boiling 202-203
Boundary cavitation 203
Boundary layers 184-196, 299
Boundary-layer friction 286-290
Boundary-layer turbulence 187-193, 299
Boundary-layer velocity profiles 185-188
Breaking waves 68-71
Broadband noise 142-143, 299, 313
Bubble collapse 205-220
Bubble dynamics 205-215
Bubble growth 205-208
Bubble pulse frequency 244
Bubble sounds 62-69
Bubble temperatures 211
Bulk modulus 29, 107-108
Bulk waves in solids 107-108
Buoyant bodies 195

Camber of airfoils 233-235
Cartesian coordinates 11-14, 20-22
Cavitation 202-242, 269-279, 317
Cavitation blade rates 270
Cavitation damage 223
Cavitation dynamics 205-215
Cavitation erosion 223
Cavitation hysteresis 224
Cavitation in uniform inflows 264-265
Cavitation inception 203-205, 224, 227-229, 265, 269-270, 272
Cavitation inception scaling 227-229
Cavitation noise 202-203, 215-222, 269-279
Cavitation noise modulation 278-279
Cavitation nuclei 203-205, 228
Cavitation of hydrofoils 202, 223, 231-240
Cavitation of marine propellers 253-259, 270-273

Cavitation of submarine propellers 270-273
Cavitation parameters 224-226, 269-272
Cavitation tonals 270
Cavity resonances 96-97, 318-319
Centrifugal blowers and fans 313-315
Characteristic impedance 32, 162
Chemical reactions 222
*Chevron London* (tanker) 279
Circumferential wake variations 265-270
Clamped beams vibrations 123-130
Coastal region enhancement effect 283
Coastal shipping 283-284
Coefficient of relative rotatory inertia 114
Coincidence 163-169, 175, 181
Coincidence frequency 163-168, 176
Complex quantities 15-16
Compressibility 29, 209
Compressors 288, 299-300
Constrained-layer damping treatments 147-149
Continuity equation 24-26, 47
Continuous line radiators 83-88
Continuous spectra 9
Contour integrals 15
Contrails 231
Cosine radiation pattern 288-291
Critical angle 40
Critical cavitation index 224
Cruiser *Cardiff* 274
Curl of a vector 13
Curved plates 178
Cylinders 99
Cylindrical shells 178

Damped beam structures 149
Damped oscillation of a gas bubble 63-68
Damped sound waves 37
Damping 139-142, 145-149, 176, 317, 331
Damping of bubble motions 66-68
Damping treatments for plates 145-149
Decibels defined 4, 8
Decibel arithmetic 8, 360-362
Dependence of cavitation noise on depth 259-260
Desinent cavitation 224
Detection threshold 10
Diesel engines 315, 332-345
Dipoles 45-53, 76-81, 171, 195, 288-293
Dipole strength 77, 292
Direction cosines 20-22
Directional radiation 75-77, 82-93, 171-173, 195
Directivity factor 85-87, 93
Directivity function 75-77, 82-88, 90-91, 93
Directivity index 86-88
Displacement thickness of boundary layer 185
Dissipation coefficient 63-64
Dissolved gases 209-215
Divergence operator 13
Domed sonar self-noise 196
Doppler shift 55
Double-layer damping treatment 149

Drag force 233-234, 237
Droplets 68
Dyadics 11
Dynamic tensile strength 205
Dynamic unbalance 326-327

Edge tones 308
Eggbeater-type rotating blade apparatus 255-260
Eigen-frequencies 140
Electric motors 328-329
Electrical analogy methods 100, 131
Electrical steering of arrays 75
Electromagnetic force fluctuations 328-329
Electromechanical feedback vibration suppressors 150
Elementary force dipole 288-292
Elementary pistons 89-90
Entrained mass 60-63, 113, 150-151, 164-166
Equation of continuity 24-26, 47
Equation of motion 26-28
Equation of state 24
Equilibrium boundary layers 188, 191
Equivalent spectrum level 8
Erosion damage 222-223
Erosion of marine propellers 202, 222-223
Euler-Bernoulli equation 115-123
Exhaust systems 97
Explosions 242-245
Explosion-like impulsive sources 242

Fans 288, 299-300, 313-315, 327
Far acoustic field 34, 74-75, 91
Filter bandwidth 8
Finite-amplitude effects 43-44
Finite-element methods 99-100, 130-131
Fleet submarines 270-272
Flexural resonances 123-134, 150-153
Flexural resonances of ship hulls 150-153
Flexural vibrations 106-153, 158-184
Flexural waves 100-101, 110-153, 158-184
Flexural-wave Mach number 164-169
Flexural wave speed 116-122, 159-160
Flow noise 54-55, 184-196
Flow past a piston 95
Flow-excited resonances 96-97, 318-319
Fluctuating forces 45-46, 48-50, 52-53, 288-299, 304-307
Fluctuating inflow velocity 266
Fluctuating thrust 269, 294-297
Fluctuating turbulent shear stresses 45-48, 50-53, 55, 190, 195
Fluctuating volumes 45-46, 49-52, 57-102
Fluid loading 150-151, 162-171
Fluid mechanics 23-28
Flush-mounted hydrophones 192-194
Forced flexural vibrations 135-143
Form drag 302
Fourier analysis 17-18, 169, 330
Fourier transform methods 17-18, 169
Free-free beams 123-130

Frequency of bubble oscillation 65
Frequency regimes for hull vibration 100-102
Friction velocity 186
Fuel-injection equipment 345

Garfield Thomas Water Tunnel 254, 268
Gas bubbles 62-69
Gas diffusion 215
Gas jet in water 68
Gaseous cavitation 203
Gauss' divergence theorem 25
Gauss' gradient theorem 27
Gears 327, 331-332
Geographical variability of ambient noise 281-283
Gradient operator 13-14
Gravitational force 27-28
Green's theorem 98
Guppy submarines 270
Gutin sound 56, 293

Hamburg Shipbuilding Research Establishment 317
Harmonic representation of waves 20-22, 30-35
Helical gears 331
Helicopter blade-slap noise 298
Helmholtz equation 21-22, 30-31, 33, 97-98
Helmholtz integral 151
Helmholtz integral equation 98-100
Helmholtz resonators 96-97
History effect 187
Hobbing error 331-332
Homogeneous damping treatments 145-147
Horizontal directionality of ambient noise 283
Horseshoe vortex 239-240
Hub-vortex cavitation 253-254, 269
Hull openings 95-97
Hull radiation 97
Hull vibration 106, 150-153, 295-298
Hydraulic cavitation 202, 223, 228, 240-242
Hydraulic machinery 242, 288, 299-300, 327
Hydrodynamic cavitation 223-242
Hydrodynamic damping 151
Hydrodynamic noise sources 51-55
Hydrofoil cavitation 202, 223, 231-240

Ideal vortex 229-231
Image interference 78-81
Image sources 42
Image vortex 304-307
Imaginary quantities 15-16
Impact sounds 68, 329-345
Impedance mismatches 148-150
Inception cavitation index 224, 269
Incipient cavitation index 224
Induction motors 329
Inductive pressure field 290-291, 298
Infinite beam impedance 138-140
Injector noise 345
Inner region of boundary layer 185-189
Input impedance 135-138, 162

Insertion loss 143-145
Integral equation methods 97-100, 151
Intensity 5-7, 32-33, 35-36, 58
Intensity levels 5-7
Interference patterns 79-81
Intermittency effects 191-192
Inverse-square spreading 36
Involute helical gears 331
Irrotational fields 13
Isolation mounts 143-145

Jet cavitation 223, 231
Jet noise 53-54

Karman vortex street 301-308
Knudsen ambient noise curves 69-71
Kronecker delta 12

Lamb waves 109
Laminar sublayer 185-186
Laplace's equation 20-29, 97
Laplacian operator 14, 160
Laser beams 45
Law of the wake 187
Law of the wall 187
Legendre functions 50, 95
Levels 5-8
Lift force 233-235, 239, 288
Lifting surfaces 288
Lighthill's equation 47-50, 309
Limp walls 184
Line integrals 14-15
Linear arrays 81-89
Linear bubble pulsations 62-66
Logarithmic decrement 64
Long term ambient noise trends 285
Longitudinal waves 107-109
Loss factor 63-68, 139-140
Low-frequency ambient noise 280-285
Low-frequency cavitation tonals 270

Mach number 2-3, 51-56
Magnetic force variations 328-329
Magnetostrictive hum 328
Marine diesel engines 333-345
Mass law 182-184
Mass moment of rotatory inertia 113
Material derivative 24-25
Mathematical concepts 11-18
Mechanical impedances 135-139
Mechanical unbalances 326-328
Media interfaces 38-42
Megaphone effect 283
Merchant ships 258, 266, 272-280, 298
Merchant ship trends 279-280
Micropascal 6
Microstreaming 222
Mindlin-Timoshenko thick plate equation 158-159, 161, 171-173

Mixing length 190
MKS system 5-6
Mobility 135
Modal analysis 141-143, 175-178
Modal densities 142, 178
Modal densities of cylindrical shells 178
Modulation at shaft rate 269, 298-299
Modulation of cavitation noise 269
Moment of inertia 113
Momentum equation 26-28, 47-49
Momentum theory 262-264, 268
Momentum thickness of boundary layer 185, 189
Momentum-thickness Reynolds number 189
Monopoles 45-52, 57-62, 97
Motors 328-329
Mount effectiveness 143-145
Multiply resonant systems 140-143

N.A.C.A. 233-238, 360
NACA airfoil families 233-238
NACA 4412 hydrofoils 233-238
N.A.S.A. 235, 360
N-element arrays 81-83, 87-88
Naval architecture 150-153
Navier-Stokes equations 190, 209
Near acoustic field 34, 79, 91-92
Near field of a piston radiator 91-92
Near surface sources 78-81
Noise control 3, 176
Noise measurements 81
Noltingk-Neppiras equation 210-220
Non-linear effects 43-44
Non-uniform beams 115, 130-134
Novikov gears 331
Nozzles 223
Nuclear submarines 272

Oil tankers 277, 279-280, 283
Orthotropic plates 176-178
Oscillating lift 295-298
Oscillating motion of a rigid body 288
Oscillating rigid sphere 289-292
Oscillating thrust coefficient 294
Out-of-phase sources 76-78
Outer turbulent region of boundary layer 185-188

Pancake diesels 333, 342
Partially baffled pistons 94-95
Particle velocity 31-34
Passenger ship *Astrid* 275
Passive sonar 9-11
Pennsylvania State University 254, 268
Periodic motions 55-56
Periodic structures 177-178
Permanent gases in cavitation bubbles 209-214
Pipes 97, 223, 241-242
Pipe bends 223, 242
Pipe cavitation 241-242
Pistons 89-95
Piston in a baffle 90-94
Piston in a non-rigid baffle 94
Piston in a non-planar baffle 95
Piston set in a cylinder 95
Piston slap 332-345
Planar arrays 93-94
Plane sound waves 31-33, 37-38
Plane waves 20-22
Planetary gear systems 331
Plates 106-108, 158-172
Plate flexural vibrations 158-169
Plate flexural wave radiation 158-184
Platform noise 4
Point-excited infinite plates 169-172
Poisson's ratio 108
Polar coordinates 160
Positive displacement blowers 315-316
Power level 7
Prolate spheroids 98, 298
Propellers 203, 253-273, 288, 297-300, 316-318
Propeller blade-element analysis 260-262
Propeller blade tonals 293-299
Propeller cavitation 203, 253-260, 264-265, 269-273
Propeller induced hull forces 297-298
Propeller operation in uniform flows 260-265
Propeller singing 316-318
Propulsive efficiency 262
Pseudo sound 55
Pulsating fluid motions in hole openings 95
Pulsating spheres 57-68
Pulse jets 97
Pumps 242, 288, 299-300, 327
Pump cavitation 242

Quadrupoles 45-55, 195

Radiation, of sound (see specific sources)
Radiation below coincidence 169-171
Radiation efficiency 3, 46-47, 50-51, 53-54, 60-61, 66, 92, 94, 167, 171, 289-291
Radiation from arbitrary bodies 97-100
Radiation from collapsing bubbles 215-220
Radiation from cylinders 99
Radiation from exhaust pipes 97
Radiation from finite plates 173-180
Radiation from fluctuating forces 45-46, 48-50, 52-53, 288-299, 304-309
Radiation from fluctuating volumes 45-46, 49-52, 57-102
Radiation from hulls 98-102, 178-180
Radiation from hull openings 95-97
Radiation from pipe ends 95-96
Radiation from plate flexural vibrations 158-184
Radiation from rigid pistons 89-95
Radiation from tank resonances 96-97
Radiation from two monopoles 72-81
Radiation impedance 59-62
Radiation load factor 167-169, 171
Radiation loss factor 46-47
Radiation reactance 45-46, 50, 166, 291

Radiation resistance 45-46, 50, 92, 177
Radius of gyration 113
Rain noise 71-72
Random forces 142-143
Rayleigh waves 109
Rayls 32
Real quantities 15-16
Reciprocating compressors 333
Reciprocating machinery 327-328, 332-345
Reciprocating unbalances 327-328
Recognition differential 10
Rectangular cutouts 318-319
Rectangular pistons 93
Rectilinear vortices 229-231
Reduced frequency 295-297
Reference pressures 5-7, 361
Reflection by ocean surfaces 42
Reflection of sound 39-42
Resonance frequencies of gas bubbles 65
Resonances of non-uniform beams 130-134
Resonant structures 140-143
Response of structures to sound waves 180-181
Retarded time 20
Reverberant modes 175-178, 183
Reverberant sound 2, 281-282
Reynolds number 53, 227-229, 240, 300-303, 307
Rhombic drive 333
Roots blowers 315-316
Rotary positive displacement blowers 313, 315-316
Rotating blade experiments 253-260
Rotating rods 311
Rotational unbalances 326-327
Rotor-slot motor noise 329
Rotor-stator interactions 299
Rough walls 189-190
Roughness effects on cavitation 228-229

Scalars 11-12
Scalar potentials 13-14
Scale effects 227-229, 237
Sear's function 295-297, 299
Second law of thermodynamics 1-2
Seismic profiling 242-243
Self-noise 4, 184, 193-194, 196
Semi-infinite beams 135-136
Shaft-rate modulation 269, 278-279, 298-299
Shaft-rate tonals 298-299
Shear modulus 107
Shear parameter 114, 159
Shear waves 107, 118
Ships 152-153, 280-285
Ship-generated ambient noise 280-285
Ship resonances 152-153
Side lobes 84-85
Signal excess 10
Signal-to-noise ratio 10
Simply-supported beams 123-130
Singing blades 300, 308, 316-318
Single bubble cavitation noise 215-220
Single bubble growth and collapse 205-220
Skewed propellers 297
Skin-friction coefficient 228
Slender body theory 98-99
Snell's law 38-39, 148, 162, 177
Solid rectangular bars 119-122
Sonar background noise 4
Sonar domes 196
Sonar equation 9-11
Sonar self-noise 4, 184, 193-194, 196
Sonoluminescence 222
Sound (see also radiation)
Sound isolation by walls 184
Sound pressure levels 5-8
Sound radiated by cavitation bubbles 215-220
Sound speed in solids 107-109
Sound waves 19-44, 107-109
Sounds from gas bubbles 62-69
Sounds from rotating rods 311
Sounds from splashes 68-71
Sounds from surface impacts 68-69
Sounds of running water 62-68
Source level 7
Source stability 9
Sources in motion 55-56
Space-rate-of-decay of vibration 140
Spatial filters 88-89
Specific acoustic impedance 32-35, 46, 169, 290
Specific radiation reactance 46
Specific radiation resistance 46, 169, 290
Spectral analysis 9, 18
Spectral width 9
Spectrum level 8
Spectrum of cavitation noise 220-222
Speed of sound 29, 107-109
Spheres pulsating out of phase 292
Spherical coordinates 14, 33, 50-51
Spherical sources 50-51
Spherical symmetry 14
Spherical waves 33-38
Spheroidal wave functions 98
Splash noise 68-72
Spur gears 331
Standing waves 33, 35
Static tensile strength of liquids 203-205
Static unbalance 326
Stirling engine 333
Stress tensor 48-50
Strouhal number 300-304, 318
Structural damping 145-149, 331
Structural vibrations 106-153
Structure-borne sound 106-151, 158-184
Strut cavitation 231-233
Strut oscillating forces 298
Submarines 253, 266, 270-273
Submarine propeller cavitation 270-273
Submicroscopic nuclei in liquids 203-205
Substantial 24-25
Supercavitating hydrofoils 240

Supertankers 277, 279, 283
Surface cavitation 203
Surface image interference 78-81
Surface integrals 15
Surface roughness on cavitation 228-229
Surface ships 253, 272-280
Surface tension 204, 208-209, 228
Surface waves 109

Tankers 277, 279-280, 283
Tapered cantilever beams 133-134
Temporal fluctuations 283-285
Tensile strength of liquids 203-205, 209
Tensors 11-13
Tensor notation 11-12
Thermal sources of sound 45-46
Three-dimensional body cavitation 224-229
Thrust coefficient 262
Thrust loading factor 263
Time-rate-of-decay of vibration 140
Timoshenko beam equation 115-117, 125, 130, 158-159
Tip-cavitation parameter 256, 264, 272
Tip-vortex cavitation 253, 269
TNT charges 243-245
Tonal radiation from rotating propellers 56, 269-270, 293-299, 327
Tooth impacts of gears 331
Torpedoes 253, 266, 287
Torque coefficient 262
Traffic noise 280-285
Trailing edge shape 311-312, 316-318
Transducer size effects 192-194
Transfer impedance 135
Transformer hum 328
Transient cavitation 256-257
Transmission anomaly 36-37
Transmission at boundaries 38-42
Transmission loss 5, 9-11, 35-37, 40-42, 181-184
Transmission ratio 181-184
Transmission through a plane boundary 40-42
Transmission through wall structures 180-184
Transport theorem 25
Turbines 288, 299, 316
Turbulence noise 45-46, 49-50, 53-55
Turbulent boundary layers 184-196
Turbulent pressure fluctuations 184, 192-196
Turbulent stresses 45-46, 49-52, 57-102, 190, 195
Two-element array (two-pole) 72-83

U.S. Naval Oceanographic Office (N.O.O.) 279
U.S. Navy Bureau of Ships 6
U.S. Office of Scientific Research and Development (O.S.R.D.) 273
Ultrasonics applications 202, 222
Unbaffled pistons 94-95
Unbalance forces 326-328
Underwater explosions 242-245
Uniform beams vibrations 115-130
Unsteady airfoil theory 295-297

Valves 223, 242
Valve cavitation 242
Van der Waals' equation of state 203
Vapor cavitation 203
Vectors 11-15
Vector arithmetic 12
Vector differentiation 12-13
Vector operations 12-13
Vector operators 13-14
Velocity potential 30
Venturis 223, 241
Vertical directionality of ambient noise 283
Vibration absorbers 150
Vibration damping 139-142, 145-149, 176, 317
Vibration suppressors 150
Viscoelastic materials 145-149
Volume cavitation 203
Volume integrals 15
Volume pulsations of gas bubbles 62-68
Vortex cavitation 223, 228-231, 239-240, 253-254
Vortex shedding sounds 299-319
Vortex sounds from rotating blades 312-313
Vortex streets 301-308
Vortex wakes 299-312

Wake cavitation 231
Wake diagrams 266-268
Wake operation of propellers 265-270, 294-299
Wake turbulence 54, 223
Wake turbulence cavitation 223
Wake vortices 299-312
Wall pressure fluctuations 192-196
Wall shear stress 185-191, 228
Wall-shear-stress velocity 186
Water-to-air transmission 41-42, 182
Water-to-water transmission 181-182
Wave approach to resonance calculation 128-132, 152-153
Wave equation 19-31, 47-50
Wave motion 19, 106
Wave motions in solids 106-110
Wave number 21-22
Wave speeds 19-22, 107-109
Wave vectors 22
Wave-vector filters 27, 194
Waves in plates 108-109
Weber number 228
Whipping modes 100-101, 106
Wind-generated ambient sea noise 69-71
Wing-tip vortex cavitation 239-240, 253
Wing-tip vortices 239-240

Young's modulus 107